CBSE Board Exams 2023

CW00420583

i Succeed

15 Sample Question Papers

As Per Latest CBSE Sample Paper Issued on 16 Sep. 2022

MATHEMATICS
Class 12

Authors
Laxman Prasad
Sagar Verma

Arihant Prakashan (School Division Series)

✳arihant

Arihant Prakashan (School Division Series)

All Rights Reserved

卐 **Administrative & Production Offices**

Regd. Office

'Ramchhaya' 4577/15, Agarwal Road, Darya Ganj, New Delhi -110002
Tele: 011- 47630600, 43518550

卐 **Head Office**

Kalindi, TP Nagar, Meerut (UP) - 250002
Tel: 0121-7156203, 7156204

卐 **Sales & Support Offices**

Agra, Ahmedabad, Bengaluru, Bareilly, Chennai, Delhi, Guwahati, Hyderabad, Jaipur, Jhansi, Kolkata, Lucknow, Nagpur & Pune.

卐 **PRICE** ₹215.00

PO No : TXT-XX-XXXXXXX-X-XX

Published by Arihant Publications (India) Ltd.

For further information about the books published by Arihant, log on to www.arihantbooks.com or e-mail at info@arihantbooks.com

Follow us on

REAL PRACTICE
A Key to Achieve Perfection

Practice is the key to achieve perfection; one should practice to achieve perfection in any field and school examinations are not an exception to this fact. Constant practice can help one to overcome his weakness. The practice done in a right way with proper guidelines helps to attain grasp over the subject and result in a 'Perfect Performance'.

Sample paper is a must have study resource for each and every student, as it helps them to make themselves acquainted with the real exam paper pattern. They can check and update different aspects like enough speed to complete the paper within the prescribed time limit, identifying those topics/chapter, they are not comfortable with, polishing their skills of writing the solution as per the need of the question, etc.

i Succeed 15 Sample Question Papers will serve the above cited purpose in a perfect manner. This book will help you to master all the skills required to attempt the CBSE Class XII Examination Paper perfectly. This series is not just another Sample Paper series in the market, there are some special features associated with *i Succeed* which make it stand apart.

Some of them are :

○ A special section at the start, **Fast Track Revision** to have a quick revision as the whole syllabus before attempting the full length Sample Question Papers.

○ For Step-by-Step Upgradation, Sample Question Papers grouped into **Three Stages: Stage I, II & III**. Through these stages one can enhance his/her performance gradually .

○ All Sample Papers strictly follow the **Latest CBSE Sample Paper Pattern 2023**.

○ At the end, there are fully solved **Latest CBSE Sample Paper** & a separate sample paper for **One Day Before Exam**.

○ Solutions given with each question has Stepwise Marking.

○ **Online Guidance** is available for unsolved Sample Question Papers.

To gain maximum benefit from Sample Papers, it is advised that you attempt the papers at a stretch in 3 hours without any help.

Although, We have put our best efforts to preparing this book, but if any error or discrepancy has skipped our attention, or you have any suggestion, send your feedbacks. We will welcome your feedback. We thank everyone involved in the process of preparing this book and especially acknowledge the contribution of Ashwani (Project Head). With the hope that this book will be of great help to the students, we wish great success to our readers.

Authors

STAGES
of Real Practice

FAST TRACK REVISION
(Brush up Your Concepts) 1-17

STAGE I

Fully Solved

STAGE II

Fully Solved

STAGE III

Unsolved

To Give You Interactive &

STEP-BY-STEP PRACTICE

Sample Papers in *i Succeed* books have been divided in
3 STAGES

STAGE I (Sample Papers 1 to 5)

The solution to individual question has been given with the question itself, by attempting this stage you can practice along with the learning. If you have any doubt while solution any question you can refer the solution instantly, in this way you will learn and will be able to make your concepts clear.

STAGE II (Sample Papers 6 to 10)

The solution to the questions has been given at the end of the question paper. You can check what you have learnt in the Stage I. This is the stage which will seriously assess your knowledge, if you go through this stage without referring to the solution then you can be sure of getting a high end success in the exam.

STAGE III (Sample Papers 11 to 15)

No solution to the questions has been given, But Online guidelines has been provided this stage. You are advised to attempt this stage within the prescribed time limit of three hours (however, we advice you to attempt all the Sample Question Papers in the prescribed time limit), this is the stage of real assessment. If you find yourself in problem while solving some of the questions, then attempt the same question again and again till you get it correct.

"After going through all the three stages, you will find yourself confident about the coming examination and will come out with the flying colours."

SAMPLE QUESTION PAPERS
a need of the students

It is a question which may rise in the mind of the students that inspite of all the Classroom studies, reading good books, completing homework, etc.

Why there is a need of separate book having simulated Sample Question Papers ?

The answer will be, YES it is needed.

Following points will successfully explain the need of Sample Question Papers

- *i Succeed* 15 Sample Question Papers help you to practice for the CBSE class 12th Examination 2023 and finally will make you getting high end success.

- This series is not just another Sample Papers series in the market but there are some special features associated with *i Succeed* Series books which make them stand apart from others.

TAKING THE SAMPLE QUESTION PAPERS

In order to maximise the benefits of the Sample Question Papers, it is recommended that you take these Papers under conditions similar to the conditions under which the real examinations are administered. T ry to take the Sample Papers in a quiet atmosphere with few interruptions and limit yourself to the three hour time period allotted for the real examination. You will find your results to be more useful if you refer to the answer key only after you have completed the Sample Question Papers.

PURPOSE OF SAMPLE QUESTION PAPERS

The Sample Question Papers are designed to provide an additional resource to help you effectively prepare for the School Examinations. The primary purpose of the Sample Question Papers is to help you become familiar with the structure and content of the examination. It is also intended to help you to identify the areas in which you need to focus on your studies.

INCORPORATING SAMPLE QUESTION PAPERS in Your Study Plan

Adequate preparation prior to taking the real examination is strongly recommended. How much preparation and study you need depends on how comfortable and knowledgeable you are with the content of the examination.

The Sample Question Papers may be used as one indicator of potential strengths and weaknesses in your knowledge of the content in the examination. Because of the similarities in the format and difficulty level between the Sample Question Papers and real examinations, it is possible to predict precisely how you might score in the examination. So, by incorporating the Sample Question Papers in your study plan you can assess yourself from the examination point of view in a better and realistic manner.

COURSE STRUCTURE
(2022-23)

Paper: One   **Time: 3 Hrs**   **Max. Marks : 80**

Units		No. of Periods	Marks
Unit I	Relations and Functions	30	08
Unit II	Algebra	50	10
Unit III	Calculus	80	35
Unit IV	Vectors and Three-Dimensional Geometry	30	14
Unit V	Linear Programming	20	05
Unit VI	Probability	30	08
	Total	**240**	**80**
	Internal Assessment		**20**

Unit I Relations and Functions

Relations and Functions   **15 Periods**

Types of relations: reflexive, symmetric, transitive and equivalence relations. One to one and onto functions.

Inverse Trigonometric Functions   **15 Periods**

Definition, range, domain, principal value branch. Graph of inverse trigonometric functions.

Unit II Algebra

Matrices   **25 Periods**

Concept, notation, order, equality, types of matrices, zero and identity matrix, transpose of a matrix, symmetric and skew symmetric matrices. Operation on matrices: Addition and multiplication and multiplication with a scalar. Simple properties of addition, multiplication and scalar multiplication.

On commutativity of multiplication of matrices and existance of non-zero matrices whose product is the zero matrix (restict of square matrices of order 2), Invertible matrices and proof of the uniqueness of inverse, if it exists. (Here all matrices will have real entries).

Determinants   **25 Periods**

Determinant of a square matrix (up to 3 x 3 matrices), minors, co-factors and applications of determinants in finding the area of a triangle. Adjoint and inverse of a square matrix. solving system of linear equations in two or three variables (having unique solution) using inverse of a matrix.

Unit III Calculus

Continuity and Differentiability   **20 Periods**

Continuity and differentiability, chain rule, derivative of inverse trigonometric functions like $\sin^{-1} x, \cos^{-1} x$ and $\tan^{-1} x$, derivative of implicit functions. Concept of exponential and logarithmic functions. Derivatives of logarithmic and exponential functions. Logarithmic differentiation, derivative of functions expressed in parametric forms. Second order derivatives.

Applications of Derivatives   **10 Periods**

Applications of derivatives: rate of change of bodies, increasing/decreasing functions, maxima and minima (first derivative test motivated geometrically and second derivative test given as a provable tool). Simple problems (that illustrate basic principles and understanding of the subject as well as reallife situations).

Integrals   **20 Periods**

Integration as inverse process of differentiation. Integration of a variety of functions by substitution, by partial fractions and by parts, Evaluation of simple integrals of the following types and problems based on them.

$$\int\frac{dx}{x^2\pm a^2},\ \int\frac{dx}{\sqrt{x^2\pm a^2}},\ \int\frac{dx}{\sqrt{a^2-x^2}},\ \int\frac{dx}{ax^2+bx+c},\ \int\frac{dx}{\sqrt{ax^2+bx+c}},$$

$$\int\frac{px+q}{ax^2+bx+c}\,dx,\ \int\frac{px+q}{\sqrt{ax^2+bx+c}},\ \int\sqrt{a^2\pm x^2}\,dx,\ \int\sqrt{x^2-a^2}\,dx,\ \sqrt{ax^2+bx+c}\,dx$$

Fundamental Theorem of Calculus (without proof). Basic properties of definite integrals and evaluation of definite integrals.

Applications of the Integrals   **15 Periods**

Applications in finding the area under simple curves, especially lines, parabolas/ellipses (in standard form only).

Differential Equations   **15 Periods**

Definition, order and degree, general and particular solutions of a differential equation. Solution of differential equations by method of separation of variables, solutions of homogeneous differential equations of first order and first degree. Solutions of linear differential equation of the type:

$$\frac{dy}{dx}+py=q,\text{ where }p\text{ and }q\text{ are functions of }x\text{ or constants.}$$

$$\frac{dx}{dy}+p(x)=q,\text{ where }p\text{ and }q\text{ are functions of }y\text{ or constant.}$$

Unit IV   Vectors and Three Dimensional Geometry

Vectors   **15 Periods**

Vectors and scalars, magnitude and direction of a vector. Direction cosines and direction ratios of a vector. Types of vectors (equal, unit, zero, parallel and collinear vectors), position vector of a point, negative of a vector, components of a vector, addition of vectors, multiplication of a vector by a scalar, position vector of a point dividing a line segment in a given ratio. Definition, Geometrical Interpretation, properties and application of scalar (dot) product of vectors, vector (cross) product of vectors.

Three Dimensional Geometry   **15 Periods**

Direction cosines and direction ratios of a line joining two points. Cartesian equation and vector equation of a line, skew lines, shortest distance between two lines. Angle between two lines.

Unit V   Linear Programming

Linear Programming   **20 Periods**

Introduction, related terminology such as constraints, objective function, optimization, graphical method of solution for problems in two variables, feasible and infeasible regions (bounded and unbounded), feasible and infeasible solutions, optimal feasible solutions (up to three non-trivial constraints).

Unit VI   Probability

Probability   **30 Periods**

Conditional probability, multiplication theorem on probability, independent events, total probability, Bayes' theorem, Random variable and its probability distribution, mean of random variable.

QUESTION PAPER DESIGN
Class XII (2022-23)

Max. Marks : 80

Duration : 3 Hours

S. N.	Typology of Questions	Total Marks	% Weightage (approx.)
1	**Remembering:** Exhibit memory of previously learned material by recalling facts, terms, basic concepts, and answers. **Understanding:** Demonstrate understanding of facts and ideas by organizing, comparing, translating, interpreting, giving descriptions, and stating main ideas	44	55
2	**Applying:** Solve problems to new situations by applying acquired knowledge, facts, techniques and rules in a different way.	20	25
3	**Analysing :** Examine and break information into parts by identifying motives or causes. Make inferences and find evidence to support generalizations. **Evaluating :** Present and defend opinions by making judgments about information, validity of ideas, or quality of work based on a set of criteria. **Creating :** Compile information together in a different way by combining elements in a new pattern or proposing alternative solutions.	16	20
	Total	**80**	**100**

1. No chapter wise weightage. Care to be taken to cover all the chapters.
2. Suitable internal variations may be made for generating various templates keeping the overall weightage to different form of questions and typology of questions same.

Choice(s):
There will be no overall choice in the question paper.
However, 33% internal choices will be given in all the sections

INTERNAL ASSESSMENT	20 MARKS
Periodic Tests (Best 2 out of 3 tests conducted)	10 Marks
Mathematics Activities	10 Marks

Fast Track
REVISION

Brush Up Your Concepts in Fast Track Mode Before Attempting the Sample Question Paper

■ Relations and Functions

1. Relation

Let A be a non-empty set and $R \subseteq A \times A$. Then, R is called a relation on A. If $(a, b) \in R$, then we say that a is related to b and we write aRb and if $(a, b) \notin R$, then we write $a\cancel{R}b$.

2. Domain, Range and Codomain of a Relation

Let R be a relation from set A to set B, such that $R = \{(a, b) : a \in A$ and $b \in R\}$. The set of all first and second elements of the ordered pairs in R is called the domain and range respectively, i.e. Domain $(R) = \{a : (a, b) \in R\}$ and Range $(R) = \{b : (a, b) \in R\}$. The set B is called the codomain of relation R.

3. Types of Relations

(i) **Empty (void) Relation** A relation R on a set A is called empty relation, if no element of A is related to any element of A, i.e. $R = \phi \subset A \times A$.

(ii) **Universal Relation** A relation R on a set A is called universal relation, if each element of A is related to every element of A, i.e. $R = A \times A$.

(iii) **Identity Relation** A relation R on a set A is called an identity relation, if each element of A is related to itself only. It is denoted by I_A. i.e. $I_A = R = \{(a, a) : a \in A\}$

(iv) **Reflexive Relation** A relation R defined on set A is said to be reflexive, if $(x, x) \in R, \forall x \in A$ i.e. $xRx, \forall x \in A$.

(v) **Symmetric Relation** A relation R defined on set A is said to be symmetric, if $(x, y) \in R \Rightarrow (y, x) \in R$, $\forall x, y \in A$ i.e. $xRy \Rightarrow yRx, \forall x, y \in A$.

(vi) **Transitive Relation** A relation R defined on set A is said to be transitive, if $(x, y) \in R$ and $(y, z) \in R \Rightarrow (x, z) \in R, \forall x, y, z \in A$ i.e. xRy and $yRz \Rightarrow xRz, \forall x, y, z \in A$.

4. Equivalence Relation

A relation R on a set A is called an equivalence relation, if it is reflexive, symmetric and transitive.

5. Equivalence Classes

Consider an arbitrary equivalence relation R on an arbitrary set X, R divides X into mutually disjoint subsets A_i, called partitions or subdivisions of X, satisfying

(i) For each i all elements of A_i are related to each other i.e. $A_i \cup A_j = X, i \neq j$.

(ii) no element of A_i is related to any element of A_j, i.e. $A_i \cap A_j = \phi$, for $i \neq j$.

(iii) $\cup A_i = X$ and $A_i \cap A_j = \phi, i \neq j$.

Here, subset A_i are also called equivalence classes.

6. Function

Let A and B be two non-empty sets. Then, a rule f from A to B which associates each element $x \in A$, to a unique element of $f(x) \in B$ is called a function or mapping from A to B and we write $f : A \rightarrow B$. Here, element of A is called the **domain** of f and element of B is called the **codomain** of f.

Also, $\{f(x) : x \in A\} \subseteq B$ is called the **range** of f.

Note *Every function is a relation but every relation is not a function.*

7. Types of Functions

(i) **One-one** (Injective) **Function** A function $f : A \rightarrow B$ is said to be one-one, if distinct elements of A have distinct images in B,

i.e. $f(x_1) = f(x_2) \Rightarrow x_1 = x_2$

or $x_1 \neq x_2 \Rightarrow f(x_1) \neq f(x_2)$

where, $x_1, x_2 \in A$.

(ii) **Many-one Function** A function $f : A \to B$ is said to be many-one, if two or more than two elements in A have the same image in B.

(iii) **Onto** (Surjective) **Function** A function $f : A \to B$ is said to be onto or surjective, if every element in B has atleast one pre-image in A, i.e. if for each $y \in B$, there exists an element $x \in A$, such that $f(x) = y$.

(iv) **Into Function** A function $f : A \to B$ is said to be into, if atleast one element of B does not have a pre-image in A.

(v) **One-one and Onto** (Bijective) **Function** A function $f : X \to Y$ is said to be bijective, if f is both one-one and onto.

Inverse Trigonometric Functions

Trigonometric functions are not one-one on their natural domains, so their inverse does not exist in all values but their inverse may exists in some interval of their restricted domains. Thus, we can say that, inverse of trigonometric functions are defined within restricted domains of corresponding trigonometric functions. Inverse of f is denoted by f^{-1}.

Note
- $\sin^{-1} x \neq (\sin x)^{-1}$
- $\sin^{-1} x \neq \sin^{-1}\left(\dfrac{1}{x}\right)$
- $\sin^{-1} x \neq \dfrac{1}{\sin x}$

Domain and Principal Value Branch (Range) of Inverse Trigonometric Functions

Function	Domain	Principal value branch (Range)
$\sin^{-1} x$	$[-1, 1]$	$\left[-\dfrac{\pi}{2}, \dfrac{\pi}{2}\right]$
$\cos^{-1} x$	$[-1, 1]$	$[0, \pi]$
$\tan^{-1} x$	R	$\left(-\dfrac{\pi}{2}, \dfrac{\pi}{2}\right)$
$\text{cosec}^{-1} x$	$(-\infty, -1] \cup [1, \infty)$	$\left[-\dfrac{\pi}{2}, \dfrac{\pi}{2}\right] - \{0\}$
$\sec^{-1} x$	$(-\infty, -1] \cup [1, \infty)$	$[0, \pi] - \left\{\dfrac{\pi}{2}\right\}$
$\cot^{-1} x$	R	$(0, \pi)$

Matrices

1. Matrix
A matrix is an ordered rectangular array of numbers or functions. The number or functions are called the elements or the entries of the matrix.

2. Order of Matrix
A matrix of order $m \times n$ is of the form

$$A = \begin{bmatrix} a_{11} & a_{12} & a_{13} & \cdots & a_{1n} \\ a_{21} & a_{22} & a_{23} & \cdots & a_{2n} \\ \vdots & \vdots & \vdots & \vdots & \vdots \\ a_{m1} & a_{m2} & a_{m3} & \cdots & a_{mn} \end{bmatrix}$$

where, m represents number of rows and n represents number of columns.
In notation form, it can be rewritten as
$$A = [a_{ij}]_{m \times n}$$
where, $1 \le i \le m, 1 \le j \le n$ and $i, j \in N$.
Here, a_{ij} is an element lying in the ith row and jth column.

3. Types of Matrices
(i) **Row matrix** A matrix having only one row, is called a row matrix.

(ii) **Column matrix** A matrix having only one column, is called a column matrix.

(iii) **Zero or Null matrix** If all the elements of a matrix are zero, then it is called a zero matrix or null matrix. It is denoted by symbol O.

(iv) **Square matrix** A matrix in which number of rows and number of columns are equal, is called a square matrix.

(v) **Diagonal matrix** A square matrix is said to be a diagonal matrix, if all the elements lying outside the diagonal elements are zero.

(vi) **Scalar matrix** A diagonal matrix in which all diagonal elements are equal, is called a scalar matrix.

Note *A scalar matrix is a diagonal matrix but a diagonal matrix may or may not be a scalar matrix.*

(vii) **Unit or Identity matrix** A diagonal matrix in which all the diagonal elements are equal to unity (one), is called an identity matrix. It is denoted by I.

4. Equality of Matrices
Two matrices are said to be equal, if their order are same and their corresponding elements are also equal, i.e. $a_{ij} = b_{ij}, \forall i, j$.

5. Addition of Matrices
Let A and B be two matrices each of same order $m \times n$. Then, the sum of matrices $A + B$ is a matrix whose elements are obtained by adding the corresponding elements of A and B.

i.e. if $\qquad A = [a_{ij}]_{m \times n}$
and $\qquad B = [b_{ij}]_{m \times n}$
Then, $\qquad A + B = [a_{ij} + b_{ij}]_{m \times n}$

6. Properties of Matrix Addition

Let A, B and C are three matrices of same order $m \times n$, then

(i) Matrix addition is commutative, i.e. $A + B = B + A$

(ii) Matrix addition is associative, i.e. $(A + B) + C = A + (B + C)$

(iii) **Existence of additive identity** Zero matrix (O) of order $m \times n$ (same as of A) is called additive identity, as $A + O = A = O + A$.

(iv) **Existence of additive inverse** For the square matrix, the matrix ($-A$) is called additive inverse, if $A + (-A) = O = (-A) + A$.

Note *If A and B are not of same order, then $A + B$ is not defined.*

7. Multiplication of a Matrix by a Scalar

Let $A = [a_{ij}]_{m \times n}$ be a matrix and k be any scalar. Then, kA is another matrix which is obtained by multiplying each element of A by k, i.e. $kA = k[a_{ij}]_{m \times n} = [k(a_{ij})]_{m \times n}$.

8. Negative of a Matrix

If we multiply a matrix A by a scalar quantity (-1), then the negative of a matrix (i.e. $-A$) is obtained.

In negative of A, each element is multiplied by (-1).

9. Properties of Scalar Multiplication

Let A and B be the two matrices of same order, then

(i) $k(A + B) = kA + kB$, where k is scalar.

(ii) $(k_1 + k_2)A = k_1 A + k_2 A$, where k_1 and k_2 are scalars.

(iii) $(kl)A = k(lA) = l(kA)$, where l and k are scalars.

10. Difference (or Subtraction) of Matrices

If $A = [a_{ij}]$ and $B = [b_{ij}]$ are two matrices of the same order $m \times n$, then difference of these matrices $A - B$ is defined as a matrix $D = [d_{ij}]$, where $d_{ij} = a_{ij} - b_{ij}, \forall\, i, j$.

11. Multiplication of Matrices

Let $A = [a_{ij}]_{m \times n}$ and $B = [b_{jk}]_{n \times p}$ be two matrices such that the number of columns of A is equal to the number of rows of B, then multiplication of A and B is denoted by AB and it is given by $c_{ik} = \sum_{j=1}^{n} a_{ij} b_{jk}$, where c_{ik} is the (i, k)th element of matrix C of order $m \times p$ where $C = AB$.

Note *Generally, multiplication of matrices is not commutative, i.e. $AB \neq BA$.*

12. Properties of Multiplication of Matrices

(i) Let A, B and C be three matrices of same order. Then, matrix multiplication is associative i.e. $(AB)C = A(BC)$.

(ii) **Existence of multiplicative identity** For every square matrix A, there exists an identity matrix I of same order such that $A \cdot I = A = I \cdot A$.

(iii) Matrix multiplication is distributive over addition. i.e. $A(B + C) = AB + AC$

(iv) **Non-commutativity** Generally, matrix multiplication is not commutative i.e. if A and B are two matrices and AB, BA both exist, then it is not necessary that $AB = BA$.

(v) If the product of two matrices is a zero matrix, then it is not necessary that one of the matrices is zero matrix.

13. Transpose of a Matrix

The matrix obtained by interchanging the rows and columns of a given matrix A, is called transpose of a matrix A. It is denoted by A' or A^T or A^c.

14. Properties of Transpose of Matrices

(i) $(A')' = A$

(ii) $(A \pm B)' = A' \pm B'$

(iii) $(kA)' = kA'$, where k is any constant.

(iv) $(AB)' = B'A'$ [reversal law]

15. Symmetric and Skew-symmetric Matrices

A square matrix A is called symmetric matrix, if $A' = A$ and a square matrix A is called skew-symmetric, if $A' = -A$.

16. Properties of Symmetric and Skew-symmetric Matrices

(i) For a square matrix A with real number entries, $A + A'$ is a symmetric matrix and $A - A'$ is a skew-symmetric matrix.

(ii) Any square matrix A can be expressed as the sum of a symmetric and a skew-symmetric matrices.

i.e. $A = \dfrac{1}{2}(A + A') + \dfrac{1}{2}(A - A')$

■ Determinants

1. Determinant

Every square matrix A of order n is associated with a number, called its determinant and it is denoted by $\det(A)$ or $|A|$.

2. Determinant of Matrix of Order 1

Let $A = [a]$ be a square matrix of order 1, then $|A| = |a| = a$, i.e. element itself is determinant.

3. Determinant of Matrix of Order 2

$$\det(A) \text{ or } |A| = \begin{vmatrix} a_{11} & a_{12} \\ a_{21} & a_{22} \end{vmatrix} = a_{11} a_{22} - a_{12} a_{21}$$

4. Determinant of Matrix of Order 3

$$\det(A) = |A| = \begin{vmatrix} a_{11} & a_{12} & a_{13} \\ a_{21} & a_{22} & a_{23} \\ a_{31} & a_{32} & a_{33} \end{vmatrix}$$

$$= a_{11}(a_{22}a_{33} - a_{32}a_{23}) - a_{12}(a_{21}a_{33} - a_{31}a_{23}) + a_{13}(a_{21}a_{32} - a_{31}a_{22}) \text{ [expanding along } R_1]$$

Note *We can expand the above determinant corresponding to any row or column. If A is $n \times n$ matrix, then $|kA| = k^n |A|$.*

5. Area of Triangle

Let $A(x_1, y_1)$, $B(x_2, y_2)$ and $C(x_3, y_3)$ be the vertices of a $\triangle ABC$. Then, its area is given by

$$\Delta = \frac{1}{2} \begin{Vmatrix} x_1 & y_1 & 1 \\ x_2 & y_2 & 1 \\ x_3 & y_3 & 1 \end{Vmatrix}$$

$$= \frac{1}{2} \cdot |[x_1(y_2 - y_3) + x_2(y_3 - y_1) + x_3(y_1 - y_2)]|$$

Note ▪ *Area is positive quantity. So, we always take the absolute value of the determinant.*
▪ *If area is given, then use both positive and negative values of the determinant for calculation.*

6. Condition of Collinearity for Three Points

Three points $A(x_1, y_1)$, $B(x_2, y_2)$ and $C(x_3, y_3)$ are collinear if and only if the area of triangle formed by these three points is zero.

i.e. $\begin{vmatrix} x_1 & y_1 & 1 \\ x_2 & y_2 & 1 \\ x_3 & y_3 & 1 \end{vmatrix} = 0$

7. Minors

Minor of an element a_{ij} of a determinant is the determinant obtained by deleting ith row and jth column in which element a_{ij} lies. It is denoted by M_{ij}.

e.g.   If $A = \begin{vmatrix} a_{11} & a_{12} & a_{13} \\ a_{21} & a_{22} & a_{23} \\ a_{31} & a_{32} & a_{33} \end{vmatrix}$, then

minors of elements of A are

$$M_{11} = \begin{vmatrix} a_{22} & a_{23} \\ a_{32} & a_{33} \end{vmatrix}, \quad M_{12} = \begin{vmatrix} a_{21} & a_{23} \\ a_{31} & a_{33} \end{vmatrix}$$

and $\quad M_{13} = \begin{vmatrix} a_{21} & a_{22} \\ a_{31} & a_{32} \end{vmatrix}$, etc.

Note *The minor of an element of a determinant of order n ($n \geq 2$) is a determinant of order $n - 1$.*

8. Cofactors

If M_{ij} is the minor of an element a_{ij}, then the cofactor of a_{ij} is denoted by C_{ij} or A_{ij} and defined as follows

$$A_{ij} \text{ or } C_{ij} = (-1)^{i+j} M_{ij}$$

Note *If elements of a row (column) are multiplied with cofactors of any other row (column), then their sum is zero.*

9. Singular and Non-singular Matrices

A square matrix A is said to be a singular matrix, if $|A| = 0$ and if $|A| \neq 0$, then matrix A is said to be non-singular matrix.

10. Adjoint of a Matrix

The adjoint of a square matrix A is defined as the transpose of the matrix formed by cofactors of elements of A.

Let $A = [a_{ij}]_{n \times n}$ be a square matrix, then adjoint of A,

i.e. $\quad\quad \text{adj}(A) = C^T$,

where $C = [c_{ij}]$ is the cofactor matrix of A.

11. Properties of Adjoint of Square Matrix

If A and B are two square matrices of order n, then

(i) $\text{adj}(A^T) = (\text{adj } A)^T$

(ii) $\text{adj}(kA) = k^{n-1}(\text{adj } A), k \in R$

(iii) $(\text{adj } AB) = (\text{adj } B)(\text{adj } A)$

(iv) $|\text{adj } A| = |A|^{n-1}$, if $|A| \neq 0$

(v) $|\text{adj}[\text{adj}(A)]| = |A|^{(n-1)^2}$, if $|A| \neq 0$

(vi) $\text{adj}(\text{adj } A) = |A|^{n-2} \cdot A$

12. Inverse of a Matrix

Suppose A is a non-zero square matrix of order n and there exists matrix B of same order n such that $AB = BA = I_n$, then such matrix B is called an inverse of matrix A. It is denoted by A^{-1} and is given by

$$A^{-1} = \frac{1}{|A|}[\text{adj}(A)].$$

13. Properties of Inverse of a Matrix

(i) $(A^{-1})^{-1} = A$

(ii) $(AB)^{-1} = B^{-1}A^{-1}$

(iii) $(A^T)^{-1} = (A^{-1})^T$

(iv) $|A^{-1}| = |A|^{-1}$

(v) $AA^{-1} = A^{-1}A = I$

(vi) $(kA)^{-1} = \frac{1}{k}A^{-1}$, where $k \neq 0$

14. Solution of System of Linear Equations by Using Inverse of a Matrix (or by matrix method)

Let the system of linear equations be

$a_1x + b_1y + c_1z = d_1$; $a_2x + b_2y + c_2z = d_2$ and $a_3x + b_3y + c_3z = d_3$.

We can write the above system of linear equations in matrix form as $AX = B$, where

$$A = \begin{bmatrix} a_1 & b_1 & c_1 \\ a_2 & b_2 & c_2 \\ a_3 & b_3 & c_3 \end{bmatrix}, X = \begin{bmatrix} x \\ y \\ z \end{bmatrix} \text{ and } B = \begin{bmatrix} d_1 \\ d_2 \\ d_3 \end{bmatrix}$$

Case I If $|A| \neq 0$, then system is consistent and has a unique solution which is given by

$$X = A^{-1}B.$$

Case II If $|A| = 0$ and $(\text{adj } A) B \neq O$, then the system is inconsistent and has no solution.

Case III If $|A| = 0$ and $(\text{adj } A) B = O$, then the system is consistent and has infinitely many solutions.

■ Continuity and Differentiability

1. Continuous Function

A real valued function f is said to be continuous, if it is continuous at every point in the domain of f.

2. Continuity of a Function at a Point

Suppose, f is a real valued function on a subset of the real numbers and let c be a point in the domain of f. Then, f is continuous at $x = c$, if $\lim_{x \to c} f(x) = f(c)$.

i.e. if $f(c) = \lim_{x \to c^+} f(x) = \lim_{x \to c^-} f(x)$, then $f(x)$ is continuous at $x = c$.

Otherwise, $f(x)$ is discontinuous at $x = c$.

> **Note** *Graphically, a function f(x) is said to be continuous at a point, if the graph of the function has no break either on the left or on the right in the neighbourhood of a point.*

3. Some Basic Continuous Function

(i) Every constant function is continuous.
(ii) Every identity function is continuous.
(iii) Every rational function is always continuous.
(iv) Every polynomial function is continuous.
(v) Modulus function $f(x) = |x|$ is continuous.
(vi) All trigonometric functions are continuous in their domain.

4. Algebra of Continuous Function

Theorem

Let f and g be two real functions continuous at a real number c, then

(i) $(f + g)$ is continuous at $x = c$.
(ii) $(f - g)$ is continuous at $x = c$.
(iii) fg is continuous at $x = c$.
(iv) $\dfrac{f}{g}$ is continuous at $x = c$ provided that, $g(x) \neq 0$.

5. Differentiability or Derivability

A real valued function f is said to be derivable or differentiable at $x = c$ in its domain, if its left hand and right hand derivatives at $x = c$ exist and are equal.

At $x = a$,

Right hand derivative, $Rf'(a) = \lim_{h \to 0} \dfrac{f(a+h) - f(a)}{h}$

and left hand derivative, $Lf'(a) = \lim_{h \to 0} \dfrac{f(a-h) - f(a)}{-h}$

Thus, $f(x)$ is differentiable at $x = a$, if $Rf'(a) = Lf'(a)$. Otherwise, $f(x)$ is not differentiable at $x = a$.

6. Differentiation

The process of finding derivative of a function is called the differentiation.

7. Derivatives of Some Standard Functions

(i) $\dfrac{d}{dx}(\text{constant}) = 0$

(ii) $\dfrac{d}{dx}(x^n) = nx^{n-1}$

(iii) $\dfrac{d}{dx}(cx^n) = cn\, x^{n-1}$, where c is a constant.

(iv) $\dfrac{d}{dx}(\sin x) = \cos x$

(v) $\dfrac{d}{dx}(\cos x) = -\sin x$

(vi) $\dfrac{d}{dx}(\tan x) = \sec^2 x$

(vii) $\dfrac{d}{dx}(\operatorname{cosec} x) = -\operatorname{cosec} x \cot x$

(viii) $\dfrac{d}{dx}(\sec x) = \sec x \tan x$

(ix) $\dfrac{d}{dx}(\cot x) = -\operatorname{cosec}^2 x$

(x) $\dfrac{d}{dx}(e^x) = e^x$

(xi) $\dfrac{d}{dx}(a^x) = a^x \log_e a, a > 0$

(xii) $\dfrac{d}{dx}(\log_e x) = \dfrac{1}{x},\ x > 0$

(xiii) $\dfrac{d}{dx}(\log_a x) = \dfrac{1}{x \log_e a},\ a > 0, a \neq 1$

8. Algebra of Derivatives

(i) $\dfrac{d}{dx}(u \pm v) = \dfrac{du}{dx} \pm \dfrac{dv}{dx}$ [sum and difference rule]

(ii) $\dfrac{d}{dx}(u \cdot v) = u\dfrac{d}{dx}(v) + v\dfrac{d}{dx}(u)$ [product rule]

(iii) $\dfrac{d}{dx}\left(\dfrac{u}{v}\right) = \dfrac{v\dfrac{d}{dx}(u) - u\dfrac{d}{dx}(v)}{v^2}$ [quotient rule]

where, u and v are functions of x.

9. Derivatives of Implicit Functions

Let $f(x, y) = 0$ be an implicit function of x. Then, to find $\dfrac{dy}{dx}$ we first differentiate both sides of equation w.r.t. x and then take all terms involving $\dfrac{dy}{dx}$ on LHS and remaining terms on RHS to get required value.

10. Derivatives of Inverse Trigonometric Functions

(i) $\dfrac{d}{dx}(\sin^{-1} x) = \dfrac{1}{\sqrt{1 - x^2}},\ -1 < x < 1$

(ii) $\dfrac{d}{dx}(\cos^{-1} x) = \dfrac{-1}{\sqrt{1 - x^2}},\ -1 < x < 1$

(iii) $\dfrac{d}{dx}(\tan^{-1} x) = \dfrac{1}{1 + x^2}$

(iv) $\dfrac{d}{dx}(\cot^{-1} x) = \dfrac{-1}{1 + x^2}$

(v) $\dfrac{d}{dx}(\sec^{-1}x) = \dfrac{1}{x\sqrt{x^2-1}}, |x| > 1$

(vi) $\dfrac{d}{dx}(\csc^{-1}x) = \dfrac{-1}{x\sqrt{x^2-1}}, |x| > 1$

11. Derivative of a Function with Respect to Another Function

Let $y = f(x)$ and $z = g(x)$ be two given functions, we firstly differentiate both functions with respect to x separately and then put these values in the following formulae

$$\dfrac{dy}{dz} = \dfrac{dy/dx}{dz/dx} \text{ or } \dfrac{dz}{dy} = \dfrac{dz/dx}{dy/dx}.$$

12. Differentiation of Logarithmic Function

Suppose, given function is of the form $[u(x)]^{v(x)}$, where $u(x)$ and $v(x)$ are functions of x. In such cases, we take logarithm on both sides and use properties of logarithm to simplify it and then differentiate it.

13. Differentiation of Parametric Functions

If $x = \phi(t)$ and $y = \psi(t)$, then $\dfrac{dy}{dx} = \dfrac{dy/dt}{dx/dt}$

14. Differentiation of Infinite Series

When the value of y is given as an infinite series, then the process to find the derivatives of such infinite series is called differentiation of infinite series. In this case, we use the fact that if one term is deleted from an infinite series, it remains unaffected to replace all terms except first form by y. Thus, we convert it into a finite series or function. Then, we differentiate it to find the required value.

15. Second Order Derivative

Let $y = f(x)$ be a given function, then $\dfrac{dy}{dx} = f'(x)$ is called

the first derivative of y or $f(x)$ and $\dfrac{d}{dx}\left(\dfrac{dy}{dx}\right)$ is called the

second order derivative of y w.r.t. x and it is denoted by $\dfrac{d^2y}{dx^2}$ or y'' or y_2.

■ Application of Derivatives

• Thre **rate of change** of y with respect to x at point $x = x_0$ is given by $\left(\dfrac{dy}{dx}\right)_{x=x_0}$ or $f'(x_0)$.

• Suppose $y = f(t)$ and $x = g(t)$. Then, **rate of change** of y with respect to x is given by
$\dfrac{dy}{dx} = \dfrac{dy/dt}{dx/dt}$ provided $\dfrac{dx}{dt} \neq 0$ or $\dfrac{dy}{dx} = \dfrac{dy}{dt}\cdot\dfrac{dt}{dx}$.

1. Increasing and Decreasing Functions

(i) **Increasing functions** Let I be an open interval contained in the domain of a real valued function f. Then, f is said to be

(a) increasing on I, if $x_1 < x_2$
$\Rightarrow f(x_1) \leq f(x_2), \forall\, x_1, x_2 \in I$

(b) strictly increasing on I, if $x_1 < x_2$
$\Rightarrow f(x_1) < f(x_2), \forall x_1, x_2 \in I$

(ii) **Decreasing functions** Let I be an open interval contained in the domain of a real valued function f. Then, f is said to be

(a) decreasing on I, if $x_1 < x_2$
$\Rightarrow \qquad f(x_1) \geq f(x_2), \forall\, x_1, x_2 \in I$

(b) strictly decreasing on I, if $x_1 < x_2$
$\Rightarrow \qquad f(x_1) > f(x_2), \forall x_1, x_2 \in I$

Theorem Let f be continuous on $[a, b]$ and differentiable on (a, b).

• If $f'(x) > 0$ for each $x \in (a, b)$, then $f(x)$ is said to be increasing in $[a, b]$ and strictly increasing in (a, b).

• If $f'(x) < 0$ for each $x \in (a, b)$, then $f(x)$ is said to be decreasing in $[a, b]$ and strictly decreasing in (a, b).

• If $f'(x) = 0$ for each $x \in (a, b)$, then f is said to be a constant function in $[a, b]$.

Note *A monotonic function f in an interval I means that f is either increasing in I or decreasing in I.*

2. Maxima and Minima

Let f be a real valued function and c be an interior point in the domain of f. Then,

(i) point c is called a **local maxima**, if there is a $h > 0$ such that $f(c) > f(x), \forall\, x$ in $(c - h, c + h)$.
Here, value $f(c)$ is called the **local maximum value** of f.

(ii) point c is called a point of **local minima**, if there is a $h > 0$ such that $f(c) < f(x), \forall\, x$ in $(c - h, c + h)$.
Here, value $f(c)$ is called the **local minimum value** of f.

3. Critical Point

A point c in the domain of a function f at which either $f'(c) = 0$ or f is not differentiable, is called a critical point of f. If f is continuous at c and $f'(c) = 0$, then there exists $h > 0$ such that f is differentiable in the interval $(c - h, c + h)$.

4. First Derivative Test

Let f be a function defined on an open interval I and let f be continuous at a critical point c in I. Then,

(i) if $f'(x)$ changes sign from positive to negative as x increases through point c, then c is a point of local maxima.

(ii) if $f'(x)$ changes sign from negative to positive as x increases through point c, then c is a point of local minima.

(iii) if $f'(x)$ does not change sign as x increases through c, then c is neither a point of local maxima nor a point of local minima. Infact, such a point is called **point of inflection**.

5. Second Derivative Test

Let f be a function defined on an interval I and $c \in I$. Let f be twice differentiable at c, then

(i) $x = c$ is a point of local maxima, if $f'(c) = 0$ and $f''(c) < 0$. The value $f(c)$ is local maximum value of f.

(ii) $x = c$ is a point of local minima, if $f'(c) = 0$ and $f''(c) > 0$. Then, the value $f(c)$ is local minimum value of f.

(iii) if $f'(c) = 0$ and $f''(c) = 0$, then the test fails.

6. Absolute Maxima and Absolute Minima

Let f be a continuous function on $[a, b]$ and c be a point in $[a, b]$ such that $f'(c) = 0$. Then, find $f(a)$, $f(b)$ and $f(c)$. The maximum of these values gives a maxima or absolute maxima and minimum of these values gives a minima or absolute minima.

■ Integrals

1. Indefinite Integral

Let $F(x)$ and $f(x)$ be two functions connected together, such that $\frac{d}{dx}[F(x)] = f(x)$, then $F(x)$ is called **integral of** $f(x)$ or **indefinite integral** or **anti-derivative**. Thus,

$$\int f(x)dx = F(x) + C$$

where, C is an arbitrary constant.

2. Some Standard Formulae

(i) $\int x^n dx = \dfrac{x^{n+1}}{n+1} + C, n \neq -1$

(ii) $\int dx = x + C$

(iii) $\int \dfrac{1}{x} dx = \log |x| + C, x \neq 0$

(iv) $\int e^x dx = e^x + C$

(v) $\int a^x dx = \dfrac{a^x}{\log_e a} + C, a > 0, a \neq 1$

(vi) $\int \sin x \, dx = -\cos x + C$

(vii) $\int \cos x \, dx = \sin x + C$

(viii) $\int \tan x \, dx = \log |\sec x| + C$

(ix) $\int \cot x \, dx = \log |\sin x| + C$

(x) $\int \sec x \, dx = \log |\sec x + \tan x| + C$

$\quad\quad = \log |\tan (\pi/4 + x/2)| + C$

(xi) $\int \csc x \, dx = \log |\csc x - \cot x| + C$

$\quad\quad = \log |\tan(x/2)| + C$

(xii) $\int \sec^2 x \, dx = \tan x + C$

(xiii) $\int \csc^2 x \, dx = -\cot x + C$

(xiv) $\int \sec x \cdot \tan x \, dx = \sec x + C$

(xv) $\int \csc x \cdot \cot x \, dx = -\csc x + C$

(xvi) $\int \dfrac{1}{\sqrt{1-x^2}} dx = \sin^{-1} x + C$

(xvii) $\int \dfrac{1}{\sqrt{1-x^2}} dx = -\cos^{-1} x + C$

(xviii) $\int \dfrac{dx}{1+x^2} = \tan^{-1} x + C$

(xix) $\int \dfrac{1}{1+x^2} dx = -\cot^{-1} x + C$

(xx) $\int \dfrac{dx}{x\sqrt{x^2-1}} = \sec^{-1} x + C$

(xxi) $\int \dfrac{1}{x\sqrt{x^2-1}} dx = -\csc^{-1} x + C$

3. Properties of Indefinite Integral

(i) The process of differentiation and integration are inverse of each other.

i.e. $\dfrac{d}{dx} \int f(x)dx = f(x)$ and $\int f'(x)dx = f(x) + C$

where, C is any arbitrary constant.

(ii) $\int \{f(x) \pm g(x)\} \, dx = \int f(x)dx \pm \int g(x)dx$

(iii) $\int k \, f(x)dx = k \int f(x)dx$

(iv) In general, if $f_1, f_2, \ldots, f_n$ are functions and $k_1, k_2, \ldots, k_n$ are numbers, then

$\int [k_1 f_1(x) + k_2 f_2(x) + \ldots + k_n f_n(x)]dx$

$= k_1 \int f_1(x)dx + k_2 \int f_2(x)dx + \ldots + k_n \int f_n(x)dx + C$

where, C is the constant of integration.

4. Integration by Substitution

The method of reducing a given integral into one of the standard integrals by a proper substitution is called method of substitution. To evaluate an integral of the type $\int f\{g(x)\} \cdot g'(x)dx$, we substitute $g(x) = t$, so that $g'(x)dx = dt$

Some Standard Substitutions

	Expression	Substitution
1.	$a^2 - x^2$ or $\sqrt{a^2 - x^2}$	$x = a\sin\theta$ or $a\cos\theta$
2.	$a^2 + x^2$ or $\sqrt{a^2 + x^2}$	$x = a\tan\theta$ or $a\cot\theta$
3.	$x^2 - a^2$ or $\sqrt{x^2 - a^2}$	$x = a\sec\theta$ or $a\csc\theta$
4.	$\sqrt{\dfrac{a+x}{a-x}}$ or $\sqrt{\dfrac{a-x}{a+x}}$	$x = a\cos 2\theta$
5.	$\sqrt{\dfrac{x-\alpha}{\beta-x}}$ or $\sqrt{(x-\alpha)(\beta-x)}$	$x = \alpha\cos^2\theta + \beta\sin^2\theta, \beta > \alpha$
6.	$\sqrt{\dfrac{x}{a-x}}$ or $\sqrt{\dfrac{a-x}{x}}$	$x = a\sin^2\theta$ or $x = a\cos^2\theta$
7.	$\sqrt{\dfrac{x}{a+x}}$ or $\sqrt{\dfrac{a+x}{x}}$	$x = a\tan^2\theta$ or $x = a\cot^2\theta$

5. Integrals of Some Particular Functions

(i) $\int \dfrac{dx}{(x^2 - a^2)} = \dfrac{1}{2a} \log \left| \dfrac{x-a}{x+a} \right| + C$

(ii) $\int \dfrac{dx}{(a^2 - x^2)} = \dfrac{1}{2a} \log \left| \dfrac{a+x}{a-x} \right| + C$

(iii) $\int \dfrac{dx}{(a^2 + x^2)} = \dfrac{1}{a} \tan^{-1} \dfrac{x}{a} + C$

(iv) $\int \dfrac{dx}{\sqrt{a^2 - x^2}} = \sin^{-1} \dfrac{x}{a} + C$

(v) $\int \dfrac{dx}{\sqrt{(x^2 - a^2)}} = \log |x + \sqrt{x^2 - a^2}| + C$

(vi) $\int \dfrac{dx}{\sqrt{x^2 + a^2}} = \log \left| x + \sqrt{x^2 + a^2} \right| + C$

(vii) $\int \sqrt{x^2 - a^2}\, dx = \dfrac{x}{2} \sqrt{x^2 - a^2} - \dfrac{a^2}{2} \log |x + \sqrt{x^2 - a^2}| + C$

(viii) $\int \sqrt{x^2 + a^2}\, dx = \dfrac{x}{2} \sqrt{x^2 + a^2} + \dfrac{a^2}{2} \log |x + \sqrt{x^2 + a^2}| + C$

(x) $\int \sqrt{a^2 - x^2}\, dx = \dfrac{x}{2} \sqrt{a^2 - x^2} + \dfrac{a^2}{2} \sin^{-1} \dfrac{x}{a} + C$

6. Some Standard Integrals and Substitutions for Them

Integral	Substitution
$\int \dfrac{dx}{a \pm b\cos x}$	Put $\cos x = \dfrac{1 - \tan^2 \frac{x}{2}}{1 + \tan^2 \frac{x}{2}}$, then put $\tan\dfrac{x}{2} = t$
$\int \dfrac{dx}{a \pm b\sin x}$	Put $\sin x = \dfrac{2 \tan \frac{x}{2}}{1 + \tan^2 \frac{x}{2}}$, then put $\tan\dfrac{x}{2} = t$
$\int \dfrac{dx}{a\sin x + b\cos x}$	Put $a = r\cos\theta$ and $b = r\sin\theta$ where, $r = \sqrt{a^2 + b^2}$ and $\theta = \tan^{-1}\left(\dfrac{b}{a}\right)$
$\int \dfrac{dx}{a + b\sin^2 x}, \int \dfrac{dx}{a + b\cos^2 x},$ $\int \dfrac{dx}{a\cos^2 x + b\sin^2 x},$ $\int \dfrac{dx}{(a\sin x + b\cos x)^2}$ and $\int \dfrac{dx}{a + b\sin^2 x + c\cos^2 x}$	(a) Divide numerator and denominator by $\cos^2 x$ (b) Reduce $\sec^2 x$ in denominator as $1 + \tan^2 x$ (c) Put $\tan x = t$ and proceed for perfect square
$\int \dfrac{dx}{(ax + b)\sqrt{px + q}}$ or $\int \dfrac{dx}{(ax^2 + bx + c)\sqrt{px + q}}$	Put $\sqrt{px + q} = t$

Integral	Substitution
$\int \dfrac{dx}{(px + q)(\sqrt{ax^2 + bx + c})}$	Put $px + q = \dfrac{1}{t}$
$\int \dfrac{dx}{(px^2 + q)\sqrt{ax^2 + b}}$	Put $x = \dfrac{1}{t}$ and then put $\sqrt{a^2 + bt^2} = u$

7. Integration by Partial Fractions

Suppose, given integral is of the form $\int \dfrac{p(x)}{q(x)} dx$, where $p(x)$ and $q(x)$ are polynomials in x and $q(x) \neq 0$. Then, to solve such integrals by partial fraction, we firstly take the given integrand $\dfrac{p(x)}{q(x)}$ and express it as the sum of partial fractions and then integrate each term by using suitable method.

S.No.	Form of the rational function	Form of the partial fraction
1.	$\dfrac{px \pm q}{(x \pm a)(x \pm b)}, a \neq b$	$\dfrac{A}{x \pm a} + \dfrac{B}{x \pm b}$
2.	$\dfrac{px \pm q}{(x \pm a)^2}$	$\dfrac{A}{(x \pm a)} + \dfrac{B}{(x \pm a)^2}$
3.	$\dfrac{px^2 \pm qx \pm r}{(x \pm a)(x \pm b)(x \pm c)}$	$\dfrac{A}{(x \pm a)} + \dfrac{B}{(x \pm b)} + \dfrac{C}{(x \pm c)}$
4.	$\dfrac{px^2 \pm qx \pm r}{(x \pm a)(x \pm b)^2}$	$\dfrac{A}{(x \pm a)} + \dfrac{B}{(x \pm b)} + \dfrac{C}{(x \pm b)^2}$
5.	$\dfrac{px^2 \pm qx \pm r}{(x \pm a)^2(x \pm b)}$	$\dfrac{A}{(x \pm a)} + \dfrac{B}{(x \pm a)^2} + \dfrac{C}{(x \pm b)}$
6.	$\dfrac{px^2 \pm qx \pm r}{(x \pm a)^3}$	$\dfrac{A}{(x \pm a)} + \dfrac{B}{(x \pm a)^2} + \dfrac{C}{(x \pm a)^3}$
7.	$\dfrac{px^2 \pm qx \pm r}{(x \pm a)(x^2 \pm bx \pm c)}$	$\dfrac{A}{(x \pm a)} + \dfrac{Bx + C}{x^2 \pm bx \pm c}$ where, $x^2 \pm bx \pm c$ cannot be factorised further.

8. Integration by Parts

Let u and v be two differentiable functions of a single variable x, then the integral of the product of two functions is

$$\int \underset{\text{I} \quad \text{II}}{u\,v}\ dx = u \int v\, dx - \int \left(\dfrac{d}{dx} u \int v\, dx \right) dx$$

If two functions are of different types, then consider the 1st function (i.e. u) which comes first in word ILATE, where

I : Inverse trigonometric function e.g. $\sin^{-1} x$

L : Logarithmic function e.g. $\log x$

A : Algebraic function e.g. 1, x, x^2

T : Trigonometric function e.g. $\sin x$, $\cos x$

E : Exponential function e.g. e^x

9. Integral of the type $\int e^x[f(x)+f'(x)]dx$

If the given integrand is of the form $e^x[f(x)+f'(x)]$, then we can directly write the integral as
$$\int e^x[f(x)+f'(x)]dx = e^x f(x) + C$$

10. Definite Integral

An integral of the form $\int_a^b f(x)dx$ is known as definite

integral and is given by $\int_a^b f(x)dx = g(b)-g(a)$,

where $f(x)$ is derivative of $g(x)$, a and b are **lower** and **upper limits** of a definite integral.

11. Fundamental Theorem of Integral Calculus

(i) Let f be a continuous function defined on the closed interval $[a,b]$ and $A(x)$ be the area of function, i.e. $A(x)=\int_a^x f(x)dx$.

Then, $A'(x)=f(x), \forall x \in [a,b]$

(ii) Let f be a continuous function defined on the closed interval $[a,b]$ and F be an anti-derivative of f.

Then, $\int_a^b f(x)\,dx = [F(x)]_a^b = F(b)-F(a)$

12. Properties of Definite Integrals

(i) $\int_a^b f(x)dx = \int_a^b f(t)dt$

(ii) $\int_a^b f(x)dx = -\int_b^a f(x)dx$

(iii) $\int_a^b f(x)dx = \int_a^c f(x)dx + \int_c^b f(x)dx$, where $a<c<b$.

(iv) $\int_a^b f(x)dx = \int_a^b f(a+b-x)dx$

(v) $\int_0^a f(x)dx = \int_0^a f(a-x)dx$

(vi) $\int_0^{2a} f(x)dx = \int_0^a f(x)dx + \int_0^a f(2a-x)dx$

(vii) $\int_0^{2a} f(x)dx = \begin{cases} 2\int_0^a f(x)dx, & \text{if } f(2a-x)=f(x) \\ 0, & \text{if } f(2a-x)=-f(x) \end{cases}$

(viii) $\int_{-a}^a f(x)dx$
$$= \begin{cases} 2\int_0^a f(x)dx, & \text{if } f(-x)=f(x), \text{ i.e. even} \\ 0, & \text{if } f(-x)=-f(x), \text{i.e. odd} \end{cases}$$

■ Application of Integrals

(i) If the curve $y=f(x)$ lies above X-axis, then the area bounded by the curve $y=f(x)$, the X-axis and the lines at $x=a$ and $x=b$, is given by $\int_a^b y\,dx$.

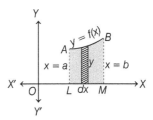

(ii) If the curve $x=f(y)$ lies to right of Y-axis, then the area bounded by the curve $x=f(y)$, the Y-axis and the lines at $y=c$ and $y=d$, is given by $\int_c^d x\,dy$.

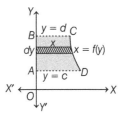

(iii) If the curve $y=f(x)$ lies below the X-axis, then area bounded by the curve $y=f(x)$, X-axis and the lines at $x=a$ and $x=b$, is given by $\left| \int_a^b y\,dx \right|$.

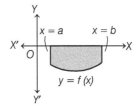

(iv) Generally, it may happen that some position of the curve is above X-axis and some is below the X-axis which is shown in the figure. The area A bounded by the curve $y=f(x)$, X-axis and the lines at $x=a$ and $x=b$, is given by $A=|A_2|+A_1$.

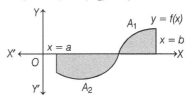

■ Differential Equations

1. **Differential Equation**
   An equation involving independent variable(s), dependent variable and derivative(s) of dependent variable with respect to independent variable(s), is called a differential equation.

2. **Ordinary Differential Equation**
   A differential equation involving derivative or derivatives of the dependent variable with respect to only one independent variable is called an **ordinary differential equation.**

3. **Order of a Differential Equation**
   The order of the highest order derivative of dependent variable with respect to independent variable occurring in the differential equation, is called the order of differential equation.

4. **Degree of a Differential Equation**
   The highest power (positive integral index) of the highest order derivative involved in a differential equation, when it is written as a polynomial in derivatives, is called degree of a differential equation.

   Note *(i) Order and degree (if defined) of a differential equation are always positive integers.*
   (ii) The order of a differential equation representing a family of curves is same as the number of arbitrary constants present in the equation.

5. **Solution of a Differential Equation**
   A function of the form $y = \phi(x) + C$, which satisfies given differential equation, is called the solution of the differential equation.

6. **General Solution of a Differential Equation**
   A solution of a differential equation which contains as many arbitrary constants as the order of the differential equation, is called the general solution or primitive solution of the differential equation.

7. **Particular Solution of a Differential Equation**
   The solution obtained by giving particular values to the arbitrary constants in general solution, is called a particular solution of the differential equation.
   In other words, the solution free from arbitrary constants is called particular solution.

8. **Differential Equation in Variable Separable Form**
   Suppose a first order and first degree differential equation, $\dfrac{dy}{dx} = f(x, y)$, is such that $f(x, y)$ can be written as $g(x) \cdot h(y)$ ...(i)
   Then, expressed the given differential equation as
   $$\frac{dy}{dx} = h(y) \cdot g(x).   \quad ...(ii)$$

If $h(y) \neq 0$, then separating the variables, Eq. (ii) can be written as $\dfrac{1}{h(y)} dy = g(x) dx$.

On integrating both sides, we get the required solution of given differential equation.

9. **Homogeneous Differential Equation**
   A function $F(x, y)$ is said to be homogeneous function of degree n, if
   $$F(x, y) = x^n\, g\!\left(\frac{y}{x}\right) \text{ or } y^n\, h\!\left(\frac{x}{y}\right).$$

   A differential equation of the form $\dfrac{dy}{dx} = F(x, y)$

   is called a homogeneous differential equation, if $F(x, y)$ is a homogeneous function of degree zero.

10. **Solution of Homogeneous Differential Equation**

    If $F(x, y) = g\!\left(\dfrac{y}{x}\right)$, then firstly put $y = vx$ and $\dfrac{dy}{dx} = v + x\dfrac{dv}{dx}$

    in given differential equation and then use variable separable method to get the required solution.

    Similarly, if $F(x, y) = h\!\left(\dfrac{x}{y}\right)$, then put $x = vy$ and

    $\dfrac{dx}{dy} = v + y\dfrac{dv}{dy}$ in the given differential equation.

    - **Linear Differential Equation** A first order differential equation in which the degree of dependent variable and its derivative is one and they do not get multiplied together, is called a **linear differential equation**.
      Type I A differential equation of the form $\dfrac{dy}{dx} + Py = Q$, where P and Q are constants or functions of x only, is called linear differential equation, whose solution is given by $y \cdot (\text{IF}) = \int Q \cdot (\text{IF}) dx + C$,
      where IF $= e^{\int P dx}$
      Type II A differential equation of the form $\dfrac{dx}{dy} + Px = Q$, where P and Q are constants or functions of y only, is called linear differential equation, whose solution is given by $x \cdot (\text{IF}) = \int Q \cdot (\text{IF}) dy + C$,
      where IF $= e^{\int P dy}$.

■ Vector Algebra

1. **Scalars**
   A quantity which has magnitude but no direction, is called a scalar.

2. **Vectors**
   A quantity which has magnitude as well as direction, is called a vector.

3. Magnitude of a Vector

The length of the vector $\overrightarrow{AB}$ or $\vec{a}$ is called the magnitude of $\overrightarrow{AB}$ or $\vec{a}$ and it is represented by $|\overrightarrow{AB}|$ or $|\vec{a}|$.

If $\vec{a} = x\,\hat{i} + y\,\hat{j} + z\,\hat{k}$, then $|\vec{a}| = \sqrt{x^2 + y^2 + z^2}$.

Note *Since, the length is never negative, so the notation $|\vec{a}| < 0$ has no meaning.*

4. Types of Vectors

(i) **Zero or Null Vector** A vector whose magnitude is zero or whose initial and terminal points coincide, is called a null vector or zero vector.

(ii) **Unit Vector** A vector whose magnitude is one unit. The unit vector in the direction of $\vec{a}$ is represented by $\hat{a}$. The unit vectors along X-axis, Y-axis and Z-axis are represented by $\hat{i}, \hat{j}$ and $\hat{k}$, respectively.

(iii) **Coinitial Vectors** Two or more vectors having the same initial point are called coinitial vectors.

(iv) **Collinear or Parallel Vectors** The vectors which have same or parallel support are called collinear vectors.

(v) **Equal Vectors** Two vectors are equal, if they have same magnitude and direction.

(vi) **Negative of a Vector** A vector whose magnitude is same as that of given vector but the direction is opposite, is called negative vector of the given vector. e.g. Let $\overrightarrow{AB}$ be a vector, then $-\overrightarrow{AB}$ or $\overrightarrow{BA}$ is a negative vector.

(vii) **Coplanar Vectors** A system of vectors is said to be coplanar, if they are parallel to the same plane.

Note *If the initial point of a vector is not specified, then it is called a **free vector**.*

5. Position Vector

Let O be any point called the origin of reference or say simply origin and a point P in space, having coordinates (x, y, z) w.r.t. origin $O(0, 0, 0)$ then vector $\overrightarrow{OP}(= \vec{r})$ having O and P as its initial and terminal point respectively, is called the position vector of the point P w.r.t. O.

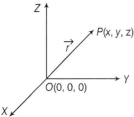

The magnitude of $\overrightarrow{OP}$ or $\vec{r}$ is given by

$$|\overrightarrow{OP}| = |\vec{r}| = \sqrt{x^2 + y^2 + z^2}$$

6. Addition of Vectors

(i) **Triangle Law of Vector Addition** If two vectors are represented along two sides of a triangle taken in order, then their resultant is represented by the third side taken in opposite direction i.e. in $\triangle ABC$, by triangle law of vector addition, we have

$$\overrightarrow{AB} + \overrightarrow{BC} = \overrightarrow{AC}$$

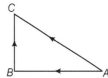

(ii) **Parallelogram Law of Vector Addition** If two vectors are represented along the two adjacent sides of a parallelogram, then their resultant is represented by the diagonal of the parallelogram, which is coinitial with the given vectors. If the sides OA and OC of parallelogram $OABC$ represents $\overrightarrow{OA}$ and $\overrightarrow{OC}$, respectively, then we get

$$\overrightarrow{OA} + \overrightarrow{OC} = \overrightarrow{OB} \quad \text{or} \quad \overrightarrow{OA} + \overrightarrow{AB} = \overrightarrow{OB} \quad [\because \overrightarrow{AB} = \overrightarrow{OC}]$$

Note *We may say that the two laws of vectors addition are equivalent to each other.*

7. Properties of Vector Addition

(i) For any two vectors $\vec{a}$ and $\vec{b}$,
$$\vec{a} + \vec{b} = \vec{b} + \vec{a} \qquad \text{[commutative law]}$$

(ii) For any three vectors $\vec{a}, \vec{b}$ and $\vec{c}$,
$$\vec{a} + (\vec{b} + \vec{c}) = (\vec{a} + \vec{b}) + \vec{c} \qquad \text{[associative law]}$$

(iii) For any vector $\vec{a}$, we have
$$\vec{a} + \vec{0} = \vec{0} + \vec{a} = \vec{a}.$$

The zero vector $\vec{0}$ is called the **additive identity** for the vector addition.

8. Multiplication of a Vector by Scalar

Let $\vec{a}$ be a given vector and λ be a scalar. Then, the product of the vector $\vec{a}$ by the scalar λ, denoted by $\lambda\vec{a}$, is called the multiplication of vector $\vec{a}$ by the scalar λ.

9. Properties of Multiplication of a Vector by a Scalar

Let $\vec{a}$ and $\vec{b}$ be any two vectors and k and m be any scalars. Then,

(i) $k\vec{a} + m\vec{a} = (k + m)\vec{a}$

(ii) $k(\vec{a} + \vec{b}) = k\vec{a} + k\vec{b}$

(iii) $k(m\vec{a}) = (km)\vec{a}$

10. Components of a Vector

If $\vec{a} = a_1\hat{i} + a_2\hat{j} + a_3\hat{k}$, then we can say that the scalar components of $\vec{a}$ along X-axis, Y-axis and Z-axis are a_1, a_2 and a_3, respectively.

11. Important Results in Component Form

If $\vec{a}$ and $\vec{b}$ are any two vectors given in the component form as $\vec{a} = a_1\hat{i} + a_2\hat{j} + a_3\hat{k}$ and $\vec{b} = b_1\hat{i} + b_2\hat{j} + b_3\hat{k}$.

Then, (a_1, a_2, a_3) and (b_1, b_2, b_3) are called **direction ratios** of $\vec{a}$ and $\vec{b}$, respectively.

(i) The sum (or resultant) of the vectors $\vec{a}$ and $\vec{b}$ is given by
$$\vec{a} + \vec{b} = (a_1 + b_1)\hat{i} + (a_2 + b_2)\hat{j} + (a_3 + b_3)\hat{k}$$

(ii) The difference of the vectors $\vec{a}$ and $\vec{b}$ is given by
$$\vec{a} - \vec{b} = (a_1 - b_1)\hat{i} + (a_2 - b_2)\hat{j} + (a_3 - b_3)\hat{k}$$

(iii) The vectors $\vec{a}$ and $\vec{b}$ are equal iff
$$a_1 = b_1, a_2 = b_2 \text{ and } a_3 = b_3$$

(iv) The multiplication of vector $\vec{a}$ by any scalar λ is given by $\lambda\vec{a} = (\lambda a_1)\hat{i} + (\lambda a_2)\hat{j} + (\lambda a_3)\hat{k}$

(v) If $\dfrac{b_1}{a_1} = \dfrac{b_2}{a_2} = \dfrac{b_3}{a_3} = k$ (constant).

Then, vectors $\vec{a}$ and $\vec{b}$ will be **collinear**.

(vi) If it is given that l, m and n are direction cosines of a vector, then
$$l\hat{i} + m\hat{j} + n\hat{k} = (\cos\alpha)\hat{i} + (\cos\beta)\hat{j} + (\cos\gamma)\hat{k}$$
is the unit vector in the direction of that vector, where α, β and γ are the angles which the vector makes with X, Y and Z-axes, respectively.

12. Vector Joining Two Points

If $P_1(x_1, y_1, z_1)$ and $P_2(x_2, y_2, z_2)$ are any two points on the plane, then vector joining of P_1 and P_2 is
$$\overrightarrow{P_1 P_2} = \overrightarrow{OP_2} - \overrightarrow{OP_1}$$
$$= (x_2\hat{i} + y_2\hat{j} + z_2\hat{k}) - (x_1\hat{i} + y_1\hat{j} + z_1\hat{k})$$
$$= (x_2 - x_1)\hat{i} + (y_2 - y_1)\hat{j} + (z_2 - z_1)\hat{k}$$

13. Section Formulae

Let A and B be two points with position vectors $\vec{a}$ and $\vec{b}$, respectively and P be a point which divides AB **internally** in the ratio $m : n$.

Then, position vector of $\vec{P} = \dfrac{m\vec{b} + n\vec{a}}{m + n}$.

If P divides AB **externally** in the ratio $m : n$. Then, position vector of $\vec{P} = \dfrac{m\vec{b} - n\vec{a}}{m - n}$.

Note If R is the mid-point of AB, then $\overrightarrow{OR} = \dfrac{\vec{a} + \vec{b}}{2}$.

14. Scalar or Dot Product

Let $\vec{a}$ and $\vec{b}$ be the two non-zero vectors inclined at an angle θ. Then, the scalar product or dot product of $\vec{a}$ and $\vec{b}$ is represented by $\vec{a}\cdot\vec{b}$ and it is defined as $\vec{a}\cdot\vec{b} = |\vec{a}||\vec{b}|\cos\theta$, where $0 \le \theta \le \pi$.

15. Important Results Based on Scalar Product

(i) $\vec{a} \perp \vec{b} \Leftrightarrow \vec{a}\cdot\vec{b} = 0$

(ii) $\hat{i}\cdot\hat{i} = \hat{j}\cdot\hat{j} = \hat{k}\cdot\hat{k} = 1$ and $\hat{i}\cdot\hat{j} = \hat{j}\cdot\hat{k} = \hat{k}\cdot\hat{i} = \vec{0}$

(iii) If $\theta = 0$, then $\vec{a}\cdot\vec{b} = |\vec{a}||\vec{b}|$
If $\theta = \pi$, then $\vec{a}\cdot\vec{b} = -|\vec{a}||\vec{b}|$

(iv) The angle between two non-zero vectors $\vec{a}$ and $\vec{b}$ is given by
$$\cos\theta = \dfrac{\vec{a}\cdot\vec{b}}{|\vec{a}||\vec{b}|} \text{ or } \theta = \cos^{-1}\left(\dfrac{\vec{a}\cdot\vec{b}}{|\vec{a}||\vec{b}|}\right)$$

16. Properties of Scalar Product

(i) $\vec{a}\cdot\vec{b} = \vec{b}\cdot\vec{a}$ \hfill [commutative]

(ii) $\vec{a}\cdot(\vec{b} + \vec{c}) = \vec{a}\cdot\vec{b} + \vec{a}\cdot\vec{c}$

(iii) $\vec{a}\cdot\vec{a} = |\vec{a}|^2 = a^2$
where, a represents magnitude of vector $\vec{a}$.

(iv) $(\vec{a} + \vec{b})\cdot(\vec{a} - \vec{b}) = a^2 - b^2$, where a and b represent the magnitude of vectors $\vec{a}$ and $\vec{b}$.

(v) $(\lambda\vec{a})\cdot\vec{b} = \lambda(\vec{a}\cdot\vec{b})$

Note If α, β and γ are the direction angles of vector $\vec{a} = a_1\hat{i} + a_2\hat{j} + a_3\hat{k}$, then its DC's is given as
$$\cos\alpha = \dfrac{a_1}{|\vec{a}|}, \quad \cos\beta = \dfrac{a_2}{|\vec{a}|}, \quad \cos\gamma = \dfrac{a_3}{|\vec{a}|}$$

17. Projection of a Vector

Let $\vec{a}$ and $\vec{b}$ be two vectors represented by $\overrightarrow{OA}$ and $\overrightarrow{OB}$ respectively and let θ be the angle made by $\vec{a}$ with directed line l in the anti-clockwise direction.

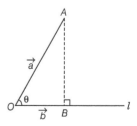

Then, the projection of $\overrightarrow{OA}$ on the line l is $\overrightarrow{OB}$, which is given by $|\overrightarrow{OA}|\cos\theta$ and the direction of $\vec{b}$, called **projection vector**, being the same (or opposite) to that of the line l, depending upon whether $\cos\theta$ is positive or negative.

Note $\vec{b} = |\overrightarrow{OA}|\cos\theta \cdot \hat{b} = |\vec{a}|\cos\theta \cdot \hat{b}$

$$\therefore \text{Projection of } \vec{a} \text{ on } \vec{b} = \frac{\vec{a} \cdot \vec{b}}{|\vec{b}|}$$

$$\text{and projection of } \vec{b} \text{ on } \vec{a} = \frac{\vec{a} \cdot \vec{b}}{|\vec{a}|}.$$

18. Cross or Vector Product

Let θ be the angle between two non-zero vectors $\vec{a}$ and $\vec{b}$, then the vector or cross product of $\vec{a}$ and $\vec{b}$ is represented by $\vec{a} \times \vec{b}$ and defined as

$\vec{a} \times \vec{b} = |\vec{a}||\vec{b}|\sin\theta\,\hat{n}$, where, $\hat{n}$ is a unit vector perpendicular to the plane of $\vec{a}$ and $\vec{b}$.

19. Properties of Cross Product

(i) $(\vec{a} \times \vec{b}) = -(\vec{b} \times \vec{a})$ [not commutative]

(ii) $\vec{a} \times (\vec{b} + \vec{c}) = \vec{a} \times \vec{b} + \vec{a} \times \vec{c}$ [distributive property]

(iii) $\lambda(\vec{a} \times \vec{b}) = (\lambda\,\vec{a}) \times \vec{b} = \vec{a} \times (\lambda\,\vec{b})$

20. Important Results Based on Cross Product

(i) A unit vector perpendicular to both $\vec{a}$ and $\vec{b}$ is given by $\hat{n} = \dfrac{(\vec{a} \times \vec{b})}{|\vec{a} \times \vec{b}|}$.

(ii) $\vec{a} \parallel \vec{b} \Leftrightarrow \vec{a} \times \vec{b} = \vec{0}$

(iii) $\vec{a} \times \vec{a} = \vec{0}$

(iv) $\hat{i} \times \hat{i} = \vec{0}, \hat{j} \times \hat{j} = \vec{0}, \hat{k} \times \hat{k} = \vec{0}$

(v) $\hat{i} \times \hat{j} = \hat{k}, \hat{j} \times \hat{k} = \hat{i}, \hat{k} \times \hat{i} = \hat{j};$
$\hat{j} \times \hat{i} = -\hat{k}, \hat{k} \times \hat{j} = -\hat{i}, \hat{i} \times \hat{k} = -\hat{j}$

(vi) If $\vec{a} = a_1\hat{i} + a_2\hat{j} + a_3\hat{k}$
and $\vec{b} = b_1\hat{i} + b_2\hat{j} + b_3\hat{k}$, then

$$\vec{a} \times \vec{b} = \begin{vmatrix} \hat{i} & \hat{j} & \hat{k} \\ a_1 & a_2 & a_3 \\ b_1 & b_2 & b_3 \end{vmatrix}$$

(vii) Area of a parallelogram with sides $\vec{a}$ and $\vec{b}$
$$= |\vec{a} \times \vec{b}|$$

(viii) Area of a parallelogram with diagonals
$$\vec{d_1} \text{ and } \vec{d_2} = \frac{1}{2}|\vec{d_1} \times \vec{d_2}|$$

(ix) Area of a $\triangle ABC = \dfrac{1}{2}|\overrightarrow{AB} \times \overrightarrow{AC}|$
$$= \frac{1}{2}|\overrightarrow{BC} \times \overrightarrow{BA}| = \frac{1}{2}|\overrightarrow{CB} \times \overrightarrow{CA}|$$

▮ Three Dimensional Geometry

1. Direction Cosines and Direction Ratios of a Line

If a line makes angles α, β and γ with X-axis, Y-axis and Z-axis, respectively, then $l = \cos\alpha$, $m = \cos\beta$ and $n = \cos\gamma$ are called the **direction cosines** of the line. The relation between direction cosines of a line is, $l^2 + m^2 + n^2 = 1$.

Numbers proportional to the direction cosines of a line are called the **direction ratios** of the line. If a, b and c are the direction ratios of a line, then

$$l = \frac{\pm a}{\sqrt{a^2 + b^2 + c^2}}, \quad m = \frac{\pm b}{\sqrt{a^2 + b^2 + c^2}}$$

and $\quad n = \dfrac{\pm c}{\sqrt{a^2 + b^2 + c^2}}$

Note *For any line, direction cosines are unique but direction ratios are not unique.*

2. Direction Cosines and Direction Ratios of a Line Passing Through Two Points

The direction cosines and direction ratios of the line passing through the points $P(x_1, y_1, z_1)$ and $Q(x_2, y_2, z_2)$ are respectively given by

$$\frac{x_2 - x_1}{PQ}, \frac{y_2 - y_1}{PQ}, \frac{z_2 - z_1}{PQ}$$

and $\quad (x_2 - x_1, y_2 - y_1, z_2 - z_1)$

where, $PQ = \sqrt{(x_2 - x_1)^2 + (y_2 - y_1)^2 + (z_2 - z_1)^2}$

3. Line

A line or straight line is a curve such that all points on the line segment joining two points of it lies on it.
A line in space can be determined uniquely, if

(i) its direction and the coordinates of a point on it are known.

(ii) it passes through two given points.

4. Equation of a Line

(i) **Equation of a line passing through a given point and parallel to a given vector**

Vector Equation The equation of a line through a given point A with position vector $\vec{a}$ and parallel to a given vector $\vec{b}$ is given by $\vec{r} = \vec{a} + \lambda\vec{b}$, where λ is a scalar.

Cartesian Equation The equation of a line passing through a point $A(x_1, y_1, z_1)$ and having direction ratios a, b and c is

$$\frac{x - x_1}{a} = \frac{y - y_1}{b} = \frac{z - z_1}{c}$$

If l, m and n are the direction cosines of the line, then equation of the line is

$$\frac{x - x_1}{l} = \frac{y - y_1}{m} = \frac{z - z_1}{n}$$

(ii) **Equation of a line passing through two given points**

Vector Equation The vector equation of a line passing through two points with position vectors $\vec{a}$ and $\vec{b}$ is given by

$$\vec{r} = \vec{a} + \lambda\,(\vec{b} - \vec{a}),$$

where λ is a scalar.

Cartesian Equation The equation of a line passing through two points $A(x_1, y_1, z_1)$ and $B(x_2, y_2, z_2)$ is

$$\frac{x - x_1}{x_2 - x_1} = \frac{y - y_1}{y_2 - y_1} = \frac{z - z_1}{z_2 - z_1}$$

5. Skew-lines

Lines which are neither parallel nor intersecting are called as skew-lines.

6. Shortest Distance between Two Skew-Lines

The shortest distance between two skew-lines is the length of line-segment perpendicular to both the lines.

In vector form Shortest distance between the skew-lines $\vec{r} = \vec{a}_1 + \lambda\,\vec{b}_1$ and $\vec{r} = \vec{a}_2 + \mu\,\vec{b}_2$ is given by

$$SD = \left| \frac{|(\vec{a}_2 - \vec{a}_1) \cdot (\vec{b}_1 \times \vec{b}_2)|}{|\vec{b}_1 \times \vec{b}_2|} \right|$$

The shortest distance between the parallel lines $\vec{r} = \vec{a}_1 + \lambda\,\vec{b}$ and $\vec{r} = \vec{a}_2 + \mu\,\vec{b}$ is given by

$$SD = \left| \frac{\vec{b} \times (\vec{a}_2 - \vec{a}_1)}{|\vec{b}|} \right|$$

In cartesian form The shortest distance between the lines

$$\frac{x - x_1}{a_1} = \frac{y - y_1}{b_1} = \frac{z - z_1}{c_1}$$

and

$$\frac{x - x_2}{a_2} = \frac{y - y_2}{b_2} = \frac{z - z_2}{c_2} \text{ is}$$

$$\left| \frac{\begin{vmatrix} x_2 - x_1 & y_2 - y_1 & z_2 - z_1 \\ a_1 & b_1 & c_1 \\ a_2 & b_2 & c_2 \end{vmatrix}}{\sqrt{(b_1 c_2 - b_2 c_1)^2 + (c_1 a_2 - c_2 a_1)^2 + (a_1 b_2 - a_2 b_1)^2}} \right|$$

Angle between Two Lines

Vector form $\cos\theta = \left| \dfrac{\vec{b}_1 \cdot \vec{b}_2}{|\vec{b}_1|\,|\vec{b}_2|} \right|$

Cartesian form

$$\cos\theta = \left| \frac{a_1 a_2 + b_1 b_2 + c_1 c_2}{\sqrt{a_1^2 + b_1^2 + c_1^2}\,\sqrt{a_2^2 + b_2^2 + c_2^2}} \right|$$

7. Coplanarity of Two Lines

In vector form Two lines $\vec{r} = \vec{a}_1 + \lambda\,\vec{b}_1$ and $\vec{r} = \vec{a}_2 + \mu\,\vec{b}_2$ are coplanar,

iff $(\vec{a}_2 - \vec{a}_1) \cdot (\vec{b}_1 \times \vec{b}_2) = 0$.

In cartesian form Suppose, cartesian equations of two lines are

$$\frac{x - x_1}{a_1} = \frac{y - y_1}{b_1} = \frac{z - z_1}{c_1}$$

and

$$\frac{x - x_2}{a_2} = \frac{y - y_2}{b_2} = \frac{z - z_2}{c_2}.$$

Then, these lines are coplanar iff

$$\begin{vmatrix} x_2 - x_1 & y_2 - y_1 & z_2 - z_1 \\ a_1 & b_1 & c_1 \\ a_2 & b_2 & c_2 \end{vmatrix} = 0.$$

■ Linear Programming

1. Linear Programming Problem (LPP)

A linear programming problem is one that is concerned with finding the optimal value (maximum or minimum value) of a linear function (called **objective function**) of several variables (say x and y called **decision variables**), subject to the constraints that the variables are non-negative and satisfy a set of linear inequalities (called **linear constraints**).

2. Mathematical Form of LPP

The general mathematical form of a linear programming problem may be written as Maximise or Minimise $Z = c_1 x + c_2 y$ subject to constraints are $a_1 x + b_1 y \le d_1$, $a_2 x + b_2 y \le d_2$, etc. and non-negative restrictions are $x \ge 0, y \ge 0$.

3. Some Terms Related to LPP

(i) **Constraints** The linear inequations or inequalities or restrictions on the variables of a linear programming problem are called **constraints**. The conditions $x \ge 0, y \ge 0$ are called **non-negative restrictions**.

(ii) **Optimisation Problem** A problem which seeks to maximise or minimise a linear function subject to certain constraints determined by a set of linear inequalities is called an optimisation problem. Linear programming problems are special type of optimisation problems.

(iii) **Objective Function** A linear function of two or more variables which has to be maximised or minimised under the given restrictions in the form of linear inequations or linear constraints is called the **objective function**. The variables used in the objective function are called **decision variables**.

(iv) **Optimal Values** The maximum or minimum value of an objective function is known as its optimal value.

(v) **Feasible and Infeasible Regions** The common region determined by all the constraints including non-negative constraints $x, y \geq 0$ of a linear programming problem is called the **feasible region** or **solution region**. Each point in this region represents a feasible choice. The region other than feasible region is called an **infeasible region**.

(vi) **Bounded and Unbounded Regions** A feasible region of a system of linear inequalities is said to be **bounded**, if it can be enclosed within a circle. Otherwise, it is said to be **unbounded region.**

(vii) **Feasible and Infeasible Solutions** Any solution to the given linear programming problem which also satisfies the non-negative restrictions of the problem is called a **feasible solution.**

Any point outside the feasible region is called an infeasible solution.

(viii) **Optimal Solution** A feasible solution at which the objective function has optimal value is called the optimal solution of the linear programming problem.

(ix) **Optimisation Technique** The process of obtaining the optimal solution is called optimisation technique.

4. Important Theorems

(i) **Theorem 1** Let R be the feasible region (convex polygon) for a linear programming problem and $Z = ax + by$ be the objective function.

When Z has an optimal value (maximum or minimum), where the variables x and y are subject to constraints described by linear inequalities, this optimal value must occur at a corner point (vertex) of the feasible region.

(A corner point of a feasible region is a point of intersection of two boundary lines in the region).

(ii) **Theorem 2** Let R be the feasible region for a linear programming problem and $Z = ax + by$ be the objective function. If R is bounded, then the objective function Z has both a maximum and a minimum value on R and each of these occurs at a corner point (vertex) of R.

Note *Maximum or minimum value of the objective function may or may not exist, if the feasible region is unbounded.*

5. Graphical Method of Solving LPP

The following steps are given below:

Step I Find the feasible region of the linear programming problem and determine its corner points (vertices) either by inspection or by solving the two equations of the lines intersecting at that point.

Step II Evaluate the objective function $Z = ax + by$ at each corner point. Let M and m respectively denote the largest and smallest values of these points.

Step III When the feasible region is bounded, M and m are the maximum and minimum values of Z.

Step IV When the feasible region is unbounded, then

   (a) M is the maximum value of Z, if the open half plane determined by $ax + by > M$ has no point in common with the feasible region. Otherwise, Z has no maximum value.

   (b) Similarly, m is the minimum value of Z, if the open half plane determined by $ax + by < m$ has no point in common with the feasible region. Otherwise, Z has no minimum value.

■ Probability

1. Some Basic Definitions

(i) **Experiment** An operation which can produce some well-defined outcomes, is called an experiment.

(ii) **Random Experiment** An experiment in which total outcomes are known in advance but occurrence of specific outcome can be told only after completion of the experiment, is known as a random experiment.

(iii) **Outcomes** A possible result of a random experiment is called its outcomes.

(iv) **Sample Space** The set of all possible outcomes of a random experiment is called its sample space. It is usually denoted by S.

(v) **Trial** When a random experiment is repeated under identical conditions and it does not give the same result each time but may result in any one of the several possible outcomes, then such experiment is called a trial and outcomes are called cases.

2. Event

A subset of the sample space associated with a random experiment is called an event.

3. Types of Events

(i) **Impossible and Sure Events** The empty set ϕ and the sample space S describe events (as S and ϕ are also subset of S). The empty set ϕ is called an impossible event and whole sample space S is called the sure event.

(ii) **Simple Event** If an event has only one sample point of a sample space, then it is called a simple or elementary event.

(iii) **Compound Event** If an event has more than one sample point, then it is called a compound event.

(iv) **Equally Likely Event** The given events are said to be equally likely, if none of them is expected to occur in preference to the other.

(v) **Mutually Exclusive Event** A set of events is said to be mutually exclusive, if the happening of one excludes the happening of the other, i.e. if A and B are mutually exclusive, then $(A \cap B) = \phi$.

(vi) **Exhaustive Event** A set of events is said to be exhaustive, if the performance of the experiment always results in the occurrence of atleast one of them. If $E_1, E_2, ..., E_n$ are exhaustive events, then $E_1 \cup E_2 \cup ... \cup E_n = S$.

(vii) **Complement of an Event** Let A be an event in a sample space S, then complement of A is the set of all sample points of the space other than the sample point in A and it is denoted by A' or $\overline{A}$,

i.e. $A' = \{n : n \in S, n \notin A\}$

4. Probability of an Event

In a random experiment, let S be the sample space and E be the event. Then,

$$P(E) = \frac{\text{Number of outcomes favourable to } E}{\text{Total number of all possible outcomes}} = \frac{n(E)}{n(S)}$$

(i) If E is an event and S is the sample space, then
(a) $0 \le P(E) \le 1$ (b) $P(\phi) = 0$ (c) $P(S) = 1$

(ii) $P(\overline{E}) = 1 - P(E)$

5. Coin

A coin has two sides, head and tail. If an event consists of more than one coin, then coins are considered as distinct, if not otherwise stated.

(i) Sample space of one coin $= \{H, T\}$

(ii) Sample space of two coins
$$= \{(H, T), (T, H), (H, H), (T, T)\}$$

(iii) Sample space of three coins
$$= \{(H, H, H), (H, H, T), (H, T, H), (T, H, H),$$
$$(H, T, T), (T, H, T), (T, T, H), (T, T, T)\}$$

6. Die

A die has six faces marked 1, 2, 3, 4, 5 and 6. If we have more than one die, then all dice are considered as distinct, if not otherwise stated.

(i) Sample space of a die $= \{1, 2, 3, 4, 5, 6\}$

(ii) Sample space of two dice

$$= \begin{cases} (1, 1), (1, 2), (1, 3), (1, 4), (1, 5), (1, 6) \\ (2, 1), (2, 2), (2, 3), (2, 4), (2, 5), (2, 6) \\ (3, 1), (3, 2), (3, 3), (3, 4), (3, 5), (3, 6) \\ (4, 1), (4, 2), (4, 3), (4, 4), (4, 5), (4, 6) \\ (5, 1), (5, 2), (5, 3), (5, 4), (5, 5), (5, 6) \\ (6, 1), (6, 2), (6, 3), (6, 4), (6, 5), (6, 6) \end{cases}$$

7. Playing Cards

A pack of playing cards has 52 cards. There are 4 suits namely spade, heart, diamond and club, each having 13 cards. There are two colours, red (heart and diamond) and black (spade and club), each having 26 cards.

In 13 cards of each suit, there are 3 face cards namely king, queen and jack, so there are in all 12 face cards.

Also, there are 16 honour cards, 4 of each suit namely ace, king, queen and jack.

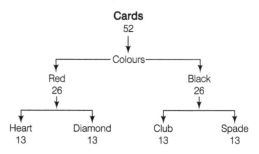

8. Important Results on Probability

(i) **Addition Theorem of Probability**

(a) For two events A and B,
$$P(A \cup B) = P(A) + P(B) - P(A \cap B)$$

If A and B are mutually exclusive events, then
$$P(A \cup B) = P(A) + P(B)$$
[for mutually exclusive, $P(A \cap B) = 0$]

(b) For three events A, B and C,
$$P(A \cup B \cup C) = P(A) + P(B) + P(C) - P(A \cap B)$$
$$- P(B \cap C) - P(A \cap C) + P(A \cap B \cap C)$$

If A, B and C are mutually exclusive events, then
$$P(A \cup B \cup C) = P(A) + P(B) + P(C)$$

$$\left[\begin{array}{c} \text{for mutually exclusive events,} \\ P(A \cap B) = P(B \cap C) = P(C \cap A) \\ = P(A \cap B \cap C) = 0 \end{array} \right]$$

(ii) If A and B are two events associated to a random experiment, then

(a) $P(\overline{A} \cap B) = P(B) - P(A \cap B)$

(b) $P(A \cap \overline{B}) = P(A) - P(A \cap B)$

(c) $P[(A \cap \overline{B}) \cup (\overline{A} \cap B)] = P(A) + P(B) - 2P(A \cap B)$

(d) $P(\overline{A} \cap \overline{B}) = 1 - P(A \cup B)$

(e) $P(\overline{A} \cup \overline{B}) = 1 - P(A \cap B)$

(f) $P(A) = P(A \cap B) + P(A \cap \overline{B})$

(g) $P(B) = P(A \cap B) + P(B \cap \overline{A})$

(iii) (a) P (exactly one of A, B occurs)
$$= P(A) + P(B) - 2P(A \cap B)$$
$$= P(A \cup B) - P(A \cap B)$$

(b) P (neither A nor B) $= P(\overline{A} \cap \overline{B}) = 1 - P(A \cup B)$

(iv) If A, B and C are three events, then
P (exactly one of A, B, C occurs)
$$= P(A) + P(B) + P(C) - 2P(A \cap B) - 2P(B \cap C)$$
$$- 2P(A \cap C) + 3P(A \cap B \cap C)$$

(v) (a) $P(\overline{A}) = 1 - P(A)$ (b) $P(A \cup \overline{A}) = P(S), P(\phi) = 0$

9. Conditional Probability

Let E and F be two events associated with a random experiment. Then, probability of occurrence of event E, when the event F has already occurred, is called conditional probability of event E over F and is denoted by $P(E/F)$.

$$P(E/F) = \frac{P(E \cap F)}{P(F)},$$

where $P(F) \neq 0$.

10. Properties of Conditional Probability

Let A, B and C be the events of a sample space S. Then,

(i) $P(S/A) = P(A/A) = 1$

(ii) $P\{(A \cup B)/C\} = P(A/C) + P(B/C) - P\{(A \cap B)/C\}$; $P(C) \neq 0$

(iii) $P(A'/B) = 1 - P(A/B)$, where A' is complement of A.

11. Multiplication Theorem of Probability

Let A and B are two events associated with a random experiment, then

$$P(A \cap B) = \begin{cases} P(A) \cdot P(B/A), \text{ where } P(A) \neq 0 \\ P(B) \cdot P(A/B), \text{ where } P(B) \neq 0 \end{cases}$$

12. Multiplication Theorem for More than Two Events

Let E, F and G be three events of sample space S, then

$$P(E \cap F \cap G) = P(E) \cdot P\left(\frac{F}{E}\right) \cdot P\left(\frac{G}{E \cap F}\right)$$

13. Independent Events

Two events A and B are said to be independent, if the occurrence or non-occurrence of one event does not affect the occurrence or non-occurrence of another event.

Two events E and F are said to be independent, if

$$P(F/E) = P(F), P(E) \neq 0,$$

and $$P(E/F) = P(E), P(F) \neq 0.$$

Note *If E and F are independent events, then* $P(E \cap F) = P(E) \cdot P(F)$.

14. Theorem of Total Probability

Let S be the sample space and $E_1, E_2, E_3, \ldots, E_n$ be n mutually exclusive and exhaustive events associated with a random experiment.

If E is any event which occurs with $E_1, E_2, E_3, \ldots, E_n$.

Then, $P(E) = P(E_1) \cdot P(E/E_1) + P(E_2) \cdot P(E/E_2)$

$$+ P(E_3) \cdot P(E/E_3) + \ldots + P(E_n) \cdot P(E/E_n)$$

or $$P(E) = \sum_{i=1}^{n} P(E_i) \cdot P\left(\frac{E}{E_i}\right)$$

15. Baye's Theorem

Let S be the sample space and $E_1, E_2, \ldots, E_n$ be n mutually exclusive and exhaustive events associated with a random experiment.

If A is any event which occurs with $E_1, E_2, \ldots, E_n$, then probability of occurrence of E_i, when A occurred,

$$P(E_i/A) = \frac{P(E_i)P(A/E_i)}{\sum_{i=1}^{n} P(E_i)P(A/E_i)}; i = 1, 2, \ldots, n$$

16. Random Variable

A random variable is a real valued function, whose domain is the sample space of a random experiment. Generally, it is denoted by capital letter X.

17. Probability Distribution of a Random Variable

The system in which the value of a random variable are given along with their corresponding probability is called probability distribution.

If X is a random variable and takes the value $x_1, x_2, x_3, \ldots, x_n$ with respective probabilities $p_1, p_2, p_3, \ldots, p_n$. Then, the probability distribution of X is represented by

X	x_1	x_2	x_3	...	x_n
$P(X)$	p_1	p_2	p_3	...	p_n

where, $p_i > 0$ such that $\Sigma p_i = 1$; $i = 1, 2, 3, \ldots, n$

Mean of X denoted by μ is the number $\sum_{i=1}^{n} x_i p_i$, it is also called the **expectation** of X, denoted by $E(X)$.

Note *If x_i is one of the possible values of a random variable X, the statement $X = x_i$ is true only at some point(s) of the sample space. Hence, the probability that X takes value x_i is always non-zero, i.e. $P(X = x_i) \neq 0$.*

SAMPLE QUESTION PAPERS

Stage – I (1–5)
Stage – II (6–10)
Stage – III (11–15)

SAMPLE QUESTION PAPER 1

MATHEMATICS

Time : 3 hrs   Max. Marks : 80

General Instructions

1. This question paper contains - five sections A, B, C, D and E. Each section is compulsory. However, there are internal choices in some questions.
2. Section A has 18 MCQ's and 02 Assertion-Reason based questions of 1 mark each.
3. Section B has 5 Very Short Answer (VSA) type questions of 2 marks each.
4. Section C has 6 Short Answer (SA) type questions of 3 marks each.
5. Section D has 4 Long Answer (LA) type questions of 5 marks each.
6. Section E has 3 source based/case based/passage based/integrated units of assessment (4 marks each) with sub parts.

Section A

(Multiple Choice Questions) Each question carries 1 mark

1. From the set $\{1, 2, 3, 4, 5\}$, two numbers a and $b\,(a \neq b)$ are chosen at random. The probability that $\dfrac{a}{b}$ is an integer, is

(a) $\dfrac{1}{3}$ (b) $\dfrac{1}{4}$ (c) $\dfrac{1}{2}$ (d) $\dfrac{3}{5}$

Sol. (c) We have, set of numbers $\{1, 2, 3, 4, 5\}$.

Sample space of choosing two numbers $= {}^5C_2 = \dfrac{5 \times 4}{1 \times 2} = 10$

Favourable outcomes are $\left(\dfrac{2}{1}, \dfrac{3}{1}, \dfrac{4}{1}, \dfrac{5}{1}, \dfrac{4}{2}\right) = 5$

$\therefore$ Required probability $= \dfrac{5}{10} = \dfrac{1}{2}$

2. If $\begin{vmatrix} 2 & 3 & 2 \\ x & x & x \\ 4 & 9 & 1 \end{vmatrix} + 3 = 0$, then the value of x is

(a) 3   (b) 0   (c) –1   (d) 1

Sol. (c) We have, $\begin{vmatrix} 2 & 3 & 2 \\ x & x & x \\ 4 & 9 & 1 \end{vmatrix} + 3 = 0$

$\Rightarrow 2(x - 9x) - 3(x - 4x) + 2(9x - 4x) + 3 = 0$

$\Rightarrow \qquad\qquad -16x + 9x + 10x + 3 = 0$

$\Rightarrow \qquad\qquad\qquad\qquad 3x + 3 = 0$

$\Rightarrow \qquad\qquad\qquad\qquad\quad x = -1$

3. The graph of the inequality $2x + 3y > 6$ is

(a) half plane that contains the origin
(b) half plane that neither contains the origin nor the points of the line $2x + 3y = 6$
(c) whole XOY-plane excluding the points on the line $2x + 3y = 6$
(d) entire XOY plane

Sol. (b) The inequality $2x + 3y > 6$ represent half plane that neither contains the origin nor the points of the line $2x + 3y = 6$

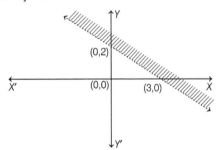

4. If A is a square matrix of order 3, such that $A(\text{adj } A) = 10\, I$, then $|\text{adj } A|$ is equal to

(a) 1   (b) 10   (c) 100   (d) 101

Sol. (c) We know that

$A (\text{adj } A) = |A| I$

Now, we have

$A (\text{adj } A) = 10I$

$\therefore \qquad |A| = 10$

Again, $\quad |\text{adj } A| = |A|^{n-1}$

$\therefore \qquad |\text{adj } A| = |A|^{3-1} = |A|^2 = (10)^2 = 100$

5. If $\vec{a} = 3\hat{i} + 2\hat{j} + 5\hat{k}$ and $\vec{b} = 6\hat{i} - \hat{j} - 5\hat{k}$, then find $(\vec{a} + \vec{b}) \cdot (\vec{a} - \vec{b})$.

(a) 24   (b) –24   (c) 18   (d) 10

Sol. (b) Given, $\vec{a} = 3\hat{i} + 2\hat{j} + 5\hat{k}$

and $\qquad \vec{b} = 6\hat{i} - \hat{j} - 5\hat{k}$

Now, $\vec{a} + \vec{b} = 9\hat{i} + \hat{j}$

and $\quad \vec{a} - \vec{b} = -3\hat{i} + 3\hat{j} + 10\hat{k}$

$\therefore (\vec{a} + \vec{b}) \cdot (\vec{a} - \vec{b}) = -27 + 3 = -24$

6. The two lines $x = ay + b,\, z = cy + d;$ and $x = a'y + b',\, z = c'y + d'$ are perpendicular to each other, if

(a) $\dfrac{a}{a'} + \dfrac{c}{c'} = 1$ (b) $\dfrac{a}{a'} + \dfrac{c}{c'} = -1$

(c) $aa' + cc' = 1$ (d) $aa' + cc' = -1$

Sol. (d) We have,

$\qquad\qquad x = ay + b,\, z = cy + d$

and $\qquad x = a'y + b',\, z = c'y + d'$

$\Rightarrow \quad \dfrac{x - b}{a} = \dfrac{y}{1} = \dfrac{z - d}{c}$ and $\dfrac{x - b'}{a'} = \dfrac{y}{1} = \dfrac{z - d'}{c'}$

Since, these lines are perpendicular.

$\therefore \qquad\qquad aa' + 1 + cc' = 0$

$[\because$ two lines are perpendicular, if $a_1 a_2 + b_1 b_2 + c_1 c_2 = 1]$

$\Rightarrow \qquad\qquad aa' + cc' = -1$

7. If $\vec{a}$ is a non-zero vector, then $(\vec{a} \cdot \hat{i})\hat{i} + (\vec{a} \cdot \hat{j})\hat{j} + (\vec{a} \cdot \hat{k})\hat{k}$ equals

(a) $\vec{a}$ (b) $2\vec{a}$ (c) $3\vec{a}$ (d) $\vec{0}$

Sol. (a) Let $\vec{a} = x\hat{i} + y\hat{j} + z\hat{k}$

$\therefore (\vec{a} \cdot \hat{i}) = (x\hat{i} + y\hat{j} + z\hat{k}) \cdot \hat{i} = x$

Similarly, $(\vec{a} \cdot \hat{j}) = y$ and $(\vec{a} \cdot \hat{k}) = z$

Now, $(\vec{a} \cdot \hat{i})\hat{i} + (\vec{a} \cdot \hat{j})\hat{j} + (\vec{a} \cdot \hat{k})\hat{k} = x\hat{i} + y\hat{j} + z\hat{k} = \vec{a}$

8. The direction ratios of the line passing through two points $(2, -4, 5)$ and $(0, 1, -1)$ is

(a) $(-2, -6, 5)$ (b) $(-2, 5, -6)$
(c) $(5, -2, -6)$ (d) $(-6, -2, 5)$

Sol. (b) Let $A(x_1, y_1, z_1) = (2, -4, 5)$

and $B(x_2, y_2, z_2) = (0, 1, -1)$

Then, DR's of line AB is $(0 - 2, 1 + 4, -1 - 5)$

i.e. $(-2, 5, -6)$.

9. If A is a 3×3 matrix such that $|A| = 8$, then $|3A|$ equals

(a) 8   (b) 24   (c) 72   (d) 216

Sol. (d) $\because |KA| = K^n |A|$

$\therefore \quad |3A| = 3^3 |A|$ $[\because n = 3]$

$\qquad\qquad = 27 \times 8 = 216$

10. $\int \dfrac{2^{x+1} - 5^{x-1}}{10^x}\, dx$ is equal to

(a) $\dfrac{1}{5}\log 2(2^{-x}) - 2\log 5(5^{-x}) + C$

(b) $\dfrac{1}{6}\log(2^{-x}) - 2\log 5(5^{-x}) + C$

(c) $\dfrac{1}{5}\log(2^{-x}) + 3\log 5(5^{-x}) + C$

(d) None of the above

Sol. (a) Let $\quad I = \int \dfrac{2^{x+1} - 5^{x-1}}{10^x}\, dx$

$\Rightarrow \quad I = \int \left(2\left(\dfrac{2}{10}\right)^x - \dfrac{1}{5}\left(\dfrac{5}{10}\right)^x \right) dx$

$\Rightarrow \quad I = \int \left(2(5)^{-x} - \dfrac{1}{5}(2)^{-x} \right) dx$

$\Rightarrow \quad I = -2 \cdot 5^{-x}\log 5 + \dfrac{1}{5}\cdot 2^{-x}\log 2 + C$

$\Rightarrow \quad I = \dfrac{1}{5}\log 2(2^{-x}) - 2\log 5(5^{-x}) + C$

11. The integrating factor of the differential equation $x\dfrac{dy}{dx} + 2y = x^2$ is

(a) x (b) x^2 (c) $3x$ (d) xy

Sol. (b) We have, $x\dfrac{dy}{dx} + 2y = x^2 \Rightarrow \dfrac{dy}{dx} + \dfrac{2}{x}y = x$

$\therefore$ Integrating factor $= e^{\int \frac{2}{x}dx} = e^{2\log x} = e^{\log x^2} = x^2$

12. If $y = \cos^{-1} x$, then $(1 - x^2)y_2$ is equal to

(a) xy (b) xy_1 (c) xy_2 (d) x^2y

Sol. (b) We have, $y = \cos^{-1}x$

$\Rightarrow \quad y_1 = \dfrac{-1}{\sqrt{1-x^2}} \qquad \ldots(i)$

$\Rightarrow \quad y_2 = \dfrac{(\sqrt{1-x^2}) \times 0 - (-1)\dfrac{1}{2\sqrt{1-x^2}}(-2x)}{(1-x^2)}$

$\Rightarrow y_2(1-x^2) = \dfrac{-x}{\sqrt{1-x^2}} \Rightarrow y_2(1-x^2) = xy_1$ [using Eq. (i)]

13. In an LPP, if the objective function has $Z = ax + by$ has the same maximum value on two corner points of the feasible region, then the number of points at which Z_{max} occurs is

(a) 0   (b) 2

(c) finite   (d) infinite

Sol. (d) An objective function has the same maximum value of two corner points the maximum value occur line joining two points.

$\therefore$ Infinite maximum value at line joining two points.

14. The number of points of discontinuity of f defined by $f(x) = |x| - |x+1|$ is

(a) 1   (b) 2   (c) 0   (d) 5

Sol. (c) We have, $f(x) = |x| - |x+1|$

$$f(x) = \begin{cases} 1, & x < -1 \\ -2x - 1, & -1 \le x < 0 \\ -1, & x \ge 0 \end{cases}$$

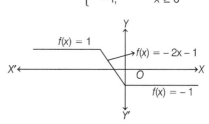

Clearly, $f(x)$ is continuous for all values of x. Hence, no discontinuous point exist.

15. The degree of the differential equation

$1 + \left(\dfrac{dy}{dx}\right)^2 = x$ is

(a) 1   (b) 2   (c) 3   (d) 4

Sol. (b) We have, $1 + \left(\dfrac{dy}{dx}\right)^2 = x$

$\therefore$ Degree $= 2$

16. If $\begin{vmatrix} 2 & 2 \\ 2 & 3 \end{vmatrix} = \begin{vmatrix} 3x & 1 \\ 4x & 2 \end{vmatrix}$, then x equals

(a) 1   (b) 2   (c) 3   (d) 4

Sol. (a) We have, $\begin{vmatrix} 2 & 2 \\ 2 & 3 \end{vmatrix} = \begin{vmatrix} 3x & 1 \\ 4x & 2 \end{vmatrix}$

$\Rightarrow \qquad 6 - 4 = 6x - 4x$

$\Rightarrow \qquad 2 = 2x$

$\Rightarrow \qquad x = 1$

17. If $\vec{a}\cdot\vec{b} = \dfrac{1}{2}|\vec{a}||\vec{b}|$, then the angle between $\vec{a}$ and $\vec{b}$ is

(a) $0°$ (b) $30°$ (c) $60°$ (d) $90°$

Sol. (c) Given $\vec{a}\cdot\vec{b} = \dfrac{1}{2}|\vec{a}||\vec{b}|$

$\Rightarrow |\vec{a}||\vec{b}|\cos\theta = \dfrac{1}{2}|\vec{a}||\vec{b}|$

$\Rightarrow \qquad \cos\theta = \dfrac{1}{2} \Rightarrow \theta = 60°$

$\therefore$ Angle between $\vec{a}$ and $\vec{b}$ is $60°$.

18. $\int_0^{\pi/8} \tan^2(2x)\, dx$ is equal to

(a) $\dfrac{4 - \pi}{8}$ (b) $\dfrac{4 + \pi}{8}$ (c) $\dfrac{4 - \pi}{4}$ (d) $\dfrac{4 - \pi}{2}$

Sol. (a) Let $I = \int_0^{\pi/8} \tan^2(2x)\,dx$

$\Rightarrow \quad I = \int_0^{\pi/8} (\sec^2(2x) - 1)\,dx$

$\Rightarrow \quad I = \left[\dfrac{\tan 2x}{2} - x\right]_0^{\pi/8}$

$\Rightarrow \quad I = \left(\dfrac{\tan \pi/4}{2} - \dfrac{\pi}{8}\right) - (0 - 0) = \dfrac{1}{2} - \dfrac{\pi}{8} = \dfrac{4 - \pi}{8}$

Assertion-Reason Based Questions

In the following questions, a statement of Assertion (A) is followed by a statement of Reason (R). Choose the correct answer out of the following choices.

(a) Both A and R are true and R is the correct explanation of A
(b) Both A and R are true but R is not the correct explanation of A
(c) A is true but R is false
(d) A is false but R is true

19. **Assertion (A)** We can write $\sin^{-1} x = (\sin x)^{-1}$

Reason (R) Any value in the range of principal value branch is called principal value of that inverse trigonometric function.

Sol. (d) **Assertion** $\sin^{-1} x$ should not be confused with $(\sin x)^{-1}$. Infact $(\sin x)^{-1} = \dfrac{1}{\sin x}$ and similarly for other trigonometric functions.

Reason The value of an inverse trigonometric function which lies in the range of principle branch, is called the principal value of that inverse trigonometric function. Hence, we can say that Assertion is false but Reason is true.

20. **Assertion (A)** A 2×2 matrix $A = [a_{ij}]$, whose elements are given by $a_{ij} = i \times j$, is $\begin{bmatrix} 1 & 2 \\ 2 & 4 \end{bmatrix}$.

Reason (R) If A is a 4×2 matrix, then the elements in A is 5.

Sol. (c) **Assertion** In general, the matrix A of order 2×2 is given by $A = \begin{bmatrix} a_{11} & a_{12} \\ a_{21} & a_{22} \end{bmatrix}$.

Now, $a_{ij} = i \times j, i = 1, 2$ and $j = 1, 2$

∴ $a_{11} = 1, a_{12} = 2, a_{21} = 2$ and $a_{22} = 4$

Thus, matrix A is $\begin{bmatrix} 1 & 2 \\ 2 & 4 \end{bmatrix}$

Reason If A is a 4×2 matrix, then A has $4 \times 2 = 8$ elements.

Hence, Assertion is true but Reason is false.

Section B

(This section comprises of very short answer type questions (VSA) of 2 marks each)

21. Check if the relation R on the set $A = \{1, 2, 3, 4, 5, 6\}$ defined as $R = \{(x, y) : y$ is divisible by $x\}$ is
   (i) symmetric
   (ii) transitive.

   Or

Find the value of $\tan^{-1}(1) + \cos^{-1}\left(-\dfrac{1}{2}\right) + \sin^{-1}\left(-\dfrac{1}{2}\right)$

Sol. (i) **For symmetry** We observe that 6 is divisible by 2 . This means that $(2, 6) \in R$ but 2 is not divisible by 6 i.e. $(6, 2) \notin R$. So, R is not symmetric.   (1)

(ii) **For transitivity** Let $(x, y) \in R$ and $(y, z) \in R$, then z is divisible by x. i.e., $(x, z) \in R$
e.g. 2 is divisible by 1, 4 is divisible by 2.
So, 4 is divisible by 1. So, R is transitive.   (1)

Or

We know that ranges of principle values of $\tan^{-1}, \cos^{-1}$ and $\sin^{-1}$ are $\left(\dfrac{-\pi}{2}, \dfrac{\pi}{2}\right), [0, \pi]$ and $\left[\dfrac{-\pi}{2}, \dfrac{\pi}{2}\right]$, respectively.

Let $\tan^{-1}(1) = \theta_1$,

$\Rightarrow \quad \tan \theta_1 = 1$

$\Rightarrow \quad \tan \theta_1 = \tan \dfrac{\pi}{4} \Rightarrow \theta_1 = \dfrac{\pi}{4} \in \left(\dfrac{-\pi}{2}, \dfrac{\pi}{2}\right)$ (1/2)

Again, let $\cos^{-1}\left(\dfrac{-1}{2}\right) = \theta_2 \Rightarrow \cos \theta_2 = \dfrac{-1}{2}$

$\Rightarrow \quad \cos \theta_2 = -\cos \dfrac{\pi}{3} = \cos\left(\pi - \dfrac{\pi}{3}\right) = \cos \dfrac{2\pi}{3}$

$\Rightarrow \quad \theta_2 = \dfrac{2\pi}{3} \in [0, \pi]$ (1/2)

Again, let $\sin^{-1}\left(\frac{-1}{2}\right) = \theta_3$

$\Rightarrow \qquad \sin\theta_3 = \frac{-1}{2} \;\Rightarrow\; \sin\theta_3 = -\sin\frac{\pi}{6}$

$\Rightarrow \qquad \sin\theta_3 = \sin\left(\frac{-\pi}{6}\right)$

$\Rightarrow \qquad \theta_3 = \frac{-\pi}{6} \in \left[\frac{-\pi}{2}, \frac{\pi}{2}\right]$ (1/2)

$\therefore\; \tan^{-1}(1) + \cos^{-1}\left(\frac{-1}{2}\right) + \sin^{-1}\left(\frac{-1}{2}\right)$

$\qquad = \frac{\pi}{4} + \frac{2\pi}{3} - \frac{\pi}{6} = \frac{3\pi}{4}$ (1/2)

22. If $x = a\cos\theta$ and $y = b\sin\theta$, then find $\dfrac{d^2 y}{dx^2}$.

Sol. We have, $x = a\cos\theta$ and $y = b\sin\theta$

$\therefore\; \dfrac{dx}{d\theta} = -a\sin\theta$ and $\dfrac{dy}{d\theta} = b\cos\theta$

$\therefore\; \dfrac{dy}{dx} = \dfrac{dy/d\theta}{dx/d\theta} = \dfrac{b\cos\theta}{-a\sin\theta} = \dfrac{-b}{a}\cot\theta$ (1)

Again, $\dfrac{d^2 y}{dx^2} = \dfrac{d}{dx}\left(\dfrac{dy}{dx}\right)$

$= \dfrac{d}{dx}\left(\dfrac{-b}{a}\cot\theta\right) = \dfrac{-b}{a}(-\csc^2\theta)\cdot\dfrac{d\theta}{dx}$

$= \dfrac{b}{a}\csc^2\theta \times \dfrac{1}{(-a\sin\theta)}$ $\left[\because \dfrac{d\theta}{dx} = \dfrac{1}{\dfrac{dx}{d\theta}}\right]$

$= \dfrac{-b}{a^2}\csc^3\theta$ (1)

23. Find $|\vec{a}|$ and $|\vec{b}|$, if $|\vec{a}| = 2|\vec{b}|$ and $(\vec{a} + \vec{b})\cdot(\vec{a} - \vec{b}) = 12$.

Or

Find the unit vector perpendicular to each of the vectors $\vec{a} = 4\hat{i} + 3\hat{j} + \hat{k}$ and $\vec{b} = 2\hat{i} - \hat{j} + 2\hat{k}$.

Sol. Given, $(\vec{a} + \vec{b})\cdot(\vec{a} - \vec{b}) = 12$ and $|\vec{a}| = 2|\vec{b}|$

$\Rightarrow \qquad |\vec{a}|^2 - |\vec{b}|^2 = 12$

$\Rightarrow \qquad (2|\vec{b}|)^2 - |\vec{b}|^2 = 12$ [given, $|\vec{a}| = 2|\vec{b}|$]

$\Rightarrow \qquad 4|\vec{b}|^2 - |\vec{b}|^2 = 12$ (1)

$\Rightarrow \qquad 3|\vec{b}|^2 = 12$

$\Rightarrow \qquad |\vec{b}|^2 = 4$

$\Rightarrow \qquad |\vec{b}| = 2$

$\therefore \qquad |\vec{a}| = 2|\vec{b}| = 2(2) = 4$ (1)

Or

Given, vectors are $\vec{a} = 4\hat{i} + 3\hat{j} + \hat{k}$

and $\qquad \vec{b} = 2\hat{i} - \hat{j} + 2\hat{k}$

Now, perpendicular vector to the given vector is

$\vec{a} \times \vec{b} = \begin{vmatrix} \hat{i} & \hat{j} & \hat{k} \\ 4 & 3 & 1 \\ 2 & -1 & 2 \end{vmatrix}$

$= \hat{i}(6+1) - \hat{j}(8-2) + \hat{k}(-4-6)$

$= 7\hat{i} - 6\hat{j} - 10\hat{k}$ (1/2)

$|\vec{a} \times \vec{b}| = \sqrt{7^2 + (-6)^2 + (-10)^2}$

$= \sqrt{49 + 36 + 100} = \sqrt{185}$ (1/2)

$\therefore$ Required unit vector $= \pm\dfrac{\vec{a} \times \vec{b}}{|\vec{a} \times \vec{b}|}$

$= \pm\dfrac{(7\hat{i} - 6\hat{j} - 10\hat{k})}{\sqrt{185}}$ (1)

24. Show that the function f defined by $f(x) = (x - 1)e^x + 1$ is an increasing function for all $x > 0$.

Sol. We have, $f(x) = (x - 1)e^x + 1$

On differentiating w.r.t. x, we get

$f'(x) = (x - 1)e^x + e^x$

$f'(x) = xe^x$ (1)

For all $x > 0 \Rightarrow f'(x) > 0$

$\therefore\; f(x)$ is an increasing function for all $x > 0$. (1)

25. If $\vec{a} = \hat{i} + \hat{j} + 3\hat{k}$ and $\vec{b} = 2\hat{i} - \hat{j} + \lambda\hat{k}$, then find the value of λ, if the vectors $\vec{a} + \vec{b}$ and $\vec{a} - \vec{b}$ are orthogonal.

Sol. Given, $\vec{a} = \hat{i} + \hat{j} + 3\hat{k}$

and $\qquad \vec{b} = 2\hat{i} - \hat{j} + \lambda\hat{k}$

$\therefore\; \vec{a} + \vec{b} = 3\hat{i} + (\lambda + 3)\hat{k}$

$\qquad \vec{a} - \vec{b} = -\hat{i} + 2\hat{j} + (3 - \lambda)\hat{k}$ (1)

According to the question,

$(\vec{a} + \vec{b})\cdot(\vec{a} - \vec{b}) = 0$

$\Rightarrow (3\hat{i} + (\lambda + 3)\hat{k})\cdot(-\hat{i} + 2\hat{j} + (3 - \lambda)\hat{k}) = 0$

$[\because$ if two vectors $\vec{a}$ and $\vec{b}$ are orthogonal, then $\vec{a}\cdot\vec{b} = 0]$

$\Rightarrow \qquad -3 + (3 + \lambda)(3 - \lambda) = 0$

$\Rightarrow \qquad -3 + 9 - \lambda^2 = 0$

$\Rightarrow \qquad 6 = \lambda^2$

$\Rightarrow \qquad \lambda = \sqrt{6}$ (1)

Section C

(This section comprises of short answer type questions (SA) of 3 marks each)

26. Find $\int \dfrac{x}{x^2+3x+2}\,dx$

Sol. Let $I = \int \dfrac{x}{x^2+3x+2}\,dx$

Again, let $x = A\dfrac{d}{dx}(x^2+3x+2) + B$

$\Rightarrow \qquad x = (2x+3)A + B$

$\Rightarrow \qquad x = 2Ax + (3A+B)$

$\therefore \qquad 2A = 1 \text{ and } 3A+B = 0$

$\Rightarrow \qquad A = \dfrac{1}{2} \text{ and } B = -\dfrac{3}{2}$

$\therefore \qquad I = \dfrac{1}{2}\int \dfrac{(2x+3)\,dx}{x^2+3x+2} - \dfrac{3}{2}\int \dfrac{dx}{x^2+3x+2}$

$\Rightarrow \qquad I = \dfrac{1}{2}I_1 - \dfrac{3}{2}I_2 \qquad \ldots(i) \; (1)$

Let $\quad I_1 = \int \dfrac{2x+3}{x^2+3x+2}\,dx \text{ and } I_2 = \int \dfrac{dx}{x^2+3x+2}$

Now, $\quad I_1 = \int \dfrac{2x+3}{x^2+3x+2}\,dx$

Put $x^2+3x+2 = t \Rightarrow (2x+3)\,dx = dt$

$\therefore \quad I_1 = \int \dfrac{dt}{t} = \log|t| + C_1 = \log|x^2+3x+2| + C_1 \qquad (1/2)$

and $I_2 = \int \dfrac{dx}{x^2+3x+2} = \int \dfrac{dx}{x^2+3x+\frac{9}{4}+2-\frac{9}{4}}$

$= \int \dfrac{dx}{\left(x+\frac{3}{2}\right)^2+2-\frac{9}{4}} = \int \dfrac{dx}{\left(x+\frac{3}{2}\right)^2-\left(\frac{1}{2}\right)^2}$

$= \dfrac{1}{2\times\frac{1}{2}}\log\left|\dfrac{x+\frac{3}{2}-\frac{1}{2}}{x+\frac{3}{2}+\frac{1}{2}}\right| + C_2$

$\Rightarrow \quad I_2 = \log\left|\dfrac{x+1}{x+2}\right| + C_2 \qquad (1/2)$

On substituting the value of I_1 and I_2 in Eq. (i), we get

$I = \dfrac{1}{2}\log|x^2+3x+2| + \dfrac{1}{2}C_1 - \dfrac{3}{2}\log\left|\dfrac{x+1}{x+2}\right| - \dfrac{3}{2}C_2$

$= \dfrac{1}{2}\log|x^2+3x+2| - \dfrac{3}{2}\log\left|\dfrac{x+1}{x+2}\right| + C,$

where $C = \dfrac{1}{2}C_1 - \dfrac{3}{2}C_2 \qquad (1)$

27. Find the value of $\int_0^1 x(1-x)^n\,dx$.

Or

Evaluate $\displaystyle\int_0^{\pi} \dfrac{x\sin x}{1+\cos^2 x}\,dx$.

Sol. Let $\quad I = \int_0^1 x(1-x)^n\,dx$

$\Rightarrow \quad I = \int_0^1 (1-x)\{1-(1-x)\}^n\,dx$

$$\left[\because \int_0^a f(x)\,dx = \int_0^a f(a-x)\,dx\right]$$

$= \int_0^1 (1-x)\,x^n\,dx = \int_0^1 (x^n - x^{n+1})\,dx \qquad (1)$

$= \left[\dfrac{x^{n+1}}{n+1} - \dfrac{x^{n+2}}{n+2}\right]_0^1 = \left[\dfrac{1}{n+1} - \dfrac{1}{n+2}\right] - 0$

$= \dfrac{(n+2)-(n+1)}{(n+1)(n+2)} = \dfrac{1}{(n+1)(n+2)} \qquad (2)$

Or

Let $I = \displaystyle\int_0^{\pi} \dfrac{x\sin x}{1+\cos^2 x}\,dx \qquad \ldots(i)$

$I = \displaystyle\int_0^{\pi} \dfrac{(\pi-x)\sin(\pi-x)}{1+\cos^2(\pi-x)}\,dx = \int_0^{\pi} \dfrac{(\pi-x)\sin x\,dx}{1+\cos^2 x} \quad \ldots(ii)$

On adding Eqs. (i) and (ii), we get

$2I = \pi\displaystyle\int_0^{\pi} \dfrac{\sin x\,dx}{1+\cos^2 x} \Rightarrow I = \dfrac{\pi}{2}\displaystyle\int_0^{\pi} \dfrac{\sin x}{1+\cos^2 x}\,dx \qquad (1)$

Using $\displaystyle\int_0^{2a} f(x)\,dx = 2\displaystyle\int_0^a f(x)\,dx$, if $f(2a-x) = f(x)$, we get

$I = \dfrac{\pi}{2}\times 2\displaystyle\int_0^{\pi/2} \dfrac{\sin x}{1+\cos^2 x}\,dx \Rightarrow I = \pi\displaystyle\int_0^{\pi/2} \dfrac{\sin x}{1+\cos^2 x}\,dx$

Put $\cos x = t$, then $-\sin x\,dx = dt$

When $x = 0$, then $t = 1$ and when $x = \dfrac{\pi}{2}$, then $t = 0 \qquad (1)$

$\therefore \qquad I = \pi\displaystyle\int_1^0 \dfrac{-dt}{1+t^2}$

$I = -\pi[\tan^{-1}t]_1^0$

$I = -\pi[\tan^{-1}0 - \tan^{-1}1]$

$I = -\pi\left[0 - \dfrac{\pi}{4}\right] = \dfrac{\pi^2}{4} \qquad (1)$

28. Solve $(x+1)\dfrac{dy}{dx} = 2e^{-y} + 1$; $y = 0$ when $x = 0$.

Or

Solve $x\sin\left(\dfrac{y}{x}\right)\dfrac{dy}{dx} + x - y\sin\left(\dfrac{y}{x}\right) = 0$; $y = \dfrac{\pi}{2}$ when $x = 1$.

Sol. Given, differential equation is

$$(x + 1)\frac{dy}{dx} = 2e^{-y} + 1$$

$$\Rightarrow \quad (x + 1)\frac{dy}{dx} = \frac{2 + e^y}{e^y} \quad \Rightarrow \quad \frac{e^y}{e^y + 2}dy = \frac{dx}{x + 1}$$

On integrating both sides, we get

$$\int\frac{e^y}{e^y + 2}dy = \int\frac{dx}{x + 1}$$

$$\Rightarrow \qquad \log(e^y + 2) = \log(x + 1) + \log C$$

$$\Rightarrow \qquad \log(e^y + 2) = \log C(x + 1) \qquad (1)$$

$$\Rightarrow \qquad e^y + 2 = C(x + 1) \qquad \ldots(i)$$

Also given, $y = 0$, when $x = 0$

On putting $x = 0$ and $y = 0$ in Eq. (i), we get

$$e^0 + 2 = C(0 + 1) \Rightarrow C = 1 + 2 = 3 \qquad (1)$$

On putting value of C in Eq. (i), we get

$$e^y + 2 = 3(x + 1)$$

$$\Rightarrow \qquad e^y = 3x + 3 - 2 \Rightarrow e^y = 3x + 1$$

$$\Rightarrow \qquad y = \log(3x + 1) \qquad (1)$$

Or

Given, differential equation can be written as

$$\frac{dy}{dx} = \frac{y}{x} - \frac{1}{\sin\left(\dfrac{y}{x}\right)}$$

Now, $(\lambda x, \lambda y) = \dfrac{\lambda y}{\lambda x} - \dfrac{1}{\sin\left(\dfrac{\lambda y}{\lambda x}\right)} = \lambda^0\left(\dfrac{y}{x} - \dfrac{1}{\sin\dfrac{y}{x}}\right)$

$$= \lambda^0 F(x, y) \qquad (1/2)$$

It is a homogeneous differential equation.

Now, put $y = vx$

$$\Rightarrow \qquad \frac{dy}{dx} = v + x\frac{dv}{dx}$$

$$\therefore \quad v + x\frac{dv}{dx} = \frac{vx}{x} - \frac{1}{\sin\left(\dfrac{vx}{x}\right)} \Rightarrow v + x\frac{dv}{dx} = v - \frac{1}{\sin v}$$

$$\Rightarrow \quad \sin v\, dv = -\frac{1}{x}dx \qquad (1/2)$$

On integrating both sides, we get

$$-\cos v = -\log|x| - C$$

$$\Rightarrow -\cos\left(\frac{y}{x}\right) = -\log|x| - C \qquad \left[\text{putting } v = \frac{y}{x}\right]$$

$$\Rightarrow \quad \cos\left(\frac{y}{x}\right) = \log|x| + C \qquad \ldots(i)\ (1)$$

Given that $x = 1$, when $y = \dfrac{\pi}{2}$

$$\therefore \quad \cos\left(\frac{\pi}{2}\right) = \log|1| + C$$

$$\Rightarrow \qquad 0 = 0 + C$$

$$\Rightarrow \qquad C = 0$$

Putting $C = 0$ in Eq. (i), we get

$$\cos\left(\frac{y}{x}\right) = \log|x| + 0$$

$$\Rightarrow \quad \cos\left(\frac{y}{x}\right) = \log|x| \qquad (1)$$

29. Three rotten apples are mixed with seven fresh apples. Find the probability distribution of the number of rotten apples, if three apples are drawn one by one with replacement. Find the mean of the number of rotten apples.

Or

In a shop X, 30 tins of ghee of type A and 40 tins of ghee of type B which look alike, are kept for sale. While in shop Y, similar 50 tins of ghee of type A and 60 tins of ghee of type B are there. One tin of ghee is purchased from one of the randomly selected shop and is found to be of type B. Find the probability that it is purchased from shop Y.

Sol. Given, rotten apples = 3 and fresh apples = 7

Here, total number of apples = $3 + 7 = 10$

Let X denotes the number of rotten apples.

Then, X takes the values 0, 1, 2, 3.

Let A be the event getting a rotten apple.

$$\therefore \quad P(A) = \frac{3}{10} \text{ and } P(A') = 1 - P(A) = 1 - \frac{3}{10} = \frac{7}{10}$$

Now, $P(X = 0) = P$ (getting 0 rotten apple)

$$= P(A')\,P(A')\,P(A')$$

$$= \frac{7}{10} \times \frac{7}{10} \times \frac{7}{10} = \frac{343}{1000} \qquad (1/2)$$

$P(X = 1) = P$(getting 1 rotten apple)

$$= 3P(A)\,P(A')\,P(A')$$

$$= 3 \times \frac{3}{10} \times \frac{7}{10} \times \frac{7}{10} = \frac{441}{1000}$$

$P(X = 2) = P$(getting 2 rotten apples)

$$= 3P(A)\,P(A)\,P(A')$$

$$= 3 \times \frac{3}{10} \times \frac{3}{10} \times \frac{7}{10} = \frac{189}{1000} \qquad (1/2)$$

and $P(X = 3) = P$(getting 3 rotten apples)

$$= P(A)\cdot P(A)\cdot P(A)$$

$$= \frac{3}{10} \times \frac{3}{10} \times \frac{3}{10} = \frac{27}{1000}$$

$\therefore$ Probability distribution is as follows:

X	0	1	2	3
$P(X)$	$\dfrac{343}{1000}$	$\dfrac{441}{1000}$	$\dfrac{189}{1000}$	$\dfrac{27}{1000}$

(1)

Now, mean $(\mu) = \Sigma X \cdot P(X)$

$$= \frac{0 \times 343}{1000} + \frac{1 \times 441}{1000} + \frac{2 \times 189}{1000} + \frac{3 \times 27}{1000}$$

$$= 0 + \frac{441}{1000} + \frac{378}{1000} + \frac{81}{1000} = \frac{900}{1000} = \frac{9}{10} \quad (1)$$

Or

Let E_1 = Getting ghee from shop X

E_2 = Getting ghee from shop Y

A = Getting type B ghee

$\therefore P(E_1) = P(E_2) = \frac{1}{2}$

[∵ both shop have equal chances]

$P(A/E_1)$ = Probability that type B ghee is purchased

from shop X

$$= \frac{40}{70} = \frac{4}{7} \quad (1)$$

$P(A/E_2)$ = Probability that type B ghee is
purchased from shop Y

$$= \frac{60}{110} = \frac{6}{11} \quad (1)$$

Now, by Baye's theorem, we get

$$P(E_2/A) = \frac{P(E_2)\,P(A/E_2)}{P(E_1)\,P(A/E_1) + P(E_2)\,P(A/E_2)}$$

$$= \frac{\dfrac{1}{2} \times \dfrac{6}{11}}{\dfrac{1}{2} \times \dfrac{4}{7} + \dfrac{1}{2} \times \dfrac{6}{11}} = \frac{\dfrac{6}{11}}{\dfrac{4}{7} + \dfrac{6}{11}}$$

$$= \frac{\dfrac{6}{11}}{\dfrac{44+42}{77}} = \frac{42}{86} = \frac{21}{43} \quad (1)$$

30. Evaluate $\displaystyle\int_1^2 \left[\frac{1}{x} - \frac{1}{2x^2}\right] e^{2x}\, dx$.

Sol. Let $I = \displaystyle\int_1^2 \left[\frac{1}{x} - \frac{1}{2x^2}\right] e^{2x}\, dx$

Put $2x = t \Rightarrow x = \frac{1}{2}t \Rightarrow dx = \frac{1}{2}dt$

When $x = 1$, then $t = 2$

and when $x = 2$, then $t = 4$ $\quad (1)$

$\therefore \quad I = \dfrac{1}{2}\displaystyle\int_2^4 \left[\dfrac{2}{t} - \dfrac{2}{t^2}\right] e^t\, dt$

$$= \int_2^4 \left(\frac{1}{t} + \frac{-1}{t^2}\right) e^t\, dt$$

$$= \left[\frac{1}{t}e^t\right]_2^4 \quad [\because \int e^x (f(x) + f'(x))\,dx = e^x f(x) + C]$$
$\quad (1)$

$$= \frac{e^4}{4} - \frac{e^2}{2} = \frac{e^2}{4}(e^2 - 2) \quad (1)$$

31. If $Z = 2x + 3y$, subject to constraints $x + 2y \le 10$, $2x + y \le 14$, $x, y \ge 0$, then find the corner point of feasible region.

Sol. Given, $Z = 2x + 3y$

Subject to constraints

$$x + 2y \le 10 \qquad \text{...(i)}$$
$$2x + y \le 14 \qquad \text{...(ii)}$$
and $\qquad x, y \ge 0 \qquad \text{...(iii)}$

Shade the region to the right of Y-axis to show $x \ge 0$ and above X-axis to show $y \ge 0$.

Table for line $x + 2y = 10$ is

x	0	4	10
y	5	3	0

$\qquad (1/2)$

So, the line is passing through the points $(0, 5)$, $(4, 3)$ and $(10, 0)$.

On putting $(0, 0)$ in the inequality $x + 2y \le 10$, we get $0 + 0 \le 10$, which is true.

So, the half plane is towards the origin.

Table for line $2x + y = 14$ is

x	4	6	7
y	6	2	0

$\qquad (1/2)$

So, the line is passing through the points $(4, 6)$, $(6, 2)$ and $(7, 0)$.

On putting $(0, 0)$ in the inequality $2x + y \le 14$, we get $0 + 0 \le 14$, which is true.

So, the half plane is towards the origin.

The intersection point of lines corresponding to Eqs. (i) and (ii) is $B(6, 2)$.

On shading the common region, we get the feasible region $OABD$.

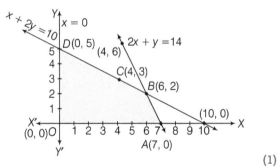

$\qquad (1)$

The corner poitns are $O(0, 0)$, $A(7, 0)$, $B(6, 2)$ and $D(0, 5)$. $\qquad (1)$

Section D

(This section comprises of long answer type questions (LA) of 5 marks each)

32. If $A = \begin{bmatrix} 2 & -3 & 5 \\ 3 & 2 & -4 \\ 1 & 1 & -2 \end{bmatrix}$, then find A^{-1}.

Using A^{-1}, solve the following system of equations:

$$2x - 3y + 5z = 11$$
$$3x + 2y - 4z = -5$$
$$x + y - 2z = -3$$

Sol. We have,

$$A = \begin{bmatrix} 2 & -3 & 5 \\ 3 & 2 & -4 \\ 1 & 1 & -2 \end{bmatrix}$$

Now, $|A| = \begin{vmatrix} 2 & -3 & 5 \\ 3 & 2 & -4 \\ 1 & 1 & -2 \end{vmatrix}$

$$= 2(-4 + 4) + 3(-6 + 4) + 5(3 - 2)$$
$$= 2(0) + 3(-2) + 5(1) = -6 + 5 = -1 \neq 0$$

Thus, A^{-1} exist.   (1)

Now, cofactor of $|A|$ are

$$C_{11} = \begin{vmatrix} 2 & -4 \\ 1 & -2 \end{vmatrix} = -4 + 4 = 0$$

$$C_{12} = \begin{vmatrix} 3 & -4 \\ 1 & -2 \end{vmatrix} = -(-6 + 4) = 2$$

$$C_{13} = \begin{vmatrix} 3 & 2 \\ 1 & 1 \end{vmatrix} = 3 - 2 = 1$$

$$C_{21} = -\begin{vmatrix} -3 & 5 \\ 1 & -2 \end{vmatrix} = -(6 - 5) = -1$$

$$C_{22} = \begin{vmatrix} 2 & 5 \\ 1 & -2 \end{vmatrix} = (-4 - 5) = -9$$

$$C_{23} = -\begin{vmatrix} 2 & -3 \\ 1 & 1 \end{vmatrix} = -(2 + 3) = -5$$

$$C_{31} = \begin{vmatrix} -3 & 5 \\ 2 & -4 \end{vmatrix} = 12 - 10 = 2$$

$$C_{32} = -\begin{vmatrix} 2 & 5 \\ 3 & -4 \end{vmatrix} = -(-8 - 15) = 23$$

$$C_{33} = \begin{vmatrix} 2 & -3 \\ 3 & 2 \end{vmatrix} = 4 + 9 = 13$$

$$\therefore \text{adj}(A) = \begin{bmatrix} C_{11} & C_{12} & C_{13} \\ C_{21} & C_{22} & C_{23} \\ C_{31} & C_{32} & C_{33} \end{bmatrix}^T$$ (1)

$$= \begin{bmatrix} 0 & 2 & 1 \\ -1 & -9 & -5 \\ 2 & 23 & 13 \end{bmatrix}^T = \begin{bmatrix} 0 & -1 & 2 \\ 2 & -9 & 23 \\ 1 & -5 & 13 \end{bmatrix}$$

$$\therefore A^{-1} = \frac{\text{adj}(A)}{|A|}$$

$$= \frac{1}{-1} \begin{bmatrix} 0 & -1 & 2 \\ 2 & -9 & 23 \\ 1 & -5 & 13 \end{bmatrix}$$

$$\Rightarrow A^{-1} = \begin{bmatrix} 0 & 1 & -2 \\ -2 & 9 & -23 \\ -1 & 5 & -13 \end{bmatrix}$$ ...(i) (1)

Now, to find the solution of system equations

$$2x - 3y + 5z = 11$$
$$3x + 2y - 4z = -5$$
$$x + y - 2z = -3$$

Given, system of equations can be written in matrix form as

$AX = B$, where $A = \begin{bmatrix} 2 & -3 & 5 \\ 3 & 2 & -4 \\ 1 & 1 & -2 \end{bmatrix}$,

$$X = \begin{bmatrix} x \\ y \\ z \end{bmatrix} \text{ and } B = \begin{bmatrix} 11 \\ -5 \\ -3 \end{bmatrix}$$

$$\Rightarrow X = A^{-1}B = \begin{bmatrix} 0 & 1 & -2 \\ -2 & 9 & -23 \\ -1 & 5 & -13 \end{bmatrix}\begin{bmatrix} 11 \\ -5 \\ -3 \end{bmatrix}$$ [∵ from Eq. (i)] (1)

$$= \begin{bmatrix} 0 - 5 + 6 \\ -22 - 45 + 69 \\ -11 - 25 + 39 \end{bmatrix}$$

$$\Rightarrow \begin{bmatrix} x \\ y \\ z \end{bmatrix} = \begin{bmatrix} 1 \\ 2 \\ 3 \end{bmatrix}$$

On comparing the corresponding elements, we get
$x = 1, y = 2$ and $z = 3$ (1)

33. Find the vector and certesian equations of the line which is perpendicular to the lines with equations $\dfrac{x+2}{1} = \dfrac{y-3}{2} = \dfrac{z+1}{4}$ and $\dfrac{x-1}{2} = \dfrac{y-2}{3} = \dfrac{z-3}{4}$ and passes through the point (1, 1, 1). Also, find the angle between the given lines.

Or

Find the shortest distance between the lines given by

$$\vec{r} = (2 + \lambda)\hat{i} - (3 + \lambda)\hat{j} + (5 + \lambda)\hat{k}$$

and $$\vec{r} = (2\mu - 1)\hat{i} + (4\mu - 1)\hat{j} + (5 - 3\mu)\hat{k}.$$

Sol. Any line through the point (1, 1, 1) is given by

$$\frac{x-1}{a} = \frac{y-1}{b} = \frac{z-1}{c} \qquad \ldots(i)$$

where a, b and c are the direction ratios of line (i). Now, the line (i) is perpendicular to the lines

$$\frac{x+2}{1} = \frac{y-3}{2} = \frac{z+1}{4} \qquad (1)$$

and $\dfrac{x-1}{2} = \dfrac{y-2}{3} = \dfrac{z-3}{4}$, where DR's of these two

lines are (1, 2, 4) and (2, 3, 4), respectively.

$$\therefore \qquad a + 2b + 4c = 0 \qquad \ldots(ii)$$
$$\text{and} \qquad 2a + 3b + 4c = 0 \qquad \ldots(iii) \quad (1)$$

[∵ if two lines having DR's (a_1, b_1, c_1) and (a_2, b_2, c_2) are perpendicular, then $a_1 a_2 + b_1 b_2 + c_1 c_2 = 0$]

By cross-multiplication method, we get

$$\frac{a}{8-12} = \frac{b}{8-4} = \frac{c}{3-4} \Rightarrow \frac{a}{-4} = \frac{b}{4} = \frac{c}{-1}$$

∴ DR's of line (i) are $-4, 4, -1$

∴ The required cartesian equation of line (i) is

$$\frac{x-1}{-4} = \frac{y-1}{4} = \frac{z-1}{-1} \qquad (1)$$

and vector equation is $\vec{r} = \hat{i} + \hat{j} + \hat{k} + \lambda(-4\hat{i} + 4\hat{j} - \hat{k})$ (1)

Again, let θ be the angle between the given lines. Then,

$$\cos\theta = \frac{|1 \times 2 + 2 \times 3 + 4 \times 4|}{\sqrt{1+4+16}\sqrt{4+9+16}} = \frac{24}{\sqrt{21}\sqrt{29}} = \frac{24}{\sqrt{609}}$$

$$\therefore \quad \theta = \cos^{-1}\left(\frac{24}{\sqrt{609}}\right) \qquad (1)$$

Or

Given, equation of lines can be rewritten as

$$\vec{r} = (2\hat{i} - 3\hat{j} + 5\hat{k}) + \lambda(\hat{i} - \hat{j} + \hat{k})$$

and $\quad \vec{r} = (-\hat{i} - \hat{j} + 5\hat{k}) + \mu(2\hat{i} + 4\hat{j} - 3\hat{k})$

On comparing the above equations with standard vector form of equation of line, $\vec{r} = \vec{a} + \lambda\vec{b}$, we get

$$\vec{a_1} = 2\hat{i} - 3\hat{j} + 5\hat{k}, \vec{b_1} = \hat{i} - \hat{j} + \hat{k},$$

and $\quad \vec{a_2} = -\hat{i} - \hat{j} + 5\hat{k}, \vec{b_2} = 2\hat{i} + 4\hat{j} - 3\hat{k}$ (1)

Now consider, $\vec{b_1} \times \vec{b_2} = \begin{vmatrix} \hat{i} & \hat{j} & \hat{k} \\ 1 & -1 & 1 \\ 2 & 4 & -3 \end{vmatrix}$

$$= \hat{i}(3-4) - \hat{j}(-3-2) + \hat{k}(4+2)$$

$$\Rightarrow \quad \vec{b_1} \times \vec{b_2} = -\hat{i} + 5\hat{j} + 6\hat{k} \qquad (1)$$

$$\Rightarrow \quad |\vec{b_1} \times \vec{b_2}| = \sqrt{(-1)^2 + (5)^2 + (6)^2}$$

$$= \sqrt{1+25+36} = \sqrt{62}$$

Also, $\vec{a_2} - \vec{a_1} = (-\hat{i} - \hat{j} + 5\hat{k}) - (2\hat{i} - 3\hat{j} + 5\hat{k})$

$$= -3\hat{i} + 2\hat{j} \qquad (1)$$

We know that shortest distance between two lines is

given by $d = \left| \dfrac{(\vec{b_1} \times \vec{b_2}) \cdot (\vec{a_2} - \vec{a_1})}{|\vec{b_1} \times \vec{b_2}|} \right|$

On putting above values, we get

$$d = \left| \frac{(-\hat{i} + 5\hat{j} + 6\hat{k}) \cdot (-3\hat{i} + 2\hat{j})}{\sqrt{62}} \right|$$

$$= \left| \frac{3 + 10 + 0}{\sqrt{62}} \right| = \frac{13}{\sqrt{62}} = \frac{13\sqrt{62}}{62}$$

Hence, required shortest distance is $\dfrac{13\sqrt{62}}{62}$ units. (2)

34. Prove that the relation R on Z, defined by $R\{(x, y): (x - y)$ is divisible by 5$\}$ is an equivalence relation.

Or

Show that the relation R in the set A of points in a plane, given by $R = \{(P, Q):$ distance of the point P from the origin is same as the distance of the point Q from the origin$\}$, is an equivalence reation. Further, show that the set of all points related to a point $P \neq (0, 0)$ is the circle passing through P with origin as centre.

Sol. Given, $R = \{(a, b): 5 \text{ divides } (a - b)\}$

and $\quad Z = $ Set of integers

Reflexive Let $a \in Z$ be any arbitrary element. Now, if $(a, a) \in R$, then 5 divides $a - a$, which is true. So, R is reflexive. (1)

Symmetric Let $a, b \in Z$, such that

$$(a, b) \in R \Rightarrow 5 \text{ divides } (a - b)$$
$$\Rightarrow \qquad 5 \text{ divides } [-(a - b)]$$
$$\Rightarrow \qquad 5 \text{ divides } (b - a) \Rightarrow (b, a) \in R$$

So, R is symmetric. (2)

Transitive Let $a, b, c \in Z$, such that $(a, b) \in R$ and $(b, c) \in R$

$\Rightarrow a - b$ and $b - c$ both are divisible by 5.

$\Rightarrow a - b + b - c$ is divisible by 5.

$\Rightarrow (a - c)$ is divisible by 5

$\Rightarrow (a, c) \in R$

So, R is transitive.

Thus, R is reflexive, symmetric and transitive.

Hence, R is an equivalence relation. (2)

Or

Here, $R = \{(P, Q):$ distance of point P from the origin is same as distance of point Q from the origin$\}$. Clearly, $(P, P) \in R$, since the distance of point P from the origin is always the same as the distance of the same point P from the origin.

Therefore, R is reflexive. (1)

Now, let $(P, Q) \in R$.

$\Rightarrow$ The distance of point P from the origin is same as the distance of point Q from the origin.

$\Rightarrow$ The distance of point Q from the origin is same as the distance of point P from the origin.

$\Rightarrow$ $(Q, P) \in R$

Therefore, R is symmetric.   (1)

Now, let $(P, Q), (Q, S) \in R$

The distance of points P and Q from the origin is same and also the distance of points Q and S from the origin is same.

$\Rightarrow$ The distance of points P and S from the origin is same.

$\Rightarrow$ $(P, S) \in R$

Therefore, R is transitive. Therefore, R is an equivalence relation.   (1)

The set of all points related to $P \neq (0, 0)$ will be those points whose distance from the origin is the same as the distance of point P from the origin.

In other words, if $O(0, 0)$ is the origin and $OP = k$, then the set of all points related to P is at a distance of k from the origin.

Hence, this set of points forms a circle with the centre as the origin and this circle passes through point P.   (2)

35. Find the area of the region lying in the first quadrant and enclosed by the X–axis, the line $y = x$ and the circle $x^2 + y^2 = 32$.

Sol. We have, circle $x^2 + y^2 = 32$ ...(i)

having centre $(0, 0)$ and radius $4\sqrt{2}$ units

and the line, $y = x$ ...(ii)

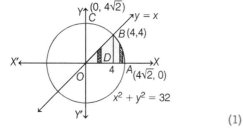

(1)

It is clear from the figure that, required region is $OABO$.

On putting the value of y from Eq. (ii) in Eq. (i), we get

$$x^2 + x^2 = 32$$

$\Rightarrow$ $2x^2 = 32$

$\Rightarrow$ $x^2 = \dfrac{32}{2} = 16$

$\Rightarrow$ $x = \pm 4$

From Eq. (ii), we get

$$y = \pm 4 \tag{1}$$

Thus, line and circle intersect at two points $(4, 4)$ and $(-4, -4)$. So, the coordinates of B are $(4, 4)$ [since, it is in I quadrant]. Also, circle cuts the X-axis at $A(4\sqrt{2}, 0)$ and Y-axis at $C(0, 4\sqrt{2})$ in I quadrant.

$$[\because 4\sqrt{2} \text{ is radius of a circle}]$$

Here, we have to draw two vertical strips, as perpendicular line drawn from intersection point to the X-axis, divides the region into two parts. Now, first strip is drawn in region $ODBO$ and then limit is taken from 0 to 4. Second strip is drawn in region $DABD$ and then limit is taken from 4 to $4\sqrt{2}$.

Now, area of region $ODBO = \int_0^4 y \, dx$, where y is the height of vertical strip

$$= \int_0^4 x \, dx = \left[\frac{x^2}{2} \right]_0^4$$

$$= \frac{(4)^2}{2} - 0 = 8 \text{ sq units} \tag{1}$$

and area of region $DABD = \int_4^{4\sqrt{2}} y \, dx$, where y is the height of vertical strip in this region

$$= \int_4^{4\sqrt{2}} \sqrt{32 - x^2} \, dx = \int_4^{4\sqrt{2}} \sqrt{(4\sqrt{2})^2 - x^2} \, dx$$

$$= \left[\frac{x}{2} \sqrt{(4\sqrt{2})^2 - x^2} + \frac{(4\sqrt{2})^2}{2} \times \sin^{-1}\left(\frac{x}{4\sqrt{2}} \right) \right]_4^{4\sqrt{2}}$$

$$= \left[\left\{ \frac{4\sqrt{2}}{2} \sqrt{(4\sqrt{2})^2 - (4\sqrt{2})^2} + \frac{32}{2} \sin^{-1}\left(\frac{4\sqrt{2}}{4\sqrt{2}} \right) \right\} \right.$$

$$\left. - \left\{ \frac{4}{2} \sqrt{(4\sqrt{2})^2 - (4)^2} + \frac{32}{2} \sin^{-1}\left(\frac{4}{4\sqrt{2}} \right) \right\} \right]$$

$$= 2\sqrt{2} \times 0 + 16 \sin^{-1}(1) - 2\sqrt{32 - 16} - 16 \sin^{-1}\left(\frac{1}{\sqrt{2}} \right)$$

$$= 16 \cdot \left(\frac{\pi}{2} \right) - 2\sqrt{16} - 16 \cdot \left(\frac{\pi}{4} \right)$$

$$= 8\pi - 8 - 4\pi = 4\pi - 8 \tag{1}$$

$\therefore$ Required area = Area of region $ODBO$

         + Area of region $DABD$

$$= 8 + 4\pi - 8 = 4\pi \text{ sq units}$$

Hence, the area of required region is 4π sq units. (1)

Section E

(This section comprises of 3 case-study/ passage-based questions of 4 marks each with two sub-parts. First two case study questions have three sub-parts (i), (ii), (iii) of marks 1, 1, 2 respectively. The third case study question has two sub-parts of 2 marks each)

36. $P(x) = -6x^2 + 120x + 25000$ (in ₹) is the total profit function of a company where x denotes the production of the company.

Based on the above information, answer the following questions.

(i) Find the profit of the company, when the production is 3 units.

(ii) Find $P'(5)$.

(iii) Find the interval in which the profit is strictly increasing.

Or

Find the production, when the profit is maximum.

Sol. (i) At $x = 3$,

$\quad P(3) = -6(3)^2 + 120(3) + 25000$

$\qquad = -54 + 360 + 25000 = ₹25306$

(ii) $P'(x) = -12x + 120$

$\quad P'(5) = -12 \times 5 + 120 = -60 + 120 = 60$

(iii) For strictly increasing, we must put $P'(x) > 0$

$\Rightarrow \qquad -12x + 120 > 0$

$\Rightarrow \qquad\qquad 120 > 12x$

$\Rightarrow \qquad\qquad\quad x < 10$

$\therefore \qquad\qquad x \in (0, 10)$

Or

$\quad P(x) = -6x^2 + 120x + 25000$

$\Rightarrow P'(x) = -12x + 120$

For maximum profit, put $P'(x) = 0$

$\Rightarrow \qquad\qquad\qquad x = 10$

Now $P''(x) = -12 < 0$

$\therefore$ At $x = 10$, profit function is maximum.

37. In a college, an architecture design a auditorium for its cultural activities purpose. The shape of the floor of the auditorium is rectangular and it has a fixed perimeter, say P.

Based on the above information, answer the following questions.

(i) If l and b represents the length and breadth of the rectangular region, then find the relationship between l, b, P.

(ii) Find the area (A) of the floor, as a function of l.

(iii) College manager is interested in maximising the area of the floor A. For this purpose, find the value of l.

Or

Find the maximum area of the floor.

Sol. (i) Perimeter of rectangular floor

$\qquad\qquad = 2$ (length + breadth)

$\Rightarrow \qquad\qquad P = 2(l + b)$

(ii) Area, $A = $ length $\times$ breadth

$\qquad\qquad A = l \times b$ ...(i)

$\because \qquad P = 2(l + b) \Rightarrow \dfrac{P}{2} = l + b$

$\Rightarrow \quad \dfrac{P}{2} - l = b \Rightarrow \dfrac{P - 2l}{2} = b$

From Eq. (i),

$\qquad\qquad A = l\left(\dfrac{P - 2l}{2}\right)$

$\Rightarrow \qquad\qquad A = \dfrac{Pl - 2l^2}{2}$

(iii) We have, $A = \dfrac{Pl - 2l^2}{2}$

On differentiating w.r.t. l, we get

$$\frac{dA}{dl} = \frac{1}{2}(P - 4l)$$

For maximum area of floor, put $\dfrac{dA}{dl} = 0$

$\therefore \quad \dfrac{1}{2}(P - 4l) = 0$

$\Rightarrow \quad P - 4l = 0$

$\Rightarrow \quad l = \dfrac{P}{4}$

Clearly at $l = \dfrac{P}{4}, \dfrac{d^2A}{dl^2} = -2 < 0$

$\therefore$ Area is maximum at $l = \dfrac{P}{4}$.

Or

We have, $A = l \times b$

For maximum area, $l = \dfrac{P}{4}$

Now, $b = \dfrac{P - 2l}{2}$ [from part (ii)]

$\quad = \dfrac{P}{2} - l = \dfrac{P}{2} - \dfrac{P}{4} = \dfrac{P}{4}$

$\therefore (A)_{max} = l \times b = \dfrac{P}{4} \times \dfrac{P}{4} = \dfrac{P^2}{16}$ sq units.

38. In an office three employees Vinay, Sonia and Iqbal process incoming copies of a certain form. Vinay process 50% of the forms. Sonia processes 20% and Iqbal the remaining 30% of the forms. Vinay has an error rate of 0.06, Sonia has an error rate of 0.04 and Iqbal has an error rate of 0.03.

Based on the above information answer the following questions.

(i) The total probability of committing an error in processing the form.

(ii) The manager of the company wants to do a quality check. During inspection he selects a form at random from the days output of processed forms. If the form selected at random has an error, the probability that the form is not processed by Vinay.

Sol. (i) Required probability = $P(A)$

$= P(E_1)P\left(\dfrac{A}{E_1}\right) + P(E_2)P\left(\dfrac{A}{E_2}\right) + P(E_3)P\left(\dfrac{A}{E_3}\right)$

$= 0.5 \times 0.06 + 0.2 \times 0.04 + 0.3 \times 0.03$

$= 0.030 + 0.008 + 0.009$

$= 0.047$

(ii) Required probability

$= P\left(\dfrac{\bar{E_1}}{A}\right)$

$= 1 - P\left(\dfrac{E_1}{A}\right)$

$= 1 - \dfrac{P(E_1)P\left(\dfrac{A}{E_1}\right)}{P(E_1)P\left(\dfrac{A}{E_1}\right) + P(E_2)P\left(\dfrac{A}{E_2}\right) + P(E_3)P\left(\dfrac{A}{E_3}\right)}$

$= 1 - \left[\dfrac{0.5 \times 0.06}{0.5 \times 0.06 + 0.2 \times 0.04 + 0.3 \times 0.03}\right]$

$= 1 - \left[\dfrac{0.030}{0.030 + 0.008 + 0.009}\right]$

$= 1 - \dfrac{0.030}{0.047}$

$= 1 - \dfrac{30}{47}$

$= \dfrac{17}{47}$

SAMPLE QUESTION PAPER 2

MATHEMATICS

Time : 3 hrs   Max. Marks : 80

General Instructions

1. This question paper contains - five sections A, B, C, D and E. Each section is compulsory. However, there are internal choices in some questions.
2. Section A has 18 MCQ's and 02 Assertion-Reason based questions of 1 mark each.
3. Section B has 5 Very Short Answer (VSA) type questions of 2 marks each.
4. Section C has 6 Short Answer (SA) type questions of 3 marks each.
5. Section D has 4 Long Answer (LA) type questions of 5 marks each.
6. Section E has 3 source based/case based/passage based/integrated units of assessment (4 marks each) with sub parts.

Section A

(Multiple Choice Questions) Each question carries 1 mark

1. If $\begin{bmatrix} x+3 & z+4 & 2y-7 \\ -6 & a-1 & 0 \\ b-3 & -21 & 0 \end{bmatrix} = \begin{bmatrix} 0 & 6 & 3y-2 \\ -6 & -3 & 2c+2 \\ 2b+4 & -21 & 0 \end{bmatrix}$, then the values of x, y, z, a, b and c are

(a) $x = -3, y = -5, z = 2, a = -2, b = -7$ and $c = -1$
(b) $x = -2, y = -7, z = -1, a = -3, b = -5$ and $c = 2$
(c) $x = -3, y = -5, z = 2, a = 2, b = 7$ and $c = 1$
(d) $x = 3, y = 5, z = 2, a = 2, b = 7$ and $c = 1$

Sol. (a) The given matrices are equal, therefore their corresponding elements must be equal.

Comparing the corresponding elements, we get

$$x + 3 = 0, \ z + 4 = 6, \ 2y - 7 = 3y - 2,$$
$$a - 1 = -3, \ 0 = 2c + 2 \text{ and } b - 3 = 2b + 4$$

On simplifying, we get

$$a = -2, b = -7, c = -1,$$
$$x = -3, y = -5 \text{ and } z = 2$$

2. A card is picked at random from a pack of 52 playing cards. Given that the picked card is a queen, the probability of this card to be a card of spade is

(a) $\dfrac{1}{3}$ (b) $\dfrac{4}{13}$ (c) $\dfrac{1}{4}$ (d) $\dfrac{1}{2}$

Sol. (c) Let A be the event that card drawn is a spade and B be the event that card drawn is a queen. We have a total of 13 spades and 4 queen and one queen is from spade.

$$\therefore \quad P(A) = \frac{13}{52} = \frac{1}{4}, \ P(B) = \frac{4}{52} = \frac{1}{13}$$

and $P(A \cap B) = \dfrac{1}{52}$

$$\therefore \quad P\left(\frac{A}{B}\right) = \frac{P(A \cap B)}{P(B)} = \frac{1/52}{1/13} = \frac{1}{4}$$

3. If matrix A given by $A = \begin{bmatrix} 1 & -1 \\ 0 & 3 \\ 2 & 5 \end{bmatrix}$, then the order of the matrix A is

(a) 1×2 (b) 2×3 (c) 3×2 (d) 2×2

Sol. (c) Given matrix, $A = \begin{bmatrix} 1 & -1 \\ 0 & 3 \\ 2 & 5 \end{bmatrix}$ has 3 rows and 2 columns.

$\therefore$ Order of matrix A is 3×2.

4. The lines $\dfrac{x-2}{1} = \dfrac{y-3}{1} = \dfrac{4-z}{k}$ and $\dfrac{x-1}{k} = \dfrac{y-4}{2} = \dfrac{z-5}{-2}$ are mutually perpendicular, if the value of k is

(a) $-\dfrac{2}{3}$ (b) $\dfrac{2}{3}$ (c) -2 (d) 2

Sol. (a) We have,

$$\frac{x-2}{1} = \frac{y-3}{1} = \frac{4-z}{k}$$

and $$\frac{x-1}{k} = \frac{y-4}{2} = \frac{z-5}{-2}$$

or $$\frac{x-2}{1} = \frac{y-3}{1} = \frac{z-4}{-k}$$

and $$\frac{x-1}{k} = \frac{y-4}{2} = \frac{z-5}{-2}$$

Since, the given lines are perpendicular.

$$\therefore \quad (1)(k) + (1)(2) + (-k)(-2) = 0$$
$$\Rightarrow \quad k + 2 + 2k = 0$$
$$\Rightarrow \quad 3k + 2 = 0 \Rightarrow k = -\frac{2}{3}$$

5. Direction cosines of the vector $2\hat{i} - \hat{j} + 3\hat{k}$ are

(a) $\dfrac{2}{\sqrt{14}}, \dfrac{-1}{\sqrt{14}}, \dfrac{3}{\sqrt{14}}$ (b) $\dfrac{-2}{\sqrt{14}}, \dfrac{1}{\sqrt{14}}, \dfrac{3}{\sqrt{14}}$

(c) $\dfrac{4}{\sqrt{14}}, \dfrac{3}{\sqrt{14}}, \dfrac{6}{\sqrt{14}}$ (d) $\dfrac{2}{\sqrt{15}}, \dfrac{-1}{\sqrt{15}}, \dfrac{3}{\sqrt{15}}$

Sol. (a) Direction cosines of the vector $2\hat{i} - \hat{j} + 3\hat{k}$ are

$$\frac{2}{\sqrt{(2)^2 + (-1)^2 + (3)^2}}, \frac{-1}{\sqrt{(2)^2 + (-1)^2 + (3)^2}},$$
$$\frac{3}{\sqrt{(2)^2 + (-1)^2 + (3)^2}}$$

$$= \frac{2}{\sqrt{14}}, \frac{-1}{\sqrt{14}}, \frac{3}{\sqrt{14}}$$

6. $\displaystyle\int \dfrac{dx}{\sqrt{x} + x}$ is equal to

(a) $2\log|\sqrt{x} + 1| + C$ (b) $\log|x + 1| + C$
(c) $\log|x - 1| + C$ (d) $2\log|x + 1| + C$

Sol. (a) Let $I = \displaystyle\int \dfrac{dx}{\sqrt{x} + x}$

$$\Rightarrow \quad I = \int \frac{dx}{\sqrt{x}\,(1 + \sqrt{x})}$$

Put $\sqrt{x} + 1 = t$, then $\dfrac{1}{2\sqrt{x}} dx = dt$

$$\therefore \quad I = 2\int \frac{dt}{t} = 2\log|t| + C$$
$$= 2\log|\sqrt{x} + 1| + C \quad [\text{putting } t = \sqrt{x} + 1]$$

7. Degree of differential equation

$$\frac{d^2 y}{dx^2} = \sqrt{1 + \left(\frac{dy}{dx}\right)^2} \text{ is}$$

(a) 1   (b) 2   (c) 3   (d) 4

Sol. (b) Given, equation can be rewritten as

$$\left(\frac{d^2 y}{dx^2}\right)^2 = 1 + \left(\frac{dy}{dx}\right)^2$$

Hence, degree $= 2$

8. If $\displaystyle\int_0^a \dfrac{dx}{1 + 4x^2} = \dfrac{\pi}{8}$, then the value of a is

(a) 1   (b) $\dfrac{1}{2}$ (c) 3   (d) 0

Sol. (b) We have, $\displaystyle\int_0^a \dfrac{dx}{1 + 4x^2} = \dfrac{\pi}{8}$

$$\Rightarrow \quad \frac{1}{2}[\tan^{-1} 2x]_0^a = \frac{\pi}{8}$$
$$\Rightarrow \quad \tan^{-1}(2a) = \frac{\pi}{4}$$
$$\Rightarrow \quad 2a = \tan\frac{\pi}{4} \Rightarrow 2a = 1 \Rightarrow a = \frac{1}{2}$$

9. General solution of $\dfrac{dy}{dx} = \dfrac{y}{x}$ is

(a) $y = kx^2$ (b) $y = kx$

(c) $y = \dfrac{k}{x}$ (d) $yx = k$

Sol. (b) We have, $\dfrac{dy}{dx} = \dfrac{y}{x} \Rightarrow \dfrac{1}{y}\,dy = \dfrac{1}{x}\,dx$

On integrating both sides, we get

$$\int \dfrac{1}{y}\,dy = \int \dfrac{1}{x}\,dx$$

$\Rightarrow \qquad \log y = \log x + \log k$

$\Rightarrow \qquad \log y = \log kx$

$\Rightarrow \qquad\qquad y = kx$

10. The projection of the vector $\hat{i} + 3\hat{j} + 7\hat{k}$ on the vector $2\hat{i} - 3\hat{j} + 6\hat{k}$ is

(a) 4   (b) 5   (c) 1   (d) 0

Sol. (b) Let $\vec{a} = \hat{i} + 3\hat{j} + 7\hat{k}$ and $\vec{b} = 2\hat{i} - 3\hat{j} + 6\hat{k}$

$\therefore$ Projection of $\vec{a}$ on $\vec{b} = \dfrac{\vec{a} \cdot \vec{b}}{|\vec{b}|}$

$= \dfrac{(\hat{i} + 3\hat{j} + 7\hat{k}) \cdot (2\hat{i} - 3\hat{j} + 6\hat{k})}{|2\hat{i} - 3\hat{j} + 6\hat{k}|}$

$= \dfrac{2 - 9 + 42}{\sqrt{4 + 9 + 36}} = \dfrac{35}{7} = 5$

11. If $|\vec{a} \times \vec{b}| = 1, |\vec{a}| = 2$ and $|\vec{b}| = 1$, then angle between $\vec{a}$ and $\vec{b}$ is equal to

(a) $\dfrac{\pi}{3}$ (b) $\dfrac{\pi}{6}$ (c) $\dfrac{\pi}{4}$ (d) $\dfrac{\pi}{2}$

Sol. (b) We have, $|\vec{a} \times \vec{b}| = 1, |\vec{a}| = 2$ and $|\vec{b}| = 1$

Let θ be angle between $\vec{a}$ and $\vec{b}$.

$\therefore \qquad \sin\theta = \dfrac{|\vec{a} \times \vec{b}|}{|\vec{a}|\,|\vec{b}|} = \dfrac{1}{2 \cdot 1} = \dfrac{1}{2}$

$\therefore \qquad \theta = \dfrac{\pi}{6}$

12. The value of determinant $\begin{vmatrix} 1 & 4 & 3 \\ 9 & -1 & 4 \\ 5 & 0 & 2 \end{vmatrix}$ is

(a) 21   (b) 166

(c) 64   (d) None of these

Sol. (a) We have, $\begin{vmatrix} 1 & 4 & 3 \\ 9 & -1 & 4 \\ 5 & 0 & 2 \end{vmatrix}$

On expanding along R_3, we get

$= 5(16 + 3) + 2(-1 - 36) = 95 - 74 = 21$

13. The value of $\begin{vmatrix} x & -7 \\ x & 5x+1 \end{vmatrix}$ at $x = -1$ is

(a) -1 (b) -3

(c) 2   (d) -5

Sol. (b) Given, $\begin{vmatrix} x & -7 \\ x & 5x+1 \end{vmatrix} = x(5x+1) + 7x$

$= 5x^2 + x + 7x = 5x^2 + 8x$

$= x(5x + 8)$

Now at $x = -1$,

Required result $= (-1)(-5 + 8) = (-1)(3) = -3$

14. The function f given by $f(x) = 3x + 17$, is

(a) strictly increasing on R

(b) strictly decreasing on R

(c) decreasing on R

(d) Both (b) and (c) are correct

Sol. (a) Given, $f(x) = 3x + 17$

On differentiating w.r.t. x, we get

$f'(x) = 3 > 0$, in every interval of R.

Thus, the function is strictly increasing on R.

15. If Radha has 15 notebooks and 6 pens, Fauzia has 10 notebooks and 2 pens and Simran has 13 notebooks and 5 pens, then the above information is expressed as

I. $\begin{bmatrix} 15 & 6 \\ 10 & 2 \\ 13 & 5 \end{bmatrix}$ II. $\begin{bmatrix} 15 & 10 & 13 \\ 6 & 2 & 5 \end{bmatrix}$

(a) Only I   (b) Only II

(c) Both I and II   (d) None of these

Sol. (c) If Radha has 15 notebooks and 6 pens, Fauzia has 10 notebooks and 2 pens and Simran has 13 notebooks and 5 pens, then this could be arranged in tabular form as

Name	Notebooks	Pens
Radha	15	6
Fauzia	10	2
Simran	13	5

This can be expressed as $\begin{bmatrix} 15 & 6 \\ 10 & 2 \\ 13 & 5 \end{bmatrix}$.

The above information can also be arranged in tabular form as

Name	Radha	Fauzia	Simran
Notebooks	15	10	13
Pens	6	2	5

This can be expressed as $\begin{bmatrix} 15 & 10 & 13 \\ 6 & 2 & 5 \end{bmatrix}$.

16. If $f(x) = \dfrac{\sqrt{4+x} - 2}{x}$, $x \neq 0$ be continuous at $x = 0$, then $4f(0)$ is equal to

(a) $\dfrac{1}{2}$ (b) $\dfrac{1}{4}$ (c) 1   (d) $\dfrac{3}{2}$

Sol. (c) Given, $f(x) = \dfrac{\sqrt{4+x} - 2}{x}$

$\because f(x)$ is continuous at $x = 0$.

$\therefore \lim\limits_{x \to 0} f(x) = f(0)$

$\Rightarrow \quad f(0) = \lim\limits_{x \to 0} f(x) = \lim\limits_{x \to 0} \dfrac{\sqrt{4+x} - 2}{x}$

$\qquad = \lim\limits_{x \to 0} \left(\dfrac{\sqrt{4+x} - 2}{x} \times \dfrac{\sqrt{4+x} + 2}{\sqrt{4+x} + 2} \right)$

$\qquad = \lim\limits_{x \to 0} \dfrac{4 + x - 4}{x(\sqrt{4+x} + 2)} = \lim\limits_{x \to 0} \dfrac{x}{x(\sqrt{4+x} + 2)}$

$\qquad = \lim\limits_{x \to 0} \dfrac{1}{\sqrt{4+x} + 2} = \dfrac{1}{2+2} = \dfrac{1}{4}$

$\therefore \quad 4f(0) = 1$

17. All the points of discontinuity of f defined by $f(x) = |x| - |x+1|$ is/are

(a) 0, 1
(b) 1, 0, 2
(c) no point of discontinuity
(d) None of the above

Sol. (c) Let $g(x) = |x|$ and $h(x) = |x+1|$

Now, $g(x) = |x|$ is the absolute value function, so it is a continuous function for all $x \in R$.

$h(x) = |x+1|$ is the absolute value function, so it is a continuous function for all $x \in R$.

Since, $g(x)$ and $h(x)$ are both continuous functions for all $x \in R$, so difference of two continuous function is a continuous function for all $x \in R$.

Thus, $f(x) = |x| - |x+1|$ is a continuous function at all points.

Hence, there is no point at which $f(x)$ is discontinuous.

18. Degree of differential equation $\dfrac{d^2 y}{dx^2} + e^{dy/dx} = 0$ is

(a) 1   (b) 2
(c) 3   (d) not defined

Sol. (d) Given, $\dfrac{d^2 y}{dx^2} + e^{dy/dx} = 0$

Degree of the equation is not defined.

Since, differential equation is not a polynomial equation.

Assertion-Reason Based Questions

In the following questions, a statement of Assertion (A) is followed by a statement of Reason (R). Choose the correct answer out of the following choices.

(a) Both A and R are true and R is the correct explanation of A
(b) Both A and R are true but R is not the correct explanation of A
(c) A is true but R is false
(d) A is false but R is true

19. **Assertion (A)** The linear programming problem, maximise $Z = x + 2y$, subject to the constraints $x - y \leq 10$, $2x + 3y \leq 20$ and $x, y \geq 0$. It gives the maximum value of Z as $\dfrac{40}{3}$.

Reason (R) To obtain maximum value of Z, we need to compare value of Z at all the corner points of the shaded region.

Sol. (a) **Assertion** We have, maximise $Z = x + 2y$

Subject to the constraints,

$\qquad x - y \leq 10$, $2x + 3y \leq 20$ and $x, y \geq 0$

The graph of constraints are given below

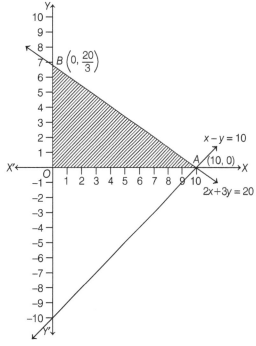

Here, OAB is the required feasible region whose corner points are $O\,(0, 0)$, $A\,(10, 0)$ and $B\left(0, \dfrac{20}{3}\right)$.

Corner point	Value of $Z = x + 2y$
$O\,(0, 0)$	0
$A\,(10, 0)$	10
$B\left(0, \dfrac{20}{3}\right)$	$\dfrac{40}{3}$ (Maximum)

The maximum value of Z is $\dfrac{40}{3}$, which is obtained at $B\left(0, \dfrac{20}{3}\right)$.

Hence, both Assertion and Reason are true and Reason is the correct explanation of Assertion.

20. Assertion (A) Maximum value of $Z = 3x + 2y$, subject to the constraints $x + y \leq 2$; $x \geq 0$; $y \geq 0$ will be obtained at point $(2, 0)$.

Reason (R) In a bounded feasible region, it always exist a maximum and minimum value.

Sol. (b) **Assertion** Given, $x + y \leq 2$, $x \geq 0$ and $y \geq 0$

Maximum $Z = 3x + 2y$

Now, table for $x + y = 2$

x	0	2	1
y	2	0	1

At $(0, 0)$,

$$0 + 0 \leq 2$$
$$\Rightarrow \qquad 0 \leq 2, \text{ which is true.}$$

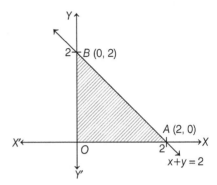

So, shaded portion is towards the origin.

Here, OAB is the required feasible region whose corner points are $O(0, 0)$, $A(2, 0)$ and $B(0, 2)$.

Corner points	Value of $Z = 3x + 2y$
$O(0, 0)$	0
$A(2, 0)$	6 (Maximum)
$B(0, 2)$	4

So, maximum value of Z is 6 at point $A(2, 0)$.

Hence both Assertion and Reason are true but Reason is not the correct explanation of Assertion.

Section B

(This section comprises of very short answer type questions (VSA) of 2 marks each)

21. Evaluate $\displaystyle\int_{0}^{\pi/2} \sin^2 x\, dx$.

Or

Evaluate $\displaystyle\int_{0}^{\pi/2} \dfrac{\sin x}{1 + \cos^2 x}\, dx$.

Sol. Let $I = \displaystyle\int_{0}^{\pi/2} \sin^2 x\, dx = \int_{0}^{\pi/2} \dfrac{1 - \cos 2x}{2}\, dx$

$$= \dfrac{1}{2} \int_{0}^{\pi/2} (1 - \cos 2x)\, dx = \dfrac{1}{2}\left[x - \dfrac{\sin 2x}{2}\right]_{0}^{\pi/2} \qquad (1)$$

$$= \dfrac{1}{2}\left[\left(\dfrac{\pi}{2} - \dfrac{1}{2}\sin \pi\right) - (0 - 0)\right] = \dfrac{1}{2} \times \dfrac{\pi}{2} = \dfrac{\pi}{4} \qquad (1)$$

Or

Let $I = \displaystyle\int_{0}^{\pi/2} \dfrac{\sin x}{1 + \cos^2 x}\, dx$

Put $\cos x = t \Rightarrow -\sin x\, dx = dt$

Also, $x = 0 \Rightarrow t = \cos 0 = 1$

and $x = \dfrac{\pi}{2} \Rightarrow t = \cos \dfrac{\pi}{2} = 0 \qquad (1)$

$$\therefore \qquad I = -\int_{1}^{0} \dfrac{dt}{1 + t^2} = -[\tan^{-1} t]_{1}^{0}$$

$$= -[\tan^{-1} 0 - \tan^{-1} 1] = -\left(-\dfrac{\pi}{4}\right) = \dfrac{\pi}{4} \qquad (1)$$

22. The minimum value of Z, where $Z = 2x + 3y$, subject to constraints $2x + y \geq 23$, $x + 3y \leq 24$ and $x, y \geq 0$, is

Sol. Given, objective function is minimise $Z = 2x + 3y$

Subject to constraints,

$2x + y \geq 23$, $x + 3y \leq 24$ and $x, y \geq 0$

Now, table for line $2x + y = 23$

x	0	11.5
y	23	0

At $(0, 0)$, $2 \cdot 0 + 0 \geq 23 \Rightarrow 0 \geq 23$, which is false.

So, shaded portion is away from the origin.

Table for line $x + 3y = 24$

x	0	24
y	8	0

On putting (0, 0) in $x + 3y \le 24$,

$0 + 3 \cdot 0 \le 24 \Rightarrow 0 \le 24$, which is true.   (1/2)

So, shaded portion is towards the origin.

Also, $x, y \ge 0$.

On drawing the graph of each linear equation, we get the following graph

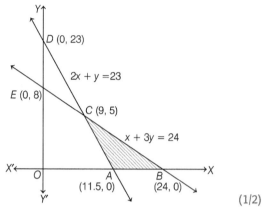

(1/2)

The feasible region is ABC and corner points are $A(11.5, 0)$, $B(24, 0)$ and $C(9, 5)$.

Corner points	Value of $Z = 2x + 3y$
$A(11.5, 0)$	23 (Minimum)
$B(24, 0)$	48
$C(9, 5)$	33

Hence, minimum value of Z is 23 at $A(11.5, 0)$.   (1)

23. If $x = \cos t + \sin t$ and $y = \sin t - \cos t$, then find $\dfrac{dy}{dx}$ at $t = \dfrac{\pi}{2}$.

Or

If $x = at^2$ and $y = 2at$, then find $\dfrac{dy}{dx}$ at $t = 1$.

Sol. Given, $x = \cos t + \sin t \Rightarrow \dfrac{dx}{dt} = -\sin t + \cos t$

and $y = \sin t - \cos t \Rightarrow \dfrac{dy}{dt} = \cos t + \sin t$

$\therefore \quad \dfrac{dy}{dx} = \dfrac{\left(\dfrac{dy}{dt}\right)}{\left(\dfrac{dx}{dt}\right)} = \dfrac{\cos t + \sin t}{\cos t - \sin t}$ (1)

Now, $\left(\dfrac{dy}{dx}\right)_{t = \frac{\pi}{2}} = \dfrac{\cos\left(\dfrac{\pi}{2}\right) + \sin\left(\dfrac{\pi}{2}\right)}{\cos\left(\dfrac{\pi}{2}\right) - \sin\left(\dfrac{\pi}{2}\right)} = \dfrac{0 + 1}{0 - 1} = -1$ (1)

Or

Given that $x = at^2$ and $y = 2at$

Now, $x = at^2$

On differentiating w.r.t. t, we get

$\dfrac{dx}{dt} = 2at$ ...(i)

and $y = 2at$

On differentiating w.r.t. t, we get

$\dfrac{dy}{dt} = 2a$ ...(ii) (1)

From Eqs. (i) and (ii), we get

$\dfrac{dy}{dx} = \dfrac{dy / dt}{dx / dt} = \dfrac{2a}{2at} = \dfrac{1}{t}$

Hence, $\left(\dfrac{dy}{dx}\right)$ at $t = 1$,

$\left(\dfrac{dy}{dx}\right)_{t=1} = 1$ (1)

24. Find the maximum value of $Z = 11x + 7y$

Subject to the constraints $2x + y \le 6$, $x \le 2$ and $x, y \ge 0$.

Sol. We have, maximise $Z = 11x + 7y$ ...(i)

Subject to the constraints

$2x + y \le 6$ ...(ii)

$x \le 2$ ...(iii)

and $x, y \ge 0$ ...(iv)

We see that, the feasible region as shaded determined by the system of constraints (ii) to (iv) is $OABC$ and is bounded.

So, now we shall use corner point method to determine the maximum value of Z.

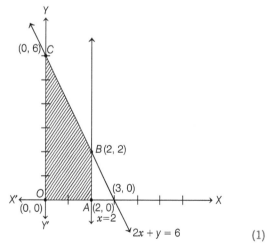

(1)

Corner points	Value of $Z = 11x + 7y$
$O(0, 0)$	0
$A(2, 0)$	22
$B(2, 2)$	36
$C(0, 6)$	42 (Maximum)

Hence, the maximum value of Z is 42 at $C(0, 6)$.   (1)

25. One card is drawn at random from a pack of well-shuffled deck of cards.

Let E: the card drawn is a spade

F: the card drawn is an ace

Are the events E and F independent?

Sol. Let S be the sample space.

Given, E = the event that the card drawn is a spade

and F = the event that the card drawn is an ace

Then, $E \cap F$ = the event that the card drawn is an ace and spade

Total number of cards = 52,

number of spade cards = 13,

number of ace cards = 4

and number of ace of spade card = 1

i.e. $n(S) = {}^{52}C_1 = 52$,

$n(E) = {}^{13}C_1 = 13$, $n(F) = {}^4C_1 = 4$ and $n(E \cap F) = 1$ (1)

Now, $P(E \cap F) = \dfrac{n(E \cap F)}{n(S)} = \dfrac{1}{52}$,

$P(E) = \dfrac{n(E)}{n(S)} = \dfrac{13}{52} = \dfrac{1}{4}$

and $P(F) = \dfrac{n(F)}{n(S)} = \dfrac{4}{52} = \dfrac{1}{13}$

Here, we see that $P(E \cap F) = \dfrac{1}{52} = P(E) \cdot P(F)$

Hence, the events E and F are independent. (1)

Section C

(This section comprises of short answer type questions (SA) of 3 marks each)

26. Find the derivative of $\dfrac{1 - \sin x}{1 + \sin x}$ w.r.t. to $\sin x$.

Sol. Let $v = \dfrac{1 - \sin x}{1 + \sin x}$ and $u = \sin x$

Now, on differentiating w.r.t. x, we get

$\dfrac{dv}{dx} = \dfrac{(1 + \sin x)\dfrac{d}{dx}(1 - \sin x) - (1 - \sin x)\dfrac{d}{dx}(1 + \sin x)}{(1 + \sin x)^2}$

$= \dfrac{(1 + \sin x)(0 - \cos x) - (1 - \sin x)(\cos x)}{(1 + \sin x)^2}$

$= \dfrac{\cos x[-(1 + \sin x) - 1 + \sin x]}{(1 + \sin x)^2}$

$= \dfrac{\cos x(-1 - \sin x - 1 + \sin x)}{(1 + \sin x)^2} = \dfrac{-2\cos x}{(1 + \sin x)^2}$ (2)

and $\dfrac{du}{dx} = \dfrac{d}{dx}(\sin x) \Rightarrow \dfrac{du}{dx} = \cos x$

∴ Derivative of $\dfrac{1 - \sin x}{1 + \sin x}$ w.r.t. $\sin x$,

$= \dfrac{dv/dx}{du/dx} = \dfrac{(-2\cos x)/(1 + \sin x)^2}{\cos x} = \dfrac{-2}{(1 + \sin x)^2}$ (1)

27. If $A = \begin{bmatrix} 4 & 2 \\ -1 & 1 \end{bmatrix}$,

show that $(A - 2I)(A - 3I) = O$.

Or If $A = \begin{bmatrix} 2 & 0 & 1 \\ 2 & 1 & 3 \\ 1 & -1 & 0 \end{bmatrix}$, then find the value of $A^2 - 5A$.

Sol. Given, $A = \begin{bmatrix} 4 & 2 \\ -1 & 1 \end{bmatrix}$, here $I = \begin{bmatrix} 1 & 0 \\ 0 & 1 \end{bmatrix}$

LHS = $(A - 2I)(A - 3I)$

$= \left\{ \begin{bmatrix} 4 & 2 \\ -1 & 1 \end{bmatrix} - 2\begin{bmatrix} 1 & 0 \\ 0 & 1 \end{bmatrix} \right\} \left\{ \begin{bmatrix} 4 & 2 \\ -1 & 1 \end{bmatrix} - 3\begin{bmatrix} 1 & 0 \\ 0 & 1 \end{bmatrix} \right\}$

$= \left\{ \begin{bmatrix} 4 & 2 \\ -1 & 1 \end{bmatrix} - \begin{bmatrix} 2 & 0 \\ 0 & 2 \end{bmatrix} \right\} \left\{ \begin{bmatrix} 4 & 2 \\ -1 & 1 \end{bmatrix} - \begin{bmatrix} 3 & 0 \\ 0 & 3 \end{bmatrix} \right\}$

$= \begin{bmatrix} 2 & 2 \\ -1 & -1 \end{bmatrix} \begin{bmatrix} 1 & 2 \\ -1 & -2 \end{bmatrix}$ (1½)

$= \begin{bmatrix} 2 - 2 & 4 - 4 \\ -1 + 1 & -2 + 2 \end{bmatrix}$

$= \begin{bmatrix} 0 & 0 \\ 0 & 0 \end{bmatrix} = O = $ RHS   **Hence proved.** (1½)

Or

Given, $A = \begin{bmatrix} 2 & 0 & 1 \\ 2 & 1 & 3 \\ 1 & -1 & 0 \end{bmatrix}$

$A^2 = A \times A = \begin{bmatrix} 2 & 0 & 1 \\ 2 & 1 & 3 \\ 1 & -1 & 0 \end{bmatrix} \times \begin{bmatrix} 2 & 0 & 1 \\ 2 & 1 & 3 \\ 1 & -1 & 0 \end{bmatrix}$

$= \begin{bmatrix} 4 + 0 + 1 & 0 + 0 - 1 & 2 + 0 + 0 \\ 4 + 2 + 3 & 0 + 1 - 3 & 2 + 3 + 0 \\ 2 - 2 + 0 & 0 - 1 + 0 & 1 - 3 - 0 \end{bmatrix}$

$A^2 = \begin{bmatrix} 5 & -1 & 2 \\ 9 & -2 & 5 \\ 0 & -1 & -2 \end{bmatrix}$ (1)

Now, $A^2 - 5A = \begin{bmatrix} 5 & -1 & 2 \\ 9 & -2 & 5 \\ 0 & -1 & -2 \end{bmatrix} - 5\begin{bmatrix} 2 & 0 & 1 \\ 2 & 1 & 3 \\ 1 & -1 & 0 \end{bmatrix}$

$$= \begin{bmatrix} 5 & -1 & 2 \\ 9 & -2 & 5 \\ 0 & -1 & -2 \end{bmatrix} - \begin{bmatrix} 10 & 0 & 5 \\ 10 & 5 & 15 \\ 5 & -5 & 0 \end{bmatrix}$$

$$= \begin{bmatrix} 5-10 & -1-0 & 2-5 \\ 9-10 & -2-5 & 5-15 \\ 0-5 & -1+5 & -2-0 \end{bmatrix} = \begin{bmatrix} -5 & -1 & -3 \\ -1 & -7 & -10 \\ -5 & 4 & -2 \end{bmatrix}$$ (2)

28. For the determinant $\begin{vmatrix} 1 & 3 & -4 \\ 1 & 0 & 6 \\ 2 & 1 & 4 \end{vmatrix}$, find the cofactor of each element.

Or

For the determinant $\begin{vmatrix} 2 & 1 & 6 \\ -1 & 4 & 2 \\ 0 & 1 & 2 \end{vmatrix}$, find the minor of each element and evaluate

$$a_{11}M_{11} + a_{12}M_{12} + a_{13}M_{13}$$

Sol. Let $\Delta = \begin{vmatrix} 1 & 3 & -4 \\ 1 & 0 & 6 \\ 2 & 1 & 4 \end{vmatrix}$

$A_{11} = \begin{vmatrix} 0 & 6 \\ 1 & 4 \end{vmatrix} = -6,\ A_{12} = -\begin{vmatrix} 1 & 6 \\ 2 & 4 \end{vmatrix} = 8,\ A_{13} = \begin{vmatrix} 1 & 0 \\ 2 & 1 \end{vmatrix} = 1,$

$A_{21} = -\begin{vmatrix} 3 & -4 \\ 1 & 4 \end{vmatrix} = -16,\ A_{22} = \begin{vmatrix} 1 & -4 \\ 2 & 4 \end{vmatrix} = 12,$ (1)

$A_{23} = -\begin{vmatrix} 1 & 3 \\ 2 & 1 \end{vmatrix} = 5$

$A_{31} = \begin{vmatrix} 3 & -4 \\ 0 & 6 \end{vmatrix} = 18,\ A_{32} = -\begin{vmatrix} 1 & -4 \\ 1 & 6 \end{vmatrix} = -10,$

$A_{33} = \begin{vmatrix} 1 & 3 \\ 1 & 0 \end{vmatrix} = -3$ (2)

Or

Let $\Delta = \begin{vmatrix} 2 & 1 & 6 \\ -1 & 4 & 2 \\ 0 & 1 & 2 \end{vmatrix}$

$M_{11} = \begin{vmatrix} 4 & 2 \\ 1 & 2 \end{vmatrix} = 6,\ M_{12} = \begin{vmatrix} -1 & 2 \\ 0 & 2 \end{vmatrix} = -2,$

$M_{13} = \begin{vmatrix} -1 & 4 \\ 0 & 1 \end{vmatrix} = -1$

$M_{21} = \begin{vmatrix} 1 & 6 \\ 1 & 2 \end{vmatrix} = -4,\ M_{22} = \begin{vmatrix} 2 & 6 \\ 0 & 2 \end{vmatrix} = 4,\ M_{23} = \begin{vmatrix} 2 & 1 \\ 0 & 1 \end{vmatrix} = 2$ (1)

$M_{31} = \begin{vmatrix} 1 & 6 \\ 4 & 2 \end{vmatrix} = -22,\ M_{32} = \begin{vmatrix} 2 & 6 \\ -1 & 2 \end{vmatrix} = 10,$

$M_{33} = \begin{vmatrix} 2 & 1 \\ -1 & 4 \end{vmatrix} = 9$

Now, $a_{11}M_{11} + a_{12}M_{12} + a_{13}M_{13}$

$= 2(6) + 1(-2) + 6(-1)$

$= 12 - 2 - 6 = 4$ (2)

29. Find the particular solution of the differential equation $(1 + e^{2x})\,dy + (1 + y^2)\,e^x\,dx = 0$, given that $y = 1$ when $x = 0$.

Or

Solve the following differential equation $y^2\,dx + (x^2 - xy + y^2)\,dy = 0$

Sol. Given, differential equation is

$(1 + e^{2x})\,dy + (1 + y^2)\,e^x\,dx = 0$

$\Rightarrow \quad (1 + e^{2x})\,dy = -(1 + y^2)\,e^x\,dx$

$\Rightarrow \quad \dfrac{dy}{1 + y^2} = -\dfrac{e^x}{1 + e^{2x}}\,dx$

On integrating both sides, we get

$$\int \dfrac{dy}{1 + y^2} = -\int \dfrac{e^x}{1 + e^{2x}}\,dx$$

Put $e^x = t \Rightarrow e^x\,dx = dt$ (1)

$\therefore$ We have, $\displaystyle\int \dfrac{dy}{1 + y^2} = -\int \dfrac{dt}{1 + t^2}$

$\Rightarrow \quad \tan^{-1}y = -\tan^{-1}t + C$

$\Rightarrow \quad \tan^{-1}y + \tan^{-1}e^x = C$ [putting $t = e^x$] (1)

Now, it is given that, $y = 1$ when $x = 0$.

$\therefore \quad \tan^{-1}(1) + \tan^{-1}(1) = C$

$\Rightarrow \quad \dfrac{\pi}{4} + \dfrac{\pi}{4} = C$

$\Rightarrow \quad C = 2 \times \dfrac{\pi}{4} = \dfrac{\pi}{2}$

Hence, the required particular solution is

$$\tan^{-1}y + \tan^{-1}e^x = \dfrac{\pi}{2}$$ (1)

Or

We have, $y^2\,dx + (x^2 - xy + y^2)\,dy = 0$

$\Rightarrow \quad \dfrac{dy}{dx} = \dfrac{-y^2}{x^2 - xy + y^2}$ ...(i)

This is homogeneous differential equation.

Now, on putting $y = vx \Rightarrow \dfrac{dy}{dx} = v + x\dfrac{dv}{dx}$ in Eq. (i), we get

$$v + x\dfrac{dv}{dx} = \dfrac{-v^2 x^2}{x^2 - vx^2 + v^2 x^2}$$

$\Rightarrow \quad v + x\dfrac{dv}{dx} = \dfrac{-v^2}{1 - v + v^2}$

$\Rightarrow \quad x\dfrac{dv}{dx} = \dfrac{-v^2}{1 - v + v^2} - v$

$\Rightarrow \quad x\dfrac{dv}{dx} = \dfrac{-v - v^3}{1 - v + v^2}$

$\therefore \quad \dfrac{1 - v + v^2}{v(1 + v^2)}\,dv = -\dfrac{1}{x}\,dx$ (1)

On integrating both sides, we get

$$\int \frac{1 + v^2}{v(1 + v^2)} dv - \int \frac{v}{v(1 + v^2)} dv = -\int \frac{1}{x} dx$$

$$\Rightarrow \qquad \int \frac{1}{v} dv - \int \frac{1}{1 + v^2} dv = -\int \frac{1}{x} dx$$

$$\Rightarrow \qquad \log|v| - \tan^{-1} v = -\log|x| + \log C \qquad (1)$$

$$\Rightarrow \qquad \log\left|\frac{vx}{C}\right| = \tan^{-1} v$$

$$\Rightarrow \qquad \frac{vx}{C} = e^{\tan^{-1} v}$$

$$\Rightarrow \qquad \frac{y}{C} = e^{\tan^{-1}(y/x)} \qquad \left[\text{putting } v = \frac{y}{x}\right]$$

$$\therefore \quad y = C \, e^{\tan^{-1}(y/x)}, \text{ which is the required solution.} \qquad (1)$$

30. Find the shortest distance between lines $\dfrac{x - 3}{1} = \dfrac{y - 5}{-2} = \dfrac{z - 7}{1}$ and $\dfrac{x + 1}{7} = \dfrac{y + 1}{-6} = \dfrac{z + 1}{1}$.

Sol. Given, equations of lines are

$$\frac{x - 3}{1} = \frac{y - 5}{-2} = \frac{z - 7}{1} \qquad ...(i)$$

and

$$\frac{x + 1}{7} = \frac{y + 1}{-6} = \frac{z + 1}{1} \qquad ...(ii)$$

On comparing above equations with one point form of equation of line which is

$$\frac{x - x_1}{a} = \frac{y - y_1}{b} = \frac{z - z_1}{c}, \text{ we get}$$

$$a_1 = 1, b_1 = -2, c_1 = 1, x_1 = 3, y_1 = 5, z_1 = 7$$

and $a_2 = 7, b_2 = -6, c_2 = 1, x_2 = -1, y_2 = -1, z_2 = -1$ (1)

We know that the shortest distance between two lines is given by

$$d = \frac{\begin{vmatrix} x_2 - x_1 & y_2 - y_1 & z_2 - z_1 \\ a_1 & b_1 & c_1 \\ a_2 & b_2 & c_2 \end{vmatrix}}{\sqrt{(b_1 c_2 - b_2 c_1)^2 + (c_1 a_2 - c_2 a_1)^2 + (a_1 b_2 - a_2 b_1)^2}}$$

$$\therefore \quad d = \frac{\begin{vmatrix} -4 & -6 & -8 \\ 1 & -2 & 1 \\ 7 & -6 & 1 \end{vmatrix}}{\sqrt{(-2 + 6)^2 + (7 - 1)^2 + (-6 + 14)^2}} \qquad (1)$$

$$= \left|\frac{-4(-2 + 6) + 6(1 - 7) - 8(-6 + 14)}{\sqrt{(4)^2 + (6)^2 + (8)^2}}\right|$$

$$= \left|\frac{-4(4) + 6(-6) - 8(8)}{\sqrt{16 + 36 + 64}}\right|$$

$$= \left|\frac{-16 - 36 - 64}{\sqrt{116}}\right|$$

$$= \left|\frac{-116}{\sqrt{116}}\right|$$

$$= \frac{116}{\sqrt{116}}$$

$$= \sqrt{116} \qquad (1)$$

Hence, the required shortest distance is $\sqrt{116}$ units.

31. Evaluate $\displaystyle\int \frac{x^2 + 1}{(x^2 + 2)(2x^2 + 1)} dx$.

Sol. Let $x^2 = y$.

Then, $\dfrac{x^2 + 1}{(x^2 + 2)(2x^2 + 1)} = \dfrac{y + 1}{(y + 2)(2y + 1)}$

Let $\dfrac{y + 1}{(y + 2)(2y + 1)} = \dfrac{A}{y + 2} + \dfrac{B}{(2y + 1)}$ \qquad ...(i)

$$\Rightarrow \qquad y + 1 = A(2y + 1) + B(y + 2) \qquad ...(ii)$$

Putting $y + 2 = 0$ i.e. $y = -2$ in Eq. (ii), we get

$$-1 = -3A$$

$$\Rightarrow \qquad A = \frac{1}{3}$$

Putting $2y + 1 = 0$ i.e. $y = -\dfrac{1}{2}$ in Eq. (ii), we get

$$\frac{1}{2} = B\left(\frac{3}{2}\right)$$

$$\Rightarrow \qquad B = \frac{1}{3} \qquad (1)$$

On substituting the values of A and B in Eq. (i), we obtain

$$\frac{y + 1}{(y + 2)(2y + 1)} = \frac{1}{3} \cdot \frac{1}{y + 2} + \frac{1}{3} \frac{1}{(2y + 1)}$$

Replacing y by x^2, we get

$$\frac{x^2 + 1}{(x^2 + 2)(2x^2 + 1)} = \frac{1}{3} \cdot \frac{1}{x^2 + 2} + \frac{1}{3} \cdot \frac{1}{(2x^2 + 1)} \qquad (1)$$

$$\therefore \quad I = \int \frac{x^2 + 1}{(x^2 + 2)(2x^2 + 1)} dx$$

$$= \frac{1}{3} \int \frac{1}{x^2 + (\sqrt{2})^2} dx + \frac{1}{3} \int \frac{1}{(\sqrt{2}x)^2 + 1^2} dx$$

$$\Rightarrow \quad I = \frac{1}{3} \times \frac{1}{\sqrt{2}} \tan^{-1}\left(\frac{x}{\sqrt{2}}\right) + \frac{1}{3\sqrt{2}} \tan^{-1}(\sqrt{2}x) + C$$

$$= \frac{1}{3\sqrt{2}} \left\{\tan^{-1} \frac{x}{\sqrt{2}} + \tan^{-1} \sqrt{2}x\right\} + C \qquad (1)$$

Section D

(This section comprises of long answer type questions (LA) of 5 marks each)

32. Evaluate $\int_{-1}^{2} |x^3 - x|\, dx$

Sol. Let $I = \int_{-1}^{2} |x^3 - x|\, dx$

Again, let $f(x) = x^3 - x = x(x^2 - 1) = x(x - 1)(x + 1)$

Now, break the given limit at $x = 0, 1$

[putting $f(x) = 0$, we get $x = 0, 1, -1$]

$$\therefore \quad f(x) = (x^3 - x) = \begin{cases} \geq 0, \forall\, x \in [-1, 0] \\ \leq 0, \forall\, x \in [0, 1] \\ \geq 0, \forall\, x \in [1, 2] \end{cases} \quad (1)$$

$$\therefore I = \int_{-1}^{0} (x^3 - x)\, dx + \int_{0}^{1} -(x^3 - x)\, dx + \int_{1}^{2} (x^3 - x)\, dx$$

$$= \left[\frac{x^4}{4} - \frac{x^2}{2}\right]_{-1}^{0} - \left[\frac{x^4}{4} - \frac{x^2}{2}\right]_{0}^{1} + \left[\frac{x^4}{4} - \frac{x^2}{2}\right]_{1}^{2} \quad (2)$$

$$= \left[0 - 0 - \left\{\frac{1}{4} - \frac{1}{2}\right\}\right] - \left[\left\{\frac{1}{4} - \frac{1}{2}\right\} - 0 + 0\right]$$

$$\qquad + \left[\left\{\frac{16}{4} - \frac{4}{2}\right\} - \left\{\frac{1}{4} - \frac{1}{2}\right\}\right]$$

$$= -\frac{3}{4} + \frac{3}{2} + 4 - 2 = \frac{3}{4} + 2 = \frac{11}{4} \quad (2)$$

33. Find the intervals on which the function $f(x) = (x - 1)^3 (x - 2)^2$ is strictly increasing and strictly decreasing.

Or Find the dimensions of the rectangle of perimeter 36 cm which will sweep out a volume as large as possible, when revolved about one of its side. Also, find the maximum volume.

Sol. Given, function is $f(x) = (x - 1)^3 (x - 2)^2$.

On differentiating w.r.t. x, we get

$$f'(x) = 3(x - 1)^2 (x - 2)^2 + 2(x - 2)(x - 1)^3$$
$$= (x - 1)^2 (x - 2)[3(x - 2) + 2(x - 1)]$$
$$= (x - 1)^2 (x - 2)(5x - 8)$$
$$= (x - 1)^2 (2 - x)(8 - 5x) \quad (2)$$

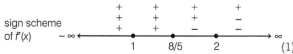

sign scheme of $f'(x)$

For strictly increasing $f'(x) > 0$.

We get positive $f'(x)$ in the interval

$\left(-\infty, \dfrac{8}{5}\right) \cup (2, \infty)$.

And for strictly decreasing $f'(x) < 0$, we get

negative $f'(x)$ in the interval $\left(\dfrac{8}{5}, 2\right)$. $\quad (2)$

Or

Here $ABCD$ is a rectangle with length $AD = y$ cm and breadth $AB = x$ cm

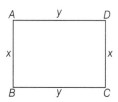

The rectangle is rotated about AD. Let V be the volume of the cylinder so formed

$$\therefore \qquad V = \pi x^2 y \quad [\because r = x \text{ and } h = y] \quad ...(i) \quad (1)$$

Perimeter of rectangle $= 2(x + y)$

$$\Rightarrow \qquad 36 = 2(x + y) \Rightarrow y = 18 - x$$

From Eq. (i), $\quad V = \pi x^2 (18 - x)$

$$\Rightarrow \qquad V = \pi (18x^2 - x^3)$$

$$\Rightarrow \qquad \frac{dV}{dx} = \pi (36x - 3x^2) \quad (1)$$

For maxima or minima, put $\dfrac{dV}{dx} = 0$

$$\pi(36x - 3x^2) = 0 \Rightarrow x = 12, \, x \neq 0$$

Now, $\qquad \dfrac{d^2V}{dx^2} = \pi (36 - 6x)$

$$\left(\frac{d^2V}{dx^2}\right)_{x = 12} = \pi(36 - 72) = -36\pi < 0 \quad (1)$$

$\therefore$ Volume is maximum when $x = 12$ cm

$$\therefore \qquad y = 18 - x = 18 - 12 = 6\,\text{cm}$$

Hence, the dimension of rectangle, which have maximum volume, when revolved about of its side is 12×6. $\quad (2)$

34. If $\vec{a} = \hat{i} + 2\hat{j} + 3\hat{k}$ and $\vec{b} = 2\hat{i} + 4\hat{j} - 5\hat{k}$ represent two adjacent sides of a parallelogram, find unit vectors parallel to the diagonals of the parallelogram.

Or Using vectors, find the area of the ΔABC with vertices A (1, 2, 3), $B(2, -1, 4)$ and $C(4, 5, -1)$.

Sol. We have, $\vec{a} = \hat{i} + 2\hat{j} + 3\hat{k}$ and $\vec{b} = 2\hat{i} + 4\hat{j} - 5\hat{k}$

So, the diagonals of the parallelogram whose adjacent sides are $\vec{a}$ and $\vec{b}$ are given by

$$\vec{p} = \vec{a} + \vec{b} \text{ and } \vec{q} = \vec{a} - \vec{b}$$

Now, $\vec{p} = (\hat{i} + 2\hat{j} + 3\hat{k}) + (2\hat{i} + 4\hat{j} - 5\hat{k})$
$$= 3\hat{i} + 6\hat{j} - 2\hat{k}$$

and $\quad \vec{q} = (\hat{i} + 2\hat{j} + 3\hat{k}) - (2\hat{i} + 4\hat{j} - 5\hat{k})$
$$= -\hat{i} - 2\hat{j} + 8\hat{k} \qquad (1)$$

$\therefore \qquad \hat{p} = \dfrac{\vec{p}}{|\vec{p}|} = \dfrac{3\hat{i} + 6\hat{j} - 2\hat{k}}{\sqrt{9 + 36 + 4}}$

$$= \dfrac{3\hat{i} + 6\hat{j} - 2\hat{k}}{7} = \dfrac{3}{7}\hat{i} + \dfrac{6}{7}\hat{j} - \dfrac{2}{7}\hat{k} \qquad (2)$$

and $\quad \hat{q} = \dfrac{\vec{q}}{|\vec{q}|} = \dfrac{-\hat{i} - 2\hat{j} + 8\hat{k}}{\sqrt{1 + 4 + 64}} = \dfrac{-\hat{i} - 2\hat{j} + 8\hat{k}}{\sqrt{69}}$

$$= \dfrac{-1}{\sqrt{69}}\hat{i} - \dfrac{2}{\sqrt{69}}\hat{j} + \dfrac{8}{\sqrt{69}}\hat{k} \qquad (2)$$

Or

Let $\vec{a}, \vec{b}$ and $\vec{c}$ be the position vectors of points A, B and C, respectively.

Then, $\vec{a} = \hat{i} + 2\hat{j} + 3\hat{k}, \vec{b} = 2\hat{i} - \hat{j} + 4\hat{k}$ and $\vec{c} = 4\hat{i} + 5\hat{j} - \hat{k}$.

Clearly, the area of $\triangle ABC = \dfrac{1}{2}|\vec{AB} \times \vec{AC}|$

Now, $\vec{AB}$ = Position vector of B − Position vector of A.

$$= \vec{b} - \vec{a} = 2\hat{i} - \hat{j} + 4\hat{k} - (\hat{i} + 2\hat{j} + 3\hat{k})$$
$$= \hat{i} - 3\hat{j} + \hat{k} \qquad (1)$$

$\vec{AC}$ = Position vector of C − Position vector of A

$$= \vec{c} - \vec{a} = 4\hat{i} + 5\hat{j} - \hat{k} - (\hat{i} + 2\hat{j} + 3\hat{k}) = 3\hat{i} + 3\hat{j} - 4\hat{k} \qquad (1)$$

$$\therefore \vec{AB} \times \vec{AC} = \begin{vmatrix} \hat{i} & \hat{j} & \hat{k} \\ 1 & -3 & 1 \\ 3 & 3 & -4 \end{vmatrix}$$

$$= (12 - 3)\hat{i} - (-4 - 3)\hat{j} + (3 + 9)\hat{k}$$
$$= 9\hat{i} + 7\hat{j} + 12\hat{k} \qquad (1)$$

and $|\vec{AB} \times \vec{AC}| = \sqrt{(9)^2 + (7)^2 + (12)^2}$

$$= \sqrt{81 + 49 + 144} = \sqrt{274}$$

So, area of $\triangle ABC = \dfrac{1}{2}|\vec{AB} \times \vec{AC}| = \dfrac{1}{2}\sqrt{274}$ sq units $\quad (2)$

35. Using integration find the area of the region.

$$\{(x, y) : 0 \le y \le x^2, 0 \le y \le x, 0 \le x \le 2\}$$

Sol. Given, equations of curve and lines are

$$y = x^2 \qquad \qquad \dots(i)$$
$$y = x \qquad \qquad \dots(ii)$$
and $\qquad x = 2 \qquad \qquad \dots(iii)$

Eq. (i) represent a parabola with vertex $A(0, 0)$ and axis along the positive direction of Y-axis.

Eq. (ii) represents a line which passes through $(0, 0)$.

Eq. (iii) represents a line which is perpendicular to the X-axis.

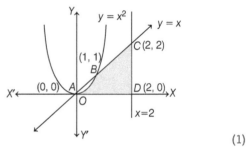

(1)

As, $0 \le y \le x^2$, it means the area outside the parabola and above the X-axis.

Similarly, $0 \le y \le x$ means the area below the line AB and above X-axis and $0 \le x \le 2$ represents the area between the parallel lines $x = 0$ and $x = 2$.

∴ The required region is shown in the shaded region.

The point of intersection of curve and line is

$$x^2 = x \Rightarrow x = 0, 1 \Rightarrow y = 0, 1$$

Thus, the points of intersection are $A(0, 0)$ and $B(1, 1)$. $\quad (2)$

∴ Required area = Area of shaded region $ABCD$

$$= \int_0^1 y(\text{parabola})\, dx + \int_1^2 y(\text{line})\, dx$$

$$= \int_0^1 x^2\, dx + \int_1^2 x\, dx = \left[\dfrac{x^3}{3}\right]_0^1 + \left[\dfrac{x^2}{2}\right]_1^2$$

$$= \left[\dfrac{1}{3} - 0\right] + \left[\dfrac{4}{2} - \dfrac{1}{2}\right] = \dfrac{1}{3} + \dfrac{3}{2} = \dfrac{2 + 9}{6} = \dfrac{11}{6}$$ sq units $\quad (2)$

Section E

(This section comprises of 3 case-study/ passage-based questions of 4 marks each with two sub-parts. First two case study questions have three sub-parts (i), (ii), (iii) of marks 1, 1, 2 respectively. The third case study question has two sub-parts of 2 marks each)

36. A relation R in a set A is called:

Reflexive, if $(a, a) \in R$, for every $a \in A$.

Symmetric, if $(a_1, a_2) \in R$, implies that $(a_2, a_1) \in R, \forall a_1, a_2 \in A$

Transitive, if $(a_1, a_2) \in R$ and $(a_2, a_3) \in R$ implies that $(a_1, a_3) \in R \forall a_1, a_2, a_3 \in A$.

On the basis of above information, answer the following questions.

(i) Show that the relation $R = \{(x, y): x$ is father of $y\}$, is neither reflexive nor symmetric nor transitive.

(ii) Show that the relation $R = \{(x, y): x$ is exactly 7cm taller than $y\}$, is neither reflexive nor symmetric nor transitive

(iii) Let R be the relation in the set A of all books in a library of a college given by $R = \{\{x, y\}: x$ and y have same number of pages$\}$. Then, show that R is an equivalence relation.

Or

Show that the relation $R = \{(a, b) : a$ and b work at the same place$\}$, is an equivalence relation.

Sol. (i) Here, R is not reflexive; as x cannot be father of x, for any x.

R is not symmetric as, if x is father of y, then y cannot be father of x.

R is not transitive as, if x is father of y and y is father of z, then x is grandfather (not father) of z.

(ii) Here, R is not reflexive as x is not 7 cm taller than x.

R is not symmetric as, if x is exactly 7 cm taller than y, then y cannot be 7 cm taller than x. And R is not transitive as, if x is exactly 7 cm taller than y and y is exactly 7 cm taller than z, then x is exactly 14 cm taller than z.

(iii) Here, A is the set of all books in the library of a college and $R = \{(x, y) : x$ and y have the same number of pages$\}$.

Now, R is reflexive, since $(x, x) \in R \ \forall \ x \in A$, as x and x has the same number of pages.

Let $(x, y) \in R$.

$\Rightarrow x$ and y have the same number of pages.

$\Rightarrow y$ and x have the same number of pages.

$\Rightarrow (y, x) \in R$. So, R is symmetric.

Now, let $(x, y) \in R$ and $(y, z) \in R$.

$\Rightarrow x$ and y have the same number of pages and y and z have the same number of pages.

$\Rightarrow x$ and z have the same number of pages

$\Rightarrow (x, z) \in R$

Therefore, R is transitive.

Hence, R is an equivalence relation.

Or

Here, $R = \{(a, b): a$ and b work at the same place$\}$. Then, R is reflexive as a works at same place of a.

$\Rightarrow (a, a) \in R \ \forall \ a \in A$

If a and b work at same place, then b and a also work at same place,

i.e. if $(a, b) \in R \Rightarrow (b, a) \in R$

$\Rightarrow R$ is symmetric.

Let $(a, b) \in R, (b, c) \in R$

$\Rightarrow a$ and b work at same place and b and c work at same place.

Since, all three work at same place.

$\Rightarrow a$ and c work at same place.

$\Rightarrow (a, c) \in R$

$\Rightarrow R$ is transitive.

$\Rightarrow R$ is an equivalence relation.

37. For awareness on Covid-19 protocol, Indian Government planned to fix a hoarding board at the face of a building on the road of a busy market. Sagar, Roy and Asif are the three engineers who are working on the project, P and P' are considered to be two person viewing the hoarding board 40 m and 50 m respectively, away from the building. All three engineers suggested to the firm to place the hoarding board at three different locations namely R, S and T. R is at the height of 20 m from the ground level. For the viewer P, the angle of elevation of S is double the angle of elevation of R. The angle of elevation of T is triple the angle of elevation of R for the same viewer. Look at the given figure.

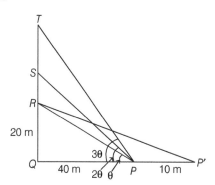

On the basis of above information, answer the following questions.

(i) Write the domain and range of $\tan^{-1} x$.

(ii) Find $\angle RPQ$.

(iii) Find $\angle SPQ$.

Or

Find $\angle TPQ$.

Sol. (i) Domain of $\tan^{-1} x = R$

Range of $\tan^{-1} x = \left(-\dfrac{\pi}{2}, \dfrac{\pi}{2}\right)$

(ii) In $\triangle PQR$, $\tan \angle RPQ = \dfrac{QR}{PQ}$

$$\tan \angle RPQ = \dfrac{20}{40} = \dfrac{1}{2}$$

$$\Rightarrow \qquad \angle RPQ = \tan^{-1}\left(\dfrac{1}{2}\right)$$

(iii) Given, $\angle SPQ = 2\angle RPQ$

$$\Rightarrow \quad \tan \angle SPQ = \tan 2\angle RPQ$$

$$\tan \angle SPQ = \dfrac{2\tan \angle RPQ}{1 - \tan^2 \angle RPQ}$$

$$= \dfrac{2 \cdot \dfrac{1}{2}}{1 - \left(\dfrac{1}{2}\right)^2} = \dfrac{1}{1 - \dfrac{1}{4}} = \dfrac{4}{3}$$

$$\Rightarrow \quad \tan \angle SPQ = \dfrac{4}{3}$$

$$\Rightarrow \qquad \angle SPQ = \tan^{-1}\left(\dfrac{4}{3}\right)$$

Or

Given, $\angle TPQ = 3\angle RPQ$

$$\tan \angle TPQ = \tan 3\angle RPQ$$

$$\Rightarrow \quad \tan \angle TPQ = \dfrac{3\tan \angle RPQ - \tan^3 \angle RPQ}{1 - 3\tan^2 \angle RPQ}$$

$$= \dfrac{3 \times \dfrac{1}{2} - \left(\dfrac{1}{2}\right)^3}{1 - 3\left(\dfrac{1}{2}\right)^2} = \dfrac{\dfrac{3}{2} - \dfrac{1}{8}}{1 - \dfrac{3}{4}}$$

$$= \dfrac{\dfrac{12 - 1}{8}}{\dfrac{4 - 3}{4}} = \dfrac{11}{2}$$

$$\Rightarrow \quad \tan \angle TPQ = \dfrac{11}{2}$$

$$\Rightarrow \qquad \angle TPQ = \tan^{-1}\left(\dfrac{11}{2}\right)$$

38. A doctor is to visit a patient. From the post experience, it is known that the probabilities that he will come by train, bus, scooter and by other means of transport are respectively $\dfrac{3}{10}, \dfrac{1}{5}, \dfrac{1}{10}$ and $\dfrac{2}{5}$. The probability that he will be late are $\dfrac{1}{4}, \dfrac{1}{3}$ and $\dfrac{1}{12}$, if he comes by train, bus and scooter respectively, but if he comes by other means of transport, then he will not be late.

On the basis of above information, answer the following questions.

(i) Find the probability that he is late.

(ii) Find the probability that he come by scooter given that he is late and also find the probability that he comes late given that he comes by other means of transport.

Sol. Let E_1, E_2, E_3 and E_4 be the events that the doctor comes by train, bus, scooter and other means of transport, respectively.

It is given that

$$P(E_1) = \dfrac{3}{10}, \ P(E_2) = \dfrac{1}{5},$$

$$P(E_3) = \dfrac{1}{10} \text{ and } P(E_4) = \dfrac{2}{5}$$

Let A denotes the event that the doctor visits the patient late. It is given that

$$P\left(\dfrac{A}{E_1}\right) = \dfrac{1}{4}, \ P\left(\dfrac{A}{E_2}\right) = \dfrac{1}{3},$$

$$P\left(\dfrac{A}{E_3}\right) = \dfrac{1}{12} \text{ and } P\left(\dfrac{A}{E_4}\right) = 0$$

(i) Required probability $= P(A) = \displaystyle\sum_{i=1}^{4} P(E_i)\, P\left(\dfrac{A}{E_i}\right)$

$$= P(E_1)\, P\left(\dfrac{A}{E_1}\right) + P(E_2)\, P\left(\dfrac{A}{E_2}\right)$$

$$+ P(E_3)\, P\left(\dfrac{A}{E_3}\right) + P(E_4)\, P\left(\dfrac{A}{E_4}\right)$$

$$= \dfrac{3}{10} \times \dfrac{1}{4} + \dfrac{1}{5} \times \dfrac{1}{3} + \dfrac{1}{10} \times \dfrac{1}{12} + \dfrac{2}{5} \times 0$$

$$= \dfrac{3}{40} + \dfrac{1}{15} + \dfrac{1}{120} = \dfrac{9 + 8 + 1}{120} = \dfrac{18}{120} = \dfrac{3}{20}$$

(ii) Probability that he comes by scooter given that he is late is $P\left(\dfrac{E_3}{A}\right)$

$$\therefore \ P\left(\dfrac{E_3}{A}\right) = \dfrac{P(E_3)\, P\left(\dfrac{A}{E_3}\right)}{P(A)} = \dfrac{\dfrac{1}{10} \times \dfrac{1}{12}}{\dfrac{3}{20}}$$

$$= \dfrac{1}{18}$$

Probability that he comes late given that he comes by other means of transport

$$= P\left(\dfrac{A}{E_4}\right) = 0$$

SAMPLE QUESTION PAPER 3

MATHEMATICS

Time : 3 hrs   Max. Marks : 80

General Instructions

1. This question paper contains - five sections A, B, C, D and E. Each section is compulsory. However, there are internal choices in some questions.
2. Section A has 18 MCQ's and 02 Assertion-Reason based questions of 1 mark each.
3. Section B has 5 Very Short Answer (VSA) type questions of 2 marks each.
4. Section C has 6 Short Answer (SA) type questions of 3 marks each.
5. Section D has 4 Long Answer (LA) type questions of 5 marks each.
6. Section E has 3 source based/case based/passage based/integrated units of assessment (4 marks each) with sub parts.

Section A

(Multiple Choice Questions) Each question carries 1 mark

1. Let $\begin{vmatrix} 3 & y \\ x & 1 \end{vmatrix} = \begin{vmatrix} 3 & 2 \\ 4 & 1 \end{vmatrix}$. Find the number of all possible pair of values of x and y, if x and y are natural numbers.

(a) 1   (b) 2   (c) 3   (d) 4

Sol. (d) We have, $\begin{vmatrix} 3 & y \\ x & 1 \end{vmatrix} = \begin{vmatrix} 3 & 2 \\ 4 & 1 \end{vmatrix}$

$\Rightarrow \quad 3 - xy = 3 - 8 \Rightarrow xy = 8$

$\Rightarrow \quad (x, y) = (1, 8), (2, 4), (4, 2), (8, 1)$

2. The area of the region bounded by the parabola $y = x^2$ and the line $y = x$ is

(a) $\dfrac{1}{6}$ sq unit   (b) $\dfrac{3}{5}$ sq unit   (c) $\dfrac{7}{2}$ sq units   (d) 5 sq units

Sol. (a) The given equations are $y = x^2$ ...(i)

and $\quad\quad\quad\quad\quad\quad\quad\quad\quad y = x$ ...(ii)

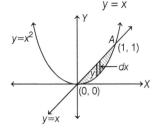

From Eqs. (i) and (ii), we get

$$x = x^2$$

$$\Rightarrow \quad\quad x^2 - x = 0$$

$$\Rightarrow \quad\quad x(x-1) = 0 \Rightarrow x = 0, x = 1$$

For $x = 0$, $\quad\quad y = 0$

and for $x = 1$, $\quad y = 1$

So, the line and the parabola meet at $O(0, 0)$ and $A(1, 1)$.

So, required area $= \int_0^1 y \, dx = \int_0^1 (x - x^2) \, dx = \left[\dfrac{x^2}{2} - \dfrac{x^3}{3}\right]_0^1$

$$= \left(\dfrac{1}{2} - \dfrac{1}{3}\right) - 0 = \dfrac{1}{6} \text{ sq unit}$$

3. The rate of change of the area of a circle with respect to its radius r, when $r = 3$ cm, is

(a) $\dfrac{6\pi}{5}$ cm^2/cm   (b) 3π cm^2/cm

(c) 6π cm^2/cm   (d) $\dfrac{3\pi}{5}$ cm^2/cm

Sol. (c) Area of circle $= \pi r^2$

i.e. $\quad\quad\quad A = \pi r^2$

$$\dfrac{dA}{dr} = 2\pi r$$

$$\left(\dfrac{dA}{dr}\right)_{r=3} = 2\pi(3) = 6\pi \text{ cm}^2/\text{cm}$$

4. The least value of the function

$f(x) = ax + \dfrac{b}{x} \, (a > 0, b > 0, x > 0)$ is

(a) $\sqrt{ab}$ (b) $2\sqrt{ab}$ (c) $3\sqrt{ab}$ (d) $5\sqrt{ab}$

Sol. (b) We have,

$$f(x) = ax + \dfrac{b}{x} \, (a > 0, b > 0, x > 0)$$

$$\therefore \quad f'(x) = a - \dfrac{b}{x^2} \text{ and } f''(x) = \dfrac{2b}{x^3}$$

For maxima and minima of $f(x)$,

$$f'(x) = 0$$

$$\Rightarrow \quad a - \dfrac{b}{x^2} = 0 \Rightarrow x^2 = \dfrac{b}{a} \Rightarrow x = \sqrt{\dfrac{b}{a}} \quad [\because x > 0]$$

Again, $f''\left(\sqrt{\dfrac{b}{a}}\right) = \dfrac{2b}{\left(\dfrac{b}{a}\right)^{3/2}} = \dfrac{2a^{3/2}}{\sqrt{b}} > 0 \quad [\because a > 0, b > 0]$

So, $f(x)$ has least value at $x = \sqrt{\dfrac{b}{a}}$

$$\therefore f_{\min}(x) = f\left(\sqrt{\dfrac{b}{a}}\right) = a\sqrt{\dfrac{b}{a}} + \dfrac{b}{\sqrt{\dfrac{b}{a}}}$$

$$= \sqrt{ab} + \sqrt{ab} = 2\sqrt{ab}$$

5. If the function f defined as

$f(x) = \begin{cases} \dfrac{x^2 - 9}{x - 3}, & x \neq 3 \\ k, & x = 3 \end{cases}$ is continuous at

$x = 3$, then the value of k is

(a) 1   (b) 2   (c) 6   (d) 5

Sol. (c) Given, $f(x) = \begin{cases} \dfrac{x^2 - 9}{x - 3}, & x \neq 3 \\ k, & x = 3 \end{cases}$

Since, $f(x)$ is continuous at $x = 3$.

$$\therefore \quad \lim_{x \to 3} f(x) = f(3)$$

$$\Rightarrow \lim_{x \to 3} \dfrac{x^2 - 9}{x - 3} = k \Rightarrow \lim_{x \to 3} \dfrac{(x-3)(x+3)}{(x-3)} = k$$

$$\Rightarrow \lim_{x \to 3} (x + 3) = k$$

$$\Rightarrow \quad\quad 3 + 3 = k \Rightarrow k = 6$$

6. The value of $\int x^2 e^{x^3} dx$ is

(a) $\dfrac{1}{3} e^{x^3} + C$ (b) $\dfrac{1}{3} e^{x^4} + C$

(c) $\dfrac{1}{2} e^{x^3} + C$ (d) $\dfrac{1}{2} e^{x^2} + C$

Sol. (a) Let $I = \int x^2 e^{x^3} dx$

Put $x^3 = t \Rightarrow 3x^2 dx = dt$

$$\therefore \quad I = \dfrac{1}{3} \int e^t dt = \dfrac{1}{3} e^t + C \Rightarrow I = \dfrac{1}{3} e^{x^3} + C$$

7. If $y = 3e^{2x} + 2e^{3x}$, then the value of $y_2 - 5y_1 + 6y$ is

(a) 1   (b) 0   (c) 2   (d) 3

Sol. (b) We have, $y = 3e^{2x} + 2e^{3x}$

$$y_1 = 6e^{2x} + 6e^{3x}$$

$$y_2 = 12e^{2x} + 18e^{3x}$$

$$y_2 = 6(2e^{2x} + 3e^{3x})$$

Hence, $y_2 - 5y_1 + 6y = 6(2e^{2x} + 3e^{3x}) - 30(e^{2x} + e^{3x})$

$$+ 6(3e^{2x} + 2e^{3x})$$

$$= 0$$

8. If $x^{2/3} + y^{2/3} = a^{2/3}$, then find $\dfrac{dy}{dx}$.

(a) $-\left(\dfrac{y}{x}\right)^{1/3}$ (b) $\left(\dfrac{y}{x}\right)^{1/3}$ (c) $\left(\dfrac{x}{y}\right)^{1/3}$ (d) $\dfrac{x}{y}$

Sol. (a) We have, $x^{2/3} + y^{2/3} = a^{2/3}$

On differentiating both sides w.r.t. x, we get

$$\dfrac{2}{3}x^{2/3-1} + \dfrac{2}{3}y^{2/3-1}\dfrac{dy}{dx} = 0$$

$$\Rightarrow \qquad y^{-1/3}\dfrac{dy}{dx} = -x^{-1/3}$$

$$\Rightarrow \qquad \dfrac{dy}{dx} = \dfrac{-x^{-1/3}}{y^{-1/3}} = -\left(\dfrac{y}{x}\right)^{1/3}$$

9. If $f'(1) = 2$ and $y = f(\log_e x)$, find $\dfrac{dy}{dx}$ at $x = e$.

(a) $\dfrac{2}{e}$ (b) $\dfrac{3}{e}$ (c) $\dfrac{1}{e}$ (d) $\dfrac{2}{5e}$

Sol. (a) We have, $y = f(\log_e x)$

$$\therefore \qquad \dfrac{dy}{dx} = f'(\log_e x)\cdot\dfrac{1}{x}$$

Now, putting $x = e$, we get

$$\left.\dfrac{dy}{dx}\right|_{x=e} = f'(\log_e e)\cdot\dfrac{1}{e} = \dfrac{1}{e}f'(1) \qquad [\because \log_e e = 1]$$

$$= \dfrac{2}{e} \qquad\qquad [\because f'(1) = 2]$$

10. The particular solution of the differential equation $\dfrac{dy}{dx} = y\tan x$ at $y = 1$, $x = 0$ is

(a) $y = \cos x$ (b) $y = \sec x$

(c) $y\sin x = 6$ (d) $y = \tan x$

Sol. (b) We have, $\dfrac{dy}{dx} = y\tan x \Rightarrow \dfrac{dy}{y} = \tan x\, dx$

$$\Rightarrow \qquad \int\dfrac{dy}{y} = \int\tan x\, dx$$

$$\Rightarrow \qquad \log y = \log|\sec x| + C \qquad \ldots\text{(i)}$$

Putting $y = 1$ and $x = 0$ in (i), we get

$$C = 0$$

$$\therefore \quad y = \sec x$$

11. $\displaystyle\int_1^4 |x - 5|\, dx$ is equal to

(a) $\dfrac{15}{2}$ (b) $\dfrac{13}{2}$

(c) 1 (d) 4

Sol. (a) Let $I = \displaystyle\int_1^4 |x - 5|\, dx$

$$= \int_1^4 -(x-5)\, dx \qquad [\because |x-5| = -(x-5),\ x < 5]$$

$$= -\left[\dfrac{x^2}{2} - 5x\right]_1^4 = -\left[\left(\dfrac{16}{2} - 20\right) - \left(\dfrac{1}{2} - 5\right)\right]$$

$$= -\left[-12 + \dfrac{9}{2}\right] = \dfrac{15}{2}$$

12. The area of the region bounded by the curve $y = \dfrac{1}{x}$, the X-axis and between $x = 1$ to $x = 6$ is

(a) $\log_e 3$ sq units   (b) $\log_e 6$ sq units

(c) $\log 5$ sq units   (d) 6 sq units

Sol. (b) Required area $= \displaystyle\int_1^6 y\, dx = \int_1^6 \dfrac{1}{x}\, dx = [\log x]_1^6$

$$= \log_e 6 \text{ sq units}$$

13. The degree of the differential equation

$$\left(\dfrac{dy}{dx}\right)^5 + 2x^2\left(\dfrac{d^2 y}{dx^2}\right)^4 = 0 \text{ is}$$

(a) 1 (b) 2 (c) 3 (d) 4

Sol. (d) Degree $= 4$

14. The minimum value of the function $f(x) = |x - 4|$ exists at

(a) $x = 0$ (b) $x = 2$

(c) $x = 4$ (d) $x = -4$

Sol. (c) Given function, $f(x) = |x - 4|$

Graph of $f(x)$,

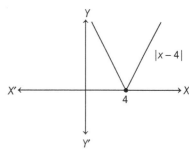

From graph, we observe that $f(x)$ has minimum value at $x = 4$.

15. The function $f : N \to N$, N being the set of natural numbers, defined by $f(x) = 2x + 3$ is

(a) injective and surjective

(b) injective but not surjective

(c) not injective but surjective

(d) neither injective nor surjective

Sol. (b) Given, $f : N \to N$ defined by $f(x) = 2x + 3$

Let $f(x_1) = f(x_2)$

$$\Rightarrow 2x_1 + 3 = 2x_2 + 3 \Rightarrow x_1 = x_2$$

Hence, $f(x)$ is injective.

Let $f(x) = y$

$\Rightarrow \qquad y = 2x + 3$

$\Rightarrow \qquad x = \dfrac{y-3}{2}$

Let $y = 4 \Rightarrow x = \dfrac{1}{2}$

i.e. $y \in N$ but $x \notin N$.

Hence, $f(x)$ is not surjective.

16. Suppose there is a relation R between the positive numbers x and y given by xRy if and only if $x \le y^2$. Then, which one of the following is correct?

(a) R is reflexive but not symmetric
(b) R is symmetric but not reflexive
(c) R is neither reflexive nor symmetric
(d) None of the above

Sol. (a) **Reflexive** Given, $xRy \Rightarrow x$ is less than y^2.

$\therefore xRx \Rightarrow x$ is less than x^2, which is true.

Hence, R is reflexive.

Symmetric xRy is not equivalent to yRx because

$1R2 \Rightarrow 1$ is less than 2^2.

$2R1 \Rightarrow 2$ is less than 1^2.

Thus, it is not symmetric.

17. The corner points of the feasible region determined by the following system of linear inequalities $2x + y \le 10$, $x + 3y \le 15$, $x, y \ge 0$ are $(0, 0)$ $(5, 0)$ $(3, 4)$ and $(0, 5)$. Let $Z = px + qy$, where $p, q > 0$. Condition on p and q, so that the maximum of Z occurs at both $(3, 4)$ and $(0, 5)$, is

(a) $p = q$ (b) $p = 2q$
(c) $p = 3q$ (d) $q = 3p$

Sol. (d) The maximum value of Z is unique.

It is given that the maximum value of Z occurs at two points $(3, 4)$ and $(0, 5)$.

Value of Z at $(3, 4) =$ Value of Z at $(0, 5)$

$\Rightarrow \qquad p(3) + q(4) = p(0) + q(5)$

$\Rightarrow \qquad 3p + 4q = 5q \Rightarrow 3p = q$

18. $\sin^{-1}\left(\cos\dfrac{3\pi}{5}\right)$ is equal to

(a) $\dfrac{\pi}{10}$ (b) $\dfrac{3\pi}{5}$
(c) $\dfrac{-\pi}{10}$ (d) $\dfrac{-3\pi}{5}$

Sol. (c) We have, $\sin^{-1}\left(\cos\left(\dfrac{3\pi}{5}\right)\right)$

$= \sin^{-1}\left(\sin\left(\dfrac{\pi}{2} - \dfrac{3\pi}{5}\right)\right)$

$\qquad \left[\because \cos\theta = \sin\left(\dfrac{\pi}{2} - \theta\right)\right]$

$= \sin^{-1}\left(\sin\left(-\dfrac{\pi}{10}\right)\right) = -\dfrac{\pi}{10}$

Assertion-Reason Based Questions

In the following questions, a statement of Assertion (A) is followed by a statement of Reason (R). Choose the correct answer out of the following choices.

(a) Both A and R are true and R is the correct explanation of A
(b) Both A and R are true but R is not the correct explanation of A
(c) A is true but R is false
(d) A is false but R is true

19. Assertion (A) $f(x)$ is continuous at $x = a$, if $\lim\limits_{x \to a} f(x)$ exists and equals to $f(a)$.

Reason (R) If $f(x)$ is continuous at a point, then $\dfrac{1}{f(x)}$ is also continuous at the point.

Sol. (c) **Assertion** We know that

If $f(a) = \lim\limits_{x \to a} f(x)$, then $f(x)$ is continuous at $x = a$, while both limits must exist.

Reason If $f(x)$ is continuous at a point, then it is not necessary that $\dfrac{1}{f(x)}$ is also continuous at that point.

e.g. $f(x) = x$ is continuous at $x = 0$ but $\dfrac{1}{f(x)} = \dfrac{1}{x}$ is not continuous at $x = 0$.

20. Assertion (A) The matrix

$A = \begin{bmatrix} 3 & -1 & 0 \\ 3/2 & 3\sqrt{2} & 1 \\ 4 & 3 & -1 \end{bmatrix}$ is rectangular matrix of order 3.

Reason (R) If $A = [a_{ij}]_{m \times 1}$, then A is column matrix.

Sol. (d) **Assertion** $A = \begin{bmatrix} 3 & -1 & 0 \\ \dfrac{3}{2} & 3\sqrt{2} & 1 \\ 4 & 3 & -1 \end{bmatrix}$ is a square matrix of order 3.

Reason In general, $A = [a_{ij}]_{m \times 1}$ is a column matrix.

Section B

(This section comprises of very short answer type questions (VSA) of 2 marks each)

21. Evaluate $\int_0^1 \dfrac{2x}{5x^2+1}\,dx$.

Or Evaluate $\int_0^2 [x^2]\,dx$, where $[\cdot]$ is the greatest integer function.

Sol. Given, $I = \int_0^1 \dfrac{2x}{5x^2+1}dx$

Let $5x^2 + 1 = t$

Differentiating w.r.t. x, we get

$\dfrac{d}{dx}(5x^2+1) = \dfrac{dt}{dx} \Rightarrow 10x\,dx = dt$

When, $x = 0$, then $t = 5x^2 + 1 \Rightarrow t = 1$

When, $x = 1$, then $t = 5x^2 + 1 \Rightarrow t = 6$ (1)

$\therefore \int_0^1 \dfrac{2x}{5x^2+1}dx = \int_1^6 \dfrac{2x}{t} \times \dfrac{dt}{10x}$

$= \dfrac{1}{5}\int_1^6 \dfrac{dt}{t} = \dfrac{1}{5}[\log t]_1^6$

$= \dfrac{1}{5}[\log 6 - \log 1] = \dfrac{1}{5}\log 6$ (1)

Or

Here, $\quad [x^2] = \begin{cases} 0, & \text{when } 0 < x < 1 \\ 1, & \text{when } 1 < x < \sqrt{2} \\ 2, & \text{when } \sqrt{2} < x < \sqrt{3} \\ 3, & \text{when } \sqrt{3} < x < 2 \end{cases}$ (1)

$\therefore \int_0^2 [x^2]dx = \int_0^1 0\,dx + \int_1^{\sqrt{2}} 1\,dx + \int_{\sqrt{2}}^{\sqrt{3}} 2\,dx + \int_{\sqrt{3}}^2 3\,dx$

$= 0 + [x]_1^{\sqrt{2}} + [2x]_{\sqrt{2}}^{\sqrt{3}} + [3x]_{\sqrt{3}}^2$

$= (\sqrt{2}-1) + 2(\sqrt{3}-\sqrt{2}) + 3(2-\sqrt{3})$

$= \sqrt{2} - 1 + 2\sqrt{3} - 2\sqrt{2} + 6 - 3\sqrt{3}$

$= 5 - \sqrt{2} - \sqrt{3}$ (1)

22. Evaluate $\int (x+1)e^x \log(xe^x)\,dx$.

Sol. Let $I = \int (x+1)e^x \log(xe^x)dx$

On putting, $xe^x = t \Rightarrow (e^x + xe^x)dx = dt$

$\Rightarrow (1+x)e^x dx = dt$

$\therefore \quad I = \int 1 \cdot \log t\,dt = \log t \cdot t - \int t \cdot \dfrac{1}{t}dt$ (1)

[using integration by parts]

$= t \cdot \log t - \int 1\,dt = t \cdot \log t - t + C$

$= xe^x \log(xe^x) - xe^x + C$ [putting $t = xe^x$]

$= xe^x [\log(xe^x) - 1] + C$ (1)

23. A committee of 4 students is selected at random from a group consisting of 8 boys and 4 girls. If there is atleast one girl in the committee, then calculate the probability that there are exactly 2 girls in the committee.

Or

If $P(A) = \dfrac{1}{4}$, $P(B) = \dfrac{1}{5}$ and $P(A \cap B) = \dfrac{1}{7}$, find $P(\overline{A}/\overline{B})$.

Sol. Let A denotes the event that atleast one girl will be chosen and B denotes the event that exactly 2 girls will be chosen. Then, to find $P(B/A)$

Now, $P(A) = 1 - P(\overline{A}) = 1 - P$ (no girl is chosen)

$= 1 - P$ (4 boys are chosen)

$= 1 - \dfrac{{}^8C_4}{{}^{12}C_4}$

$= 1 - \dfrac{70}{495}$

$= 1 - \dfrac{14}{99} = \dfrac{85}{99}$ (1/2)

and $P(A \cap B) = P$ (2 boys and 2 girls are chosen)

$= \dfrac{{}^8C_2 \times {}^4C_2}{{}^{12}C_4} = \dfrac{28 \times 6}{495} = \dfrac{56}{165}$ (1/2)

Hence, $P\left(\dfrac{B}{A}\right) = \dfrac{P(A \cap B)}{P(A)} = \dfrac{\frac{56}{165}}{\frac{85}{99}} = \dfrac{56}{165} \times \dfrac{99}{85} = \dfrac{168}{425}$ (1)

Or

Given, $P(A) = \dfrac{1}{4}$, $P(B) = \dfrac{1}{5}$ and $P(A \cap B) = \dfrac{1}{7}$

$\therefore \quad P\left(\dfrac{\overline{A}}{\overline{B}}\right) = \dfrac{P(\overline{A} \cap \overline{B})}{P(\overline{B})} = \dfrac{1 - P(A \cup B)}{1 - P(B)}$

$= \dfrac{1 - [P(A) + P(B) - P(A \cap B)]}{1 - \dfrac{1}{5}}$ (1)

$= \dfrac{1 - \left(\dfrac{1}{4} + \dfrac{1}{5} - \dfrac{1}{7}\right)}{\dfrac{4}{5}} = \dfrac{1 - \left(\dfrac{35 + 28 - 20}{140}\right)}{\dfrac{4}{5}}$

$= \dfrac{1 - \dfrac{43}{140}}{\dfrac{4}{5}} = \dfrac{(140 - 43)}{140} \times \dfrac{5}{4}$

$= \dfrac{97}{28 \times 4} = \dfrac{97}{112}$ (1)

24. Find the values of λ for which the angle between the vectors $\vec{a} = 2\lambda^2\hat{i} + 4\lambda\hat{j} + \hat{k}$ and $\vec{b} = 7\hat{i} - 2\hat{j} + \lambda\hat{k}$ is obtuse.

Sol. Let θ be the angle between $\vec{a}$ and $\vec{b}$. Then,

$$\cos\theta = \frac{\vec{a} \cdot \vec{b}}{|\vec{a}||\vec{b}|} = \frac{(2\lambda^2\hat{i} + 4\lambda\hat{j} + \hat{k}) \cdot (7\hat{i} - 2\hat{j} + \lambda\hat{k})}{|2\lambda^2\hat{i} + 4\lambda\hat{j} + \hat{k}||7\hat{i} - 2\hat{j} + \lambda\hat{k}|}$$

Now, θ is obtuse.

$\therefore \qquad\qquad \cos\theta < 0$

$\Rightarrow \qquad \dfrac{\vec{a} \cdot \vec{b}}{|\vec{a}||\vec{b}|} < 0 \qquad\qquad$ (1)

$\Rightarrow \qquad\qquad \vec{a} \cdot \vec{b} < 0$

$\Rightarrow \qquad 14\lambda^2 - 8\lambda + \lambda < 0$

$\Rightarrow \qquad\qquad 14\lambda^2 - 7\lambda < 0$

$\Rightarrow \qquad\qquad 7\lambda\,(2\lambda - 1) < 0$

$\Rightarrow \qquad\qquad \lambda\,(2\lambda - 1) < 0$

$\Rightarrow \quad \lambda < 0 \text{ and } 2\lambda - 1 > 0 \text{ or } \lambda > 0 \text{ and } 2\lambda - 1 < 0$

$\Rightarrow \quad \lambda < 0 \text{ and } \lambda > \dfrac{1}{2} \text{ or } \lambda > 0 \text{ and } \lambda < \dfrac{1}{2}$

$\Rightarrow \quad \lambda > 0 \text{ and } \lambda < \dfrac{1}{2}$

[as there cannot be any number less than zero and greater than $\frac{1}{2}$]

$\Rightarrow \qquad\qquad \lambda \in \left(0, \dfrac{1}{2}\right) \qquad\qquad$ (1)

25. If $\vec{a} + \vec{b} + \vec{c} = 0$ and $|\vec{a}| = 5, |\vec{b}| = 6$ and $|\vec{c}| = 9$, then find angle between $\vec{a}$ and $\vec{b}$.

Sol. Given, $\vec{a} + \vec{b} + \vec{c} = 0$

$\Rightarrow \qquad\qquad \vec{a} + \vec{b} = -\vec{c}$

$\Rightarrow \qquad\qquad (\vec{a} + \vec{b})^2 = (-\vec{c})^2 \qquad$ [squaring both sides]

$\Rightarrow \qquad (\vec{a} + \vec{b})(\vec{a} + \vec{b}) = (-\vec{c}) \cdot (-\vec{c})$

$\Rightarrow \quad \vec{a} \cdot \vec{a} + \vec{a} \cdot \vec{b} + \vec{b} \cdot \vec{a} + \vec{b} \cdot \vec{b} = \vec{c} \cdot \vec{c}$

$\Rightarrow \quad |\vec{a}|^2 + 2\vec{a} \cdot \vec{b} + |\vec{b}|^2 = |\vec{c}|^2 \quad [\because \vec{a} \cdot \vec{b} = \vec{b} \cdot \vec{a}]$

$\Rightarrow |\vec{a}|^2 + 2|\vec{a}||\vec{b}|\cos\theta + |\vec{b}|^2 = |\vec{c}|^2 \qquad \text{...(i)} \text{ (1)}$

$[\because \vec{a} \cdot \vec{b} = |\vec{a}||\vec{b}|\cos\theta]$

Putting the values of $|\vec{a}| = 5, |\vec{b}| = 6$ and $|\vec{c}| = 9$ in Eq. (i), we get

$$(5)^2 + 2 \times 5 \times 6 \times \cos\theta + (6)^2 = (9)^2$$

$\Rightarrow \qquad\qquad 25 + 60\cos\theta + 36 = 81$

$\Rightarrow \qquad\qquad 60\cos\theta = 81 - 61 = 20$

$\Rightarrow \qquad\qquad \cos\theta = \dfrac{20}{60} = \dfrac{1}{3}$

$\Rightarrow \qquad\qquad \theta = \cos^{-1}\left(\dfrac{1}{3}\right) \qquad$ (1)

Section C

(This section comprises of short answer type questions (SA) of 3 marks each)

26. Three persons A, B and C apply for the job of Manager in a private company. Chances of their selection (A, B and C) are in the ratio $1 : 2 : 4$. The probabilities that A, B and C can introduce changes to improve profits of the company are 0.8, 0.5 and 0.3, respectively. If the change does not take place, find the probability that it is due to the appointment of C.

Sol. Let us define the following events

$A = $ Selecting person A

$B = $ Selecting person B

$C = $ Selecting person C

$$P(A) = \frac{1}{1+2+4}, \; P(B) = \frac{2}{1+2+4} \text{ and } P(C) = \frac{4}{1+2+4}$$

$\Rightarrow \quad P(A) = \dfrac{1}{7}, P(B) = \dfrac{2}{7} \text{ and } P(C) = \dfrac{4}{7} \qquad$ (1)

Let $E = $ Event of introducing the changes in their profit.

Also, given $P\left(\dfrac{E}{A}\right) = 0.8$, $P\left(\dfrac{E}{B}\right) = 0.5$ and $P\left(\dfrac{E}{C}\right) = 0.3$

$\Rightarrow \qquad P\left(\dfrac{\overline{E}}{A}\right) = 1 - 0.8 = 0.2,$

$\qquad\qquad P\left(\dfrac{\overline{E}}{B}\right) = 1 - 0.5 = 0.5$

and $\qquad P\left(\dfrac{\overline{E}}{C}\right) = 1 - 0.3 = 0.7 \qquad$ (1)

The probability that change does not take place by the appointment of C,

$$P\left(\dfrac{C}{\overline{E}}\right) = \frac{P(C) \cdot P\left(\dfrac{\overline{E}}{C}\right)}{P(A) \cdot P\left(\dfrac{\overline{E}}{A}\right) + P(B) \cdot P\left(\dfrac{\overline{E}}{B}\right) + P(C) \cdot P\left(\dfrac{\overline{E}}{C}\right)}$$

$$= \frac{\frac{4}{7} \times 0.7}{\frac{1}{7} \times 0.2 + \frac{2}{7} \times 0.5 + \frac{4}{7} \times 0.7}$$

$$= \frac{2.8}{0.2 + 1.0 + 2.8} = \frac{2.8}{4} = 0.7 \qquad (1)$$

27. Evaluate $\int \dfrac{dx}{1 - 3\sin x}$.

Or

Evaluate $\int \sqrt{\dfrac{1 - \sqrt{x}}{1 + \sqrt{x}}}\, dx$.

Sol. Let $I = \int \dfrac{dx}{1 - 3\sin x}$

$$= \int \frac{dx}{1 - 3\left(\dfrac{2\tan\dfrac{x}{2}}{1 + \tan^2\dfrac{x}{2}}\right)} \qquad \left[\because \sin x = \frac{2\tan\dfrac{x}{2}}{1 + \tan^2\dfrac{x}{2}}\right]$$

$$= \int \frac{dx}{\dfrac{1 + \tan^2\dfrac{x}{2} - 6\tan\dfrac{x}{2}}{1 + \tan^2\dfrac{x}{2}}} = \int \frac{\sec^2\dfrac{x}{2}}{\tan^2\dfrac{x}{2} - 6\tan\dfrac{x}{2} + 1}\, dx$$

$$(1)$$

$$[\because 1 + \tan^2\theta = \sec^2\theta]$$

Put $\tan\dfrac{x}{2} = t$

On differentiating both sides w.r.t. x, we get

$$\sec^2\frac{x}{2} \cdot \frac{1}{2} = \frac{dt}{dx} \Rightarrow \sec^2\frac{x}{2}\,dx = 2\,dt \qquad (1)$$

$$\therefore \quad I = 2\int \frac{dt}{t^2 - 6t + 1} = 2\int \frac{dt}{t^2 - 6t + 1 + (3)^2 - (3)^2}$$

$$= 2\int \frac{dt}{(t - 3)^2 - 8} = 2\int \frac{dt}{(t - 3)^2 - (2\sqrt{2})^2}$$

$$= 2 \times \frac{1}{2 \times 2\sqrt{2}} \log\left|\frac{t - 3 - 2\sqrt{2}}{t - 3 + 2\sqrt{2}}\right| + C$$

$$\left[\because \int \frac{1}{x^2 - a^2}\, dx = \frac{1}{2a} \log\left|\frac{x - a}{x + a}\right|\right]$$

$$= \frac{1}{2\sqrt{2}} \log\left|\frac{\tan\dfrac{x}{2} - 3 - 2\sqrt{2}}{\tan\dfrac{x}{2} - 3 + 2\sqrt{2}}\right| + C \quad \left[\because t = \tan\frac{x}{2}\right]$$

$$(1)$$

Or

Let $I = \int \sqrt{\dfrac{1 - \sqrt{x}}{1 + \sqrt{x}}}\, dx$

Put $\sqrt{x} = \cos t$ or $x = \cos^2 t \Rightarrow dx = -2\sin t \cdot \cos t \cdot dt$

$$\therefore \quad I = \int \sqrt{\frac{1 - \cos t}{1 + \cos t}} \cdot (-2\sin t \cdot \cos t)\, dt$$

$$= \int \sqrt{\frac{2\sin^2 t/2}{2\cos^2 t/2}} \, (-2\sin t \cdot \cos t)\, dt$$

$$[\because 1 - \cos\theta = 2\sin^2(\theta/2) \text{ and } 1 + \cos\theta = 2\cos^2(\theta/2)]$$

$$= \int \frac{\sin t/2}{\cos t/2} \times (-2 \times 2 \times \sin(t/2)\cos(t/2) \times \cos t\, dt$$

$$[\because \sin 2\theta = 2\sin\theta\cos\theta] \;(1)$$

$$= -\int 4\sin^2(t/2) \times \cos t\, dt$$

$$= -\int 4\left(\frac{1 - \cos t}{2}\right)\cos t\, dt \quad \left[\because 1 - \cos\theta = 2\sin^2\frac{\theta}{2}\right]$$

$$= -\int 2(1 - \cos t)\cos t\, dt$$

$$= -2\int (\cos t - \cos^2 t)\, dt$$

$$= -2\int \left[\cos t - \left(\frac{1 + \cos 2t}{2}\right)\right]dt$$

$$[\because \cos 2\theta = 2\cos^2\theta - 1]$$

$$= -2\int \left[\frac{2\cos t - 1 - \cos 2t}{2}\right]dt \qquad (1)$$

$$= -\int (2\cos t - 1 - \cos 2t)\, dt$$

$$= -\left(2\sin t - t - \frac{\sin 2t}{2}\right) + C$$

$$= -\left(2\sin t - t - \frac{2\sin t \cdot \cos t}{2}\right) + C$$

$$= -2\sin t + t + \sin t \cdot \cos t + C$$

$$= -2\sqrt{1 - \cos^2 t} + t + \sqrt{1 - \cos^2 t} \cdot \cos t + C$$

$$[\because \sin^2\theta + \cos^2\theta = 1 \Rightarrow \sin\theta = \sqrt{1 - \cos^2\theta}]$$

$$= -2\sqrt{1 - x} + \cos^{-1}\sqrt{x} + \sqrt{x} \cdot \sqrt{1 - x} + C \qquad (1)$$

$$[\because \sqrt{x} = \cos t]$$

28. Solve the following differential equation

$$x\frac{dy}{dx} = y - x\tan\left(\frac{y}{x}\right).$$

Or

Solve the following differential equation

$$x\cos\left(\frac{y}{x}\right)\frac{dy}{dx} = y\cos\left(\frac{y}{x}\right) + x;\, x \neq 0.$$

Sol. Given, differential equation is

$$x\frac{dy}{dx} = y - x\tan\left(\frac{y}{x}\right)$$

$$\Rightarrow \quad \frac{dy}{dx} = \frac{y - x\tan\left(\dfrac{y}{x}\right)}{x}$$

$$\Rightarrow \quad \frac{dy}{dx} = \frac{y}{x} - \tan\left(\frac{y}{x}\right) \qquad \ldots\text{(i)} \;(1)$$

which is a homogeneous differential equation

as $\dfrac{dy}{dx} = F\left(\dfrac{y}{x}\right)$.

On putting $y = vx \Rightarrow \dfrac{dy}{dx} = v + x\dfrac{dv}{dx}$ in Eq. (i), we get

$$v + x\dfrac{dv}{dx} = v - \tan v \Rightarrow x\dfrac{dv}{dx} = -\tan v$$

$$\Rightarrow \quad \dfrac{dv}{\tan v} = -\dfrac{dx}{x} \Rightarrow \cot v \, dv = -\dfrac{dx}{x}$$

On integrating both sides, we get

$$\int \cot v \, dv = -\int \dfrac{dx}{x}$$

$\Rightarrow \quad \log|\sin v| = -\log|x| + C$ (1)

$\Rightarrow \quad \log|\sin v| + \log|x| = C$

$\Rightarrow \quad \log|x \sin v| = C$

$$[\because \log m + \log n = \log mn]$$

$\therefore \quad \log\left|x \sin \dfrac{y}{x}\right| = C \quad \left[\text{putting } v = \dfrac{y}{x}\right]$

$\Rightarrow \quad x \sin\dfrac{y}{x} = e^C$

$\Rightarrow \quad x \sin\dfrac{y}{x} = A \quad [e^C = A = \text{constant}]$

$\Rightarrow \quad \sin\dfrac{y}{x} = \dfrac{A}{x}$

$\Rightarrow \quad y = x\sin^{-1}\left(\dfrac{A}{x}\right).$ (1)

which is the required solution.

Or

Given, differential equation is

$$x\cos\left(\dfrac{y}{x}\right)\dfrac{dy}{dx} = y\cos\left(\dfrac{y}{x}\right) + x \qquad \dots\text{(i)}$$

which is a homogeneous differential equation as

$$\dfrac{dy}{dx} = F\left(\dfrac{y}{x}\right)$$

On putting $y = vx \Rightarrow \dfrac{dy}{dx} = v + x\dfrac{dv}{dx}$ in Eq. (i),

we get

$$x\cos v\left[v + x\dfrac{dv}{dx}\right] = vx\cos v + x$$

$\Rightarrow \quad vx\cos v + x^2\cos v\dfrac{dv}{dx} = vx\cos v + x$

$\Rightarrow \quad x^2\cos v\dfrac{dv}{dx} = x$

$\Rightarrow \quad \cos v\, dv = \dfrac{dx}{x}$ (1)

On integrating both sides, we get

$$\int \cos v\, dv = \int \dfrac{dx}{x}$$

$\Rightarrow \quad \sin v = \log|x| + C$

$\Rightarrow \quad \sin\left(\dfrac{y}{x}\right) = \log|x| + C \quad \left[\text{putting } v = \dfrac{y}{x}\right]$

which is the required solution of given differential equation.   (2)

29. For any two vectors $\vec{a}$ and $\vec{b}$, show that

$$(1 + |\vec{a}|^2)(1 + |\vec{b}|^2) = \{(1 - \vec{a}\cdot\vec{b})\}^2 + |\vec{a} + \vec{b} + (\vec{a}\times\vec{b})|^2.$$

Or

If $\vec{a} = \hat{i} + \hat{j} + \hat{k}$ and $\vec{b} = \hat{j} - \hat{k}$, then find a vector $\vec{c}$ such that $\vec{a}\times\vec{c} = \vec{b}$ and $\vec{a}\cdot\vec{c} = 3$.

Sol. We have,

$$(1 - \vec{a}\cdot\vec{b})^2 + |\vec{a} + \vec{b} + (\vec{a}\times\vec{b})|^2$$

$$= \{1 - 2(\vec{a}\cdot\vec{b}) + (\vec{a}\cdot\vec{b})^2\}$$
$$+ \{(\vec{a} + \vec{b} + \vec{a}\times\vec{b})\cdot(\vec{a} + \vec{b} + \vec{a}\times\vec{b})\}$$

$$= \{1 - 2(\vec{a}\cdot\vec{b}) + (\vec{a}\cdot\vec{b})^2\} + \{(\vec{a} + \vec{b})$$
$$\cdot(\vec{a} + \vec{b}) + (\vec{a} + \vec{b})\cdot(\vec{a}\times\vec{b}) + (\vec{a}\times\vec{b})$$
$$\cdot(\vec{a} + \vec{b}) + (\vec{a}\times\vec{b})\cdot(\vec{a}\times\vec{b})\}$$ (1)

$$= \{1 - 2(\vec{a}\cdot\vec{b}) + (\vec{a}\cdot\vec{b})^2\} + \{|\vec{a} + \vec{b}|^2 +$$
$$\vec{a}\cdot(\vec{a}\times\vec{b}) + \vec{b}\cdot(\vec{a}\times\vec{b}) + (\vec{a}\times\vec{b})\cdot\vec{a}$$
$$+ (\vec{a}\times\vec{b})\cdot\vec{b} + |\vec{a}\times\vec{b}|^2\}$$

$$= \{1 - 2(\vec{a}\cdot\vec{b}) + (\vec{a}\cdot\vec{b})^2\} + \{|\vec{a} + \vec{b}|^2 + |\vec{a}\times\vec{b}|^2\}$$
$$\left[\begin{array}{l}\because \vec{a}\perp(\vec{a}\times\vec{b}), \vec{b}\perp(\vec{a}\times\vec{b}) \\ \therefore \vec{a}\cdot(\vec{a}\times\vec{b}) = \vec{b}\cdot(\vec{a}\times\vec{b}) = 0\end{array}\right]$$ (1)

$$= 1 - 2(\vec{a}\cdot\vec{b}) + (\vec{a}\cdot\vec{b})^2 + |\vec{a}|^2 + |\vec{b}|^2$$
$$+ 2(\vec{a}\cdot\vec{b}) + |\vec{a}\times\vec{b}|^2$$

$$= 1 + |\vec{a}|^2 + |\vec{b}|^2 + (\vec{a}\cdot\vec{b})^2 + |\vec{a}\times\vec{b}|^2$$

$$= 1 + |\vec{a}|^2 + |\vec{b}|^2 + |\vec{a}|^2|\vec{b}|^2$$
$$[\because (\vec{a}\cdot\vec{b})^2 + |\vec{a}\times\vec{b}|^2 = |\vec{a}|^2|\vec{b}|^2]$$

$$= (1 + |\vec{a}|^2)(1 + |\vec{b}|^2)$$

Hence, $(1 + |\vec{a}|^2)(1 + |\vec{b}|^2) = 1 - (\vec{a}\cdot\vec{b})^2$
$$+ |\vec{a} + \vec{b} + (\vec{a}\times\vec{b})|^2$$ (1)

Or

Given, $\vec{a} = \hat{i} + \hat{j} + \hat{k}$ and $\vec{b} = \hat{j} - \hat{k}$

Let $\quad \vec{c} = x\hat{i} + y\hat{j} + z\hat{k}$

Then, $\vec{a}\times\vec{c} = \vec{b} \Rightarrow \begin{vmatrix} \hat{i} & \hat{j} & \hat{k} \\ 1 & 1 & 1 \\ x & y & z \end{vmatrix} = \hat{j} - \hat{k}$

$\Rightarrow \quad \hat{i}(z - y) - \hat{j}(z - x) + \hat{k}(y - x) = \hat{j} - \hat{k}$ (1)

On comparing the coefficients of $\hat{i}, \hat{j}$ and $\hat{k}$ on both sides, we get

$$z - y = 0 \qquad \ldots(i)$$
$$x - z = 1 \qquad \ldots(ii)$$
and
$$x - y = 1 \qquad \ldots(iii)$$

Also, $\qquad \vec{a} \cdot \vec{c} = 3$

$\Rightarrow (\hat{i} + \hat{j} + \hat{k}) \cdot (x\hat{i} + y\hat{j} + z\hat{k}) = 3$

$\Rightarrow \qquad\qquad x + y + z = 3 \qquad \ldots(iv)$ (1)

On adding Eqs. (ii) and (iii), we get

$$2x - y - z = 2 \qquad \ldots(v)$$

On adding Eqs. (iv) and (v), we get

$$3x = 5 \quad \Rightarrow x = \frac{5}{3}$$

Then, from Eq. (iii), $y = \dfrac{5}{3} - 1 = \dfrac{2}{3}$

and from Eq. (i), $\qquad z = \dfrac{2}{3}$

Hence, $\vec{c} = \dfrac{5}{3}\hat{i} + \dfrac{2}{3}\hat{j} + \dfrac{2}{3}\hat{k} = \dfrac{1}{3}(5\hat{i} + 2\hat{j} + 2\hat{k})$ (1)

30. Bag A contains 4 black and 6 red balls and bag B contains 7 black and 3 red balls. A die is thrown. If 1 or 2 appears on it, then bag A is chosen, otherwise bag B. If two balls are drawn at random (without replacement) from the selected bag, find the probability of one of them being red and another black.

Sol. Given, bag A = 4 black and 6 red balls

and bag B = 7 black and 3 red balls.

Let E_1 = The event that die shows 1 or 2

E_2 = The event that die show 3 or 4 or 5 or 6

E = The event that among two drawn balls, one of them is red and other is black

Here, $P(E_1) = \dfrac{2}{6}$ and $P(E_2) = \dfrac{4}{6}$

[∵ total number in a die is six]

$\therefore \; P\left(\dfrac{E}{E_1}\right) = P$ (getting one red and one black ball from bag A)

$= \dfrac{{}^4C_1 \times {}^6C_1}{{}^{10}C_2} = \dfrac{4 \times 6 \times 2}{10 \times 9}$ (1)

$\Rightarrow P\left(\dfrac{E}{E_2}\right) = P$ (getting one red and one black ball from bag B)

$= \dfrac{{}^7C_1 \times {}^3C_1}{{}^{10}C_2} = \dfrac{7 \times 3 \times 2}{10 \times 9}$ (1)

Now, by theorem of total probability

$P(E) = P(E_1) \cdot P\left(\dfrac{E}{E_1}\right) + P(E_2) \cdot P\left(\dfrac{E}{E_2}\right)$

$= \dfrac{2}{6} \cdot \left(\dfrac{4 \times 6 \times 2}{10 \times 9}\right) + \dfrac{4}{6} \cdot \left(\dfrac{7 \times 3 \times 2}{10 \times 9}\right)$

$= \dfrac{4 \times 6}{6 \times 10 \times 9}(4 + 7) = \dfrac{4 \times 6 \times 11}{6 \times 10 \times 9} = \dfrac{22}{45}$ (1)

31. Find the shortest distance between the lines $\dfrac{x - 3}{1} = \dfrac{y - 5}{-2} = \dfrac{z - 7}{1}$

and $\dfrac{x + 1}{7} = \dfrac{y + 1}{-6} = \dfrac{z + 1}{1}$.

Sol. Given, equations of lines are

$$\dfrac{x - 3}{1} = \dfrac{y - 5}{-2} = \dfrac{z - 7}{1} \qquad \ldots(i)$$

and $\dfrac{x + 1}{7} = \dfrac{y + 1}{-6} = \dfrac{z + 1}{1} \qquad \ldots(ii)$

On comparing above equations with one point form of equation of line, which is $\dfrac{x - x_1}{a} = \dfrac{y - y_1}{b} = \dfrac{z - z_1}{c}$,

we get

$a_1 = 1, b_1 = -2, c_1 = 1, x_1 = 3, y_1 = 5, z_1 = 7$

and $a_2 = 7, b_2 = -6, c_2 = 1, x_2 = -1,$

$y_2 = -1, z_2 = -1$ (1)

We know that the shortest distance between two lines is given by

$$d = \dfrac{\begin{vmatrix} x_2 - x_1 & y_2 - y_1 & z_2 - z_1 \\ a_1 & b_1 & c_1 \\ a_2 & b_2 & c_2 \end{vmatrix}}{\sqrt{(b_1 c_2 - b_2 c_1)^2 + (c_1 a_2 - c_2 a_1)^2 + (a_1 b_2 - a_2 b_1)^2}}$$

$$\therefore \; d = \dfrac{\begin{vmatrix} -4 & -6 & -8 \\ 1 & -2 & 1 \\ 7 & -6 & 1 \end{vmatrix}}{\sqrt{(-2 + 6)^2 + (7 - 1)^2 + (-6 + 14)^2}}$$

[∵ $x_2 - x_1 = -1 - 3 = -4, y_2 - y_1 = -1 - 5 = -6$ and $z_2 - z_1 = -1 - 7 = -8$]

$= \left|\dfrac{-4(-2 + 6) + 6(1 - 7) - 8(-6 + 14)}{\sqrt{(4)^2 + (6)^2 + (8)^2}}\right|$ (1)

$= \left|\dfrac{-4(4) + 6(-6) - 8(8)}{\sqrt{16 + 36 + 64}}\right|$

$= \left|\dfrac{-16 - 36 - 64}{\sqrt{116}}\right|$

$= \left|\dfrac{-116}{\sqrt{116}}\right| = \dfrac{116}{\sqrt{116}} = \dfrac{116\sqrt{116}}{(\sqrt{116})^2} = \sqrt{116}$

Hence, the required shortest distance is $\sqrt{116}$ units. (1)

Section D

(This section comprises of long answer type questions (LA) of 5 marks each)

32. Show that the function $f : R \to R$ defined by
$f(x) = \dfrac{x}{x^2 + 1}, \forall x \in R$ is neither one-one nor onto.

Sol. Given, $f : R \to R$, defined by

$$f(x) = \frac{x}{x^2 + 1}, \forall x \in R$$

Let $x_1, x_2 \in R$ such that $f(x_1) = f(x_2)$

$\Rightarrow \qquad \dfrac{x_1}{x_1^2 + 1} = \dfrac{x_2}{x_2^2 + 1}$

$\Rightarrow \qquad x_1 x_2^2 + x_1 = x_2 x_1^2 + x_2$

$\Rightarrow \qquad x_1 x_2^2 - x_2 x_1^2 + x_1 - x_2 = 0 \qquad (1)$

$\Rightarrow \qquad x_1 x_2 (x_2 - x_1) - 1(x_2 - x_1) = 0$

$\Rightarrow \qquad (x_2 - x_1)(x_1 x_2 - 1) = 0$

$\Rightarrow \qquad x_2 = x_1$ or $x_1 x_2 = 1$

$\Rightarrow \qquad x_1 = x_2$ or $x_1 = \dfrac{1}{x_2}$

$\therefore$ f is not one-one, as if we take $x_1 = 3$ and $x_2 = \dfrac{1}{3}$,
then

$$f(3) = \frac{3}{10} = f\left(\frac{1}{3}\right) \text{ but } 3 \neq \frac{1}{3} \qquad (2)$$

Now, let $k \in R$ be any arbitrary element
and let $f(x) = k$

$\Rightarrow \qquad \dfrac{x}{x^2 + 1} = k \qquad \left[\because f(x) = \dfrac{x}{x^2 + 1}\right]$

$\Rightarrow \qquad kx^2 + k = x$

$\Rightarrow kx^2 - x + k = 0$

$\Rightarrow \qquad x = \dfrac{1 \pm \sqrt{1 - 4k^2}}{2k} \notin R, \text{ if } 1 - 4k^2 < 0$

or $(1 - 2k)(1 + 2k) < 0$, i.e. $k > 1/2$ or $k < -1/2$

So, f is not onto.

Hence, f is neither one-one nor onto. $\qquad (2)$

33. Solve the following system of equations by matrix method when $x \neq 0, y \neq 0$ and $z \neq 0$.

$\dfrac{2}{x} - \dfrac{3}{y} + \dfrac{3}{z} = 10, \dfrac{1}{x} + \dfrac{1}{y} + \dfrac{1}{z} = 10$

and $\qquad \dfrac{3}{x} - \dfrac{1}{y} + \dfrac{2}{z} = 13$

Or The sum of three numbers is 6. Twice the third number when added to the first number gives 7. On adding the sum of the second and third numbers to thrice the first number, we get 12. Find the numbers, using matrix method.

Sol. Given, system of equations is

$$\frac{2}{x} - \frac{3}{y} + \frac{3}{z} = 10 \qquad \ldots(i)$$

$$\frac{1}{x} + \frac{1}{y} + \frac{1}{z} = 10 \qquad \ldots(ii)$$

and $\qquad \dfrac{3}{x} - \dfrac{1}{y} + \dfrac{2}{z} = 13 \qquad \ldots(iii)$

Given equations can be written in matrix form as

$$AX = B$$

where, $A = \begin{bmatrix} 2 & -3 & 3 \\ 1 & 1 & 1 \\ 3 & -1 & 2 \end{bmatrix}$, $X = \begin{bmatrix} 1/x \\ 1/y \\ 1/z \end{bmatrix}$ and $B = \begin{bmatrix} 10 \\ 10 \\ 13 \end{bmatrix}$

Now, $|A| = \begin{vmatrix} 2 & -3 & 3 \\ 1 & 1 & 1 \\ 3 & -1 & 2 \end{vmatrix} = 2(2+1) + 3(2-3) + 3(-1-3)$

$= 6 - 3 - 12 = -9 \neq 0$

$\therefore$ A^{-1} exists. $\qquad (1)$

Now, cofactors of elements of $|A|$ are

$C_{11} = (-1)^2 \begin{vmatrix} 1 & 1 \\ -1 & 2 \end{vmatrix} = 2 + 1 = 3$

$C_{12} = (-1)^3 \begin{vmatrix} 1 & 1 \\ 3 & 2 \end{vmatrix} = -(2-3) = 1$

$C_{13} = (-1)^4 \begin{vmatrix} 1 & 1 \\ 3 & -1 \end{vmatrix} = -1 - 3 = -4$

$C_{21} = (-1)^3 \begin{vmatrix} -3 & 3 \\ -1 & 2 \end{vmatrix} = -(-6+3) = 3$

$C_{22} = (-1)^4 \begin{vmatrix} 2 & 3 \\ 3 & 2 \end{vmatrix} = 4 - 9 = -5$

$C_{23} = (-1)^5 \begin{vmatrix} 2 & -3 \\ 3 & -1 \end{vmatrix} = -(-2+9) = -7 \qquad (1)$

$C_{31} = (-1)^4 \begin{vmatrix} -3 & 3 \\ 1 & 1 \end{vmatrix} = -3 - 3 = -6$

$C_{32} = (-1)^5 \begin{vmatrix} 2 & 3 \\ 1 & 1 \end{vmatrix} = -(2-3) = 1$

$C_{33} = (-1)^6 \begin{vmatrix} 2 & -3 \\ 1 & 1 \end{vmatrix} = 2 + 3 = 5$

$\therefore \quad A^{-1} = \frac{1}{|A|} (\text{adj } A)$

$= \frac{1}{|A|} \begin{bmatrix} C_{11} & C_{21} & C_{31} \\ C_{12} & C_{22} & C_{32} \\ C_{13} & C_{23} & C_{33} \end{bmatrix} = \frac{1}{-9} \begin{bmatrix} 3 & 3 & -6 \\ 1 & -5 & 1 \\ -4 & -7 & 5 \end{bmatrix}$ (1)

$\therefore \quad X = A^{-1}B$

$\therefore \quad \begin{bmatrix} 1/x \\ 1/y \\ 1/z \end{bmatrix} = -\frac{1}{9} \begin{bmatrix} 3 & 3 & -6 \\ 1 & -5 & 1 \\ -4 & -7 & 5 \end{bmatrix} \begin{bmatrix} 10 \\ 10 \\ 13 \end{bmatrix}$

$\Rightarrow \begin{bmatrix} 1/x \\ 1/y \\ 1/z \end{bmatrix} = -\frac{1}{9} \begin{bmatrix} 30+30-78 \\ 10-50+13 \\ -40-70+65 \end{bmatrix} = -\frac{1}{9} \begin{bmatrix} -18 \\ -27 \\ -45 \end{bmatrix} = \begin{bmatrix} 2 \\ 3 \\ 5 \end{bmatrix}$

$\Rightarrow \begin{bmatrix} 1/x \\ 1/y \\ 1/z \end{bmatrix} = \begin{bmatrix} 2 \\ 3 \\ 5 \end{bmatrix}$ (1)

On comparing the corresponding elements, we get

$\frac{1}{x} = 2 \Rightarrow x = \frac{1}{2}$

$\frac{1}{y} = 3 \Rightarrow y = \frac{1}{3}$

and $\frac{1}{z} = 5 \Rightarrow z = \frac{1}{5}$ (1)

Or

Let the first, second and third numbers be x, y and z, respectively. Then,

$x + y + z = 6$ ...(i)

$x + 2z = 7$ ...(ii)

$3x + y + z = 12$ ...(iii)

Let $A = \begin{bmatrix} 1 & 1 & 1 \\ 1 & 0 & 2 \\ 3 & 1 & 1 \end{bmatrix}$, $X = \begin{bmatrix} x \\ y \\ z \end{bmatrix}$ and $B = \begin{bmatrix} 6 \\ 7 \\ 12 \end{bmatrix}$.

Then, the given system in matrix form is $AX = B$.

Now, $|A| = \begin{vmatrix} 1 & 1 & 1 \\ 1 & 0 & 2 \\ 3 & 1 & 1 \end{vmatrix} = 1(0-2) - 1(1-6) + 1(1-0)$

$= -2 + 5 + 1 = 4 \neq 0$ (1)

$\therefore A$ is invertible.

So, the given system has a unique solution, $X = A^{-1}B$.

The minors of the elements of $|A|$ are

$M_{11} = -2, M_{12} = -5, M_{13} = 1,$

$M_{21} = 0, M_{22} = -2, M_{23} = -2,$

$M_{31} = 2, M_{32} = 1, M_{33} = -1.$

The cofactors of the elements of $|A|$ are

$A_{11} = -2, A_{12} = 5, A_{13} = 1,$

$A_{21} = 0, A_{22} = -2, A_{23} = 2,$

$A_{31} = 2, A_{32} = -1, A_{33} = -1$ (2)

$\therefore (\text{adj } A) = \begin{bmatrix} -2 & 5 & 1 \\ 0 & -2 & 2 \\ 2 & -1 & -1 \end{bmatrix}^T = \begin{bmatrix} -2 & 0 & 2 \\ 5 & -2 & -1 \\ 1 & 2 & -1 \end{bmatrix}$

$\Rightarrow \quad A^{-1} = \frac{1}{|A|} \cdot (\text{adj } A) = \frac{1}{4} \cdot \begin{bmatrix} -2 & 0 & 2 \\ 5 & -2 & -1 \\ 1 & 2 & -1 \end{bmatrix}$ (1)

$\Rightarrow \quad X = A^{-1}B$

$\Rightarrow \quad \begin{bmatrix} x \\ y \\ z \end{bmatrix} = \frac{1}{4} \cdot \begin{bmatrix} -2 & 0 & 2 \\ 5 & -2 & -1 \\ 1 & 2 & -1 \end{bmatrix} \begin{bmatrix} 6 \\ 7 \\ 12 \end{bmatrix}$

$= \frac{1}{4} \cdot \begin{bmatrix} -12+0+24 \\ 30-14-12 \\ 6+14-12 \end{bmatrix} = \frac{1}{4} \cdot \begin{bmatrix} 12 \\ 4 \\ 8 \end{bmatrix} = \begin{bmatrix} 3 \\ 1 \\ 2 \end{bmatrix}$

$\Rightarrow \quad x = 3, y = 1 \text{ and } z = 2$

Hence, the required numbers are 3, 1 and 2.   (1)

34. Find the vector and cartesian equation of a plane containing the two lines $\vec{r} = (2\hat{i} + \hat{j} - 3\hat{k}) + \lambda (\hat{i} + 2\hat{j} + 5\hat{k})$ and $\vec{r} = (3\hat{i} + 3\hat{j} + 2\hat{k}) + \mu (3\hat{i} - 2\hat{j} + 5\hat{k})$.

Or

Show that the lines $\vec{r} = (-3\hat{i} + \hat{j} + 5\hat{k}) + \lambda(-3\hat{i} + \hat{j} + 5\hat{k})$ and $\vec{r} = (-\hat{i} + 2\hat{j} + 5\hat{k}) + \mu(-\hat{i} + 2\hat{j} + 5\hat{k})$ are coplanar. Also, find the equation of the plane containing these lines.

Sol. Given, equations of lines are

$\vec{r} = (2\hat{i} + \hat{j} - 3\hat{k}) + \lambda (\hat{i} + 2\hat{j} + 5\hat{k})$ ...(i)

and $\vec{r} = (3\hat{i} + 3\hat{j} + 2\hat{k}) + \mu (3\hat{i} - 2\hat{j} + 5\hat{k})$ ...(ii)

On comparing Eqs. (i) and (ii) with the vector equation of line $\vec{r} = \vec{a_1} + \lambda \vec{b_1}$ and $\vec{r} = \vec{a_2} + \mu \vec{b_2}$ respectively, we get

$\vec{a_1} = 2\hat{i} + \hat{j} - 3\hat{k}, \vec{b_1} = \hat{i} + 2\hat{j} + 5\hat{k}$

and $\vec{a_2} = 3\hat{i} + 3\hat{j} + 2\hat{k}, \vec{b_2} = 3\hat{i} - 2\hat{j} + 5\hat{k}$ (1)

Now, the required plane which contains the lines (i) and (ii), will passes through $\vec{a_1} = 2\hat{i} + \hat{j} - 3\hat{k}$.

Also, the required plane has $\vec{b_1}$ and $\vec{b_2}$ parallel to it.

$\therefore$ The normal vector to the required plane is

$\vec{n} = \vec{b_1} \times \vec{b_2} = \begin{vmatrix} \hat{i} & \hat{j} & \hat{k} \\ 1 & 2 & 5 \\ 3 & -2 & 5 \end{vmatrix}$

$= \hat{i} (10 + 10) - \hat{j} (5 - 15) + \hat{k} (-2 - 6)$

$= 20\hat{i} + 10\hat{j} - 8\hat{k}$ (1½)

∴ The vector equation of required plane is given by

$$(\vec{r} - \vec{a}) \cdot \vec{n} = 0$$

$$\Rightarrow \qquad \vec{r} \cdot \vec{n} = \vec{a}_1 \cdot \vec{n} \qquad [\because \vec{a} = \vec{a}_1]$$

$$\Rightarrow \vec{r} \cdot (20\hat{i} + 10\hat{j} - 8\hat{k}) = (2\hat{i} + \hat{j} - 3\hat{k}) \cdot (20\hat{i} + 10\hat{j} - 8\hat{k})$$

$$\Rightarrow \vec{r} \cdot (20\hat{i} + 10\hat{j} - 8\hat{k}) = 40 + 10 + 24 = 74$$

$$\Rightarrow \vec{r} \cdot (10\hat{i} + 5\hat{j} - 4\hat{k}) = 37 \qquad \ldots\text{(iii)}$$

which is the required equation of plane.   (1½)

Also, its cartesian equation is given by

$$10x + 5y - 4z = 37$$

$$\left[\begin{array}{l} \because \text{ vector form of plane } \vec{r} \cdot (a_1\hat{i} + a_2\hat{j} + a_3\hat{k}) = d \\ \text{can be written in its cartesian form as} \\ \qquad a_1 x + a_2 y + a_3 z = d \end{array}\right] \quad (1)$$

Or

Given, equation of lines are

$$\vec{r} = (-3\hat{i} + \hat{j} + 5\hat{k}) + \lambda(-3\hat{i} + \hat{j} + 5\hat{k})$$

and $\vec{r} = (-\hat{i} + 2\hat{j} + 5\hat{k}) + \mu(-\hat{i} + 2\hat{j} + 5\hat{k})$

On comparing with $\vec{r} = \vec{a}_1 + \lambda\vec{b}_1$ and $\vec{r} = \vec{a}_2 + \mu\vec{b}_2$, we get

$$\vec{a}_1 = -3\hat{i} + \hat{j} + 5\hat{k}, \vec{b}_1 = -3\hat{i} + \hat{j} + 5\hat{k}$$

and $\qquad \vec{a}_2 = -\hat{i} + 2\hat{j} + 5\hat{k}, \vec{b}_2 = -\hat{i} + 2\hat{j} + 5\hat{k}$ (1)

Now, $\vec{a}_2 - \vec{a}_1 = (-\hat{i} + 2\hat{j} + 5\hat{k}) - (-3\hat{i} + \hat{j} + 5\hat{k})$

$$= 2\hat{i} + \hat{j} + 0\hat{k}$$

Condition for coplanarity of two lines is

$$(\vec{a}_2 - \vec{a}_1) \cdot (\vec{b}_1 \times \vec{b}_2) = 0$$

$$\therefore \qquad \begin{vmatrix} 2 & 1 & 0 \\ -3 & 1 & 5 \\ -1 & 2 & 5 \end{vmatrix} = 0$$

$$\Rightarrow 2(5 - 10) - 1(-15 + 5) + 0 = 0$$

$$\Rightarrow \qquad -10 + 10 + 0 = 0$$

$$\Rightarrow \qquad 0 = 0 \qquad \text{[true]}$$

So, the given lines are coplanar.   (1½)

Now, the equation of a plane containing two lines is

$$(\vec{r} - \vec{a}_1) \cdot (\vec{b}_1 \times \vec{b}_2) = 0 \text{ or } \vec{r} \cdot (\vec{b}_1 \times \vec{b}_2) = \vec{a}_1 \cdot (\vec{b}_1 \times \vec{b}_2).$$

Here, $\vec{b}_1 \times \vec{b}_2 = \begin{vmatrix} \hat{i} & \hat{j} & \hat{k} \\ -3 & 1 & 5 \\ -1 & 2 & 5 \end{vmatrix}$

$$= \hat{i}(5 - 10) - \hat{j}(-15 + 5) + \hat{k}(-6 + 1)$$

$$= -5\hat{i} + 10\hat{j} - 5\hat{k} = 5(-\hat{i} + 2\hat{j} - \hat{k}) \qquad (1)$$

∴ Required equation of the plane is

$$\vec{r} \cdot 5(-\hat{i} + 2\hat{j} - \hat{k}) = (-3\hat{i} + \hat{j} + 5\hat{k}) \cdot [5(-\hat{i} + 2\hat{j} - \hat{k})]$$

$$\Rightarrow \vec{r} \cdot 5(-\hat{i} + 2\hat{j} - \hat{k}) = 5(3 + 2 - 5)$$

$$\Rightarrow \qquad \vec{r} \cdot (-\hat{i} + 2\hat{j} - \hat{k}) = 0 \qquad (1½)$$

35. Find the minimum value of $(ax + by)$, where $xy = c^2$.

Sol. Let $f(x) = ax + by$, whose minimum value is required.

Then, $f(x) = ax + \dfrac{bc^2}{x} \qquad \left[\because xy = c^2 \Rightarrow y = \dfrac{c^2}{x}\right]$

On differentiating both sides w.r.t. x, we get

$$f'(x) = a - \frac{bc^2}{x^2} \qquad (1)$$

For maximum or minimum value of $f(x)$, put $f'(x) = 0$

$$\Rightarrow \qquad a - \frac{bc^2}{x^2} = 0$$

$$\Rightarrow \qquad a = \frac{bc^2}{x^2}$$

$$\Rightarrow \qquad x^2 = \frac{bc^2}{a}$$

$$\Rightarrow \qquad x = \pm\sqrt{\frac{b}{a}}\, c$$

Now, $\qquad f''(x) = 0 + \dfrac{2bc^2}{x^3}$

At $x = +\sqrt{\dfrac{b}{a}}\, c, \quad f''(x) = \dfrac{2bc^2}{\left(\sqrt{\dfrac{b}{a}}\, c\right)^3} = + \text{ve}$

Hence, $f(x)$ has minimum value at $x = \sqrt{\dfrac{b}{a}}\, c$.   (1)

At $x = -\sqrt{\dfrac{b}{a}}\, c, f''(x) = \dfrac{2bc^2}{\left(-\sqrt{\dfrac{b}{a}}\, c\right)^3} = - \text{ve}$

Hence, $f(x)$ has maximum value at

$$x = -\sqrt{\frac{b}{a}}\, c. \qquad (1)$$

When $x = \sqrt{\dfrac{b}{a}}\, c$, then

$$y = \frac{c^2}{x} = \frac{c^2}{\left(\sqrt{\dfrac{b}{a}}\, c\right)} = \sqrt{\frac{a}{b}}\, c$$

∴ Minimum value of $f(x) = a\sqrt{\dfrac{b}{a}} \cdot c + b\sqrt{\dfrac{a}{b}} \cdot c$

$$= \sqrt{ab} \cdot c + \sqrt{ab} \cdot c$$

$$= 2\sqrt{ab} \cdot c \qquad (2)$$

Section E

(This section comprises of 3 case-study/ passage-based questions of 4 marks each with two sub-parts. First two case study questions have three sub-parts (i), (ii), (iii) of marks 1, 1, 2 respectively. The third case study question has two sub-parts of 2 marks each)

36. If $A = [a_{ij}]$ be a $m \times n$ matrix, then the matrix obtained by interchanging the rows and columns of A is called the transpose of A.

A square matrix $A = [a_{ij}]$ is said to be symmetric, if $A^T = A$ for all possible values of i and j.

A square matrix $A = [a_{ij}]$ is said to be skew-symmetric, if $A^T = -A$ for all possible values of i and j.

Based on the above information, answer the following questions.

(i) Find the transpose of $[1 - 2 - 5]$.

(ii) Find the transpose of matrix (ABC).

(iii) Evaluate $(A + B)^T - A$, where $A = \begin{bmatrix} 0 & 1 \\ 2 & -1 \end{bmatrix}$

and $B = \begin{bmatrix} 1 & 2 \\ 3 & 4 \end{bmatrix}$

Or

Evaluate $(AB)^T$, where $A = \begin{bmatrix} 1 & 1 \\ 0 & 1 \end{bmatrix}$ and

$B = \begin{bmatrix} 3 & 2 \\ 1 & 4 \end{bmatrix}$

Sol. (i) $[1 \;\; -2 \;\; -5]^T = \begin{bmatrix} 1 \\ -2 \\ -5 \end{bmatrix}$

(ii) $(ABC)^T = C^T B^T A^T$

(iii) $(A + B) = \begin{bmatrix} 0 & 1 \\ 2 & -1 \end{bmatrix} + \begin{bmatrix} 1 & 2 \\ 3 & 4 \end{bmatrix} = \begin{bmatrix} 1 & 3 \\ 5 & 3 \end{bmatrix}$

Now, $(A + B)^T - A = \begin{bmatrix} 1 & 5 \\ 3 & 3 \end{bmatrix} - \begin{bmatrix} 0 & 1 \\ 2 & -1 \end{bmatrix} = \begin{bmatrix} 1 & 4 \\ 1 & 4 \end{bmatrix}$

Or

$AB = \begin{bmatrix} 1 & 1 \\ 0 & 1 \end{bmatrix} \begin{bmatrix} 3 & 2 \\ 1 & 4 \end{bmatrix} = \begin{bmatrix} 4 & 6 \\ 1 & 4 \end{bmatrix}$

$\therefore (AB)^T = \begin{bmatrix} 4 & 1 \\ 6 & 4 \end{bmatrix}$

37. The feasible solution for a LPP is shown below.

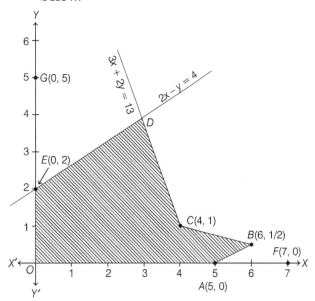

and the objective function is $Z = 15x - 4y$.

Based on the above information, answer the following questions.

(i) Find the value of $(n-1)^2$, where n is number of corner points.

(ii) Find $Z_{\left(6, \frac{1}{2}\right)} + Z_{(0, 2)}$

(iii) Find the coordinate of point D.

Or

Find the maximum of Z.

Sol. (i) Since, shaded region is $OABCDEO$.

The number of corner points, $n = 6$

$\therefore (n-1)^2 = (6-1)^2 = 5^2 = 25$

(ii) $Z_{\left(6, \frac{1}{2}\right)} + Z_{(0, 2)} = 88 + (-8) = 80$

(iii) Given, equation of lines $3x + 2y = 13$ ...(i)

and $ 2x - y = 4$ ...(ii)

The point D is the intersection point of the above two lines.

Multiplying by 2 from Eq. (ii), we get

$$4x - 2y = 8 \qquad \ldots\text{(iii)}$$

Adding Eqs. (i) and (iii), we get

$$7x = 21$$
$$\Rightarrow \qquad x = 3$$

From Eq. (ii),

$$2x - 4 = y$$
$$\Rightarrow \qquad y = 2 \times 3 - 4 = 2$$

Hence, the coordinates of point D are $(3, 2)$.

Or

Value of objective function at all corner points.

Corner points	Value of $Z = 15x - 4y$
$O(0,0)$	$15(0) - 4(0) = 0$
$A(5, 0)$	$15 \times 5 - 4 \times 0 = 75$
$B\left(6, \dfrac{1}{2}\right)$	$15 \times 6 - 4 \times \dfrac{1}{2} = 88$ (Maximum)
$C(4, 1)$	$15 \times 4 - 4 \times 1 = 56$
$D(3,2)$	$15 \times 3 - 4 \times 2 = 37$
$E(0, 2)$	$15 \times 0 - 4 \times 2 = -8$ (Minimum)

$\therefore$ Maximum of Z is 88.

38. Consider the given equation $\dfrac{dy}{dx} + Py = Q$.

The above equation is known as linear differential equation. Here, $\text{IF} = e^{\int P dx}$ and solution is given by $y \cdot \text{IF} = \int Q \cdot \text{IF}\, dx + C$

Now, consider the given equation $(1 + \sin x)\dfrac{dy}{dx} + y \cos x + x = 0.$

On the basis of above information, answer the following questions.

(i) What is the solution of the given equation?

(ii) If $y(0) = 1$, then what is the value of $y\left(\dfrac{\pi}{2}\right)$?

Sol. We have, $(1 + \sin x)\dfrac{dy}{dx} + y \cos x + x = 0$

$$\Rightarrow \qquad \dfrac{dy}{dx} + \dfrac{\cos x}{1 + \sin x} y = \dfrac{-x}{1 + \sin x}$$

$\therefore \quad P = \dfrac{\cos x}{1 + \sin x}$ and $Q = \dfrac{-x}{1 + \sin x}$

$\therefore \quad \text{IF} = e^{\int P dx} = e^{\int \frac{\cos x}{1 + \sin x} dx}$

Put $1 + \sin x = t \Rightarrow \cos x\, dx = dt$

$\therefore \quad \text{IF} = e^{\int \frac{1}{t} dt} = e^{\log t} = t = 1 + \sin x$

(i) The solution of the given equation is

$$y(1 + \sin x) = \int \dfrac{-x}{1 + \sin x} \cdot (1 + \sin x)\, dx + C$$

$$y(1 + \sin x) = -\dfrac{x^2}{2} + C$$

(ii) We have, $\qquad y(0) = 1$

$$\therefore \qquad 1 = C$$

$$\therefore \qquad y(1 + \sin x) = -\dfrac{1}{2}x^2 + 1$$

$$\Rightarrow \qquad y = \dfrac{2 - x^2}{2(1 + \sin x)}$$

Now, $y\left(\dfrac{\pi}{2}\right) = \dfrac{2 - \dfrac{\pi^2}{4}}{2\left(1 + \sin\dfrac{\pi}{2}\right)} = \dfrac{8 - \pi^2}{16}$

SAMPLE QUESTION PAPER 4

MATHEMATICS

Time : 3 hrs   Max. Marks : 80

General Instructions

1. This question paper contains - five sections A, B, C, D and E. Each section is compulsory. However, there are internal choices in some questions.
2. Section A has 18 MCQ's and 02 Assertion-Reason based questions of 1 mark each.
3. Section B has 5 Very Short Answer (VSA) type questions of 2 marks each.
4. Section C has 6 Short Answer (SA) type questions of 3 marks each.
5. Section D has 4 Long Answer (LA) type questions of 5 marks each.
6. Section E has 3 source based/case based/passage based/integrated units of assessment (4 marks each) with sub parts.

Section A
(Multiple Choice Questions) Each question carries 1 mark

1. If a leap year is selected at random, then what is the chance that it will contain 53 Tuesday?

(a) $\dfrac{1}{7}$ (b) $\dfrac{2}{7}$ (c) $\dfrac{3}{7}$ (d) $\dfrac{5}{7}$

Sol. (b) In a leap year, there are 366 days i.e. 52 weeks and 2 days.

The two days can be

(1) Sunday and Monday   (2) Monday and Tuesday
(3) Tuesday and Wednesday   (4) Wednesday and Thursday
(5) Thursday and Friday   (6) Friday and Saturday
(7) Saturday and Sunday

∴ Total number of cases = 7

Number of favourable cases = 2

∴ Required probability = $\dfrac{2}{7}$

2. Evaluate $\int_0^{2\pi} \dfrac{3^{\sin x}}{1+3^{\sin x}}\,dx$

(a) 2π (b) $\dfrac{\pi}{2}$ (c) 3π (d) π

Sol. (d) Let $I = \int_0^{2\pi} \dfrac{3^{\sin x}}{1+3^{\sin x}}\,dx$ ...(i)

$$= \int_0^{2\pi} \dfrac{3^{\sin(2\pi-x)}}{1+3^{\sin(2\pi-x)}}\,dx$$

$$\left[\because \int_0^a f(x)\,dx = \int_0^a f(a-x)\,dx\right]$$

$$= \int_0^{2\pi} \dfrac{3^{-\sin(x)}}{1+3^{-\sin x}}\,dx$$

$$I = \int_0^{2\pi} \dfrac{1}{1+3^{\sin x}}\,dx \qquad ...(ii)$$

On adding Eqs. (i) and (ii), we get

$$2I = \int_0^{2\pi} \dfrac{3^{\sin x}}{1+3^{\sin x}}\,dx + \int_0^{2\pi} \dfrac{1}{1+3^{\sin x}}\,dx$$

$$= \int_0^{2\pi} \dfrac{1+3^{\sin x}}{1+3^{\sin x}}\,dx = \int_0^{2\pi} 1\,dx = [x]_0^{2\pi} = 2\pi$$

$\Rightarrow \qquad I = \pi$

3. If $y = \log_a x$, then $\dfrac{dy}{dx}$ equals

(a) $\dfrac{1}{x\log a}$ (b) $\dfrac{1}{\log a}$

(c) $\dfrac{3x}{\log a}$ (d) $\dfrac{1}{x}$

Sol. (a) We have,

$$y = \log_a x = \dfrac{\log x}{\log a} \qquad \left[\because \log_b a = \dfrac{\log a}{\log b}\right]$$

$$\therefore \quad \dfrac{dy}{dx} = \dfrac{1}{\log a}\cdot\dfrac{1}{x} = \dfrac{1}{x\log a}$$

4. The least value of $f(x) = e^x + e^{-x}$ is

(a) -2 (b) 2
(c) 0 (d) 1

Sol. (b) Given, $f(x) = e^x + e^{-x}$

On differentiating w.r.t. x, we get

$$f'(x) = e^x - e^{-x}$$

For least value of $f(x)$, put $f'(x) = 0$

$\therefore \qquad e^x - e^{-x} = 0 \Rightarrow e^x = e^{-x}$

$\Rightarrow \qquad e^{2x} = 1 \Rightarrow 2x = 0$

$\Rightarrow \qquad x = 0$

Now, $f''(x) = e^x + e^{-x}$

At $x = 0$, $f''(0) = e^0 + e^{-0} = 1+1 = 2 > 0$

$\therefore f(x)$ is least (or minima) at $x = 0$.

So, the least value of $f(x)$ at $x = 0$ is

$$f(0) = e^0 + e^{-0} = 1+1 = 2$$

5. The feasible region for an LPP is shown in the following figure.

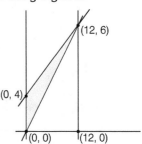

Let $F = 3x - 4y$ be the objective function. Maximum value of F is

(a) 0 (b) 8 (c) 12 (d) -18

Sol. (c) The feasible region as shown in the figure, has objective function $F = 3x - 4y$.

Corner points	Corresponding value of $F = 3x - 4y$
(0, 0)	0
(12, 6)	12 ← Maximum
(0, 4)	−16

Hence, the maximum value of F is 12.

6. The sum of order and degree of the differential equation $\left(\dfrac{dy}{dx}\right)^4 + 3y\left(\dfrac{d^2y}{dx^2}\right) = 0$

is

(a) 1 (b) 2 (c) 3 (d) 4

Sol. (c) We have,

$$\left(\dfrac{dy}{dx}\right)^4 + 3y\left(\dfrac{d^2y}{dx^2}\right) = 0$$

Here, order = 2 and degree = 1

$\therefore$ Required Sum $= 2+1 = 3$

7. The value of λ, so that the vectors $\vec{a} = 3\hat{i} + 2\hat{j} + 9\hat{k}$ and $\vec{b} = \hat{i} + \lambda\hat{j} + 3\hat{k}$ are perpendicular to each other is

(a) 15 (b) -15 (c) 12 (d) -12

Sol. (b) Given, $\vec{a} = 3\hat{i} + 2\hat{j} + 9\hat{k}$ and $\vec{b} = \hat{i} + \lambda\hat{j} + 3\hat{k}$

Since, vectors $\vec{a}$ and $\vec{b}$ are perpendicular to each other.

$\therefore \qquad\qquad \vec{a}\cdot\vec{b} = 0$

$\Rightarrow \quad (3\hat{i} + 2\hat{j} + 9\hat{k})\cdot(\hat{i} + \lambda\hat{j} + 3\hat{k}) = 0$

$\Rightarrow \qquad\qquad 3 + 2\lambda + 27 = 0 \Rightarrow 2\lambda = -30$

$\Rightarrow \qquad\qquad \lambda = -\dfrac{30}{2} = -15$

Hence, the required value of λ is -15.

8. Solve $x^3 y \, dx = dy$, given that $y = 1$ when $x = 1$

(a) $y = e^{\left(\frac{x^4-1}{3}\right)}$ (b) $y = e^{\left(\frac{x^4-1}{4}\right)}$

(c) $y = e^x$ (d) $y = e^{-x^4/4}$

Sol. (b) We have, $x^3 y \, dx = dy \Rightarrow x^3 dx = \dfrac{dy}{y}$

On integrating both sides, we get

$$\int x^3 dx = \int \frac{dy}{y}$$

$$\frac{x^4}{4} = \log y + C \qquad \ldots(i)$$

which is a general solution of the given differential equation.

Also, given $y = 1$, when $x = 1$

∴ From Eq. (i), we get $C = \dfrac{1}{4}$

On putting the value of C in Eq. (i), we get

∴ $\dfrac{x^4}{4} = \log y + \dfrac{1}{4} \Rightarrow \log y = \dfrac{x^4-1}{4} \Rightarrow y = e^{\left(\frac{x^4-1}{4}\right)}$

9. If $P(A) = \dfrac{7}{13}$, $P(B) = \dfrac{9}{13}$ and $P(A \cap B) = \dfrac{4}{13}$, then $P\left(\dfrac{A}{B}\right)$ equals

(a) $\dfrac{1}{9}$ (b) $\dfrac{2}{9}$ (c) $\dfrac{3}{9}$ (d) $\dfrac{4}{9}$

Sol. (d) We know that $P\left(\dfrac{A}{B}\right) = \dfrac{P(A \cap B)}{P(B)}$

∴ $P\left(\dfrac{A}{B}\right) = \dfrac{\frac{4}{13}}{\frac{9}{13}} = \dfrac{4}{9}$

10. Which of the following statements is true for $f(x) = 4x^3 - 6x^2 - 72x + 30$?

I. f is strictly increasing in the interval $(-\infty, -2)$.

II. f is strictly increasing in the interval $(3, \infty)$.

III. f is strictly decreasing in the interval $(-2, 3)$.

IV. f is neither increasing nor decreasing in R.

(a) I and II are true (b) II and III are true
(c) II and IV are true (d) All are true

Sol. (d) We have, $f(x) = 4x^3 - 6x^2 - 72x + 30$

On differentiating w.r.t. x, we get

$$f'(x) = 12x^2 - 12x - 72$$

$$= 12(x^2 - x - 6)$$

$$= 12(x - 3)(x + 2)$$

Therefore, $f'(x) = 0$ gives $x = -2, 3$.

The points $x = -2$ and $x = 3$ divides the real line into three disjoint intervals, namely,

$(-\infty, -2)$, $(-2, 3)$ and $(3, \infty)$.

In the intervals $(-\infty, -2)$ and $(3, \infty)$, $f'(x)$ is positive while in the interval $(-2, 3)$, $f'(x)$ is negative. Consequently, the function f is strictly increasing in the intervals $(-\infty, -2)$ and $(3, \infty)$ while the function is strictly decreasing in the interval $(-2, 3)$. However, f is neither increasing nor decreasing in R.

Interval	Sign of $f'(x)$	Nature of function f
$(-\infty, -2)$	$(-)(-) > 0$	f is strictly increasing
$(-2, 3)$	$(-)(+) < 0$	f is strictly decreasing
$(3, \infty)$	$(+)(+) > 0$	f is strictly increasing

11. The function $f(x) = 4\sin^3 x - 6\sin^2 x + 12\sin x + 100$ is strictly

(a) increasing in $\left(\pi, \dfrac{3\pi}{2}\right)$

(b) decreasing in $\left(\dfrac{\pi}{2}, \pi\right)$

(c) decreasing in $\left[-\dfrac{\pi}{2}, \dfrac{\pi}{2}\right]$

(d) decreasing in $\left[0, \dfrac{\pi}{2}\right]$

Sol. (b) ∵ $f(x) = 4\sin^3 x - 6\sin^2 x + 12\sin x + 100$

On differentiating w.r.t. x, we get

$f'(x) = 12\sin^2 x \cdot \cos x - 12\sin x \cdot \cos x + 12\cos x + 0$

$= 12\cos x(\sin^2 x - \sin x + 1)$

Since, in II quadrant $\sin x$ is $+$ve and the $\cos x$ is $-$ve.

So, $f'(x) < 0$ for all $x \in \left(\dfrac{\pi}{2}, \pi\right)$.

12. The function $f(x) = \begin{cases} \dfrac{k\cos x}{\pi - 2x}, & \text{if } x \neq \dfrac{\pi}{2} \\ 3, & \text{if } x = \dfrac{\pi}{2} \end{cases}$ is continuous at $x = \dfrac{\pi}{2}$, when k equals

(a) -6 (b) 6 (c) 5 (d) -5

Sol. (b) Given, $f(x) = \begin{cases} \dfrac{k\cos x}{\pi - 2x}, & \text{if } x \neq \dfrac{\pi}{2} \\ 3, & \text{if } x = \dfrac{\pi}{2} \end{cases}$

$\therefore$ $\text{LHL} = \lim\limits_{x \to \frac{\pi}{2}^-} f(x) = \lim\limits_{x \to \frac{\pi}{2}^-} \dfrac{k\cos x}{\pi - 2x}$

Putting $x = \dfrac{\pi}{2} - h$ as $x \to \dfrac{\pi}{2}$, then $h \to 0$

$\therefore \lim\limits_{h \to 0} \dfrac{k\cos\left(\dfrac{\pi}{2} - h\right)}{\pi - 2\left(\dfrac{\pi}{2} - h\right)} = \lim\limits_{h \to 0} \dfrac{k\sin h}{2h}$

$= \dfrac{k}{2}\lim\limits_{h \to 0} \dfrac{\sin h}{h} = \dfrac{k}{2} \times 1 = \dfrac{k}{2}$

$$\left[\because \lim\limits_{x \to 0} \dfrac{\sin x}{x} = 1 \right]$$

$\text{RHL} = \lim\limits_{x \to \frac{\pi}{2}^+} f(x) = \lim\limits_{x \to \frac{\pi}{2}^+} \dfrac{k\cos x}{\pi - 2x}$

Putting $x = \dfrac{\pi}{2} + h$ as $x \to \dfrac{\pi}{2}$, then $h \to 0$

$\therefore \lim\limits_{h \to 0} \dfrac{k\cos\left(\dfrac{\pi}{2} + h\right)}{\pi - 2\left(\dfrac{\pi}{2} + h\right)} = \lim\limits_{h \to 0} \dfrac{-k\sin h}{-2h}$

$= \dfrac{k}{2}\lim\limits_{h \to 0} \times \dfrac{\sin h}{h} = \dfrac{k}{2} \times 1 = \dfrac{k}{2}$ $\left[\because \lim\limits_{x \to 0} \dfrac{\sin x}{x} = 1 \right]$

Also, $f\left(\dfrac{\pi}{2}\right) = 3$

Since, $f(x)$ is continuous at $x = \dfrac{\pi}{2}$.

$\therefore$ $\text{LHL} = \text{RHL} = f\left(\dfrac{\pi}{2}\right) \Rightarrow \dfrac{k}{2} = 3 \Rightarrow k = 6$

13. If $y = x^3 + \tan x$, then $y'' - 2\sec^2 x \tan x$ equals
(a) 6   (b) 6x   (c) 3   (d) 3x

Sol. (b) Given that $y = x^3 + \tan x$

On differentiating both sides w.r.t. x, we get
$$y' = 3x^2 + \sec^2 x$$

Again, on differentiating both sides w.r.t. x, we get
$$y'' = 6x + 2\sec^2 x \tan x$$
$$\Rightarrow \qquad y'' - 2\sec^2 x \tan x = 6x$$

14. If $y = \tan x - \dfrac{1}{3}\log x - \dfrac{2}{x}$, then $\dfrac{dy}{dx}$ is equal to

(a) $\sec x - \dfrac{1}{3x} + \dfrac{2}{x^2}$ (b) $\sec^2 x - \dfrac{1}{3x} + \dfrac{2}{x^2}$

(c) $\sec x - 3x + x^2$ (d) None of these

Sol. (b) We have, $y = \tan x - \dfrac{1}{3}\log x - \dfrac{2}{x}$

On differentiating both the sides w.r.t. x, we get
$$\dfrac{dy}{dx} = \sec^2 x - \dfrac{1}{3} \times \dfrac{1}{x} - 2\left(-\dfrac{1}{x^2}\right)$$
$$\Rightarrow \qquad \dfrac{dy}{dx} = \sec^2 x - \dfrac{1}{3x} + \dfrac{2}{x^2}$$

15. If $y = a^x + x^a + a^a$, then $\dfrac{dy}{dx}$ is equal to

(a) $a^x \log a + ax^a$ (b) $a^x \log a + ax^{a-1}$

(c) $a^{x-1}\log a + x$ (d) $x^{a-1}\log a + a^x \log a$

Sol. (b) We have, $y = a^x + x^a + a^a$

On differentiating both sides, we get
$$\dfrac{dy}{dx} = a^x \log a + ax^{a-1} + 0 = a^x \log a + ax^{a-1}$$

16. Evaluate $\displaystyle\int_{-1}^{1} \dfrac{3x^2}{1 + 4^{\tan x}}\,dx$.

(a) 1   (b) 2   (c) 3   (d) 0

Sol. (a) We have, $I = \displaystyle\int_{-1}^{1} \dfrac{3x^2}{1 + 4^{\tan x}}\,dx$ ...(i)

$\Rightarrow I = \displaystyle\int_{-1}^{1} \dfrac{3x^2}{1 + 4^{-\tan x}}\,dx$ $\left[\because \displaystyle\int_a^b f(x)dx = \displaystyle\int_a^b f(a+b-x)dx \right]$

$\Rightarrow I = \displaystyle\int_{-1}^{1} \dfrac{3x^2 4^{\tan x}}{1 + 4^{\tan x}}\,dx$ ...(ii)

On adding Eqs. (i) and (ii), we get

$2I = \displaystyle\int_{-1}^{1} \dfrac{3x^2(1 + 4^{\tan x})}{1 + 4^{\tan x}}\,dx \Rightarrow 2I = 3\displaystyle\int_{-1}^{1} x^2 dx$

$\Rightarrow 2I = 3\left[\dfrac{x^3}{3}\right]_{-1}^{1} = [x^3]_{-1}^{1} = 1 + 1 = 2 \Rightarrow I = \dfrac{2}{2} = 1$

17. If $|\vec{a}| = 10$, $|\vec{b}| = 2$ and $\vec{a} \cdot \vec{b} = 12$, then $|\vec{a} \times \vec{b}|$ is equal to
(a) 15   (b) 16   (c) 0   (d) 12

Sol. (b) We have, $|\vec{a}| = 10, |\vec{b}| = 2$ and $\vec{a} \cdot \vec{b} = 12$

We know that $|\vec{a} \times \vec{b}| = |\vec{a}||\vec{b}|\sin\theta$ ...(i)

and $\vec{a} \cdot \vec{b} = |\vec{a}||\vec{b}|\cos\theta$ ...(ii)

On squaring and adding both sides, we get

$|\vec{a} \times \vec{b}|^2 + (\vec{a} \cdot \vec{b})^2 = |\vec{a}|^2|\vec{b}|^2\sin^2\theta + |\vec{a}|^2|\vec{b}|^2\cos^2\theta$

$\Rightarrow |\vec{a} \times \vec{b}|^2 + (\vec{a} \cdot \vec{b})^2 = |\vec{a}|^2|\vec{b}|^2(\sin^2\theta + \cos^2\theta)$

$|\vec{a} \times \vec{b}|^2 + (\vec{a} \cdot \vec{b})^2 = |\vec{a}|^2|\vec{b}|^2$

$\Rightarrow \qquad |\vec{a} \times \vec{b}|^2 + (12)^2 = (10)^2(2)^2$

$\Rightarrow \quad |\vec{a} \times \vec{b}| = \sqrt{400 - 144} \Rightarrow |\vec{a} \times \vec{b}| = \sqrt{256} = 16$

18. If $A \subset B$, then $P(B / A)$ equals

(a) 1   (b) 0   (c) 0.5   (d) 0.25

Sol. (a) We know that $P(B / A) = \dfrac{P(B \cap A)}{P(A)} = \dfrac{P(A)}{P(A)}$

$$[\because A \subset B \Rightarrow P(A \cap B) = P(A)]$$
$$= 1$$

Assertion-Reason Based Questions

In the following questions, a statement of Assertion (A) is followed by a statement of Reason (R). Choose the correct answer out of the following choices.

(a) Both A and R are true and R is the correct explanation of A

(b) Both A and R are true but R is not the correct explanation of A

(c) A is true but R is false

(d) A is false but R is true

19. Assertion (A) Let a relation R defined from set $A = \{1, 2, 5, 6\}$ to A is $R = \{(1, 1), (1, 6), (6, 1)\}$, then R is symmetric relation.

Reason (R) A relation R in set A is called symmetric, if $(a, b) \in R$ $\Rightarrow (b, a) \in R$ for every $a, b \in A$.

Sol. (a) **Assertion** We have, $A = \{1, 2, 5, 6\}$ and $R = \{(1, 1), (1, 6), (6, 1)\}$

Here, $(1, 6) \in R$

$\Rightarrow \quad (6, 1) \in R$

So, R is symmetric relation.

Hence, Assertion is true and Reason is also true and Reason is the correct explanation of Assertion.

20. Assertion (A) The inverse of sine function is define in the interval $[-\pi, 0]$, $[0, \pi]$ etc.

Reason (R) The inverse of sine function is denoted by $\sin^{-1}$.

Sol. (d) **Assertion** Sine function is one-one and onto in the interval $\left[\dfrac{-3\pi}{2}, \dfrac{-\pi}{2}\right] \left[\dfrac{-\pi}{2}, \dfrac{\pi}{2}\right] \left[\dfrac{\pi}{2}, \dfrac{3\pi}{2}\right]$ etc; and its range is $[-1, 1]$.

So, inverse of sine function is define in each of these intervals.

Reason We denote the inverse of sine function by $\sin^{-1}$ (arc sine function).

Hence, we can say that the Reason is true and Assertion is false.

Section B

(This section comprises of very short answer type questions (VSA) of 2 marks each)

21. Show that the function $f(x) = (x^3 - 6x^2 + 12x - 18)$ is an increasing function on R.

Or Prove that the function f given by $f(x) = \log \cos x$ is strictly decreasing.

Sol. We have, $f(x) = x^3 - 6x^2 + 12x - 18$

$\therefore \quad f'(x) = 3x^2 - 12x + 12 = 3(x^2 - 4x + 4)$

$= 3(x - 2)^2 \geq \forall x \in R$ (1)

$\therefore \quad f'(x) \geq 0 \, \forall x \in R$

Hence, $f(x)$ is increasing function on R.   (1)

Or

Given, $f(x) = \log \cos x$

On differentiating both sides w.r.t. x, we get

$$f'(x) = \frac{1}{\cos x} \cdot \frac{d}{dx} (\cos x)$$

$$= \frac{1}{\cos x} \cdot (-\sin x) = -\tan x \quad (1)$$

We know that for $x \in \left(0, \dfrac{\pi}{2}\right)$, $\tan x > 0$

$\therefore \quad f'(x) = -\tan x < 0$

Hence, $f(x)$ is strictly decreasing. **Hence proved.** (1)

22. Solve $\dfrac{dy}{dx} = \dfrac{3e^{2x} + 3e^{4x}}{e^x + e^{-x}}$.

Sol. We have, $\dfrac{dy}{dx} = \dfrac{3e^{2x} + 3e^{4x}}{e^x + e^{-x}}$

$\Rightarrow \quad \dfrac{dy}{dx} = \dfrac{3e^{2x}(1 + e^{2x})}{e^{-x}(e^{2x} + 1)} \Rightarrow \dfrac{dy}{dx} = 3e^{3x}$ (1)

$\Rightarrow \quad dy = 3e^{3x} dx$

On integrating both sides, we get

$$\int 1 dy = 3 \int e^{3x} dx \Rightarrow y = e^{3x} + C \quad (1)$$

23. Evaluate $\int \sin x \sin 2x \sin 3x \, dx$.

Or

Evaluate $\int \tan^4 x \, dx$

Sol. Let $I = \int \sin x \sin 2x \sin 3x$

$= \dfrac{1}{2} \int (2 \sin x \sin 2x) \sin 3x \, dx$

$= \dfrac{1}{2} \int (\cos x - \cos 3x) \sin 3x \, dx$

$= \dfrac{1}{4} \int (2 \sin 3x \cos x - 2 \sin 3x \cos 3x) dx$ (1)

$$= \frac{1}{4} \int (\sin 4x + \sin 2x - \sin 6x)\, dx$$

$$= \frac{1}{4} \left[-\frac{\cos 4x}{4} - \frac{\cos 2x}{2} + \frac{\cos 6x}{6} \right] + C \qquad (1)$$

Or

Let $I = \int \tan^4 x\, dx$

$$= \int \tan^2 x (\sec^2 x - 1)\, dx$$

$$= \int \tan^2 x \sec^2 x\, dx - \int \tan^2 x\, dx$$

$$= \int \tan^2 x \sec^2 x\, dx - \int (\sec^2 x - 1)\, dx \qquad (1)$$

Putting $\tan x = t$ and $\sec^2 x\, dx = dt$ in first integral, we get

$$= \int t^2 - \int (\sec^2 x - 1)\, dx$$

$$= \int t^2 dt - \int \sec^2 x\, dx + \int 1\, dx$$

$$= \frac{t^3}{3} - \tan x + x + C = \frac{\tan^3 x}{3} - (\tan x - x) + C \qquad (1)$$

24. Solve $\dfrac{dy}{dx} + 2y = e^{3x}$.

Sol. We have, $\dfrac{dy}{dx} + 2y = e^{3x}$

This is of the form $\dfrac{dy}{dx} + Py = Q$.

Here, $P = 2$ and $Q = e^{3x}$ (1/2)

$$\therefore \qquad \text{IF} = e^{\int 2\, dx} = e^{2x}$$

The solution is given by

$$y \times \text{IF} = \int (Q \times \text{IF})\, dx + C$$

$$\Rightarrow \qquad y \cdot e^{2x} = \int e^{2x} \cdot e^{3x}\, dx + C \qquad (1/2)$$

$$\Rightarrow \qquad y e^{2x} = \int e^{5x}\, dx + C$$

$$\Rightarrow \qquad y e^{2x} = \frac{1}{5} e^{5x} + C$$

$$\Rightarrow \qquad y = \frac{1}{5} e^{3x} + C e^{-2x} \qquad (1)$$

25. If the points $A(-1, 3, 2)$, $B(-4, 2, -2)$ and $C(5, 5, \lambda)$ are collinear, find the value of λ.

Sol. The equations of line passing through $A(-1, 3, 2)$ and $B(-4, 2, -2)$ is

$$\frac{x+1}{-4+1} = \frac{y-3}{2-3} = \frac{z-2}{-2-2}$$

$$\Rightarrow \qquad \frac{x+1}{-3} = \frac{y-3}{-1} = \frac{z-2}{-4}$$

$$\Rightarrow \qquad \frac{x+1}{3} = \frac{y-3}{1} = \frac{z-2}{4} \qquad \ldots\text{(i) (1)}$$

Since, A, B, C are collinear, then C must satisfy Eq. (i).

$$\therefore \qquad \underset{\text{I}}{\frac{5+1}{3}} = \underset{\text{II}}{\frac{5-3}{1}} = \underset{\text{III}}{\frac{\lambda-2}{4}}$$

On taking II and III, we get

$$\frac{\lambda - 2}{4} = 2 \quad \Rightarrow \quad \lambda = 10 \qquad (1)$$

Section C

(This section comprises of short answer type questions (SA) of 3 marks each)

26. Let $A = R - \{3\}$, $B = R - \{1\}$. If $f : A \to B$ be defined by $f(x) = \dfrac{x-2}{x-3}$, $\forall\, x \in A$. Show that f is bijective.

Sol. Given, $A = R - \{3\}$, $B = R - \{1\}$ and

$$f : A \to B \text{ defined by } f(x) = \frac{x-2}{x-3}, \forall\, x \in A.$$

For one-one

Let $f(x_1) = f(x_2)$

$$\Rightarrow \qquad \frac{x_1 - 2}{x_1 - 3} = \frac{x_2 - 2}{x_2 - 3}$$

$$\Rightarrow \qquad (x_1 - 2)(x_2 - 3) = (x_2 - 2)(x_1 - 3)$$

$$\Rightarrow \quad x_1 x_2 - 3x_1 - 2x_2 + 6 = x_1 x_2 - 3x_2 - 2x_1 + 6$$

$$\Rightarrow \qquad -3x_1 - 2x_2 = -3x_2 - 2x_1$$

$$\Rightarrow \qquad -x_1 = -x_2$$

$$\Rightarrow \qquad x_1 = x_2$$

So, $f(x)$ is one-one.   (1)

For onto

Let $\qquad y = \dfrac{x-2}{x-3} \Rightarrow x - 2 = xy - 3y$

$$\Rightarrow x(1 - y) = 2 - 3y$$

$$\Rightarrow \qquad x = \frac{2 - 3y}{1 - y} \qquad (1)$$

$$\because \qquad x = \frac{3y - 2}{y - 1}$$

Clearly, $x \in R - \{3\}$, $\forall\, y \in R - \{1\}$

So, range of $f(x) = R - \{1\}$

$\therefore$ Range = codomain

So, $f(x)$ is onto.

Thus, $f(x)$ is bijective.   (1)

27. Let $A = \{1, 2, 3, \ldots, 9\}$ and R be the relation in $A \times A$ defined by $(a, b)\, R\, (c, d)$, if $a + d = b + c$ for $(a, b), (c, d)$ in $A \times A$. Prove that R is an equivalence relation.

Or

Prove that the relation R in set $A = \{1, 2, 3, 4, 5\}$ given by $R = \{(a, b) : |a - b|$ is even$\}$ is an equivalence relation.

Sol. Given, $A = \{1, 2, 3, ..., 9\}$ and a relation R in $A \times A$ defined by $(a, b)R(c, d)$, if $a + d = b + c$.

Reflexivity Let $(a, b) \in A \times A$ be any arbitrary element.

Now, $\qquad a + b = b + a$

[∵ addition is commutative on the set of real numbers]

Therefore, $(a, b)R(a, b)$.

∵ $\qquad (a, b) \in A \times A$ was arbitrary.

∴ $\quad R$ is reflexive. $\hfill (1)$

Symmetricity Let $(a, b), (c, d) \in A \times A$

such that $\qquad (a, b)R(c, d)$.

∵ $\qquad (a, b)R(c, d)$

∴ $\qquad a + d = b + c \Rightarrow c + b = d + a$

[∵ addition is commutative on the set of real numbers]

$\Rightarrow \qquad (c, d)R(a, b)$

So, R is symmetric. $\hfill (1)$

Transitivity Let $(a, b), (c, d), (e, f) \in A \times A$ such that $(a, b)R(c, d)$ and $(c, d)R(e, f)$.

Since, $(a, b)R(c, d)$ and $(c, d)R(e, f)$.

So, we have $\quad a + d = b + c \hfill ...(i)$

and $\qquad c + f = d + e \hfill ...(ii)$

On adding Eqs. (i) and (ii), we get

$(a + d) + (c + f) = (b + c) + (d + e)$

$\Rightarrow \qquad a + f = b + e \Rightarrow (a, b)R(e, f)$

So, R is transitive.

Thus, R is reflexive, symmetric and transitive.

Hence, R is an equivalence relation. $\hfill (1)$

Or

The given relation is $R = \{(a, b) : |a - b|$ is even$\}$ defined on set $A = \{1, 2, 3, 4, 5\}$.

To show that R is an equivalence relation, we show that it is reflexive, symmetric and transitive.

(i) **Reflexive** As $|x - x| = 0$ is even, $\forall \, x \in A$.

$\Rightarrow \qquad (x, x) \in R, \forall \, x \in A$

Hence, R is reflexive. $\hfill (1/2)$

(ii) **Symmetric** As, $(x, y) \in R \Rightarrow |x - y|$ is even

[by the definition of given relation]

$\Rightarrow |y - x|$ is also even $\quad$ [∵ $|a| = |-a|, \forall \, a \in R$]

$\Rightarrow (y, x) \in R, \forall \, x, y \in A$

We have shown that $(x, y) \in R$

$\Rightarrow (y, x) \in R, \forall \, x, y \in A$

Hence, R is symmetric. $\hfill (1/2)$

(iii) **Transitive** As $(x, y) \in R$ and $(y, z) \in R$

$\Rightarrow |x - y|$ is even and $|y - z|$ is even.

[by using definition of given relation]

Now, $|x - y|$ is even

$\Rightarrow \quad x$ and y both are even or odd

and $\quad |y - x|$ is even

$\Rightarrow \quad y$ and x both are even or odd. $\hfill (1/2)$

There are two cases arise

Case I When y is even.

Now, $(x, y) \in R$ and $(y, z) \in R$.

$\Rightarrow \quad |x - y|$ is even and $|y - z|$ is even

$\Rightarrow \quad x$ is even and z is even $\Rightarrow |x - z|$ is even

[∵ difference of two even numbers is also even]

$\Rightarrow (x, z) \in R \hfill (1/2)$

Case II When y is odd.

Now, $(x, y) \in R$ and $(y, z) \in R$

$\Rightarrow \quad |x - y|$ is even and $|y - z|$ is even

$\Rightarrow \quad x$ is odd and z is odd $\Rightarrow |x - z|$ is even

[∵ difference of two odd numbers is even]

$\Rightarrow \qquad (x, z) \in R$

So, we have shown that $(x, y) \in R$ and $(y, z) \in R$

$\Rightarrow \qquad (x, z) \in R, \forall \, x, y, z \in A$

∴ R is transitive.

Since, R is reflexive, symmetric and transitive. So, it is an equivalence relation. $\hfill (1)$

28. Evaluate $\int_{\pi/3}^{\pi/2} \dfrac{\sqrt{1 + \cos x}}{(1 - \cos x)^{5/2}} \, dx$.

Or

Evaluate $I = \int_0^1 \log \left| \dfrac{1}{x} - 1 \right| dx$

Sol. Let $I = \int_{\pi/3}^{\pi/2} \dfrac{\sqrt{1 + \cos x}}{(1 - \cos x)^{5/2}} \, dx$

$I = \int_{\pi/3}^{\pi/2} \dfrac{(2\cos^2 x/2)^{1/2}}{(2\sin^2 x/2)^{5/2}} \, dx = \dfrac{1}{4} \int_{\pi/3}^{\pi/2} \dfrac{\cos x/2}{\sin^5 x/2} \, dx \hfill (1)$

Put $\sin \dfrac{x}{2} = t \Rightarrow \cos \dfrac{x}{2} dx = 2dt$

When $x = \dfrac{\pi}{3} \Rightarrow t = \dfrac{1}{2}$ and $x = \dfrac{\pi}{2} \Rightarrow t = \dfrac{1}{\sqrt{2}} \hfill (1)$

∵ $I = \dfrac{2}{4} \int_{1/2}^{1/\sqrt{2}} \dfrac{1}{t^5} \, dt \Rightarrow I = \dfrac{1}{2} \left[\dfrac{1}{-4t^4} \right]_{1/2}^{1/\sqrt{2}}$

$I = -\dfrac{1}{8} \left[\dfrac{1}{\left(\dfrac{1}{\sqrt{2}}\right)^4} - \dfrac{1}{\left(\dfrac{1}{2}\right)^4} \right] \Rightarrow I = -\dfrac{1}{8}[4 - 16] = \dfrac{12}{8}$

$I = \dfrac{3}{2} \hfill (1)$

Or

Let $\qquad I = \int_0^1 \log \left| \dfrac{1}{x} - 1 \right| dx$

$\Rightarrow \qquad I = \int_0^1 \log \left| \dfrac{1 - x}{x} \right| dx \hfill ...(i)$

$\Rightarrow \qquad I = \int_0^1 \log \left| \dfrac{1-(1-x)}{1-x} \right| dx$

$$\left[\because \int_0^a f(x)\, dx = \int_0^a f(a-x)\, dx \right]$$

$\Rightarrow \qquad I = \int_0^1 \log \left| \dfrac{x}{1-x} \right| dx \qquad \text{...(ii)}$

(1)

On adding Eqs. (i) and (ii), we get

$2I = \int_0^1 \log \left| \dfrac{1-x}{x} \right| dx + \int_0^1 \log \left| \dfrac{x}{1-x} \right| dx$

$\Rightarrow \quad 2I = \int_0^1 \left[\log \left| \dfrac{1-x}{x} \right| + \log \left| \dfrac{x}{1-x} \right| \right] dx$

(1)

$\Rightarrow \quad 2I = \int_0^1 \log \left| \left(\dfrac{1-x}{x} \times \dfrac{x}{1-x} \right) \right| dx$

$$[\because \log m + \log n = \log (m \times n)]$$

$\Rightarrow \quad 2I = \int_0^1 \log 1 \, dx$

$\Rightarrow \quad 2I = \int_0^1 0 \, dx = 0 \qquad [\because \log 1 = 0]$

$\therefore \qquad I = 0$

(1)

29. Find the area bounded by the curve $y = \cos x$ between $x = 0$ and $x = 2\pi$.

Or

Find the area bounded by the curve $y^2 = 4a^2(x-1)$ and the lines $x = 1$ and $y = 4a$.

Sol. The graph of $y = \cos x$ between 0 to 2π is the curve shown in given figure.

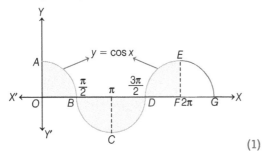

(1)

$\therefore$ Required area = Area of region $OABO$

$\qquad\qquad$ + Area of region $BCDB$

$\qquad\qquad$ + Area of region $DEFD$

$= \int_0^{\pi/2} \cos x \, dx + \left| \int_{\pi/2}^{3\pi/2} \cos x \, dx \right| + \int_{3\pi/2}^{2\pi} \cos x \, dx$

[$\because$ in region $BCDB$, the curve is below the X-axis, where value come out to be negative, so we take the absolute value]

$= [\sin x]_0^{\pi/2} + \left| [\sin x]_{\pi/2}^{3\pi/2} \right| + [\sin x]_{3\pi/2}^{2\pi}$

$= \left(\sin \dfrac{\pi}{2} - \sin 0 \right) + \left| \sin \dfrac{3\pi}{2} - \sin \dfrac{\pi}{2} \right|$

$\qquad\qquad + \left(\sin 2\pi - \sin \dfrac{3\pi}{2} \right)$

(1)

$= (1-0) + |-1-1| + [0-(-1)]$

$= 1 + 2 + 1 = 4 \text{ sq units}$

Therefore, the required area is 4 sq units.   (1)

Or

The equation of the given curve is $y^2 = 4a^2(x-1)$

or $\qquad\qquad (y-0)^2 = 4a^2(x-1)$.

Clearly, this equation represents a parabola with vertex at (1, 0) as shown in figure.

The region enclosed by $y^2 = 4a^2(x-1)$, $x = 1$ and $y = 4a$ is the area of shaded portion in figure.   (1/2)

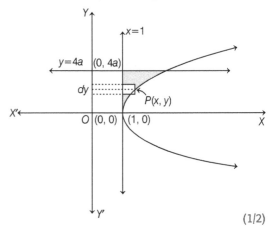

(1/2)

When we slice the area of the shaded portion in horizontal strips, we observe that each strip has left end on the line $x = 1$ and the right end on the parabola $y^2 = 4a^2(x-1)$.

So, the approximating rectangle shown in figure has, length $= x - 1$, width $= dy$ and area $= (x-1)dy$.

Since, the approximating rectangle can move from $y = 0$ to $y = 4a$.   (1)

So, required area A is given by

$A = \int_0^{4a} (x-1)\, dy$

$\Rightarrow \quad A = \int_0^{4a} \dfrac{y^2}{4a^2}\, dy \quad [\because P(x, y) \text{ lies on } y^2 = 4a^2(x-1)$

$\qquad\qquad\qquad\qquad\qquad \therefore x - 1 = y^2/4a^2]$

$\Rightarrow \quad A = \dfrac{1}{4a^2} \left[\dfrac{y^3}{3} \right]_0^{4a} = \dfrac{1}{4a^2} \left(\dfrac{64a^3}{3} \right)$

$\qquad\qquad = \dfrac{16a}{3} \text{ sq units}$

(1)

30. If $y = (x)^x + (\sin x)^x$, then find $\dfrac{dy}{dx}$.

Sol. Given, $y = (x)^x + (\sin x)^x$

Let $\quad u = (x)^x$

and $\quad v = (\sin x)^x$

Then, given equation becomes, $y = u + v$

On differentiating both sides w.r.t. x, we get

$$\frac{dy}{dx} = \frac{du}{dx} + \frac{dv}{dx} \qquad \ldots(i) \ (1/2)$$

Consider, $u = x^x$

On taking log both sides, we get

$$\log u = \log x^x$$

$$\Rightarrow \quad \log u = x \log x \qquad [\because \log m^n = n \log m]$$

On differentiating both sides w.r.t. x, we get

$$\frac{1}{u} \frac{du}{dx} = x \cdot \frac{d}{dx} (\log x) + \log x \cdot \frac{d}{dx} (x)$$

[by using product rule of derivative]

$$\Rightarrow \quad \frac{1}{u} \frac{du}{dx} = x \cdot \frac{1}{x} + \log x \cdot 1 \Rightarrow \frac{1}{u} \frac{du}{dx} = 1 + \log x$$

$$\Rightarrow \quad \frac{du}{dx} = u \, (1 + \log x)$$

$$\Rightarrow \quad \frac{du}{dx} = x^x \, (1 + \log x) \quad [\because \text{put } u = x^x] \ \ldots(ii) \ (1/2)$$

Now consider, $v = (\sin x)^x$

On taking log both sides, we get

$$\log v = \log (\sin x)^x$$

$$\Rightarrow \quad \log v = x \log (\sin x) \qquad [\because \log m^n = n \log m]$$

On differentiating both sides w.r.t. x, we get

$$\frac{1}{v} \frac{dv}{dx} = x \cdot \frac{d}{dx} \log (\sin x) + \log (\sin x) \cdot \frac{d}{dx} (x)$$

[by using product rule of derivative]

$$\Rightarrow \quad \frac{1}{v} \frac{dv}{dx} = x \cdot \frac{1}{\sin x} \cdot \frac{d}{dx} (\sin x) + \log \sin x \qquad (1/2)$$

$$\Rightarrow \quad \frac{1}{v} \frac{dv}{dx} = x \cdot \frac{1}{\sin x} \cdot \cos x + \log \sin x$$

$$\Rightarrow \quad \frac{1}{v} \frac{dv}{dx} = x \cot x + \log \sin x$$

$$\Rightarrow \quad \frac{dv}{dx} = v \, (x \cot x + \log \sin x)$$

$$\Rightarrow \quad \frac{dv}{dx} = (\sin x)^x \, (x \cot x + \log \sin x) \qquad \ldots(iii) \ (1/2)$$

$$[\text{putting } v = (\sin x)^x]$$

Now, from Eqs. (i), (ii) and (iii), we get

$$\frac{dy}{dx} = x^x (1 + \log x) + (\sin x)^x (x \cot x + \log \sin x) \qquad (1)$$

31. Find the values of p and q for which

$$f(x) = \begin{cases} \dfrac{1 - \sin^3 x}{3 \cos^2 x}, & \text{if } x < \dfrac{\pi}{2} \\[2mm] p, & \text{if } x = \dfrac{\pi}{2} \\[2mm] \dfrac{q \, (1 - \sin x)}{(\pi - 2x)^2}, & \text{if } x > \dfrac{\pi}{2} \end{cases}$$

is continuous at $x = \dfrac{\pi}{2}$.

Sol. Let $f(x) = \begin{cases} \dfrac{1 - \sin^3 x}{3 \cos^2 x}, & \text{if } x < \dfrac{\pi}{2} \\[2mm] p, & \text{if } x = \dfrac{\pi}{2} \\[2mm] \dfrac{q(1 - \sin x)}{(\pi - 2x)^2}, & \text{if } x > \dfrac{\pi}{2} \end{cases}$

is continuous at $x = \dfrac{\pi}{2}$.

Then, $(\text{LHL})_{x = \frac{\pi}{2}} = (\text{RHL})_{x = \frac{\pi}{2}} = f\left(\dfrac{\pi}{2}\right) \qquad \ldots(i)$

Now, LHL $= \lim\limits_{x \to \frac{\pi}{2}^-} f(x) = \lim\limits_{h \to 0} f\left(\dfrac{\pi}{2} - h\right)$

$$\left[\text{putting } x = \dfrac{\pi}{2} - h; \text{when } x \to \dfrac{\pi}{2}^-, \text{then } h \to 0\right]$$

$$= \lim_{h \to 0} \frac{1 - \sin^3\left(\dfrac{\pi}{2} - h\right)}{3 \cos^2\left(\dfrac{\pi}{2} - h\right)} = \lim_{h \to 0} \frac{1 - \cos^3 h}{3 \sin^2 h} \qquad (1/2)$$

$$\left[\because \cos\left(\dfrac{\pi}{2} - \theta\right) = \sin \theta, \sin\left(\dfrac{\pi}{2} - \theta\right) = \cos\theta\right]$$

$$= \lim_{h \to 0} \frac{(1 - \cos h)(1^2 + \cos^2 h + 1 \times \cos h)}{3 \, (1 - \cos^2 h)}$$

$$= \lim_{h \to 0} \frac{(1 - \cos h)(1 + \cos^2 h + \cos h)}{3 \, (1 - \cos h)(1 + \cos h)}$$

$$= \lim_{h \to 0} \frac{(1 + \cos^2 h + \cos h)}{3 \, (1 + \cos h)}$$

$$= \frac{1 + \cos^2 0 + \cos 0}{3(1 + \cos 0)} = \frac{1 + 1 + 1}{3(1 + 1)} = \frac{3}{3 \times 2} = \frac{1}{2}$$

$$\ldots(ii) \ (1/2)$$

and RHL $= \lim\limits_{x \to \frac{\pi}{2}^+} f(x) = \lim\limits_{h \to 0} f\left(\dfrac{\pi}{2} + h\right)$

$$\left[\text{putting } x = \dfrac{\pi}{2} + h; \text{when } x \to \dfrac{\pi}{2}^+, \text{then } h \to 0\right]$$

$$= \lim_{h \to 0} \frac{q\left[1 - \sin\left(\dfrac{\pi}{2} + h\right)\right]}{\left[\pi - 2\left(\dfrac{\pi}{2} + h\right)\right]^2} \qquad (1/2)$$

$$= \lim_{h \to 0} \frac{q(1 - \cos h)}{(\pi - \pi - 2h)^2}$$

$$= \lim_{h \to 0} \frac{q \, (1 - \cos h)}{4 h^2}$$

$$= \lim_{h \to 0} \frac{q\left(2 \sin^2 \dfrac{h}{2}\right)}{4 h^2} \qquad \left[\because 1 - \cos x = 2 \sin^2 \dfrac{x}{2}\right]$$

$$= \frac{q}{8} \lim_{h \to 0} \left[\frac{\sin\left(\frac{h}{2}\right)}{\frac{h}{2}} \right]^2$$

$$= \frac{q}{8} \times 1 = \frac{q}{8} \qquad \left[\because \lim_{x \to 0} \frac{\sin x}{x} = 1 \right] \dots \text{(iii)} \ \ (1/2)$$

On substituting the values from Eqs. (ii) and (iii) to Eq. (i), we get

$$\frac{1}{2} = \frac{q}{8} = f\left(\frac{\pi}{2}\right)$$

$$\Rightarrow \qquad \frac{1}{2} = \frac{q}{8} = p \qquad \left[\because f\left(\frac{\pi}{2}\right) = p \text{ (given)} \right]$$

$$\Rightarrow \qquad \frac{1}{2} = \frac{q}{8} \text{ and } \frac{1}{2} = p$$

$$\therefore \qquad q = 4 \text{ and } p = \frac{1}{2} \tag{1}$$

Section D

(This section comprises of long answer type questions (LA) of 5 marks each)

32. Find the angle between the lines whose direction cosines are given by the equations $3l + m + 5n = 0$ and $6mn - 2nl + 5lm = 0$.

Sol. The given equations are $3l + m + 5n = 0$ ...(i)

and $6mn - 2nl + 5lm = 0$ ...(ii)

From Eq. (i), we have

$$m = -3l - 5n$$

On putting the value of m in Eq. (ii), we get

$$6(-5n - 3l)n - 2nl + 5l(-3l - 5n) = 0 \tag{1}$$

$$\Rightarrow \ -30n^2 - 18ln - 2nl - 25ln - 15l^2 = 0$$

$$\Rightarrow \qquad -30n^2 - 45nl - 15l^2 = 0$$

$$\Rightarrow \qquad 2n^2 + 3nl + l^2 = 0$$

[dividing both sides by (–15)] (1)

$$\Rightarrow \qquad (n + l)(2n + l) = 0$$

Either $n = -l$ or $l = -2n$

Now, if $l = -n$, then $m = -2n$

and if $l = -2n$, then $m = n$ (1)

Thus, the direction ratios of two lines are proportional to $(-n, -2n, n)$ and $(-2n, n, n)$

i.e. $(-1, -2, 1)$ and $(-2, 1, 1)$. (1)

Let the required angle be θ.

Then, $\cos\theta = \dfrac{a_1 a_2 + b_1 b_2 + c_1 c_2}{\sqrt{a_1^2 + b_1^2 + c_1^2} \sqrt{a_2^2 + b_2^2 + c_2^2}}$

$$\cos\theta = \frac{-1(-2) - 2(1) + 1(1)}{\sqrt{(-1)^2 + (-2)^2 + (1)^2} \sqrt{(-2)^2 + (1)^2 + (1)^2}}$$

$$= \frac{1}{\sqrt{6} \cdot \sqrt{6}} = \frac{1}{6}$$

$$\therefore \qquad \theta = \cos^{-1}\left(\frac{1}{6}\right) \tag{1}$$

33. If $A = \begin{bmatrix} 1 & -1 & 0 \\ 2 & 3 & 4 \\ 0 & 1 & 2 \end{bmatrix}$ and $B = \begin{bmatrix} 2 & 2 & -4 \\ -4 & 2 & -4 \\ 2 & -1 & 5 \end{bmatrix}$,

find AB. Use this to solve the system of equations

$$x - y = 3, \ 2x + 3y + 4z = 17 \text{ and } y + 2z = 7.$$

Or

Show that $A = \begin{bmatrix} 1 & 0 & -2 \\ -2 & -1 & 2 \\ 3 & 4 & 1 \end{bmatrix}$ satisfies the

equation $A^3 - A^2 - 3A - 1 = O$ and hence find A^{-1}.

Sol. We have, $AB = \begin{bmatrix} 1 & -1 & 0 \\ 2 & 3 & 4 \\ 0 & 1 & 2 \end{bmatrix} \begin{bmatrix} 2 & 2 & -4 \\ -4 & 2 & -4 \\ 2 & -1 & 5 \end{bmatrix}$

$$= \begin{bmatrix} 2 + 4 + 0 & 2 - 2 + 0 & -4 + 4 + 0 \\ 4 - 12 + 8 & 4 + 6 - 4 & -8 - 12 + 20 \\ 0 - 4 + 4 & 0 + 2 - 2 & 0 - 4 + 10 \end{bmatrix}$$

$$= \begin{bmatrix} 6 & 0 & 0 \\ 0 & 6 & 0 \\ 0 & 0 & 6 \end{bmatrix} = 6 \begin{bmatrix} 1 & 0 & 0 \\ 0 & 1 & 0 \\ 0 & 0 & 1 \end{bmatrix} = 6I$$

$$\therefore \qquad AB = 6I \qquad \dots \text{(i)} \ \ (1\frac{1}{2})$$

Now, given system of equations can be written in matrix form as $AX = C$

$$\Rightarrow \qquad X = A^{-1}C \qquad \dots \text{(ii)}$$

Where, $A = \begin{bmatrix} 1 & -1 & 0 \\ 2 & 3 & 4 \\ 0 & 1 & 2 \end{bmatrix}$, $X = \begin{bmatrix} x \\ y \\ z \end{bmatrix}$ and $C = \begin{bmatrix} 3 \\ 17 \\ 7 \end{bmatrix}$

Now, from Eq. (i), we get

$$AB = 6I$$

$$\Rightarrow \qquad A^{-1}(AB) = A^{-1}(6I)$$

[pre-multiply both sides by A^{-1}]

$\Rightarrow \qquad (A^{-1}A)B = 6(A^{-1}I)$

$\Rightarrow \qquad IB = 6A^{-1}$

$\qquad\qquad [\because AA^{-1} = A^{-1}A = I \text{ and } AI = A = IA]$

$\Rightarrow \qquad B = 6A^{-1}$

$\Rightarrow \qquad A^{-1} = \dfrac{1}{6}B$

$\Rightarrow \qquad A^{-1} = \dfrac{1}{6}\begin{bmatrix} 2 & 2 & -4 \\ -4 & 2 & -4 \\ 2 & -1 & 5 \end{bmatrix}$ (1½)

Now, from Eq. (ii), we get

$\qquad X = A^{-1}C$

$\Rightarrow \quad \begin{bmatrix} x \\ y \\ z \end{bmatrix} = \dfrac{1}{6}\begin{bmatrix} 2 & 2 & -4 \\ -4 & 2 & -4 \\ 2 & -1 & 5 \end{bmatrix}\begin{bmatrix} 3 \\ 17 \\ 7 \end{bmatrix}$ (1)

$\Rightarrow \quad \begin{bmatrix} x \\ y \\ z \end{bmatrix} = \dfrac{1}{6}\begin{bmatrix} 6+34-28 \\ -12+34-28 \\ 6-17+35 \end{bmatrix}$

$\qquad = \dfrac{1}{6}\begin{bmatrix} 12 \\ -6 \\ 24 \end{bmatrix} = \begin{bmatrix} 2 \\ -1 \\ 4 \end{bmatrix}$

On comparing corresponding elements, we get

$\qquad x = 2,\ y = -1 \text{ and } z = 4$ (1)

Or

We have, $A^2 = \begin{bmatrix} 1 & 0 & -2 \\ -2 & -1 & 2 \\ 3 & 4 & 1 \end{bmatrix}\begin{bmatrix} 1 & 0 & -2 \\ -2 & -1 & 2 \\ 3 & 4 & 1 \end{bmatrix}$

$= \begin{bmatrix} 1+0-6 & 0+0-8 & -2+0-2 \\ -2+2+6 & 0+1+8 & 4-2+2 \\ 3-8+3 & 0-4+4 & -6+8+1 \end{bmatrix}$

$= \begin{bmatrix} -5 & -8 & -4 \\ 6 & 9 & 4 \\ -2 & 0 & 3 \end{bmatrix}$ (1)

$A^3 = A^2 \cdot A = \begin{bmatrix} -5 & -8 & -4 \\ 6 & 9 & 4 \\ -2 & 0 & 3 \end{bmatrix}\begin{bmatrix} 1 & 0 & -2 \\ -2 & -1 & 2 \\ 3 & 4 & 1 \end{bmatrix}$

$= \begin{bmatrix} -5+16-12 & 0+8-16 & 10-16-4 \\ 6-18+12 & 0-9+16 & -12+18+4 \\ -2+0+9 & 0+0+12 & 4+0+3 \end{bmatrix}$

$= \begin{bmatrix} -1 & -8 & -10 \\ 0 & 7 & 10 \\ 7 & 12 & 7 \end{bmatrix}$ (1)

$-3A = (-3)\begin{bmatrix} 1 & 0 & -2 \\ -2 & -1 & 2 \\ 3 & 4 & 1 \end{bmatrix}$

$= \begin{bmatrix} -3 & 0 & 6 \\ 6 & 3 & -6 \\ -9 & -12 & -3 \end{bmatrix}$

$\therefore A^3 - A^2 - 3A - 1 = \begin{bmatrix} -1 & -8 & -10 \\ 0 & 7 & 10 \\ 7 & 12 & 7 \end{bmatrix} - \begin{bmatrix} -5 & -8 & -4 \\ 6 & 9 & 4 \\ -2 & 0 & 3 \end{bmatrix}$

$\qquad + \begin{bmatrix} -3 & 0 & 6 \\ 6 & 3 & -6 \\ -9 & -12 & -3 \end{bmatrix} - \begin{bmatrix} 1 & 0 & 0 \\ 0 & 1 & 0 \\ 0 & 0 & 1 \end{bmatrix}$

$= \begin{bmatrix} 0 & 0 & 0 \\ 0 & 0 & 0 \\ 0 & 0 & 0 \end{bmatrix} = O$ (1)

We have, $A = \begin{bmatrix} 1 & 0 & -2 \\ -2 & -1 & 2 \\ 3 & 4 & 1 \end{bmatrix}$

Now, $\quad |A| = 1(-1-8) - 0 + (-2)(-8+3)$

$\Rightarrow \qquad |A| = -9 + 10 = 1$

$\Rightarrow \qquad |A| \neq 0$

$\therefore A^{-1}$ exists.

Now, cofactors of elements of $|A|$ are

$C_{11} = (-1)^{1+1}\begin{vmatrix} -1 & 2 \\ 4 & 1 \end{vmatrix} = -1-8 = -9$

$C_{12} = (-1)^{1+2}\begin{vmatrix} -2 & 2 \\ 3 & 1 \end{vmatrix} = -(-2-6) = 8$

$C_{13} = (-1)^{1+3}\begin{vmatrix} -2 & -1 \\ 3 & 4 \end{vmatrix} = (-8+3) = -5$

$C_{21} = (-1)^{2+1}\begin{vmatrix} 0 & -2 \\ 4 & 1 \end{vmatrix} = -\{-(-8)\} = -8$

$C_{22} = (-1)^{2+2}\begin{vmatrix} 1 & -2 \\ 3 & 1 \end{vmatrix} = 1+6 = 7$

$C_{23} = (-1)^{2+3}\begin{vmatrix} 1 & 0 \\ 3 & 4 \end{vmatrix} = -(4) = -4$

$C_{31} = (-1)^{3+1}\begin{vmatrix} 0 & -2 \\ -1 & 2 \end{vmatrix} = (-2) = -2$

$C_{32} = (-1)^{3+2}\begin{vmatrix} 1 & -2 \\ -2 & 2 \end{vmatrix} = -(2-4) = 2$

$C_{33} = (-1)^{3+3}\begin{vmatrix} 1 & 0 \\ -2 & -1 \end{vmatrix} = -1$ (1)

$\therefore \text{adj}(A) = \begin{bmatrix} C_{11} & C_{12} & C_{13} \\ C_{21} & C_{22} & C_{23} \\ C_{31} & C_{32} & C_{33} \end{bmatrix}^T$

$= \begin{bmatrix} -9 & 8 & -5 \\ -8 & 7 & -4 \\ -2 & 2 & -1 \end{bmatrix}^T = \begin{bmatrix} -9 & -8 & -2 \\ 8 & 7 & 2 \\ -5 & -4 & -1 \end{bmatrix}$

and $A^{-1} = \dfrac{1}{|A|}\text{adj}(A)$

$= \dfrac{1}{1}\begin{bmatrix} -9 & -8 & -2 \\ 8 & 7 & 2 \\ -5 & -4 & -1 \end{bmatrix}$ (1)

34. Given, $A = \begin{bmatrix} 5 & 0 & 4 \\ 2 & 3 & 2 \\ 1 & 2 & 1 \end{bmatrix}$, $B^{-1} = \begin{bmatrix} 1 & 3 & 3 \\ 1 & 4 & 3 \\ 1 & 3 & 4 \end{bmatrix}$

Compute $(AB)^{-1}$.

Or

Show that the matrix $A = \begin{bmatrix} 1 & 2 & 2 \\ 2 & 1 & 2 \\ 2 & 2 & 1 \end{bmatrix}$

satisfies the equation $A^2 - 4A - 5I_3 = O$ and hence find A^{-1}.

Sol. We have, $A = \begin{bmatrix} 5 & 0 & 4 \\ 2 & 3 & 2 \\ 1 & 2 & 1 \end{bmatrix}$

Now, $|A| = \begin{vmatrix} 5 & 0 & 4 \\ 2 & 3 & 2 \\ 1 & 2 & 1 \end{vmatrix} = 5(3-4) - 0 + 4(4-3)$

$= -5 + 4 = -1 \neq 0$ (1)

Thus, A is non-singular matrix, so A^{-1} exists.
Now, cofactors of elements of $|A|$ are

$A_{11} = (-1)^2 \begin{vmatrix} 3 & 2 \\ 2 & 1 \end{vmatrix} = (3-4) = -1$

$A_{12} = (-1)^3 \begin{vmatrix} 2 & 2 \\ 1 & 1 \end{vmatrix} = -(2-2) = 0$

$A_{13} = (-1)^4 \begin{vmatrix} 2 & 3 \\ 1 & 2 \end{vmatrix} = (4-3) = 1$

$A_{21} = (-1)^3 \begin{vmatrix} 0 & 4 \\ 2 & 1 \end{vmatrix} = -(0-8) = 8$

$A_{22} = (-1)^4 \begin{vmatrix} 5 & 4 \\ 1 & 1 \end{vmatrix} = (5-4) = 1$ (1)

$A_{23} = (-1)^5 \begin{vmatrix} 5 & 0 \\ 1 & 2 \end{vmatrix} = -(10-0) = -10$

$A_{31} = (-1)^4 \begin{vmatrix} 0 & 4 \\ 3 & 2 \end{vmatrix} = (0-12) = -12$

$A_{32} = (-1)^5 \begin{vmatrix} 5 & 4 \\ 2 & 2 \end{vmatrix} = -(10-8) = -2$

$A_{33} = (-1)^6 \begin{vmatrix} 5 & 0 \\ 2 & 3 \end{vmatrix} = (15-0) = 15$ (1)

$\therefore \text{adj } A = \begin{bmatrix} -1 & 8 & -12 \\ 0 & 1 & -2 \\ 1 & -10 & 15 \end{bmatrix}$

$\therefore A^{-1} = \dfrac{\text{adj } A}{|A|} = \dfrac{1}{-1}\begin{bmatrix} -1 & 8 & -12 \\ 0 & 1 & -2 \\ 1 & -10 & 15 \end{bmatrix} = \begin{bmatrix} 1 & -8 & 12 \\ 0 & -1 & 2 \\ -1 & 10 & -15 \end{bmatrix}$ (1)

Now, $(AB)^{-1} = B^{-1}A^{-1}$

$= \begin{bmatrix} 1 & 3 & 3 \\ 1 & 4 & 3 \\ 1 & 3 & 4 \end{bmatrix}\begin{bmatrix} 1 & -8 & 12 \\ 0 & -1 & 2 \\ -1 & 10 & -15 \end{bmatrix}$

$= \begin{bmatrix} 1+0-3 & -8-3+30 & 12+6-45 \\ 1+0-3 & -8-4+30 & 12+8-45 \\ 1+0-4 & -8-3+40 & 12+6-60 \end{bmatrix}$

$= \begin{bmatrix} -2 & 19 & -27 \\ -2 & 18 & -25 \\ -3 & 29 & -42 \end{bmatrix}$ (1)

Or

We have, $A = \begin{bmatrix} 1 & 2 & 2 \\ 2 & 1 & 2 \\ 2 & 2 & 1 \end{bmatrix}$

Now, $A^2 = A \cdot A = \begin{bmatrix} 1 & 2 & 2 \\ 2 & 1 & 2 \\ 2 & 2 & 1 \end{bmatrix}\begin{bmatrix} 1 & 2 & 2 \\ 2 & 1 & 2 \\ 2 & 2 & 1 \end{bmatrix}$

$= \begin{bmatrix} 1+4+4 & 2+2+4 & 2+4+2 \\ 2+2+4 & 4+1+4 & 4+2+2 \\ 2+4+2 & 4+2+2 & 4+4+1 \end{bmatrix}$

$= \begin{bmatrix} 9 & 8 & 8 \\ 8 & 9 & 8 \\ 8 & 8 & 9 \end{bmatrix}$,

$4A = \begin{bmatrix} 4 & 8 & 8 \\ 8 & 4 & 8 \\ 8 & 8 & 4 \end{bmatrix}$

and $5I_3 = \begin{bmatrix} 5 & 0 & 0 \\ 0 & 5 & 0 \\ 0 & 0 & 5 \end{bmatrix}$ (1)

$\therefore A^2 - 4A - 5I_3 = \begin{bmatrix} 9 & 8 & 8 \\ 8 & 9 & 8 \\ 8 & 8 & 9 \end{bmatrix} - \begin{bmatrix} 4 & 8 & 8 \\ 8 & 4 & 8 \\ 8 & 8 & 4 \end{bmatrix} - \begin{bmatrix} 5 & 0 & 0 \\ 0 & 5 & 0 \\ 0 & 0 & 5 \end{bmatrix}$

$\Rightarrow A^2 - 4A - 5I_3 = \begin{bmatrix} 9-4-5 & 8-8-0 & 8-8-0 \\ 8-8-0 & 9-4-5 & 8-8-0 \\ 8-8-0 & 8-8-0 & 9-4-5 \end{bmatrix}$

$= \begin{bmatrix} 0 & 0 & 0 \\ 0 & 0 & 0 \\ 0 & 0 & 0 \end{bmatrix} = O$

Now, $A^2 - 4A - 5I_3 = O$ (2)

$\Rightarrow \qquad A^2 - 4A = 5I_3$

$\Rightarrow A^{-1}A^2 - 4A^{-1}A = 5A^{-1}I_3$

[pre-multiplying throughout by A^{-1}]

$\Rightarrow \qquad A - 4I = 5A^{-1}$ $[\because A^{-1}A^2 = (A^{-1}A)A = IA = A]$

$\Rightarrow \qquad A^{-1} = \dfrac{1}{5}(A - 4I)$ (1)

$\Rightarrow A^{-1} = \dfrac{1}{5}\left\{\begin{bmatrix} 1 & 2 & 2 \\ 2 & 1 & 2 \\ 2 & 2 & 1 \end{bmatrix} - \begin{bmatrix} 4 & 0 & 0 \\ 0 & 4 & 0 \\ 0 & 0 & 4 \end{bmatrix}\right\}$

$= \dfrac{1}{5}\begin{bmatrix} -3 & 2 & 2 \\ 2 & -3 & 2 \\ 2 & 2 & -3 \end{bmatrix}$ (1)

35. If $\vec{a} = \hat{i} + \hat{j} + \hat{k}$ and $\vec{b} = \hat{j} - \hat{k}$, then find a vector $\vec{c}$ such that $\vec{a} \times \vec{c} = \vec{b}$ and $\vec{a} \cdot \vec{c} = 3$.

Sol. Given, $\vec{a} = \hat{i} + \hat{j} + \hat{k}$ and $\vec{b} = \hat{j} - \hat{k}$

Let $\vec{c} = x\hat{i} + y\hat{j} + z\hat{k}$

Then, $\vec{a} \times \vec{c} = \vec{b} \Rightarrow \begin{vmatrix} \hat{i} & \hat{j} & \hat{k} \\ 1 & 1 & 1 \\ x & y & z \end{vmatrix} = \hat{j} - \hat{k}$

$\Rightarrow \hat{i}(z - y) - \hat{j}(z - x) + \hat{k}(y - x) = \hat{j} - \hat{k}$ (1)

On comparing the coefficients of $\hat{i}, \hat{j}$ and $\hat{k}$ from both sides, we get

$$z - y = 0 \qquad \qquad ...(i)$$
$$x - z = 1 \qquad \qquad ...(ii)$$
and $$x - y = 1 \qquad \qquad ...(iii) \text{ (1)}$$

Also, $\vec{a} \cdot \vec{c} = 3$

$\Rightarrow \quad (\hat{i} + \hat{j} + \hat{k}) \cdot (x\hat{i} + y\hat{j} + z\hat{k}) = 3$

$\Rightarrow \qquad\qquad x + y + z = 3 \qquad ...(iv)$

On adding Eqs. (ii) and (iii), we get

$$2x - y - z = 2 \qquad \qquad ...(v) \text{ (1)}$$

On adding Eqs. (iv) and (v), we get

$$3x = 5 \Rightarrow x = \frac{5}{3}$$

Then, from Eq. (iii), $y = \dfrac{5}{3} - 1 = \dfrac{2}{3}$

and from Eq. (i), $z = \dfrac{2}{3}$

Hence, $\vec{c} = \dfrac{5}{3}\hat{i} + \dfrac{2}{3}\hat{j} + \dfrac{2}{3}\hat{k}$

$= \dfrac{1}{3}(5\hat{i} + 2\hat{j} + 2\hat{k})$ (2)

Section E

(This section comprises of 3 case-study/ passage-based questions of 4 marks each with two sub-parts. First two case study questions have three sub-parts (i), (ii), (iii) of marks 1, 1, 2 respectively. The third case study question has two sub-parts of 2 marks each)

36. Sometimes, x and y are given as functions of one another variable, say $x = \phi(t)$, $y = \psi(t)$ are two functions and t is a variable. In such a case, x and y are called parametric functions or parametric equations and t is called the parameter.

To find the derivatives of parametric functions, we use following steps

  I. First, write the given parametric functions, suppose $x = f(t)$ and $y = g(t)$, where t is a parameter.

  II. Differentiate both functions separately w.r.t. parameter t by using suitable formula,

    i.e. find $\dfrac{dx}{dt}$ and $\dfrac{dy}{dt}$.

  III. Divide the derivative of one function w.r.t. parameter by the derivative of second function w.r.t. parameter, to get required value,

    i.e. $\dfrac{dy}{dx}$.

Thus, $\dfrac{dy}{dx} = \dfrac{\dfrac{dy}{dt}}{\dfrac{dx}{dt}} = \dfrac{g'(t)}{f'(t)}$, where $f'(t) \neq 0$.

On the basis of above information, answer the following questions.

  (i) If $x = \log t$ and $y = \cos t$, then find $\dfrac{dy}{dx}$.

  (ii) If $x = at^3$ and $y = t^2 + 1$, then find $\dfrac{dy}{dx}$ at $t = \dfrac{2}{3}$.

  (iii) If $x = \cos t + \sin t$ and $y = \sin t - \cos t$, then find $\dfrac{dy}{dx}$ at $t = \dfrac{\pi}{2}$.

            Or

    If $x = 4\cos t$ and $y = 8\tan t$, then find $\dfrac{dy}{dx}$ at $t = \dfrac{\pi}{4}$.

Sol. (i) Given, $x = \log t$

$\Rightarrow \quad \dfrac{dx}{dt} = \dfrac{1}{t}$

and $y = \cos t$

$\Rightarrow \quad \dfrac{dy}{dt} = -\sin t$

$\therefore \quad \dfrac{dy}{dx} = \dfrac{\left(\dfrac{dy}{dt}\right)}{\left(\dfrac{dx}{dt}\right)} = \dfrac{-\sin t}{\left(\dfrac{1}{t}\right)} = -t \sin t$

(ii) Given, $x = at^3$

$\Rightarrow \quad \dfrac{dx}{dt} = 3at^2$

and $\quad y = t^2 + 1$

$\Rightarrow \quad \dfrac{dy}{dt} = 2t$

$\therefore \quad \dfrac{dy}{dx} = \dfrac{\left(\dfrac{dy}{dt}\right)}{\left(\dfrac{dx}{dt}\right)} = \dfrac{2t}{3at^2} = \dfrac{2}{3at}$

Now, $\left(\dfrac{dy}{dx}\right)_{t=\frac{2}{3}} = \dfrac{2}{3a\left(\dfrac{2}{3}\right)} = \dfrac{1}{a}$

(iii) Given, $x = \cos t + \sin t$

$\Rightarrow \quad \dfrac{dx}{dt} = -\sin t + \cos t$

and $\quad y = \sin t - \cos t$

$\Rightarrow \quad \dfrac{dy}{dt} = \cos t + \sin t$

$\therefore \quad \dfrac{dy}{dx} = \dfrac{\left(\dfrac{dy}{dt}\right)}{\left(\dfrac{dx}{dt}\right)} = \dfrac{\cos t + \sin t}{\cos t - \sin t}$

Now, $\left(\dfrac{dy}{dx}\right)_{t=\frac{\pi}{2}} = \dfrac{\cos\left(\dfrac{\pi}{2}\right) + \sin\left(\dfrac{\pi}{2}\right)}{\cos\left(\dfrac{\pi}{2}\right) - \sin\left(\dfrac{\pi}{2}\right)}$

$= \dfrac{0+1}{0-1} = -1$

Or

Given, $x = 4\cos t$

$\Rightarrow \quad \dfrac{dx}{dt} = -4\sin t$

and $\quad y = 8\tan t$

$\Rightarrow \quad \dfrac{dy}{dt} = 8\sec^2 t$

Now, $\dfrac{dy}{dx} = \dfrac{\left(\dfrac{dy}{dt}\right)}{\left(\dfrac{dx}{dt}\right)} = \dfrac{8\sec^2 t}{-4\sin t} = \dfrac{-2}{\sin t \cos^2 t}$

Now, $\left(\dfrac{dy}{dx}\right)_{t=\frac{\pi}{4}} = \dfrac{-2}{\sin\dfrac{\pi}{4}\cos^2\left(\dfrac{\pi}{4}\right)}$

$= \dfrac{-2}{\dfrac{1}{\sqrt{2}}\left(\dfrac{1}{2}\right)}$

$= -4\sqrt{2}$

37. If feasible solution of a LPP is given as follows:

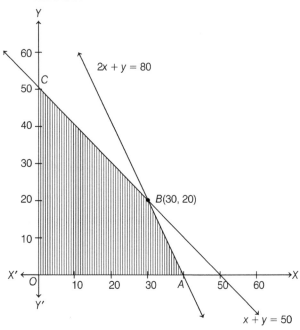

And the objective function is
$Z = 10500x + 9000y$.

On the basis of above information, answer the following question.

(i) If n is the number of corner point, then find the value of $(n+2)^3$.

(ii) Find the value of $Z_{(1,1)}$

(iii) Find the point where objective function is maximum.

Or

Evaluate $Z|_{(20,20)} - Z|_{(10,10)}$.

Sol. (i) We have, $n = 4$

$\therefore (n+2)^3 = (4+2)^3 = 6^3 = 216$

(ii) $Z_{(1,1)} = (10500 \times 1) + (9000 \times 1) = 19500$

(iii) To know the maximum value of Z, we need coordinates of all the corner points.

We have, equation of lines $x + y = 50$ ...(i)

and $\qquad\qquad\qquad 2x + y = 80$ ...(ii)

For point A, putting $y = 0$ into Eq. (ii),

$\qquad\qquad 2x + 0 = 80$

$\Rightarrow \qquad\qquad x = 40 \Rightarrow A(40, 0)$

For point C, putting $x = 0$ into Eq. (i),

$$0 + y = 50 \Rightarrow y = 50 \Rightarrow C(0, 50)$$

Now,

Corner points	Value of $Z = 10500x + 9000y$
$O(0, 0)$	$10500 \times 0 + 9000 \times 0 = 0$
$A(40, 0)$	$10500 \times 40 + 9000 \times 0 = 420000$
$B(30, 20)$	$10500 \times 30 + 9000 \times 20 = 495000$ (Maximum)
$C(0, 50)$	$10500 \times 0 + 9000 \times 50 = 450000$

Hence, Z is maximum at $B(30, 20)$.

Or

$$Z|_{(20, 20)} - Z|_{(10, 10)}$$
$$= (10500 \times 20 + 9000 \times 20)$$
$$\qquad - (10500 \times 10 + 9000 \times 10)$$
$$= 1000[(105 \times 2 + 90 \times 2) - (105 + 90)]$$
$$= 1000[(210 + 180) - (195)]$$
$$= 1000[390 - 195] = 195000$$

38. Given three identical boxes I, II and III, each containing two coins. In box I both coins are gold coins, in box II both are silver coins and in box III there is one gold and one silver coin. A person choose a box at random and takes out a coin.

On the basis of above information, answer the following questions.

(i) Find the total probability of drawing gold coin.

(ii) If drawn coin is of gold, then find the probability that other coin in box is also of gold.

Sol. Consider the following events,

$E_1 =$ Box I is choosen,

$E_2 =$ Box II is choosen,

$E_3 =$ Box III is choosen.

$A =$ The coin drawn is of gold.

Clearly, $P(E_1) = P(E_2) = P(E_3) = \dfrac{1}{3}$

Then, $P(A/E_1) =$ Probability of drawing a gold coin from box I

$$= \frac{2}{2} = 1,$$

$P(A/E_2) =$ Probability of drawing a gold coin from box II

$$= 0$$

and $P(A/E_3) =$ Probability of drawing a gold coin from box III

$$= \frac{1}{2}$$

(i) $\therefore$ Required probability

$$= P(A)$$

$$= \sum_{i=1}^{3} P(E_i)\, P\!\left(\frac{A}{E_i}\right)$$

$$= P(E_1)\, P\!\left(\frac{A}{E_1}\right) + P(E_2)\, P\!\left(\frac{A}{E_2}\right) + P(E_3)\, P\!\left(\frac{A}{E_3}\right)$$

$$= \frac{1}{3} \times 1 + \frac{1}{3} \times 0 + \frac{1}{3} \times \frac{1}{2}$$

$$= \frac{1}{3} + 0 + \frac{1}{6}$$

$$= \frac{2+1}{6} = \frac{3}{6} = \frac{1}{2}$$

(ii) $\therefore$ Required probability

Probability that the other coin in the box is of gold

$=$ Probability that gold coin is drawn from the box I

$= P(E_1/A)$

$$= \frac{P(E_1)\, P(A/E_1)}{P(E_1)\, P(A/E_1) + P(E_2)\, P(A/E_2) + P(E_3)\, P(A/E_3)}$$

[by Baye's theorem]

$$= \frac{\dfrac{1}{3} \times 1}{\dfrac{1}{3} \times 1 + \dfrac{1}{3} \times 0 + \dfrac{1}{3} \times \dfrac{1}{2}}$$

$$= \frac{1}{3} \times \frac{2}{1} = \frac{2}{3}$$

SAMPLE QUESTION PAPER 5

MATHEMATICS

Time : 3 hrs   Max. Marks : 80

General Instructions

1. This question paper contains - five sections A, B, C, D and E. Each section is compulsory. However, there are internal choices in some questions.
2. Section A has 18 MCQ's and 02 Assertion-Reason based questions of 1 mark each.
3. Section B has 5 Very Short Answer (VSA) type questions of 2 marks each.
4. Section C has 6 Short Answer (SA) type questions of 3 marks each.
5. Section D has 4 Long Answer (LA) type questions of 5 marks each.
6. Section E has 3 source based/case based/passage based/integrated units of assessment (4 marks each) with sub parts.

Section A

(Multiple Choice Questions) Each question carries 1 mark

1. The vector equation of a line which passes through the points $(3, 4, -7)$ and $(1, -1, 6)$ is
   (a) $3\hat{i} + 4\hat{j} - 7\hat{k} + \lambda(-2\hat{i} - 5\hat{j} + 13\hat{k})$
   (b) $3\hat{i} + 4\hat{j} + 7\hat{k} + \lambda(2\hat{i} - 5\hat{j} - 13\hat{k})$
   (c) $3\hat{i} + 4\hat{j} - 7\hat{k} + \lambda(2\hat{i} - 5\hat{j} + 13\hat{k})$
   (d) $-3\hat{i} + 4\hat{j} - 7\hat{k} + \lambda(-2\hat{i} + 3\hat{j} - 7\hat{k})$

Sol. (a) Any line passing through the points $\vec{a}$ and $\vec{b}$ has vector equation $\vec{r} = \vec{a} + \lambda(\vec{b} - \vec{a})$.

∴ Vector equation of the line passing through the points $\vec{a} = 3\hat{i} + 4\hat{j} - 7\hat{k}$ and $\vec{b} = \hat{i} - \hat{j} + 6\hat{k}$ is given by

$$\vec{r} = 3\hat{i} + 4\hat{j} - 7\hat{k} + \lambda[(\hat{i} - \hat{j} + 6\hat{k}) - (3\hat{i} + 4\hat{j} - 7\hat{k})]$$

$$\Rightarrow \quad \vec{r} = 3\hat{i} + 4\hat{j} - 7\hat{k} + \lambda(-2\hat{i} - 5\hat{j} + 13\hat{k})$$

2. The projection of the vector $\hat{i} - \hat{j}$ on the vector $\hat{i} + \hat{j}$ is

(a) 1   (b) 0

(c) 2   (d) 5

Sol. (b) Let $\vec{a} = \hat{i} - \hat{j}$ and $\vec{b} = \hat{i} + \hat{j}$

We know that projection of $\vec{a}$ on $\vec{b}$ is $\dfrac{\vec{a} \cdot \vec{b}}{|\vec{b}|}$

$$= \frac{(\hat{i} - \hat{j}) \cdot (\hat{i} + \hat{j})}{|\hat{i} + \hat{j}|} = \frac{1 - 1}{\sqrt{2}} = 0$$

3. If $\vec{a}$ and $\vec{b}$ are two unit vectors such that $\vec{a} + \vec{b}$ is also a unit vector, then the angle between $\vec{a}$ and $\vec{b}$ is

(a) $\dfrac{\pi}{3}$ (b) $\dfrac{\pi}{4}$ (c) $\dfrac{2\pi}{3}$ (d) $\dfrac{\pi}{6}$

Sol. (c) Given, $|\vec{a}| = |\vec{b}| = 1 = |\vec{a} + \vec{b}|$

$$|\vec{a} + \vec{b}|^2 = |\vec{a}|^2 + |\vec{b}|^2 + 2|\vec{a}||\vec{b}|\cos\theta$$

$$\Rightarrow \quad 1 = 1 + 1 + 2\cos\theta \Rightarrow 2\cos\theta = -1$$

$$\Rightarrow \quad \cos\theta = \frac{-1}{2}$$

$$\therefore \quad \theta = \frac{2\pi}{3}$$

4. $\hat{i} \times (\hat{j} \times \hat{k})$ is equal to

(a) $\hat{i}$ (b) $-\hat{j}$

(c) 0   (d) $-\hat{k}$

Sol. (c) We have, $\hat{i} \times (\hat{j} \times \hat{k})$

$$= \hat{i} \times \hat{i} \qquad [\because \hat{j} \times \hat{k} = \hat{i}]$$

$$= 0 \qquad [\because \vec{a} \times \vec{a} = 0]$$

5. The projection of $\hat{i} + \hat{j} + \hat{k}$ along the vector $\hat{j}$ is equal to

(a) 1   (b) 2   (c) $\hat{i}$ (d) $\hat{k}$

Sol. (a) Required projection $= \dfrac{(\hat{i} + \hat{j} + \hat{k}) \cdot (\hat{j})}{|\hat{j}|} = \dfrac{0 + 1 + 0}{1} = 1$

6. A vector in the direction of a vector $\vec{a} = \hat{i} - \hat{j} + \hat{k}$, which has magnitude 8 units is

(a) $\dfrac{8}{\sqrt{3}}\hat{i} + \dfrac{8}{\sqrt{3}}\hat{j} + \dfrac{8}{\sqrt{3}}\hat{k}$ (b) $\dfrac{8}{\sqrt{3}}\hat{i} - \dfrac{8}{\sqrt{3}}\hat{j} + \dfrac{8}{\sqrt{3}}\hat{k}$

(c) $\dfrac{3}{\sqrt{5}}\hat{i} + \dfrac{3}{\sqrt{5}}\hat{j} + \dfrac{3}{\sqrt{5}}\hat{k}$ (d) $\dfrac{\hat{i}}{\sqrt{2}} + \dfrac{\hat{j}}{\sqrt{2}} + \dfrac{\hat{k}}{\sqrt{2}}$

Sol. (b) Given, $\vec{a} = \hat{i} - \hat{j} + \hat{k}$

Now, unit vector in the direction of $\vec{a}$ is

$$\hat{a} = \frac{\vec{a}}{|\vec{a}|} = \frac{\hat{i} - \hat{j} + \hat{k}}{\sqrt{(1)^2 + (-1)^2 + (1)^2}} = \frac{\hat{i} - \hat{j} + \hat{k}}{\sqrt{3}}$$

$\therefore$ Vector of magnitude 8 units in direction of $\hat{a}$

$$= \frac{8(\hat{i} - \hat{j} + \hat{k})}{\sqrt{3}} = \frac{8}{\sqrt{3}}\hat{i} - \frac{8}{\sqrt{3}}\hat{j} + \frac{8}{\sqrt{3}}\hat{k}$$

7. The sum of the vectors $\vec{a} = \hat{i} - 2\hat{j} + \hat{k}$, $\vec{b} = -2\hat{i} + 4\hat{j} + 5\hat{k}$ and $\vec{c} = \hat{i} - 6\hat{j} - 7\hat{k}$ is equal to

(a) $\hat{i} + \hat{j}$ (b) $-4\hat{j} - \hat{k}$

(c) $4\hat{j} - \hat{k}$ (d) $\hat{k} - 4\hat{j}$

Sol. (b) Given vectors are $\vec{a} = \hat{i} - 2\hat{j} + \hat{k}$, $\vec{b} = -2\hat{i} + 4\hat{j} + 5\hat{k}$ and $\vec{c} = \hat{i} - 6\hat{j} - 7\hat{k}$.

Sum of the vectors $\vec{a}, \vec{b}$ and $\vec{c}$ is

$$\vec{a} + \vec{b} + \vec{c} = (\hat{i} - 2\hat{j} + \hat{k}) + (-2\hat{i} + 4\hat{j} + 5\hat{k})$$
$$+ (\hat{i} - 6\hat{j} - 7\hat{k})$$

$$= -4\hat{j} - \hat{k}$$

8. $ABCD$ is a rhombus whose diagonals intersect at E. Then, $\overrightarrow{EA} + \overrightarrow{EB} + \overrightarrow{EC} + \overrightarrow{ED}$ is equal to

(a) $\vec{0}$ (b) $\overrightarrow{AD}$ (c) $2\overrightarrow{BC}$ (d) $2\overrightarrow{AD}$

Sol. (a)

We know that diagonals of a rhombus bisect each other.

$\therefore \quad \overrightarrow{EA} = -\overrightarrow{EC}$ and $\overrightarrow{EB} = -\overrightarrow{ED}$

$\therefore \quad \overrightarrow{EA} + \overrightarrow{EB} + \overrightarrow{EC} + \overrightarrow{ED} = -\overrightarrow{EC} - \overrightarrow{ED} + \overrightarrow{EC} + \overrightarrow{ED} = \vec{0}$

9. The probability distribution of a random variable x is given as under

$$P(X = x) = \begin{cases} kx^2 & , x = 1, 2, 3 \\ 2kx & , x = 4, 5, 6 \\ 0 & , \text{otherwise} \end{cases}$$

where, k is constant. Then, k equals

(a) $\dfrac{1}{2}$ (b) $\dfrac{1}{44}$ (c) $\dfrac{3}{44}$ (d) $\dfrac{1}{3}$

Sol. (b) The probability distribution is

X	1	2	3	4	5	6	otherwise
P(X)	k	$4k$	$9k$	$8k$	$10k$	$12k$	0

We know that $\Sigma\, P_i = 1$

$\therefore k + 4k + 9k + 8k + 10k + 12k = 1$

$\Rightarrow \qquad\qquad\qquad\quad 44k = 1$

$\Rightarrow \qquad\qquad\qquad\quad k = \dfrac{1}{44}$

10. The direction cosines of a line are k, k, k, then

(a) $k > 0$ (b) $0 < k < 1$

(c) $k = 1$ (d) $k = \pm\dfrac{1}{\sqrt{3}}$

Sol. (d) We have, $l = m = n = k$

We know that $l^2 + m^2 + n^2 = 1$

$\Rightarrow \quad k^2 + k^2 + k^2 = 1 \Rightarrow 3k^2 = 1$

$\Rightarrow \qquad\quad k^2 = \dfrac{1}{3} \Rightarrow k = \pm\dfrac{1}{\sqrt{3}}$

11. A die is thrown once. Let A be the event that the number obtained is greater than 3. Let B be the event that the number obtained is less than 5. Then, $P(A \cup B)$ is

(a) $\dfrac{2}{5}$ (b) $\dfrac{3}{5}$ (c) 0   (d) 1

Sol. (d) We have, $A = \{4, 5, 6\}$

and $\qquad\qquad B = \{1, 2, 3, 4\}$

Now, $\qquad A \cap B = \{4\}$

Now, $P(A \cup B) = P(A) + P(B) - P(A \cap B)$

$\qquad\qquad = \dfrac{3}{6} + \dfrac{4}{6} - \dfrac{1}{6} = \dfrac{6}{6} = 1$

12. The direction ratios of the line $\dfrac{x+2}{2} = \dfrac{2y-5}{-3}$, $z = 2$ are

(a) 1, 1, 5   (b) 2, 1, 3

(c) 4, 6, 0   (d) 4, −6, 0

Sol. (d) Given, equation of line can be written as

$\dfrac{x+2}{2} = \dfrac{2y-5}{-3} = \dfrac{z-2}{0} \Rightarrow \dfrac{x+2}{2} = \dfrac{y-5/2}{-3/2} = \dfrac{z-2}{0}$

$\therefore$ DR's of line are $2, \dfrac{-3}{2}, 0$ or $4, -6, 0$.

13. A bag contains 3 white, 4 black and 2 red balls. If 2 balls are drawn at random (without replacement), then the probability that both the balls are white, is

(a) $\dfrac{1}{18}$ (b) $\dfrac{1}{36}$ (c) $\dfrac{1}{12}$ (d) $\dfrac{1}{24}$

Sol. (c) We have 3 white, 4 black and 2 red balls.

Total number of balls $= 3 + 4 + 2 = 9$

Two balls are drawn at random (without replacement).

Then, the probability that both the balls are white

$$= \dfrac{3}{9} \times \dfrac{2}{8} = \dfrac{6}{72} = \dfrac{1}{12}$$

14. The derivative of $\dfrac{x^3}{\cos x}$ is, when $x = 0$

(a) $\dfrac{x^3}{\sin x}$ (b) 1

(c) 0   (d) $\dfrac{x^2}{\cos^2 x}$

Sol. (c) Given, $\dfrac{x^3}{\cos x}$

Let $y = \dfrac{x^3}{\cos x}$

On differentiating w.r.t. x, we get

$$\dfrac{dy}{dx} = \dfrac{\cos x \dfrac{d}{dx}(x^3) - x^3 \dfrac{d}{dx}(\cos x)}{(\cos x)^2}$$

$\Rightarrow \qquad \dfrac{dy}{dx} = \dfrac{3x^2 \cos x + x^3 \sin x}{(\cos x)^2}$

When $x = 0$, then

$$\dfrac{dy}{dx}\Big|_{x=0} = 0$$

15. If two events A and B are mutually exclusive, then $P(A / B)$ equals

(a) 0   (b) 1

(c) 0.5   (d) 0.25

Sol. (a) We know that if A and B are mutually exclusive, then $P(A \cap B) = 0$

$\therefore \quad P\left(\dfrac{A}{B}\right) = \dfrac{P(A \cap B)}{P(B)} = 0 \qquad [\because P(A \cap B) = 0]$

16. The interval in which $y = x^2\, e^{-x}$ is increasing, is

(a) $(-\infty, \infty)$ (b) $(-2, 0)$

(c) $(2, \infty)$ (d) $(0, 2)$

Sol. (d) Given, $y = x^2 e^{-x}$

On differentiating w.r.t. x, we get

$$\dfrac{dy}{dx} = x^2 e^{-x}(-1) + e^{-x}(2x)$$

$$= x e^{-x}(-x + 2) = x e^{-x}(2 - x)$$

For increasing function, $\dfrac{dy}{dx} > 0$

$\Rightarrow \qquad\qquad x e^{-x}(2 - x) > 0$

Case I

$\Rightarrow \quad x > 0 \quad$ and $\quad 2 - x > 0$

$\Rightarrow \quad x > 0 \quad$ and $\quad x < 2$

$\Rightarrow \quad 0 < x < 2$

Case II

$\Rightarrow \quad x < 0 \quad$ and $\quad 2 - x < 0$

$\Rightarrow \quad x < 0 \quad$ and $\quad x > 2$

Hence, there is no value of x exist.

Clearly, it is increasing in $(0, 2)$.

17. If A and B are two events such that $P(A) > 0$ and $P(B) \neq 1$, then $P(A'/B')$ equals

(a) $1 - P(A / B)$ (b) $1 - P(A'/B)$

(c) $\dfrac{1 - P(A \cup B)}{P(B')}$ (d) $P(A')/P(B')$

Sol. (c) Given, $P(A) > 0$ and $P(B) \neq 1$

$\therefore \quad P\left(\dfrac{A'}{B'}\right) = \dfrac{P(A' \cap B')}{P(B')} = \dfrac{1 - P(A \cup B)}{P(B')}$

18. If a die is thrown and a card is selected at random from a deck of 52 playing cards, then the probability of getting an even number on the die and a spade card equals

(a) $\dfrac{1}{4}$ (b) $\dfrac{1}{2}$

(c) $\dfrac{1}{8}$ (d) $\dfrac{1}{3}$

Sol. (c) Let the event A and B are getting an even number on die and getting spade card, respectively.

$\therefore P(A) = \dfrac{3}{6} = \dfrac{1}{2}$ and $P(B) = \dfrac{13}{52} = \dfrac{1}{4}$

Now, both are independent events.

$\therefore P(A \cap B) = P(A) \times P(B) = \dfrac{1}{2} \times \dfrac{1}{4} = \dfrac{1}{8}$

Assertion-Reason Based Questions

In the following questions, a statement of Assertion (A) is followed by a statement of Reason (R). Choose the correct answer out of the following choices.

    (a) Both A and R are true and R is the correct explanation of A

    (b) Both A and R are true but R is not the correct explanation of A

    (c) A is true but R is false

    (d) A is false but R is true

19. Assertion (A) Let $A = \{2, 4, 6\}$ and $B = \{3, 5, 7, 9\}$ and defined a function $f = \{(2, 3), (4, 5), (6, 7)\}$ from A to B. Then, f is not onto.

Reason (R) A function $f : A \to B$ is said to be onto, if every element of B is the image of some elements of A under f.

Sol. (b) **Assertion** Given that

$$A = \{2, 4, 6\},$$
$$B = \{3, 5, 7, 9\}$$
and $\qquad R = \{(2, 3), (4, 5), (6, 7)\}$

Here, $f(2) = 3$, $f(4) = 5$ and $f(6) = 7$

It can be seen that the images of distinct elements of A under f are distinct.

Hence, function f is one-one but f is not onto, as $9 \in B$ does not have a pre-image in A.

Hence, both Assertion and Reason are true, but Reason is not the correct explanation of Assertion.

20. Assertion (A) Consider the linear programming problem. Maximise $Z = 4x + y$, subject to constraints are $x + y \leq 50$, $x + y \geq 100$, and $x, y \geq 0$

Then, maximum value of Z is 50.

Reason (R) If the shaded region is not bounded, then maximum value cannot be determined.

Sol. (d) **Assertion** Given, maximise, $Z = 4x + y$

and $x + y \leq 50$, $x + y \geq 100$; $x, y \geq 0$

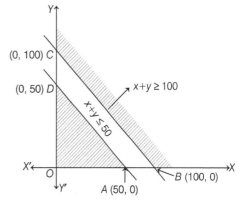

Hence, it is clear from the graph that it is not bounded region. So, maximum value cannot be determined.

Hence, Assertion is false but Reason is true.

Section B

(This section comprises of very short answer type questions (VSA) of 2 marks each)

21. Evaluate $\int_{-1}^{1} |1-x|$.

Or

Evaluate $\int_{0}^{3} [x] \, dx$, where $[x]$ is the greatest integer function.

Sol. Let $I = \int_{-1}^{1} |1-x| \, dx = \int_{-1}^{1} (1-x) \, dx$

$$\left[\because |1-x| = \begin{cases} (1-x), & x < 1 \\ -(1-x), & x \geq 1 \end{cases} \right] \quad (1)$$

$$= \left[x - \frac{x^2}{2} \right]_{-1}^{1} = \left(1 - \frac{1}{2} \right) - \left(-1 - \frac{1}{2} \right)$$

$$= \frac{1}{2} + \frac{3}{2} = 2 \quad (1)$$

Or

Let $I = \int_{0}^{3} [x] \, dx = \int_{0}^{1} [x] \, dx + \int_{1}^{2} [x] \, dx + \int_{2}^{3} [x] \, dx \quad (1)$

$$= \int_{0}^{1} 0 \, dx + \int_{1}^{2} 1 \, dx + \int_{2}^{3} 2 \, dx = 0 + [x]_{1}^{2} + 2[x]_{2}^{3}$$

$$= (2-1) + 2(3-2) = 1 + 2 = 3 \quad (1)$$

22. If two vectors $\vec{a}$ and $\vec{b}$ are such that $|\vec{a}| = 2$, $|\vec{b}| = 3$ and $\vec{a} \cdot \vec{b} = 4$, then find $|\vec{a} - \vec{b}|$.

Sol. Given, $|\vec{a}| = 2, |\vec{b}| = 3$ and $\vec{a} \cdot \vec{b} = 4$

$|\vec{a} - \vec{b}|^2 = (\vec{a} - \vec{b}) \cdot (\vec{a} - \vec{b})$

$\Rightarrow |\vec{a} - \vec{b}|^2 = \vec{a} \cdot \vec{a} - \vec{a} \cdot \vec{b} - \vec{b} \cdot \vec{a} + \vec{b} \cdot \vec{b}$

$\Rightarrow |\vec{a} - \vec{b}|^2 = \vec{a} \cdot \vec{a} + \vec{b} \cdot \vec{b} - \vec{a} \cdot \vec{b} - \vec{a} \cdot \vec{b} \quad (1)$

$$[\because \vec{a} \cdot \vec{b} = \vec{b} \cdot \vec{a}]$$

$\Rightarrow |\vec{a} - \vec{b}|^2 = |\vec{a}|^2 + |\vec{b}|^2 - 2(\vec{a} \cdot \vec{b})$

$\Rightarrow |\vec{a} - \vec{b}|^2 = 4 + 9 - 2(4) \Rightarrow |\vec{a} - \vec{b}| = \sqrt{13 - 8} = \sqrt{5} \quad (1)$

23. Evaluate $\int e^x (\cos x - \sin x) \, dx$.

Or

Evaluate $\int x e^x \, dx$.

Sol. Let $I = \int e^x (\cos x - \sin x) \, dx$

$\Rightarrow I = \int e^x \{\cos x + (-\sin x)\} \, dx \quad \ldots(i)$

Let $f(x) = \cos x \Rightarrow f'(x) = -\sin x \quad (1)$

We know that $\int e^x \{f(x) + f'(x)\} \, dx = e^x f(x) + C$

$\therefore$ From Eq. (i), we get $I = e^x \cos x + C \quad (1)$

Or

Let $I = \int x e^x \, dx$

$I = x \int e^x \, dx - \int \left(\frac{d}{dx}(x) \cdot \int e^x \, dx \right) dx$

$= x e^x - \int (1 \cdot e^x) \, dx \quad (1)$

$= x e^x - \int e^x \, dx$

$\Rightarrow I = x e^x - e^x + C$

$\Rightarrow I = e^x (x - 1) + C \quad (1)$

24. Show that the area of a parallelogram having diagonals $3\hat{i} + \hat{j} - 2\hat{k}$ and $\hat{i} - 3\hat{j} + 4\hat{k}$ is $5\sqrt{3}$ sq units.

Sol. Let $\vec{a} = 3\hat{i} + \hat{j} - 2\hat{k}$ and $\vec{b} = \hat{i} - 3\hat{j} + 4\hat{k}$. Then,

$$\vec{a} \times \vec{b} = \begin{vmatrix} \hat{i} & \hat{j} & \hat{k} \\ 3 & 1 & -2 \\ 1 & -3 & 4 \end{vmatrix} = (4-6)\hat{i} - (12+2)\hat{j} + (-9-1)\hat{k}$$

$$= -2\hat{i} - 14\hat{j} - 10\hat{k} \quad (1)$$

$\Rightarrow |\vec{a} \times \vec{b}| = \sqrt{(-2)^2 + (-14)^2 + (-10)^2} = \sqrt{300}$

$\therefore$ Area of the parallelogram $= \frac{1}{2} |\vec{a} \times \vec{b}| = \frac{1}{2} \times \sqrt{300}$

$$= 5\sqrt{3} \text{ sq units} \quad (1)$$

25. Let A and B be two events of the same sample space S of an experiment, then prove that $0 \leq P(A/B) \leq 1, B \neq \phi$.

Sol. By definition, $P\left(\frac{A}{B} \right) = \frac{P(A \cap B)}{P(B)} \quad \ldots(i)$

Also, $A \cap B \subset B \quad [\because A \cap B \text{ is a subset of } B]$

$\Rightarrow \qquad P(A \cap B) \leq P(B)$

$\Rightarrow \qquad \frac{P(A \cap B)}{P(B)} \leq 1 \quad \ldots(ii) \quad (1)$

Again, $P(A \cap B) \geq 0$ and $B \neq \phi$

$\therefore \qquad P(B) > 0$

$\therefore \qquad \frac{P(A \cap B)}{P(B)} \geq 0 \quad \ldots(iii)$

From Eqs. (ii) and (iii), we get

$$0 \leq \frac{P(A \cap B)}{P(B)} \leq 1$$

Hence, $0 \leq P(A/B) \leq 1$ [from Eq. (i)] **Hence proved.**
$$(1)$$

Section C

(This section comprises of short answer type questions (SA) of 3 marks each)

26. Show that the relation S in set $A = \{x \in Z : 0 \le x \le 12\}$ given by $S = \{(a, b) : a, b \in A, |a - b| \text{ is divisible by } 4\}$ is an equivalence relation. Find the set of all elements related to 1.

Sol. Given relation is

$S = \{(a, b) : |a - b| \text{ is divisible by 4 and } a, b \in A\}$

and $A = \{x : x \in Z \text{ and } 0 \le x \le 12\}$

Now, A can be written as

$$A = \{0, 1, 2, 3, ..., 12\} \qquad (1/2)$$

Reflexive As for any $x \in A$, we get $|x - x| = 0$, which is divisible by 4.

$\Rightarrow \quad (x, x) \in S, \forall x \in A$

Therefore, S is reflexive. $\qquad (1/2)$

Symmetric As for any $(x, y) \in S$, we get $|x - y|$ is divisible by 4.

[by using definition of given relation]

$\Rightarrow \qquad |x - y| = 4\lambda \text{, for some } \lambda \in Z$

$\Rightarrow \qquad |y - x| = 4\lambda \text{, for some } \lambda \in Z$

$\Rightarrow \qquad (y, x) \in S$

Thus, $(x, y) \in S \Rightarrow (y, x) \in S, \forall x, y \in A$

Therefore, S is symmetric. $\qquad (1)$

Transitive For any $(x, y) \in S$ and $(y, z) \in S$, we get $|x - y|$ is divisible by 4 and $|y - z|$ is divisible by 4.

[by using definition of given relation]

$\Rightarrow \quad |x - y| = 4\lambda \text{ and } |y - z| = 4\mu, \text{ for some } \lambda, \mu \in Z.$

Now, $x - z = (x - y) + (y - z)$

$\qquad = \pm 4\lambda \pm 4\mu = \pm 4(\lambda + \mu)$

$\Rightarrow \quad |x - z| \text{ is divisible by 4.} \Rightarrow (x, z) \in S$

Thus, $(x, y) \in S$ and $(y, z) \in S$

$\Rightarrow \quad (x, z) \in S, \forall x, y, z \in A$

Therefore, S is transitive.

Since, S is reflexive, symmetric and transitive, so it is an equivalence relation.

Now, set of all elements related to 1 is $\{1, 5, 9\}$. $\qquad (1)$

27. Determine $f(0)$, so that the function $f(x)$ defined by $f(x) = \dfrac{(4^x - 1)^3}{\sin \dfrac{x}{4} \log \left(1 + \dfrac{x^2}{3}\right)}$ becomes continuous at $x = 0$.

Or If $y = b \tan^{-1} \left(\dfrac{x}{a} + \tan^{-1} \dfrac{y}{x}\right)$, find $\dfrac{dy}{dx}$.

Sol. For $f(x)$ to be continuous at $x = 0$, we must have

$$\lim_{x \to 0} f(x) = f(0)$$

$\Rightarrow \qquad f(0) = \lim_{x \to 0} f(x)$

$$= \lim_{x \to 0} \frac{(4^x - 1)^3}{\sin \dfrac{x}{4} \log \left(1 + \dfrac{x^2}{3}\right)} \qquad (1)$$

$$= \lim_{x \to 0} \frac{\left(\dfrac{4^x - 1}{x}\right)^3}{\left(\dfrac{\sin \dfrac{x}{4}}{4 \times \dfrac{x}{4}}\right) \left(\dfrac{\log \left(1 + \dfrac{x^2}{3}\right)}{\dfrac{x^2}{3} \times 3}\right)}$$

$$= \frac{(\log_e 4)^3}{\dfrac{1}{4} \times \dfrac{1}{3}} = 12 (\log_e 4)^3 \qquad (2)$$

Or

Given, $y = b \tan^{-1} \left(\dfrac{x}{a} + \tan^{-1} \dfrac{y}{x}\right)$

$\Rightarrow \qquad \dfrac{y}{b} = \tan^{-1} \left(\dfrac{x}{a} + \tan^{-1} \dfrac{y}{x}\right)$

$\Rightarrow \qquad \tan \dfrac{y}{b} = \dfrac{x}{a} + \tan^{-1} \dfrac{y}{x} \qquad (1)$

On differentiating both sides w.r.t. x, we get

$$\frac{1}{b} \sec^2 \left(\frac{y}{b}\right) \frac{dy}{dx} = \frac{1}{a} + \frac{1}{1 + \left(\dfrac{y}{x}\right)^2} \times \frac{x \dfrac{dy}{dx} - y}{x^2}$$

$$\Rightarrow \frac{1}{b} \sec^2 \left(\frac{y}{b}\right) \frac{dy}{dx} = \frac{1}{a} + \frac{x \dfrac{dy}{dx} - y}{x^2 + y^2} \qquad (1)$$

$$\Rightarrow \frac{dy}{dx} \left\{\frac{1}{b} \sec^2 \left(\frac{y}{b}\right) - \frac{x}{x^2 + y^2}\right\} = \frac{1}{a} - \frac{y}{x^2 + y^2}$$

$$\therefore \qquad \frac{dy}{dx} = \frac{\dfrac{1}{a} - \dfrac{y}{x^2 + y^2}}{\dfrac{1}{b} \sec^2 \left(\dfrac{y}{b}\right) - \dfrac{x}{x^2 + y^2}} \qquad (1)$$

28. Evaluate $\int \tan(x - \theta) \tan(x + \theta) \tan 2x \, dx$.

Or

Evaluate $\int \dfrac{\sin x - x \cos x}{x(x + \sin x)} dx$.

Sol. We know that

$$2x = (x - \theta) + (x + \theta)$$

$$\Rightarrow \quad \tan 2x = \tan\{(x - \theta) + (x + \theta)\}$$

$$\Rightarrow \quad \tan 2x = \frac{\tan(x - \theta) + \tan(x + \theta)}{1 - \tan(x - \theta)\tan(x + \theta)} \quad (1)$$

$$\Rightarrow \tan 2x - \tan(x - \theta)\tan(x + \theta)\tan 2x$$
$$= \tan(x - \theta) + \tan(x + \theta)$$

$$\Rightarrow \tan(x - \theta)\tan(x + \theta)\tan 2x = \tan 2x$$
$$- \tan(x - \theta) - \tan(x + \theta) \quad (1)$$

Let $I = \int \tan(x - \theta)\tan(x + \theta)\tan 2x\, dx$

$$= \int \{\tan 2x - \tan(x - \theta) - \tan(x + \theta)\}\, dx$$

$$\Rightarrow I = -\frac{1}{2}\log|\cos 2x| + \log|\cos(x - \theta)|$$

$$+ \log|\cos(x + \theta)| + C \quad (1)$$

Or

Let $I = \int \dfrac{\sin x - x\cos x}{x(x + \sin x)}dx = \int \dfrac{(x + \sin x) - x - x\cos x}{x(x + \sin x)}dx$

$$= \int\left\{\frac{x + \sin x}{x(x + \sin x)} - \frac{x(1 + \cos x)}{x(x + \sin x)}\right\}dx \quad (1)$$

$$= \int \frac{1}{x}dx - \int \frac{1 + \cos x}{x + \sin x}dx$$

$$= \log|x| - \log|x + \sin x| + C$$

$$\left[\because \frac{d}{dx}(x + \sin x) = 1 + \cos x\right]$$

$$= \log\left|\frac{x}{x + \sin x}\right| + C \quad (2)$$

29. Find the area of the region bounded by the parabola $x^2 = 4y$ and the line $x = 4y - 2$.

Or

Sketch the region $\{(x, y) : x = \sqrt{4 - y^2}\,\}$ and Y-axis. Find the area of the region using integration.

Sol. Given, equations of curves are

$$x^2 = 4y \qquad \qquad \dots(i)$$

and $\qquad\qquad x = 4y - 2 \qquad \qquad \dots(ii)$

Eq. (i) represents a parabola which is open upward having vertex (0, 0) and Eq. (ii) represents a straight line.

On putting the value of $4y$ from Eq. (i) in Eq. (ii), we get

$$x = x^2 - 2$$

$$\Rightarrow \qquad x^2 - x - 2 = 0$$

$$\Rightarrow \qquad x^2 - 2x + x - 2 = 0$$

$$\Rightarrow \qquad x(x - 2) + 1(x - 2) = 0$$

$$\Rightarrow \qquad (x + 1)(x - 2) = 0 \Rightarrow x = -1, 2 \quad (1/2)$$

When $x = -1$, then from Eq. (i), we get

$$y = \frac{1}{4}$$

and when $x = 2$, then from Eq. (i), $y = 1$

∴ Points of intersection of given curves are

$\left(-1, \dfrac{1}{4}\right)$ and $(2, 1)$.

(1/2)

Now, the graph of given curves is as follows

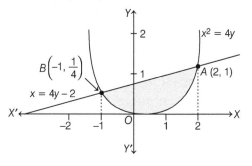

(1)

∴ Required area = Area of shaded region *BOAB*

$$= \int_{-1}^{2}[y_{(line)} - y_{(parabola)}]\, dx = \int_{-1}^{2}\left[\left(\frac{x + 2}{4}\right) - \frac{x^2}{4}\right]dx$$

$$= \frac{1}{4}\int_{-1}^{2}(x + 2 - x^2)\, dx = \frac{1}{4}\left[\frac{x^2}{2} + 2x - \frac{x^3}{3}\right]_{-1}^{2}$$

$$= \frac{1}{4}\left[\left(2 + 4 - \frac{8}{3}\right) - \left(\frac{1}{2} - 2 + \frac{1}{3}\right)\right]$$

$$= \frac{1}{4}\left(6 - \frac{8}{3} + 2 - \frac{5}{6}\right) = \frac{1}{4}\left(8 - \frac{8}{3} - \frac{5}{6}\right)$$

$$= \frac{1}{4}\left(\frac{48 - 16 - 5}{6}\right) = \frac{1}{4}\cdot\frac{27}{6} = \frac{27}{24} = \frac{9}{8}$$

Hence, the required area is $\dfrac{9}{8}$ sq units.

(1)

Or

Given region is $\{(x, y) : x = \sqrt{4 - y^2}\,\}$ and Y-axis.

We have, $x = \sqrt{4 - y^2}$

$$\Rightarrow \qquad x^2 = 4 - y^2 \Rightarrow x^2 + y^2 = 4$$

This represents the equation of circle having centre (0, 0) and radius 2.

But original equation is $x = \sqrt{4 - y^2}$, so x is positive. It means that we have to take a curve right side the Y-axis.

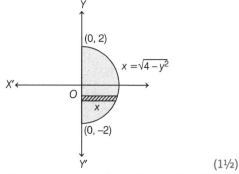

(1½)

Thus, only semi-circle is formed right side of the Y-axis.

Since, the region is symmetrical about X-axis.

∴ Area of shaded region,

$$A = 2\int_0^2 x\,dy = 2\int_0^2 \sqrt{4-y^2}\,dy$$

$$= 2\int_0^2 \sqrt{2^2 - y^2}\,dy$$

$$= 2\left[\frac{y}{2}\sqrt{2^2 - y^2} + \frac{2^2}{2}\sin^{-1}\frac{y}{2}\right]_0^2$$

$$= 2\left[\frac{2}{2}\cdot 0 + 2\cdot\frac{\pi}{2} - \frac{0}{2}\cdot 2 - 2\sin^{-1}0\right]$$

$$= 2\left[2\cdot\frac{\pi}{2}\right] = 2\pi \text{ sq units}$$

$$(1\frac{1}{2})$$

30. Find the intervals in which the function

$f(x) = 20 - 9x + 6x^2 - x^3$ is

(i) strictly increasing.

(ii) strictly decreasing.

Sol. Given function is $f(x) = 20 - 9x + 6x^2 - x^3$.

On differentiating both sides w.r.t. x, we get

$$f'(x) = -9 + 12x - 3x^2$$

On putting $f'(x) = 0$, we get

$$-9 + 12x - 3x^2 = 0$$

$$\Rightarrow \quad -3(x^2 - 4x + 3) = 0$$

$$\Rightarrow \quad -3(x-1)(x-3) = 0$$

$$\Rightarrow \quad (x-1)(x-3) = 0$$

$$\Rightarrow \quad x - 1 = 0 \text{ or } x - 3 = 0$$

$$\Rightarrow \quad x = 1 \text{ or } 3$$

Now, we find intervals in which $f(x)$ is strictly increasing or strictly decreasing.

Interval	$f'(x) = -3(x-1)(x-3)$	Sign of $f'(x)$
$x < 1$	$(-)(-)(-)$	$-$ ve
$1 < x < 3$	$(-)(+)(-)$	$+$ ve
$x > 3$	$(-)(+)(+)$	$-$ ve

$$(1)$$

We know that a function $f(x)$ is said to be strictly increasing when $f'(x) > 0$ and it is said to be strictly decreasing, if $f'(x) < 0$. So, the given function $f(x)$ is

(i) strictly increasing on the interval $(1, 3)$. $\quad(1)$

(ii) strictly decreasing on the intervals $(-\infty, 1)$ and $(3, \infty)$. $\quad(1)$

31. If $I_n = \int_0^{\pi/4} \tan^n x\,dx$, prove that

$$I_n + I_{n+2} = \frac{1}{n+1}.$$

Sol. We have, $\quad I_n = \int_0^{\pi/4} \tan^n x\,dx$

$$\Rightarrow \quad I_{n+2} = \int_0^{\pi/4} \tan^{n+2} x\,dx$$

$$\therefore \quad I_n + I_{n+2} = \int_0^{\pi/4} \tan^n x\,dx + \int_0^{\pi/4} \tan^{n+2} x\,dx$$

$$= \int_0^{\pi/4} \tan^n x\,(1 + \tan^2 x)\,dx$$

$$= \int_0^{\pi/4} \tan^n x\,\sec^2 x\,dx \quad (2)$$

Put $\tan x = t \Rightarrow \sec^2 x\,dx = dt$

Also, when $x = 0$, then $t = 0$

and when $x = \dfrac{\pi}{4}$, then $t = 1$

$$\therefore \quad I_n + I_{n+2} = \int_0^1 t^n\,dt = \left[\frac{t^{n+1}}{n+1}\right]_0^1 = \frac{1}{n+1} \quad (1)$$

Hence proved.

Section D

(This section comprises of long answer type questions (LA) of 5 marks each)

32. Solve $\dfrac{dy}{dx} + \dfrac{1}{x} = \dfrac{e^y}{x}$.

Sol. We have, $\dfrac{dy}{dx} + \dfrac{1}{x} = \dfrac{e^y}{x} \Rightarrow \dfrac{dy}{dx} = \dfrac{e^y - 1}{x}$

$$\Rightarrow \quad \frac{dy}{e^y - 1} = \frac{dx}{x} \qquad \ldots\text{(i)} \quad (1)$$

On integrating both sides of Eq. (i), we get

$$\int\frac{dy}{e^y - 1} = \int\frac{dx}{x} \Rightarrow \int\frac{e^{-y}dy}{1 - e^{-y}} = \int\frac{dx}{x}$$

$$\Rightarrow \quad \log(1 - e^{-y}) = \log x + \log C \quad (2)$$

$$\Rightarrow \quad \log(1 - e^{-y}) = (\log Cx) \Rightarrow 1 - e^{-y} = Cx$$

$$\Rightarrow \quad e^{-y} = 1 - Cx \Rightarrow -y = \log(1 - Cx)$$

$$\Rightarrow \quad y + \log(1 - Cx) = 0 \quad (2)$$

33. Let $A = \begin{bmatrix} 2 & 3 \\ -1 & 2 \end{bmatrix}$ and $f(x) = x^2 - 4x + 7$.

Show that $f(A) = O$. Use this result to find A^5.

Or Determine the product of $\begin{bmatrix} -4 & 4 & 4 \\ -7 & 1 & 3 \\ 5 & -3 & -1 \end{bmatrix}$

$\begin{bmatrix} 1 & -1 & 1 \\ 1 & -2 & -2 \\ 2 & 1 & 3 \end{bmatrix}$ and then use to solve the

system of equations

$$x - y + z = 4,\ x - 2y - 2z = 9$$

and $2x + y + 3z = 1$.

Sol. We have, $f(x) = x^2 - 4x + 7$

$\therefore f(A) = A^2 - 4A + 7I_2$

Now, $A^2 = \begin{bmatrix} 2 & 3 \\ -1 & 2 \end{bmatrix}\begin{bmatrix} 2 & 3 \\ -1 & 2 \end{bmatrix} = \begin{bmatrix} 4-3 & 6+6 \\ -2-2 & -3+4 \end{bmatrix}$

$= \begin{bmatrix} 1 & 12 \\ -4 & 1 \end{bmatrix}$ (1)

$-4A = \begin{bmatrix} -8 & -12 \\ 4 & -8 \end{bmatrix}$ and $7I_2 = \begin{bmatrix} 7 & 0 \\ 0 & 7 \end{bmatrix}$

$\therefore \quad f(A) = A^2 - 4A + 7I_2$

$\Rightarrow f(A) = \begin{bmatrix} 1 & 12 \\ -4 & 1 \end{bmatrix} + \begin{bmatrix} -8 & -12 \\ 4 & -8 \end{bmatrix} + \begin{bmatrix} 7 & 0 \\ 0 & 7 \end{bmatrix}$

$\Rightarrow f(A) = \begin{bmatrix} 1-8+7 & 12-12+0 \\ -4+4+0 & 1-8+7 \end{bmatrix} = \begin{bmatrix} 0 & 0 \\ 0 & 0 \end{bmatrix} = O$

Hence proved.

Now, $f(A) = O$

$\Rightarrow \quad A^2 - 4A + 7I_2 = O$ (1)

$\Rightarrow \quad A^2 = 4A - 7I_2$

$\Rightarrow \quad A^3 = A^2 A = (4A - 7I_2)A = 4A^2 - 7I_2A$

$\Rightarrow \quad A^3 = 4(4A - 7I_2) - 7A$ [using $A^2 = 4A - 7I_2$]
(1)

$\Rightarrow \quad A^3 = 9A - 28I_2$

$\Rightarrow \quad A^4 = A^3 A = (9A - 28I_2)A$

$\Rightarrow \quad A^4 = 9A^2 - 28A = 9(4A - 7I_2) - 28A$

[using $A^2 = 4A - 7I_2$]

$\Rightarrow \quad A^4 = 36A - 63I_2 - 28A = 8A - 63I_2$

$\Rightarrow \quad A^5 = A^4 A = (8A - 63I_2)A = 8A^2 - 63I_2A$

$\Rightarrow \quad A^5 = 8(4A - 7I_2) - 63A = -31A - 56I_2$ (1)

[using $A^2 = 4A - 7I_2$]

$\Rightarrow A^5 = -31\begin{bmatrix} 2 & 3 \\ -1 & 2 \end{bmatrix} - 56\begin{bmatrix} 1 & 0 \\ 0 & 1 \end{bmatrix}$

$= \begin{bmatrix} -62 & -93 \\ 31 & -62 \end{bmatrix} + \begin{bmatrix} -56 & 0 \\ 0 & -56 \end{bmatrix} = \begin{bmatrix} -118 & -93 \\ 31 & -118 \end{bmatrix}$ (1)

Or

Let $B = \begin{bmatrix} -4 & 4 & 4 \\ -7 & 1 & 3 \\ 5 & -3 & -1 \end{bmatrix}$ and $A = \begin{bmatrix} 1 & -1 & 1 \\ 1 & -2 & -2 \\ 2 & 1 & 3 \end{bmatrix}$

Now, $BA = \begin{bmatrix} -4 & 4 & 4 \\ -7 & 1 & 3 \\ 5 & -3 & -1 \end{bmatrix}\begin{bmatrix} 1 & -1 & 1 \\ 1 & -2 & -2 \\ 2 & 1 & 3 \end{bmatrix}$ (1)

$= \begin{bmatrix} -4+4+8 & 4-8+4 & -4-8+12 \\ -7+1+6 & 7-2+3 & -7-2+9 \\ 5-3-2 & -5+6-1 & 5+6-3 \end{bmatrix}$

$= \begin{bmatrix} 8 & 0 & 0 \\ 0 & 8 & 0 \\ 0 & 0 & 8 \end{bmatrix} = 8\begin{bmatrix} 1 & 0 & 0 \\ 0 & 1 & 0 \\ 0 & 0 & 1 \end{bmatrix} = 8I$ (1½)

$\Rightarrow \quad BA = 8I$

$\Rightarrow \quad BA(A^{-1}) = 8I \cdot A^{-1}$ (1/2)

[post-multiplying both sides by A^{-1}]

$\Rightarrow \quad B(AA^{-1}) = 8I A^{-1}$

$\Rightarrow \quad B = 8A^{-1}$ [$\because AA^{-1} = I$]

$\therefore \quad A^{-1} = \frac{1}{8}\begin{bmatrix} -4 & 4 & 4 \\ -7 & 1 & 3 \\ 5 & -3 & -1 \end{bmatrix}$ (1)

Hence, $X = \frac{1}{8}\begin{bmatrix} -4 & 4 & 4 \\ -7 & 1 & 3 \\ 5 & -3 & -1 \end{bmatrix}\begin{bmatrix} 4 \\ 9 \\ 1 \end{bmatrix}$

$\Rightarrow \begin{bmatrix} x \\ y \\ z \end{bmatrix} = \frac{1}{8}\begin{bmatrix} -16+36+4 \\ -28+9+3 \\ 20-27-1 \end{bmatrix} = \frac{1}{8}\begin{bmatrix} 24 \\ -16 \\ -8 \end{bmatrix} = \begin{bmatrix} 3 \\ -2 \\ -1 \end{bmatrix}$

On comparing corresponding elements, we get

$x = 3, y = -2$ and $z = -1$ (1)

34. If $A = \begin{bmatrix} 1 & 0 & 2 \\ 0 & 2 & 1 \\ 2 & 0 & 3 \end{bmatrix}$ and

$A^3 - 6A^2 + 7A + kI_3 = O$, find the value of k.

Or

For the following matrices A and B, verify that $(AB)' = B'A'$, where

$A = \begin{bmatrix} 1 \\ -4 \\ 3 \end{bmatrix}$ and $B = [-1 \quad 2 \quad 1]$

Sol. Given, $A = \begin{bmatrix} 1 & 0 & 2 \\ 0 & 2 & 1 \\ 2 & 0 & 3 \end{bmatrix}$

Now, $A^2 = \begin{bmatrix} 1 & 0 & 2 \\ 0 & 2 & 1 \\ 2 & 0 & 3 \end{bmatrix}\begin{bmatrix} 1 & 0 & 2 \\ 0 & 2 & 1 \\ 2 & 0 & 3 \end{bmatrix}$

$= \begin{bmatrix} 1+0+4 & 0+0+0 & 2+0+6 \\ 0+0+2 & 0+4+0 & 0+2+3 \\ 2+0+6 & 0+0+0 & 4+0+9 \end{bmatrix}$

$= \begin{bmatrix} 5 & 0 & 8 \\ 2 & 4 & 5 \\ 8 & 0 & 13 \end{bmatrix}$ (1)

and $A^3 = A \cdot A^2 = \begin{bmatrix} 1 & 0 & 2 \\ 0 & 2 & 1 \\ 2 & 0 & 3 \end{bmatrix}\begin{bmatrix} 5 & 0 & 8 \\ 2 & 4 & 5 \\ 8 & 0 & 13 \end{bmatrix}$

$= \begin{bmatrix} 5+0+16 & 0+0+0 & 8+0+26 \\ 0+4+8 & 0+8+0 & 0+10+13 \\ 10+0+24 & 0+0+0 & 16+0+39 \end{bmatrix}$

$= \begin{bmatrix} 21 & 0 & 34 \\ 12 & 8 & 23 \\ 34 & 0 & 55 \end{bmatrix}$ (1)

Also given, $A^3 - 6A^2 + 7A + kI_3 = O$

$$\therefore \begin{bmatrix} 21 & 0 & 34 \\ 12 & 8 & 23 \\ 34 & 0 & 55 \end{bmatrix} - 6\begin{bmatrix} 5 & 0 & 8 \\ 2 & 4 & 5 \\ 8 & 0 & 13 \end{bmatrix} + 7\begin{bmatrix} 1 & 0 & 2 \\ 0 & 2 & 1 \\ 2 & 0 & 3 \end{bmatrix}$$

$$+ k\begin{bmatrix} 1 & 0 & 0 \\ 0 & 1 & 0 \\ 0 & 0 & 1 \end{bmatrix} = \begin{bmatrix} 0 & 0 & 0 \\ 0 & 0 & 0 \\ 0 & 0 & 0 \end{bmatrix} \quad (1)$$

$$\Rightarrow \begin{bmatrix} 21 & 0 & 34 \\ 12 & 8 & 23 \\ 34 & 0 & 55 \end{bmatrix} - \begin{bmatrix} 30 & 0 & 48 \\ 12 & 24 & 30 \\ 48 & 0 & 78 \end{bmatrix}$$

$$+ \begin{bmatrix} 7 & 0 & 14 \\ 0 & 14 & 7 \\ 14 & 0 & 21 \end{bmatrix} + \begin{bmatrix} k & 0 & 0 \\ 0 & k & 0 \\ 0 & 0 & k \end{bmatrix} = \begin{bmatrix} 0 & 0 & 0 \\ 0 & 0 & 0 \\ 0 & 0 & 0 \end{bmatrix} \quad (1)$$

$$\Rightarrow \begin{bmatrix} 21-30+7+k & 0-0+0+0 & 34-48+14+0 \\ 12-12+0+0 & 8-24+14+k & 23-30+7+0 \\ 34-48+14+0 & 0-0+0+0 & 55-78+21+k \end{bmatrix}$$

$$= \begin{bmatrix} 0 & 0 & 0 \\ 0 & 0 & 0 \\ 0 & 0 & 0 \end{bmatrix}$$

$$\Rightarrow \begin{bmatrix} -2+k & 0 & 0 \\ 0 & -2+k & 0 \\ 0 & 0 & -2+k \end{bmatrix} = \begin{bmatrix} 0 & 0 & 0 \\ 0 & 0 & 0 \\ 0 & 0 & 0 \end{bmatrix}$$

On equating the corresponding elements, we get
$$-2 + k = 0$$
$$\therefore \qquad k = 2 \qquad (1)$$

Or

Given, $A = \begin{bmatrix} 1 \\ -4 \\ 3 \end{bmatrix}$ and $B = [-1 \ 2 \ 1]$

To verify $(AB)' = B' A'$

Here,

$$AB = \begin{bmatrix} 1 \\ -4 \\ 3 \end{bmatrix}_{3 \times 1} [-1 \ 2 \ 1]_{1 \times 3} \Rightarrow AB = \begin{bmatrix} -1 & 2 & 1 \\ 4 & -8 & -4 \\ -3 & 6 & 3 \end{bmatrix}$$

[multiplying row by column] (1)

$$\therefore \quad \text{LHS} = (AB)' = \begin{bmatrix} -1 & 4 & -3 \\ 2 & -8 & 6 \\ 1 & -4 & 3 \end{bmatrix} \quad \dots(i)$$

[interchanging the elements of rows and columns] (1½)

Now, $B' = \begin{bmatrix} -1 \\ 2 \\ 1 \end{bmatrix}$ and $A' = [1 \ -4 \ 3]$

(1)

$$\therefore \quad \text{RHS} = B' A' = \begin{bmatrix} -1 \\ 2 \\ 1 \end{bmatrix} [1 \ -4 \ 3]$$

$$= \begin{bmatrix} -1 & 4 & -3 \\ 2 & -8 & 6 \\ 1 & -4 & 3 \end{bmatrix} \quad \dots(ii)$$

[multiplying row by column] (1)

From Eqs. (i) and (ii), we get
$$(AB)' = B' A'$$
$$\therefore \qquad \text{LHS} = \text{RHS} \qquad \textbf{Hence verified.} \ (1/2)$$

35. If $(\tan^{-1} x)^y + y^{\cot x} = 1$, then find dy/dx.

Sol. Let $u = (\tan^{-1} x)^y$ and $v = y^{\cot x}$

Then, given equation becomes $u + v = 1$

On differentiating both sides w.r.t. x, we get
$$\frac{du}{dx} + \frac{dv}{dx} = 0 \qquad \dots(i)$$

Now, $\qquad u = (\tan^{-1} x)^y$

On taking log both sides, we get
$$\log u = y \log(\tan^{-1} x) \qquad (1)$$

On differentiating both sides w.r.t. x, we get
$$\frac{1}{u}\frac{du}{dx} = \frac{d}{dx}(y) \cdot \log(\tan^{-1} x) + y \frac{d}{dx}(\log \tan^{-1} x)$$

[by using product rule of derivative]

$$\Rightarrow \frac{1}{u}\frac{du}{dx} = \frac{dy}{dx}\log(\tan^{-1} x) + \frac{y}{(\tan^{-1} x)(1 + x^2)}$$

$$\Rightarrow \frac{du}{dx} = (\tan^{-1} x)^y \left[\frac{dy}{dx}\log(\tan^{-1} x) + \frac{y}{(\tan^{-1} x)(1 + x^2)}\right] \dots(ii) \ (1)$$

Also, $\quad v = y^{\cot x}$

On taking log both sides, we get $\log v = \cot x \log y$

On differentiating both sides w.r.t. x, we get
$$\frac{1}{v}\frac{dv}{dx} = \frac{d}{dx}(\cot x) \cdot \log y + \cot x \frac{d}{dx}(\log y)$$

[by using product rule of derivative]

$$\Rightarrow \frac{1}{v}\frac{dv}{dx} = -\csc^2 x \log y + \frac{\cot x}{y}\frac{dy}{dx}$$

$$\Rightarrow \frac{dv}{dx} = y^{\cot x}\left[-\csc^2 x \log y + \frac{\cot x}{y}\frac{dy}{dx}\right]$$

$$\dots(iii) \ (1)$$

On putting the values from Eqs. (ii) and (iii) in Eq. (i), we get

$$(\tan^{-1} x)^y \left[\frac{dy}{dx}\log(\tan^{-1} x) + \frac{y}{(\tan^{-1} x)(1 + x^2)}\right]$$

$$+ y^{\cot x}\left[-\csc^2 x \log y + \frac{\cot x}{y}\frac{dy}{dx}\right] = 0$$

$$\Rightarrow \frac{dy}{dx}\left[(\tan^{-1} x)^y \log(\tan^{-1} x) + \cot x \cdot y^{\cot x - 1}\right]$$

$$= -\left[\frac{y}{1 + x^2}(\tan^{-1} x)^{y-1} - y^{\cot x}\csc^2 x \log y\right]$$

$$\Rightarrow \frac{dy}{dx} = \frac{-\left[\frac{y}{1 + x^2}(\tan^{-1} x)^{y-1} - y^{\cot x} \cdot \csc^2 x \log y\right]}{[(\tan^{-1} x)^y \log(\tan^{-1} x) + \cot x \cdot y^{\cot x - 1}]} \quad (2)$$

Section E

(This section comprises of 3 case-study/ passage-based questions of 4 marks each with two sub-parts. First two case study questions have three sub-parts (i), (ii), (iii) of marks 1, 1, 2 respectively. The third case study question has two sub-parts of 2 marks each)

36. Suppose a dealer in rural area wishes to purchase a number of sewing machines. He has some money to invest and has space for few items for storage. Let x denotes the number of electronic sewing machines and y denotes the number of manually operated sewing machines purchased by the dealer. For the same, constraint related to investment is given by $3x + 2y \le 48$ and objective function is $Z = 22x + 18y$ and other constraints consists the following $x + y \le 20$, x, y ≥ 0.

Based on the above information, answer the following questions.

(i) Find $Z_{(3, 4)}$.

(ii) Evaluate $Z_{\left(\frac{1}{2}, \frac{1}{3}\right)}$.

(iii) Find the number of corner points of the feasible region.

Or Find $Z_{(max)}$.

Sol. (i) $Z_{(3, 4)} = (22 \times 3) + (18 \times 4) = 138$

(ii) $Z_{\left(\frac{1}{2}, \frac{1}{3}\right)} = \left(22 \times \frac{1}{2}\right) + \left(18 \times \frac{1}{3}\right) = 11 + 6 = 17$

(iii) Objective function, $Z = 22x + 18y$
Subject to constraints
$$x + y \le 20, \quad 3x + 2y \le 48, \quad x, y \ge 0$$

[Graph showing feasible region with points E (0, 24), C (0, 20), B (8, 12), D (20, 0), A (16,0), O (0, 0), lines x+y=20 and 3x+2y=48]

∴ Number of corner points are 4.

Or

The coordinates of the corner points A, B, C and O are (16, 0), (8, 12), (0, 20) and (0, 0), respectively.

Corner points	$Z = 22x + 18y$
(0, 0)	0 (Minimum)
(16, 0)	352
(8, 12)	392 (Maximum)
(0, 20)	360

Z is maximum at the point (8, 12).

∴To get maximum profit 8 electronic sewing machines and 12 manually operated sewing machines should be purchased by the dealer.

Hence, $Z_{(max)} = 392$

37. Ronit and Aman, two friends are standing on either side of a tower of 30 m high. They observe its top at the angle of elevation α and β respectively. (as shown in the figure below).

The distance between Ronit and Aman is $40\sqrt{3}$ m and distance between Ronit and tower is $30\sqrt{3}$ m.

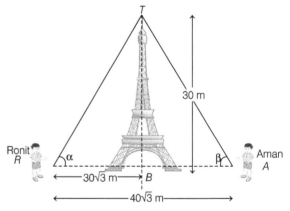

Based on the above information, answer the following questions.

(i) Find $\sin \alpha$.

(ii) Find $\angle TAR$.

(iii) If $\alpha = \cos^{-1}\left(\dfrac{k_1}{k_2}\right)$, then find $k_1 + k_2$.

Or Find $\angle ATR$.

Sol. (i) In $\triangle RTB$,

$$RB = 30\sqrt{3} \text{ and } TB = 30$$

$$\therefore \quad RT^2 = RB^2 + TB^2 = (30\sqrt{3})^2 + (30)^2$$

$$\therefore \quad RT = 60 \text{ m}$$

$$\Rightarrow \quad \sin\alpha = \frac{TB}{RT} = \frac{30}{60} = \frac{1}{2}$$

(ii) In $\triangle TAB$,

$$\tan\beta = \frac{TB}{AB}$$

$$\Rightarrow \quad \tan\beta = \frac{30}{10\sqrt{3}}$$

$$[\because AB = 40\sqrt{3} - 30\sqrt{3} = 10\sqrt{3}]$$

$$\Rightarrow \quad \beta = \tan^{-1}(\sqrt{3})$$

$$\Rightarrow \quad \beta = 60°$$

(iii) From part (i),

$$RT = 60$$

$$\Rightarrow \quad \cos\alpha = \frac{RB}{RT} = \frac{30\sqrt{3}}{60} = \frac{\sqrt{3}}{2}$$

$$\Rightarrow \quad \alpha = \cos^{-1}\left(\frac{\sqrt{3}}{2}\right)$$

$$\Rightarrow \quad k_1 + k_2 = \sqrt{3} + 2$$

Or

In $\triangle ART$, $\quad \alpha = \cos^{-1}\left(\frac{\sqrt{3}}{2}\right) = \frac{\pi}{6}$

$$\beta = \tan^{-1}(\sqrt{3}) = \frac{\pi}{3}$$

We know, sum of all three interior angles of a triangle is π.

$$\therefore \quad \alpha + \beta + \angle ATR = \pi$$

$$\Rightarrow \quad \frac{\pi}{6} + \frac{\pi}{3} + \angle ATR = \pi$$

$$\Rightarrow \quad \angle ATR = \pi - \frac{\pi}{2} = \frac{\pi}{2}$$

38. If $f(x)$ is a continuous function defined on $[0, a]$, then $\int_0^a f(x)\,dx = \int_0^a f(a-x)\,dx$.

On the basis of above information, answer the following questions.

(i) If $f(x) = \dfrac{\sin x - \cos x}{1 + \sin x \cos x}$, then evaluate $\int_0^{\pi/2} f(x)\,dx$.

(ii) If $g(x) = \log(1 + \tan x)$, then evaluate $\int_0^{\pi/4} g(x)\,dx$.

Sol. (i) Let $I = \int_0^{\pi/2} f(x)dx$

$$\Rightarrow \quad I = \int_0^{\pi/2} \frac{\sin x - \cos x}{1 + \sin x \cos x}dx \qquad \ldots(i)$$

$$\Rightarrow \quad I = \int_0^{\pi/2} \frac{\sin\left(\frac{\pi}{2} - x\right) - \cos\left(\frac{\pi}{2} - x\right)}{1 + \sin\left(\frac{\pi}{2} - x\right)\cos\left(\frac{\pi}{2} - x\right)}dx$$

$$\Rightarrow \quad I = \int_0^{\pi/2} \frac{\cos x - \sin x}{1 + \sin x \cos x}dx \qquad \ldots(ii)$$

On adding Eqs. (i) and (ii), we get

$$2I = \int_0^{\pi/2} \frac{\sin x - \cos x + \cos x - \sin x}{1 + \sin x \cos x}dx$$

$$\Rightarrow 2I = 0 \Rightarrow I = 0$$

(ii) We have, $g(x) = \log(1 + \tan x)$

$$\therefore \quad g\left(\frac{\pi}{4} - x\right) = \log\left[1 + \tan\left(\frac{\pi}{4} - x\right)\right]$$

$$= \log\left[1 + \frac{\tan\frac{\pi}{4} - \tan x}{1 + \tan\frac{\pi}{4}\tan x}\right]$$

$$= \log\left[1 + \frac{1 - \tan x}{1 + \tan x}\right]$$

$$= \log\left[\frac{2}{1 + \tan x}\right]$$

$$= \log 2 - \log(1 + \tan x)$$

$$= \log 2 - g(x)$$

$$\therefore \int_0^{\pi/4} g\left(\frac{\pi}{4} - x\right)dx$$

$$= \int_0^{\pi/4} \log 2\, dx - \int_0^{\pi/4} g(x)dx$$

$$\Rightarrow \int_0^{\pi/4} g(x)dx = \log 2\left(\frac{\pi}{4} - 0\right) - \int_0^{\pi/4} g(x)\,dx$$

$$\Rightarrow 2\int_0^{\pi/4} g(x)dx = \frac{\pi}{4}\log 2$$

$$\Rightarrow \int_0^{\pi/4} g(x)dx = \frac{\pi}{8}\log 2$$

SAMPLE QUESTION PAPER 6

MATHEMATICS

Time : 3 hrs   Max. Marks : 80

General Instructions

1. This question paper contains - five sections A, B, C, D and E. Each section is compulsory. However, there are internal choices in some questions.
2. Section A has 18 MCQ's and 02 Assertion-Reason based questions of 1 mark each.
3. Section B has 5 Very Short Answer (VSA) type questions of 2 marks each.
4. Section C has 6 Short Answer (SA) type questions of 3 marks each.
5. Section D has 4 Long Answer (LA) type questions of 5 marks each.
6. Section E has 3 source based/case based/passage based/integrated units of assessment (4 marks each) with sub parts.

Section A

(Multiple Choice Questions) Each question carries 1 mark

1. $\int_0^{2\pi} |\sin x|\, dx$ is equal to

   (a) 1   (b) 2   (c) 3   (d) 4

2. If $\begin{bmatrix} x+y & 7 \\ 9 & x-y \end{bmatrix} = \begin{bmatrix} 2 & 7 \\ 9 & 4 \end{bmatrix}$, then xy is equal to

   (a) 1   (b) 2   (c) –3   (d) –5

3. If $y = Ae^{5x} + Be^{-5x}$, then $\dfrac{d^2 y}{dx^2}$ is equal to

   (a) 25y   (b) 5y   (c) –25y   (d) 15y

4. $\int_0^{\pi} \dfrac{x\, dx}{1+\sin x}$ is equal to

   (a) π (b) 2π (c) 3π (d) $\pi/2$

5. $\int_{-\pi/4}^{\pi/4} \dfrac{dx}{1+\cos 2x}$ is equal to

(a) 1   (b) 2   (c) 3   (d) 0

6. Direction cosines of the vector $-2\hat{i}+\hat{j}-5\hat{k}$ are

(a) $\dfrac{2}{\sqrt{30}},\dfrac{1}{\sqrt{30}},\dfrac{5}{\sqrt{30}}$ (b) $\dfrac{-2}{\sqrt{30}},\dfrac{1}{\sqrt{30}},\dfrac{-5}{\sqrt{30}}$

(c) $\dfrac{-3}{\sqrt{30}},\dfrac{1}{\sqrt{30}},\dfrac{-5}{\sqrt{30}}$ (d) $\dfrac{-2}{\sqrt{30}},\dfrac{1}{\sqrt{30}},\dfrac{5}{\sqrt{30}}$

7. $\int_{0}^{\pi} \sin^{50} x \cos^{49} x \, dx$ is equal to

(a) 0   (b) 1   (c) 2   (d) 3

8. If $(\hat{i}+3\hat{j}+9\hat{k})\times(3\hat{i}-\lambda\hat{j}+\mu\hat{k})=0$, then $\lambda+\mu$ is equal to

(a) 10   (b) 18   (c) 0   (d) 1

9. Write the number of vectors of unit length perpendicular to both the vectors $\vec{a}=2\hat{i}+\hat{j}+2\hat{k}$ and $\vec{b}=\hat{j}+\hat{k}$.

(a) 1   (b) 2   (c) 3   (d) 4

10. A bag contains 5 red and 3 blue balls. If 3 balls are drawn at random without replacement, then the probability of getting exactly one red ball is

(a) $\dfrac{15}{36}$ (b) $\dfrac{15}{46}$ (c) $\dfrac{15}{56}$ (d) $\dfrac{1}{2}$

11. $(\hat{k}\times\hat{j})\cdot\hat{i}+\hat{j}\cdot\hat{k}$ is equal to

(a) −1   (b) 1   (c) 0   (d) −2

12. The cartesian equation of the line $\vec{r}=(2\hat{i}+\hat{j})+\lambda(\hat{i}-\hat{j}+4\hat{k})$ is

(a) $\dfrac{x-2}{1}=\dfrac{y-1}{1}=\dfrac{z}{4}$ (b) $\dfrac{x-2}{1}=\dfrac{y-1}{-1}=\dfrac{z}{4}$

(c) $\dfrac{x+2}{1}=\dfrac{y+1}{1}=\dfrac{z}{2}$ (d) $\dfrac{x-2}{1}=\dfrac{y+1}{-1}=\dfrac{z}{4}$

13. If A and B are two independent events, then $P(A\cap\bar{B})$ is equal to

(a) $P(A)-P(A)P(B)$ (b) $P(\bar{A})-P(A)P(B)$

(c) $P(A)-P(\bar{A})P(B)$ (d) $P(A)-P(A)P(\bar{B})$

14. If $P(A)=\dfrac{1}{2}$ and $P(B)=0$, then $P\left(\dfrac{A}{B}\right)$ is equal to

(a) 1   (b) 0

(c) not defined   (d) 0.5

15. Let A and B be the events associated with the sample space S, then the value of $P(A/B)$ lies in the interval

(a) (0, 1)   (b) [0, 1]   (c) (0, 1]   (d) [0, 1)

16. If $A=[2\ -3\ 4]$, $B=\begin{bmatrix}3\\2\\2\end{bmatrix}$, $X=[1\ 2\ 3]$ and $Y=\begin{bmatrix}2\\3\\4\end{bmatrix}$, then $AB+XY$ is equal to

(a) [28]   (b) [24]   (c) 28   (d) 24

17. $\int_{-\pi/2}^{\pi/2} \dfrac{1}{1+e^{\sin x}} dx$ is equal to

(a) $\dfrac{\pi}{2}$ (b) π (c) $\dfrac{2\pi}{3}$ (d) $\dfrac{3\pi}{4}$

18. A unit vector in the direction of vector $\vec{a}=2\hat{i}+\hat{j}+2\hat{k}$ is

(a) $\dfrac{2}{3}\hat{i}+\dfrac{1}{3}\hat{j}+\dfrac{2}{3}\hat{k}$ (b) $\dfrac{2}{5}\hat{i}+\dfrac{1}{5}\hat{j}+\dfrac{2}{5}\hat{k}$

(c) $\dfrac{2}{7}\hat{i}+\dfrac{1}{7}\hat{j}+\dfrac{2}{7}\hat{k}$ (d) $\hat{i}+\hat{j}+\hat{k}$

Assertion-Reason Based Questions

In the following questions, a statement of Assertion (A) is followed by a statement of Reason (R). Choose the correct answer out of the following choices.

(a) Both A and R are true and R is the correct explanation of A

(b) Both A and R are true but R is not the correct explanation of A

(c) A is true but R is false

(d) A is false but R is true

19. **Assertion (A)** Scalar matrix $A=[a_{ij}]=\begin{cases}k; & i=j\\0; & i\neq j\end{cases}$, where k is a scalar, is an identity matrix when $k=1$.

Reason (R) Every identity matrix is not a scalar matrix.

20. **Assertion (A)** If A is a 3×3 non-singular matrix, then $|A^{-1}\text{adj}\,A|=|A|$.

Reason (R) If A and B both are invertible matrices such that B is inverse of A, then $AB=BA=I$.

Section B

(This section comprises of very short answer type questions (VSA) of 2 marks each)

21. If $AB = BA$ for any two square matrices, then prove by mathematical induction that $(AB)^n = A^n B^n$.

Or

If (a, b), (a', b') and $(a - a', b - b')$ are collinear, then prove that $ab' = a'b$.

22. The x-coordinate of a point on the line joining the points $P(2, 2, 1)$ and $Q(5, 1, -2)$ is 4. Find its z-coordinate.

23. Show that the points $(a + 5, a - 4)$, $(a - 2, a + 3)$ and (a, a) do not lie on a straight line for any value of a.

Or

If $A = \begin{bmatrix} 4 & 2 \\ -1 & 1 \end{bmatrix}$, show that

$(A - 2I)(A - 3I) = O$.

24. Find the general solution of the differential equation $\dfrac{dy}{dx} = e^{x+y}$.

25. Find the position vector of a point R which divides the line joining the points $P(\hat{i} + 2\hat{j} - \hat{k})$ and $Q(-\hat{i} + \hat{j} + \hat{k})$ in the ratio $2 : 1$

(i) internally.　　　(ii) externally.

Section C

(This section comprises of short answer type questions (SA) of 3 marks each)

26. Let T be the set of all triangles in a plane. Let us define a relation

$R = \{(T_1, T_2) : T_1 \text{ is similar to } T_2; T_1, T_2 \in T\}$.

Show that R is an equivalence relation.

27. Find the value of a, for which the function

$f(x) = \begin{cases} \dfrac{\sqrt{1 + ax} - \sqrt{1 - ax}}{x}, & \text{if } -1 \leq x < 0 \\ \dfrac{2x + 1}{x - 1}, & \text{if } 0 \leq x < 1 \end{cases}$ is

continuous at $x = 0$.

Or

If $x = a(2t - \sin t)$ and $y = a(1 - \cos t)$, then find $\dfrac{dy}{dx}$ when $\theta = \dfrac{\pi}{6}$.

28. Find $\displaystyle\int \dfrac{x^2 + x + 1}{(x + 1)^2 (x + 2)} dx$.

Or Evaluate $\displaystyle\int \dfrac{\sin(x - \alpha)}{\sin(x + \alpha)} dx$.

29. If the sum of two unit vectors $\hat{a}$ and $\hat{b}$ is a unit vector, show that the magnitude of their difference is $\sqrt{3}$.

Or

If $|\vec{a}| = 10$, $|\vec{b}| = 2$ and $\vec{a} \cdot \vec{b} = 12$, then find the value of $|\vec{a} \times \vec{b}|$.

30. Find the value of

$\tan^{-1}\left(-\dfrac{1}{\sqrt{3}}\right) + \cot^{-1}\left(\dfrac{1}{\sqrt{3}}\right) + \tan^{-1}\left[\sin\left(\dfrac{-\pi}{2}\right)\right]$.

31. Using integration, find the area of the region bounded by the curves $y = |x + 1| + 1$, $x = -3$, $x = 3$ and $y = 0$.

Section D

(This section comprises of long answer type questions (LA) of 5 marks each)

32. If $y = (\log x)^x + x^{\log x}$, find $\dfrac{dy}{dx}$.

33. Evaluate $\displaystyle\int_0^{\pi/4} \dfrac{\sin x + \cos x}{9 + 16 \sin 2x} dx$.

Or

Evaluate $\displaystyle\int_0^{\pi} \dfrac{x}{a^2 \cos^2 x + b^2 \sin^2 x} dx$.

34. Determine graphically the minimum value of the objective function $Z = -50x + 20y$, subject to constraints

are $2x - y \geq -5, 3x + y \geq 3, 2x - 3y \leq 12$ and $x \geq 0, y \geq 0$.

Or

Find graphically, the maximum value of $Z = 2x + 5y$, subject to constraints given below

$2x + 4y \leq 8, 3x + y \leq 6,$
$x + y \leq 4, x \geq 0, y \geq 0.$

35. Solve the following differential equation

$$(x^3 + x^2 + x + 1)\dfrac{dy}{dx} = 2x^2 + x$$

Section E

(This section comprises of 3 case-study/ passage-based questions of 4 marks each with two sub-parts. First two case study questions have three sub-parts (i), (ii), (iii) of marks 1, 1, 2 respectively. The third case study question has two sub-parts of 2 marks each)

36. In a classroom, a teacher teaches a topic Relation on a set, which is defined below.

A relation R on a set A is said to be an equivalence relation on A iff it is

I. **reflexive** i.e. aRa or $(a, a) \in R, \forall\, a \in A$.

II. **symmetric** i.e. $aRb \Rightarrow bRa$
or $(a, b) \in R \Rightarrow (b, a) \in R$, where $a, b \in A$.

III. **transitive** i.e. if aRb and bRc, then aRc
or $(a, b) \in R$ and $(b, c) \in R$
$\Rightarrow (a, c) \in R$, where $a, b, c \in A$.

Based on the above information, answer the following questions.

(i) If the relation $R = \{(1, 1), (1, 2), (1, 3), (2, 2), (2, 3), (3, 1), (3, 2), (3, 3)\}$ defined on the set $A = \{1, 2, 3\}$, then show that R is reflexive but neither symmetric nor transitive.

(ii) If the relation $R = \{(1, 2), (2, 1), (1, 3), (3, 1)\}$ defined on the set $A = \{1, 2, 3\}$, then show that R is symmetric but neither reflexive nor transitive.

(iii) If the relation R on the set N of all natural numbers defined as $R = \{(x, y): y = x + 5 \text{ and } x < 4\}$, then show that R is neither reflexive, nor symmetric nor transitive.

Or

The relation R in the set Z of integers given by $R = \{(a, b): 2 \text{ divides } (a - b)\}$, show that R is an equivalence relation.

37. If a real valued function $f(x)$ is finitely derivable at any point of its domain, it is necessarily continuous at that point. But its converse need not be true.

e.g. Every polynomial, constant functions are both continuous as well as differentiable and inverse trigonometric functions are continuous and differentiable in their domain etc.

Based on the above information, answer the following questions,

(i) Write the interval in which the function $f(x) = \cos^{-1} x$ is always continuous.

(ii) Show that the function
$$f(x) = \begin{cases} 3x, & \text{for } x \leq 0 \\ 0, & \text{for } x > 0 \end{cases} \text{ is continuous at}$$
$x = 0$.

(iii) Show that the function $f(x) = |x - 2|$, $x \in R$, is continuous at $x = 2$.

Or Show that the function $f(x) = |\cos 2x|$ is continuous at $x = \dfrac{\pi}{4}$.

38. In a school, teacher asks a question to three students Ravi, Mohit and Sonia. The probability of solving the question by Ravi, Mohit and Sonia are 30%, 25% and 45%, respectively. The probability of making error by Ravi, Mohit and Sonia are 1%, 1.2% and 2%, respectively.

Based on the above information, answer the following questions.

(i) Find the total probability of committing an error in solving the question.

(ii) If the solution of question is checked by teacher and has some error, then find the probability that the question is not solved by Ravi.

SOLUTIONS

1. (d) Let $I = \int_0^{2\pi} |\sin x|\, dx$

$\Rightarrow \quad I = \int_0^{\pi} \sin x\, dx - \int_{\pi}^{2\pi} \sin x\, dx$

$\Rightarrow \quad I = [-\cos x]_0^{\pi} + [\cos x]_{\pi}^{2\pi}$

$\Rightarrow \quad I = -[\cos \pi - \cos 0] + [\cos 2\pi - \cos \pi]$

$\Rightarrow \quad I = -[-1-1] + [1+1] \Rightarrow I = 2+2 = 4$

2. (c) We have, $\begin{bmatrix} x+y & 7 \\ 9 & x-y \end{bmatrix} = \begin{bmatrix} 2 & 7 \\ 9 & 4 \end{bmatrix}$

$\Rightarrow \quad x+y = 2$ and $x-y = 4$

Since, $(x+y)^2 - (x-y)^2 = 4xy$

$\therefore \qquad 2^2 - 4^2 = 4xy$

$\Rightarrow \qquad 4xy = 4-16 = -12 \Rightarrow xy = -3$

3. (a) We have, $y = Ae^{5x} + Be^{-5x}$

$\Rightarrow \qquad \dfrac{dy}{dx} = Ae^{5x} \cdot (5) + Be^{-5x}(-5)$

$\qquad = 5Ae^{5x} - 5Be^{-5x}$

$\Rightarrow \qquad \dfrac{d^2y}{dx^2} = 5Ae^{5x}(5) - 5Be^{-5x}(-5)$

$\qquad = 25Ae^{5x} + 25Be^{-5x}$

$\therefore \qquad \dfrac{d^2y}{dx^2} = 25(Ae^{5x} + Be^{-5x}) = 25y$

4. (a) Let $I = \int_0^{\pi} \dfrac{x}{1+\sin x}\, dx$ ...(i)

$\Rightarrow \quad I = \int_0^{\pi} \dfrac{(\pi - x)}{1+\sin(\pi - x)}\, dx \Rightarrow I = \int_0^{\pi} \dfrac{(\pi - x)}{1+\sin x}\, dx$ ...(ii)

On adding Eqs. (i) and (ii), we get

$2I = \int_0^{\pi} \dfrac{x + \pi - x}{1+\sin x}\, dx$

$\Rightarrow 2I = \pi \int_0^{\pi} \dfrac{dx}{1+\sin x}$

$\Rightarrow 2I = \pi \int_0^{\pi} \dfrac{1-\sin x}{1-\sin^2 x}\, dx$

$\Rightarrow 2I = \pi \int_0^{\pi} \dfrac{1-\sin x}{\cos^2 x}\, dx$

$\Rightarrow 2I = \pi \int_0^{\pi} (\sec^2 x - \sec x \tan x)\, dx$

$\Rightarrow 2I = \pi[\tan x - \sec x]_0^{\pi}$

$\Rightarrow 2I = \pi[(\tan \pi - \sec \pi) - (\tan 0 - \sec 0)]$

$\Rightarrow 2I = \pi[(0+1) - (0-1)]$

$\Rightarrow 2I = 2\pi$

$\therefore \quad I = \pi$

5. (a) Let $I = \int_{-\pi/4}^{\pi/4} \dfrac{dx}{1+\cos 2x}\, dx$

$\qquad = \int_{-\pi/4}^{\pi/4} \dfrac{dx}{2\cos^2 x}$

$\Rightarrow \quad I = \dfrac{1}{2} \int_{-\pi/4}^{\pi/4} \sec^2 x\, dx$

$\Rightarrow \quad I = \int_0^{\pi/4} \sec^2 x\, dx$

$\qquad\qquad [\because \sec^2 x \text{ is an even function}]$

$\Rightarrow \quad I = [\tan x]_0^{\pi/4} = \tan \dfrac{\pi}{4} - \tan 0 = 1$

6. (b) Let $\vec{a} = -2\hat{i} + \hat{j} - 5\hat{k}$

∴ Direction cosines of $\vec{a}$ are

$$\frac{-2}{\sqrt{(-2)^2 + (1)^2 + (-5)^2}},$$

$$\frac{1}{\sqrt{(-2)^2 + (1)^2 + (-5)^2}}$$

and

$$\frac{-5}{\sqrt{(-2)^2 + (1)^2 + (-5)^2}}$$

i.e. $\dfrac{-2}{\sqrt{30}}, \dfrac{1}{\sqrt{30}}, \dfrac{-5}{\sqrt{30}}$

7. (a) Let $I = \int_0^{\pi} \sin^{50} x \cos^{49} x\, dx$ ...(i)

$\Rightarrow \quad I = \int_0^{\pi} \sin^{50}(\pi - x)\cos^{49}(\pi - x)\, dx$

$\Rightarrow \quad I = -\int_0^{\pi} \sin^{50} x \cos^{49} x\, dx$ ...(ii)

On adding Eqs. (i) and (ii), we get

$$2I = \int_0^{\pi} 0\, dx$$

∴ $\qquad I = 0$

8. (b) Given, $(\hat{i} + 3\hat{j} + 9\hat{k}) \times (3\hat{i} - \lambda\hat{j} + \mu\hat{k}) = \vec{0}$

∴ $\quad \begin{vmatrix} \hat{i} & \hat{j} & \hat{k} \\ 1 & 3 & 9 \\ 3 & -\lambda & \mu \end{vmatrix} = \vec{0}$

$\Rightarrow \hat{i}\,(3\mu + 9\lambda) - \hat{j}\,(\mu - 27) + \hat{k}\,(-\lambda - 9)$
$\qquad\qquad\qquad = 0\hat{i} + 0\hat{j} + 0\hat{k}$

On comparing the coefficients of $\hat{i}, \hat{j}$ and $\hat{k}$, we get

$3\mu + 9\lambda = 0, -\mu + 27 = 0$ and $-\lambda - 9 = 0$
$\Rightarrow \qquad \mu = 27$ and $\lambda = -9$

Also, the values of μ and λ satisfy the equation $3\mu + 9\lambda = 0$.

∴ $\qquad \lambda + \mu = -9 + 27 = 18$

9. (b) We know that unit vectors perpendicular to $\vec{a}$ and $\vec{b}$

are $\pm \left(\dfrac{\vec{a} \times \vec{b}}{|\vec{a} \times \vec{b}|} \right)$.

So, there are two unit vectors perpendicular to the given vectors. (1)

10. (c) We have, 5 red and 3 blue balls.
Probability of getting exactly one red ball, when 3 balls are drawn is

$$\frac{{}^5C_1 \times {}^3C_2}{{}^8C_3} = \frac{5 \times 3}{56} = \frac{15}{56}$$

11. (a) Given, $(\hat{k} \times \hat{j}) \cdot \hat{i} + \hat{j} \cdot \hat{k}$
$= (-\hat{i}) \cdot \hat{i} + \hat{j} \cdot \hat{k}$
$= -(\hat{i} \cdot \hat{i}) + 0$
$= -1 + 0 = -1$

12. (b) Given, vector equation of line is
$$\vec{r} = (2\hat{i} + \hat{j}) + \lambda(\hat{i} - \hat{j} + 4\hat{k})$$
$\Rightarrow x\hat{i} + y\hat{j} + z\hat{k} = \hat{i}(2 + \lambda) + \hat{j}(1 - \lambda) + 4\lambda\,\hat{k}$
On equating coefficients of $\hat{i}, \hat{j}$ and $\hat{k}$ from both sides, we get

$x = 2 + \lambda, \; y = 1 - \lambda$ and $z = 4\lambda$

$\Rightarrow \quad \dfrac{x-2}{1} = \lambda, \dfrac{y-1}{-1} = \lambda$ and $\dfrac{z}{4} = \lambda$

∴ $\quad \dfrac{x-2}{1} = \dfrac{y-1}{-1} = \dfrac{z}{4}$

which is the required cartesian equation of line.

13. (a) We have, $P(A \cap \bar{B}) = P(A) \cdot P(\bar{B})$

[∵ A and B are independent events]

$\Rightarrow \quad P(A \cap \bar{B}) = P(A) \cdot [1 - P(B)] = P(A) - P(A) \cdot P(B)$

14. (c) It is given that

$$P(A) = \frac{1}{2} \text{ and } P(B) = 0$$

$$P\left(\frac{A}{B}\right) = \frac{P(A \cap B)}{P(B)}$$

Since, $P(B) = 0$

∴ $P\left(\dfrac{A}{B}\right)$ is not defined.

15. (b) $0 \le P(A/B) \le 1$

16. (a) Given, $A = [2 \quad -3 \quad 4], B = \begin{bmatrix} 3 \\ 2 \\ 2 \end{bmatrix},$

$$X = [1 \quad 2 \quad 3] \text{ and } Y = \begin{bmatrix} 2 \\ 3 \\ 4 \end{bmatrix}.$$

Now, $AB = [2 \quad -3 \quad 4] \begin{bmatrix} 3 \\ 2 \\ 2 \end{bmatrix} = [6 - 6 + 8] = [8]$

and $XY = [1 \quad 2 \quad 3] \begin{bmatrix} 2 \\ 3 \\ 4 \end{bmatrix} = [2 + 6 + 12] = [20]$

∴ $\quad AB + XY = [8] + [20] = [28]$

17. (a) Let $I = \int_{-\pi/2}^{\pi/2} \dfrac{1}{1 + e^{\sin x}} dx$ ...(i)

$\Rightarrow \quad I = \int_{-\pi/2}^{\pi/2} \dfrac{1}{1 + e^{\sin\left(\frac{\pi}{2} - \frac{\pi}{2} - x\right)}} dx$

$= \int_{-\pi/2}^{\pi/2} \dfrac{1}{1 + e^{-\sin x}} dx$

$\Rightarrow \quad I = \int_{-\pi/2}^{\pi/2} \dfrac{1}{1 + \dfrac{1}{e^{\sin x}}} dx$

$= \int_{-\pi/2}^{\pi/2} \dfrac{e^{\sin x}}{1 + e^{\sin x}} dx$ ...(ii)

On adding Eqs. (i) and (ii), we get

$$2I = \int_{-\pi/2}^{\pi/2}\left(\frac{1}{1+e^{\sin x}}+\frac{e^{\sin x}}{1+e^{\sin x}}\right)dx = \int_{-\pi/2}^{\pi/2}\frac{1+e^{\sin x}}{1+e^{\sin x}}dx$$

$$\Rightarrow 2I = \int_{-\pi/2}^{\pi/2}dx = [x]_{-\pi/2}^{\pi/2} = \frac{\pi}{2}+\frac{\pi}{2}=\pi$$

$$\therefore \quad I = \frac{\pi}{2}$$

18. (a) We know that unit vector in the direction of $\vec{a}$ is

$$\hat{a}=\frac{\vec{a}}{|\vec{a}|}.$$

∴ Required unit vector in the direction of vector

$$\vec{a}=2\hat{i}+\hat{j}+2\hat{k}\text{ is}$$

$$\hat{a}=\frac{\vec{a}}{|\vec{a}|}=\frac{2\hat{i}+\hat{j}+2\hat{k}}{\sqrt{(2)^2+(1)^2+(2)^2}}$$

$$=\frac{2\hat{i}+\hat{j}+2\hat{k}}{\sqrt{9}}=\frac{2}{3}\hat{i}+\frac{1}{3}\hat{j}+\frac{2}{3}\hat{k}$$

19. (c) A scalar matrix $A=[a_{ij}]=\begin{cases}k; & i=j \\ 0; & i\ne j\end{cases}$ is an identity matrix when $k=1$.

But every identity matrix is clearly a scalar matrix as identity matrix is a diagonal matrix in which all the diagonal elements are equal.

Hence, Assertion is true but Reason is false.

20. (b) **Assertion** $|A^{-1}\text{ adj }A|=|A^{-1}|\cdot|\text{adj }A|$

$$[\because |AB|=|A|\cdot|B|]$$

$$=|A|^{-1}|\text{adj }A| \qquad [\because |A^{-1}|=|A|^{-1}]$$

$$=|A|^{-1}\cdot|A|^2$$

$$[\because A\text{ is a }3\times3\text{ non-singular matrix, so }|\text{adj }A|=|A|^2]$$

$$=|A|$$

Reason It is a true statement.

Hence, both Assertion and Reason are true but Reason is not correct explanation of Assertion.

21. Let $P(n):(AB)^n=A^nB^n$

$$\therefore \quad P(1):(AB)^1=A^1B^1 \Rightarrow AB=AB$$

So, $P(1)$ is true.

Now, $P(k):(AB)^k=A^kB^k, k\in N$ (1/2)

So, $P(k)$ is true, whenever $P(k+1)$ is true.

$$\therefore \quad P(AB)^{k+1}=A^{k+1}B^{k+1}$$

$$\Rightarrow \quad A^kB^k\cdot BA=A^kB^{k+1}A \Rightarrow A^k\cdot A\cdot B^{k+1}=A^{k+1}B^{k+1}$$

$$\Rightarrow \quad (A\cdot B)^{k+1}=A^{k+1}B^{k+1} \qquad (1)$$

So, $P(k+1)$ is true for all $n\in N$, whenever $P(k)$ is true.

By mathematical induction, $(AB)=A^nB^n$

is true for all $n\in N$.   **Hence proved.** (1/2)

Or

If given points are collinear, then

$$\begin{vmatrix} a & b & 1 \\ a' & b' & 1 \\ a-a' & b-b' & 1 \end{vmatrix}=0$$

$$\Rightarrow a[b'-(b-b')]-b[a'-(a-a')]$$

$$+1[a'(b-b')-b'(a-a')]=0$$

[expanding along R_1] (1)

$$\Rightarrow a(b'-b+b')-b(a'-a+a')$$

$$+(a'b-a'b'-ab'+a'b')=0$$

$$\Rightarrow a(2b'-b)-b(2a'-a)+(a'b-ab')=0$$

$$\Rightarrow 2ab'-ab-2a'b+ab+a'b-ab'=0$$

$$\Rightarrow \qquad\qquad ab'-a'b=0$$

$$\Rightarrow \qquad\qquad ab'=a'b \qquad\qquad \textbf{Hence proved.}(1)$$

22. The equation of line joining the points
$P(2,2,1)$ and $Q(5,1,-2)$ is

$$\frac{x-2}{5-2}=\frac{y-2}{1-2}=\frac{z-1}{-2-1}$$

$$\Rightarrow \qquad \frac{x-2}{3}=\frac{y-2}{-1}=\frac{z-1}{-3} \qquad (1)$$

Since, x-coordinate is 4.

$$\therefore \qquad \frac{4-2}{3}=\frac{z-1}{-3} \Rightarrow z-1=-2 \Rightarrow z=-1 \quad (1)$$

23. Given points are $(a+5,a-4),(a-2,a+3)$ and (a,a).

Now consider, $\Delta=\frac{1}{2}\begin{vmatrix} a+5 & a-4 & 1 \\ a-2 & a+3 & 1 \\ a & a & 1 \end{vmatrix}$

$$=\frac{1}{2}[(a+5)(a+3-a)-(a-4)(a-2-a)$$

$$+1(a(a-2)-a(a+3))]$$

$$=\frac{1}{2}[3a+15+2a-8+a^2-2a-a^2-3a]$$

$$=\frac{1}{2}[7]=\frac{7}{2}\ne0 \qquad (1)$$

which is also independent of a.

Hence, the given points form a triangle i.e. given points do not lie on a straight line for any value of a.

     Hence proved. (1)

Or

Given, $A=\begin{bmatrix} 4 & 2 \\ -1 & 1 \end{bmatrix}$

LHS $=(A-2I)(A-3I)$

$$=\left\{\begin{bmatrix} 4 & 2 \\ -1 & 1 \end{bmatrix}-\begin{bmatrix} 2 & 0 \\ 0 & 2 \end{bmatrix}\right\}\left\{\begin{bmatrix} 4 & 2 \\ -1 & 1 \end{bmatrix}-\begin{bmatrix} 3 & 0 \\ 0 & 3 \end{bmatrix}\right\}$$

$$=\begin{bmatrix} 2 & 2 \\ -1 & -1 \end{bmatrix}\begin{bmatrix} 1 & 2 \\ -1 & -2 \end{bmatrix} \qquad (1)$$

$$=\begin{bmatrix} 2-2 & 4-4 \\ -1+1 & -2+2 \end{bmatrix}=\begin{bmatrix} 0 & 0 \\ 0 & 0 \end{bmatrix}=O=\text{RHS}$$

     Hence proved. (1)

24. The given differential equation is

$$\frac{dy}{dx} = e^{x+y} \Rightarrow \frac{dy}{dx} = e^x \cdot e^y$$

$$\Rightarrow \quad dy = e^x \cdot e^y dx$$

$$\Rightarrow \quad e^{-y} dy = e^x dx \qquad (1)$$

$$\Rightarrow \quad \int e^{-y} dy = \int e^x dx$$

$$\Rightarrow \quad -e^{-y} = e^x + C$$

which is the required solution. (1)

25. Given, $\overrightarrow{OP} = \hat{i} + 2\hat{j} - \hat{k}$ and $\overrightarrow{OQ} = -\hat{i} + \hat{j} + \hat{k}$

(i) Let R divides PQ internally in the ratio 2 : 1.

Then, position vector of R

$$= \frac{2(-\hat{i} + \hat{j} + \hat{k}) + 1(\hat{i} + 2\hat{j} - \hat{k})}{2+1} = \frac{-\hat{i} + 4\hat{j} + \hat{k}}{3} \qquad (1)$$

(ii) Let R divides PQ externally in the ratio 2 : 1.

Then, position vector of R

$$= \frac{2(-\hat{i} + \hat{j} + \hat{k}) - 1(\hat{i} + 2\hat{j} - \hat{k})}{2-1} = -3\hat{i} + 3\hat{k} \qquad (1)$$

26. Given relation is

$R = \{(T_1, T_2) : T_1 \text{ is similar to } T_2; T_1, T_2 \in T\}$,

where T is the set of all triangles in a plane.

We know that two triangles are said to be similar, if they have same shape.

Reflexive Let $T_1 \in T$ be any arbitrary element.

As we know that every triangle is similar to itself.

So, $\qquad (T_1, T_1) \in R$

$\therefore$ R is reflexive. (1)

Symmetric Let $T_1, T_2 \in T$ such that $(T_1, T_2) \in R$

$\Rightarrow T_1$ is similar to T_2.

$\Rightarrow T_2$ is similar to T_1.

$\qquad$ [$\because$ two triangles are similar to each other]

$\Rightarrow (T_2, T_1) \in R$

$\therefore$ R is symmetric. (1)

Transitive Let $T_1, T_2, T_3 \in T$ such that

$\qquad (T_1, T_2) \in R$ and $(T_2, T_3) \in R$

$\Rightarrow T_1$ is similar to T_2 and T_2 is similar to T_3.

$\Rightarrow T_1$ is similar to $T_3 \Rightarrow (T_1, T_3) \in R$

$\therefore$ R is transitive.

Thus, relation R is reflexive, symmetric and transitive.

So, R is an equivalence relation. **Hence proved.** (1)

27. Given, $f(x) = \begin{cases} \dfrac{\sqrt{1+ax} - \sqrt{1-ax}}{x}, & \text{if } -1 \le x < 0 \\ \dfrac{2x+1}{x-1}, & \text{if } 0 \le x < 1 \end{cases}$

$\text{LHL} = \lim_{x \to 0^-} f(x) = \lim_{h \to 0} f(0-h) = \lim_{h \to 0} f(-h)$

$$= \lim_{h \to 0} \frac{\sqrt{1+a(-h)} - \sqrt{1-a(-h)}}{-h}$$

$$= \lim_{h \to 0} \frac{\sqrt{1-ah} - \sqrt{1+ah}}{-h} \times \frac{\sqrt{1-ah} + \sqrt{1+ah}}{\sqrt{1-ah} + \sqrt{1+ah}}$$

$$= \lim_{h \to 0} \frac{1-ah - (1+ah)}{-h(\sqrt{1-ah} + \sqrt{1+ah})}$$

$$= \lim_{h \to 0} \frac{-2ah}{-h(\sqrt{1-ah} + \sqrt{1+ah})}$$

$$= \lim_{h \to 0} \frac{2a}{\sqrt{1-ah} + \sqrt{1+ah}} = \frac{2a}{1+1} = a \qquad \dots(i) (1)$$

$\text{RHL} = \lim_{x=0} f(x) = \lim_{x \to 0^+} f(0+h) = \lim_{h \to 0} f(h)$

$$= \lim_{h \to 0} \frac{2h+1}{h-1} = \frac{0+1}{0-1} = -1 \qquad \dots(ii) (1)$$

Now, $f(0) = \frac{2(0)+1}{0-1} = -1 \qquad \dots(iii)$

$\because$ $f(x)$ is continuous at $x = 0$.

$\therefore \underset{x=0}{\text{LHL}} = \underset{x=0}{\text{RHL}} = f(0)$

From Eqs. (i), (ii) and (iii), we get

$$a = -1 \qquad (1)$$

$$Or$$

Consider, $x = a(2t - \sin t)$

On differentiating w.r.t. t, we get

$$\frac{dx}{dt} = a(2 - \cos t) \qquad \dots(i)$$

Consider, $y = a(1 - \cos t)$

On differentiating w.r.t. t, we get

$$\frac{dy}{dt} = a \sin t \qquad \dots(ii) (1)$$

Dividing Eq. (ii) by Eq. (i), we get

$$\frac{dy/dt}{dx/dt} = \frac{a \sin t}{a(2 - \cos t)} = \frac{\sin t}{2 - \cos t} \Rightarrow \frac{dy}{dx} = \frac{\sin t}{2 - \cos t} \quad (1)$$

$$\therefore \left. \frac{dy}{dx} \right|_{t=\frac{\pi}{6}} = \frac{\sin \frac{\pi}{6}}{2 - \cos \frac{\pi}{6}} = \frac{\frac{1}{2}}{2 - \frac{\sqrt{3}}{2}} = \frac{\frac{1}{2}}{\frac{4-\sqrt{3}}{2}}$$

$$= \frac{1}{4-\sqrt{3}} \times \frac{4+\sqrt{3}}{4+\sqrt{3}} = \frac{4+\sqrt{3}}{16-3} = \frac{4+\sqrt{3}}{13} \qquad (1)$$

28. We have, $\int \dfrac{x^2 + x + 1}{(x+1)^2 (x+2)} dx$

The integrand $\dfrac{x^2 + x + 1}{(x+1)^2 (x+2)}$ is a proper rational function.

Now, by using partial fraction,

Let $\dfrac{x^2 + x + 1}{(x+1)^2 (x+2)} = \dfrac{A}{(x+1)} + \dfrac{B}{(x+1)^2} + \dfrac{C}{(x+2)} \qquad \dots(i)$ (1)

$\Rightarrow \quad x^2 + x + 1 = A(x+1)(x+2) + B(x+2) + C(x+1)^2$

$\Rightarrow \qquad x^2 + x + 1 = A(x^2 + 3x + 2) + B(x + 2)$
$$+ C(x^2 + 2x + 1)$$
$\Rightarrow \qquad x^2 + x + 1 = (A + C)x^2 + (3A + B + 2C)x$
$$+ (2A + 2B + C)$$

On comparing the coefficients of like powers from both sides, we get

$$A + C = 1,$$
$$3A + B + 2C = 1$$

and $\qquad\qquad 2A + 2B + C = 1$

On solving these equations, we get $\qquad$ (1)
$$A = -2, B = 1 \text{ and } C = 3$$

From Eq. (i), we get

$$\frac{x^2 + x + 1}{(x + 1)^2 (x + 2)} = \frac{-2}{(x + 1)} + \frac{1}{(x + 1)^2} + \frac{3}{(x + 2)}$$

$$\therefore \int \frac{x^2 + x + 1}{(x + 1)^2 (x + 2)} dx = -2 \int \frac{1}{x + 1} dx$$
$$+ \int \frac{dx}{(x + 1)^2} + 3 \int \frac{dx}{(x + 2)}$$
$$= -2\log|x + 1| - \frac{1}{x + 1} + 3\log|x + 2| + C \qquad (1)$$

Or

Let $\qquad I = \int \frac{\sin(x - \alpha)}{\sin(x + \alpha)} dx$

Put $x + \alpha = t \Rightarrow x = t - \alpha \Rightarrow dx = dt \qquad (1)$
Then, given integral reduces to

$$I = \int \frac{\sin(t - 2\alpha)}{\sin t} dt$$

$\Rightarrow \quad I = \int \frac{\sin t \cos 2\alpha - \cos t \sin 2\alpha}{\sin t} dt$

$\qquad [\because \sin(x - y) = \sin x \cos y - \cos x \sin y] \quad (1)$

$\Rightarrow \quad I = \int \left(\frac{\sin t \cos 2\alpha}{\sin t} - \frac{\cos t \sin 2\alpha}{\sin t} \right) dt$

$\Rightarrow \quad I = \int \cos 2\alpha \, dt - \int \cot t \sin 2\alpha \, dt$

$$\left[\because \frac{\cos x}{\sin x} = \cot x \right]$$

$\Rightarrow \quad I = \cos 2\alpha \int dt - \sin 2\alpha \int \cot t \, dt$

$\Rightarrow \quad I = t \cos 2\alpha - \sin 2\alpha \cdot \log|\sin t| + C$

$$[\because \int \cot x \, dx = \log|\sin x|]$$

$\therefore \quad I = (x + \alpha)\cos 2\alpha - \sin 2\alpha \cdot \log|\sin(x + \alpha)| + C$

$$[\text{putting } t = x + \alpha] \quad (1)$$

29. Let $\vec{c} = \hat{a} + \hat{b}$. Then, according to given condition $\vec{c}$ is

a unit vector i.e. $|\vec{c}| = 1 \qquad\qquad$ ...(i)
To show $|\hat{a} - \hat{b}| = \sqrt{3} \qquad\qquad (1)$

Consider, $\qquad\qquad \vec{c} = \hat{a} + \hat{b}$

$\Rightarrow \qquad\qquad |\vec{c}| = |\hat{a} + \hat{b}|$

$\Rightarrow \qquad\qquad 1 = |\hat{a} + \hat{b}| \qquad$ [from Eq. (i)]

$\Rightarrow \qquad\qquad |\hat{a} + \hat{b}|^2 = 1$

$\Rightarrow \qquad (\hat{a} + \hat{b}) \cdot (\hat{a} + \hat{b}) = 1$

$\Rightarrow |\hat{a}|^2 + 2\hat{a} \cdot \hat{b} + |\hat{b}|^2 = 1$

$\Rightarrow \quad 1 + 2\hat{a} \cdot \hat{b} + 1 = 1 \Rightarrow 2\hat{a} \cdot \hat{b} = -1 \qquad$ ...(ii) (1)

Now consider, $|\hat{a} - \hat{b}|^2 = (\hat{a} - \hat{b}) \cdot (\hat{a} - \hat{b})$

$$= |\hat{a}|^2 - 2\hat{a} \cdot \hat{b} + |\hat{b}|^2$$
$$= 1 - (-1) + 1 \quad [\text{using Eq. (ii)}]$$
$$= 3$$

$\Rightarrow \qquad\qquad |\hat{a} - \hat{b}| = \sqrt{3}$

[taking positive square root, as magnitude cannot be negative]

Hence proved. (1)

Or

We have, $|\vec{a}| = 10, |\vec{b}| = 2$ and $\vec{a} \cdot \vec{b} = 12$

We know that $|\vec{a} \times \vec{b}| = |\vec{a}||\vec{b}|\sin\theta \qquad$ ...(i)

and $\qquad\qquad \vec{a} \cdot \vec{b} = |\vec{a}||\vec{b}|\cos\theta \qquad$ ...(ii)(1)

On squaring and adding Eqs. (i) and (ii), we get

$|\vec{a} \times \vec{b}|^2 + (\vec{a} \cdot \vec{b})^2 = |\vec{a}|^2|\vec{b}|^2\sin^2\theta + |\vec{a}|^2|\vec{b}|^2\cos^2\theta$

$\Rightarrow |\vec{a} \times \vec{b}|^2 + (\vec{a} \cdot \vec{b})^2 = |\vec{a}|^2|\vec{b}|^2(\sin^2\theta + \cos^2\theta) \qquad (1)$

$\Rightarrow |\vec{a} \times \vec{b}|^2 + (\vec{a} \cdot \vec{b})^2 = |\vec{a}|^2|\vec{b}|^2$

$\Rightarrow \quad |\vec{a} \times \vec{b}|^2 + (12)^2 = (10)^2(2)^2$

$\Rightarrow \qquad |\vec{a} \times \vec{b}| = \sqrt{400 - 144}$

$\Rightarrow \qquad |\vec{a} \times \vec{b}| = \sqrt{256} = 16 \qquad (1)$

30. Let $\tan^{-1}\left(-\frac{1}{\sqrt{3}} \right) = \theta_1$

$\Rightarrow \tan\theta_1 = -\frac{1}{\sqrt{3}} \Rightarrow \tan\theta_1 = -\tan\frac{\pi}{6} \quad \left[\because \tan\frac{\pi}{6} = \frac{1}{\sqrt{3}} \right]$

$\Rightarrow \tan\theta_1 = \tan\left(-\frac{\pi}{6} \right) \qquad [\because \tan(-\theta) = -\tan\theta]$

$\Rightarrow \quad \theta_1 = -\frac{\pi}{6} \Rightarrow \tan^{-1}\left(-\frac{1}{\sqrt{3}} \right) = -\frac{\pi}{6} \qquad (1)$

$$\left[\because -\frac{\pi}{6} \in \left(-\frac{\pi}{2}, \frac{\pi}{2} \right) \right]$$

Again, let $\cot^{-1}\left(\frac{1}{\sqrt{3}} \right) = \theta_2 \Rightarrow \cot\theta_2 = \frac{1}{\sqrt{3}}$

$\Rightarrow \qquad\qquad \cot\theta_2 = \cot\frac{\pi}{3} \qquad \left[\because \cot\frac{\pi}{3} = \frac{1}{\sqrt{3}} \right]$

$\Rightarrow \qquad \theta_2 = \dfrac{\pi}{3} \Rightarrow \cot^{-1}\dfrac{1}{\sqrt{3}} = \dfrac{\pi}{3} \qquad \left[\because \dfrac{\pi}{3} \in (0, \pi)\right]$

and let $\tan^{-1}\left[\sin\left(-\dfrac{\pi}{2}\right)\right] = \theta_3$

$\Rightarrow \qquad \tan^{-1}\left(-\sin\dfrac{\pi}{2}\right) = \theta_3 \qquad [\because \sin(-\theta) = -\sin\theta]$

$\Rightarrow \qquad \tan^{-1}(-1) = \theta_3 \qquad \left[\because \sin\dfrac{\pi}{2} = 1\right]$ (1)

$\Rightarrow \qquad \tan\theta_3 = -1$

$\Rightarrow \qquad \tan\theta_3 = -\tan\dfrac{\pi}{4} \qquad \left[\because \tan\dfrac{\pi}{4} = 1\right]$

$\Rightarrow \qquad \tan\theta_3 = \tan\left(-\dfrac{\pi}{4}\right) \qquad [\because \tan(-\theta) = -\tan\theta]$

$\Rightarrow \qquad \theta_3 = -\dfrac{\pi}{4} \qquad \left[\because -\dfrac{\pi}{4} \in \left(-\dfrac{\pi}{2}, \dfrac{\pi}{2}\right)\right]$

$\Rightarrow \qquad \tan^{-1}\left[\sin\left(-\dfrac{\pi}{2}\right)\right] = -\dfrac{\pi}{4}$

$\therefore \quad \tan^{-1}\left(-\dfrac{1}{\sqrt{3}}\right) + \cot^{-1}\left(\dfrac{1}{\sqrt{3}}\right) + \tan^{-1}\left[\sin\left(-\dfrac{\pi}{2}\right)\right]$

$= -\dfrac{\pi}{6} + \dfrac{\pi}{3} - \dfrac{\pi}{4} = \dfrac{-2\pi + 4\pi - 3\pi}{12} = -\dfrac{\pi}{12}$ (1)

31. Given curves are

$y = |x + 1| + 1 = \begin{cases} (x+1) + 1, & \text{if } x + 1 \geq 0 \\ -(x+1) + 1, & \text{if } x + 1 < 0 \end{cases} \quad \ldots(i)$

$\qquad = \begin{cases} x + 2, & \text{if } x \geq -1 \\ -x, & \text{if } x < -1 \end{cases}$

$x = -3 \qquad \qquad \ldots(ii)$

$x = 3 \qquad \qquad \ldots(iii)$

and $\qquad y = 0 \qquad \qquad \ldots(iv)$ (1)

Eq. (ii) represents the line parallel to Y-axis and passes through the point $(-3, 0)$.

Eq. (iii) represents the line parallel to Y-axis and passes through the point $(3, 0)$.

Eq. (iv) represents X-axis.

Now, Eqs. (i), (ii), (iii) and (iv) can be represented in graph as shown below:

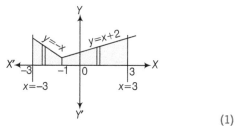

(1)

Clearly, required area

$= \int_{-3}^{-1}(-x)\,dx + \int_{-1}^{3}(x + 2)\,dx$

$= -\left[\dfrac{x^2}{2}\right]_{-3}^{-1} + \left[\dfrac{x^2}{2} + 2x\right]_{-1}^{3}$

$= -\dfrac{1}{2}(1 - 9) + \left[\left(\dfrac{9}{2} + 6\right) - \left(\dfrac{1}{2} - 2\right)\right]$

$= 4 + \dfrac{21}{2} + \dfrac{3}{2} = 16 \text{ sq units}$

Hence, the required area is 16 sq units. (1)

32. We have, $y = (\log x)^x + x^{\log x}$

Let $u = (\log x)^x$ and $v = x^{\log x}$

Then, $y = u + v \Rightarrow \dfrac{dy}{dx} = \dfrac{du}{dx} + \dfrac{dv}{dx} \qquad \ldots(i)$ (1)

Consider, $u = (\log x)^x$

On taking log both sides, we get

$\log u = \log(\log x)^x = x\log(\log x)$ (1)

On differentiating both sides w.r.t. x, we get

$\dfrac{1}{u}\dfrac{du}{dx} = x \cdot \dfrac{d}{dx}\log(\log x) + \log(\log x) \cdot \dfrac{d}{dx}(x)$

$\qquad = \dfrac{x}{\log x} \cdot \dfrac{1}{x} + \log(\log x)$

$\Rightarrow \qquad \dfrac{du}{dx} = u\left[\dfrac{1}{\log x} + \log(\log x)\right]$

$\Rightarrow \qquad \dfrac{du}{dx} = (\log x)^x\left[\dfrac{1}{\log x} + \log(\log x)\right] \qquad \ldots(ii)$

$[\because u = (\log x)^x]$ (1)

Now, $v = x^{\log x}$

On taking log both sides, we get

$\log v = \log(x^{\log x}) = (\log x)(\log x) = (\log x)^2$

On differentiating both sides w.r.t. x, we get

$\dfrac{1}{v}\dfrac{dv}{dx} = 2\log x \cdot \dfrac{1}{x} \Rightarrow \dfrac{dv}{dx} = v\left[\dfrac{2\log x}{x}\right]$

$\Rightarrow \qquad \dfrac{dv}{dx} = x^{\log x}\left[\dfrac{2\log x}{x}\right] \qquad [\because v = x^{\log x}] \ldots(iii)$

From Eqs. (i), (ii) and (iii), we get

$\dfrac{dy}{dx} = (\log x)^x\left\{\dfrac{1}{\log x} + \log(\log x)\right\} + 2\left(\dfrac{\log x}{x}\right)x^{\log x}$ (2)

33. Let $\quad I = \int_0^{\pi/4}\dfrac{\sin x + \cos x}{9 + 16\sin 2x}\,dx$

$\Rightarrow \quad I = \int_0^{\pi/4}\dfrac{\sin x + \cos x}{9 + 16(1 + \sin 2x - 1)}\,dx$

[adding and subtracting 16 in denominator]

$\Rightarrow \quad I = \int_0^{\pi/4}\dfrac{\sin x + \cos x}{9 + 16[1 - (1 - \sin 2x)]}\,dx$ (1)

$\Rightarrow \quad I = \int_0^{\pi/4}\dfrac{\sin x + \cos x}{9 + 16\left[1 - \begin{matrix}(\cos^2 x + \sin^2 x \\ -2\sin x \cos x)\end{matrix}\right]}\,dx$

$\left[\begin{matrix}\because \cos^2 x + \sin^2 x = 1 \\ \text{and } \sin 2x = 2\sin x \cos x\end{matrix}\right]$

$\Rightarrow \quad I = \int_0^{\pi/4}\dfrac{\sin x + \cos x}{9 + 16[1 - (\cos x - \sin x)^2]}\,dx$ (1)

Put $\cos x - \sin x = t$

$\Rightarrow (-\sin x - \cos x)\,dx = dt$

$\Rightarrow (\sin x + \cos x)\,dx = -dt$

Lower limit When $x = 0$, then $t = \cos 0 - \sin 0 = 1$

Upper limit When $x = \dfrac{\pi}{4}$, then

$$t = \cos\frac{\pi}{4} - \sin\frac{\pi}{4} = \frac{1}{\sqrt{2}} - \frac{1}{\sqrt{2}} = 0 \qquad (1)$$

$\therefore \quad I = \displaystyle\int_{1}^{0} \frac{-dt}{9 + 16(1 - t^2)}$

$\Rightarrow \quad I = \displaystyle\int_{0}^{1} \frac{dt}{9 + 16(1 - t^2)} \qquad \left[\because \int_{a}^{b} f(x)\,dx = -\int_{b}^{a} f(x)\,dx \right]$

$= \displaystyle\int_{0}^{1} \frac{dt}{25 - 16t^2} = \frac{1}{16}\int_{0}^{1} \frac{dt}{\left(\frac{5}{4}\right)^2 - t^2}$

$$= \frac{1}{2 \times \frac{5}{4} \times 16} \left[\log\left| \frac{5 + 4t}{5 - 4t} \right| \right]_0^1 \qquad (1)$$

$$\left[\because \int \frac{1}{a^2 - x^2}\,dx = \frac{1}{2a} \log\left| \frac{a + x}{a - x} \right| + C \right]$$

$= \dfrac{1}{40} \left[\log\left| \dfrac{5 + 4}{5 - 4} \right| - \log\left| \dfrac{5}{5} \right| \right]$

$= \dfrac{1}{40} \left[\log\left(\dfrac{9}{1} \right) - \log\left(\dfrac{5}{5} \right) \right]$

$= \dfrac{1}{40}(\log 9 - \log 1) = \dfrac{1}{40}(\log 9) \quad [\because \log 1 = 0]$

$\Rightarrow \quad I = \dfrac{1}{40}\log (3)^2 = \dfrac{2}{40}\log 3 \quad [\because \log a^n = n\log a]$

$\therefore \quad I = \dfrac{1}{20}\log 3 \qquad (1)$

Or

Let $I = \displaystyle\int_{0}^{\pi} \frac{x}{a^2\cos^2 x + b^2\sin^2 x}\,dx \qquad \dots(i)$

$\Rightarrow \quad I = \displaystyle\int_{0}^{\pi} \frac{(\pi - x)}{a^2\cos^2(\pi - x) + b^2\sin^2(\pi - x)}\,dx$

$$\left[\because \int_0^a f(x)\,dx = \int_0^a f(a - x)\,dx \right]$$

$\Rightarrow \quad I = \displaystyle\int_{0}^{\pi} \frac{(\pi - x)}{a^2\cos^2 x + b^2\sin^2 x}\,dx \qquad \dots(ii)\ (1)$

On adding Eqs. (i) and (ii), we get

$$2I = \int_{0}^{\pi} \frac{(x + \pi - x)}{a^2\cos^2 x + b^2\sin^2 x}\,dx$$

$\Rightarrow \quad 2I = \pi\displaystyle\int_{0}^{\pi} \frac{dx}{a^2\cos^2 x + b^2\sin^2 x}$

We know that

$$\int_{0}^{2a} f(x)\,dx = 2\int_{0}^{a} f(x)\,dx, \text{ if } f(2a - x) = f(x)$$

Here, $a^2\cos^2(\pi - x) + b^2\sin^2(\pi - x)$

$\qquad\qquad = a^2\cos^2 x + b^2\sin^2 x$

$\therefore \quad 2I = 2\pi\displaystyle\int_{0}^{\pi/2} \frac{dx}{a^2\cos^2 x + b^2\sin^2 x} \qquad (1)$

On dividing numerator and denominator by $\cos^2 x$, we get

$$I = \pi\int_{0}^{\pi/2} \frac{\sec^2 x}{a^2 + b^2\tan^2 x}\,dx \qquad (1)$$

Put $\tan x = t \Rightarrow \sec^2 x\,dx = dt$

Lower limit When $x = 0$, then $t = \tan 0 = 0$

Upper limit When $x = \dfrac{\pi}{2}$, then $t = \tan\dfrac{\pi}{2} = \infty$.

$\therefore \quad I = \pi\displaystyle\int_{0}^{\infty} \frac{dt}{a^2 + b^2 t^2}$

$= \pi\displaystyle\int_{0}^{\infty} \frac{dt}{a^2 + (bt)^2} = \frac{\pi}{b^2}\int_{0}^{\infty} \frac{dt}{\left(\frac{a}{b}\right)^2 + t^2}$

$\Rightarrow \quad I = \dfrac{\pi}{ab}\left[\tan^{-1}\dfrac{bt}{a} \right]_0^{\infty} \left[\because \int \dfrac{dx}{a^2 + x^2} = \dfrac{1}{a}\tan^{-1}\dfrac{x}{a} + C \right]$

$\Rightarrow \quad I = \dfrac{\pi}{ab}[\tan^{-1}\infty - \tan^{-1}0]$

$\Rightarrow \quad I = \dfrac{\pi}{ab}\left[\dfrac{\pi}{2} - 0 \right] \quad \begin{bmatrix} \because \tan^{-1}\infty = \tan^{-1}\left(\tan\dfrac{\pi}{2}\right) = \dfrac{\pi}{2} \\ \text{and } \tan^{-1}0 = \tan^{-1}(\tan 0°) = 0 \end{bmatrix}$

$\therefore \quad I = \dfrac{\pi^2}{2ab} \qquad (2)$

34. Given objective function is

Minimise $Z = -50x + 20y$

Subject to constraints, $2x - y \geq -5 \qquad \dots(i)$

$\qquad\qquad\qquad\quad 3x + y \geq 3 \qquad \dots(ii)$

$\qquad\qquad\qquad\quad 2x - 3y \leq 12 \qquad \dots(iii)$

and $\qquad\qquad\qquad x \geq 0, y \geq 0 \qquad \dots(iv)$

Table for line $2x - y = -5$ is

x	−5/2	0
y	0	5

(1)

So, the line passes through the points $\left(\dfrac{-5}{2}, 0\right)$ and $(0, 5)$.

On putting $(0, 0)$ in the inequality $2x - y \geq -5$, we get

$\qquad\qquad 0 - 0 \geq -5$

$\Rightarrow \qquad\qquad 0 \geq -5$, which is true.

So, the half plane is towards the origin.

Table for line $3x + y = 3$ is

x	0	1
y	3	0

So, the line passes through the points $(0, 3)$ and $(1, 0)$.

On putting $(0, 0)$ in the inequality $3x + y \geq 3$, we get

$\qquad\qquad 0 + 0 \geq 3$

$\Rightarrow \qquad\qquad 0 \geq 3$, which is not true. $\qquad (1)$

So, the half plane is away from the origin.

Table for line $2x - 3y = 12$ is

x	0	6
y	−4	0

So, the line passes through the points $(0, −4)$ and $(6, 0)$.
On putting $(0, 0)$ in the inequality $2x - 3y \leq 12$, we get

$$0 - 0 \leq 12$$

$$\Rightarrow \qquad 0 \leq 12, \text{ which is true.}$$

So, the half plane is towards the origin.
Also, $x \geq 0$ and $y \geq 0$, so the region lies in the I quadrant.
On drawing the graph of each linear equation, we get the following graph. In first quadrant, these equations has no intersection point. (1)

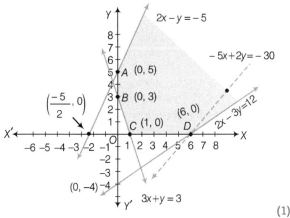

(1)

Thus, we get the common shaded region $ABCD$, which gives the feasible region and it is unbounded.
The corner points of feasible region are $A(0, 5)$, $B(0, 3)$, $C(1, 0)$ and $D(6, 0)$.
The value of Z at corner points are given below

Corner points	$Z = -50x + 20y$
$A(0, 5)$	$Z = -50(0) + 20(5) = 100$
$B(0, 3)$	$Z = -50(0) + 20(3) = 60$
$C(1, 0)$	$Z = -50(1) + 20(0) = -50$
$D(6, 0)$	$Z = -50(6) + 20(0) = -300$

Here, feasible region is unbounded so the minimum and maximum value may or may not exist.
Now, we draw a dotted line of inequation

$$-50x + 20y < -300 \text{ or } -5x + 2y < -30$$

Here, we see that half plane determined by $-5x + 2y < -30$ has a point in common with the feasible region.
Hence, no minimum value exists. (1)

Or

We have the following LPP,
Maximise, $Z = 2x + 5y$

Subject to constraints,

$$2x + 4y \leq 8 \text{ or } x + 2y \leq 4$$
$$3x + y \leq 6$$
$$x + y \leq 4$$

and $\quad x \geq 0, y \geq 0$ (1)

Now, considering the inequations as equations, we get

$$x + 2y = 4 \qquad \ldots(i)$$
$$3x + y = 6 \qquad \ldots(ii)$$

and $\quad x + y = 4 \qquad \ldots(iii)$

Table for line $x + 2y = 4$ is

x	4	0
y	0	2

So, the line passes through $(4, 0)$ and $(0, 2)$.
On putting $(0, 0)$ in the inequality $x + 2y \leq 4$, we get

$$0 + 0 \leq 4, \text{ (which is true)}$$

So, the half plane is towards the origin.
Table for line $3x + y = 6$ is

x	2	0
y	0	6

So, the line passes through $(2, 0)$ and $(0, 6)$.
On putting $(0, 0)$ in the inequality $3x + y \leq 6$, we get

$$0 + 0 \leq 6, \text{ (which is true)}$$

So, the half plane is towards the origin. (1)
Table for line $x + y = 4$ is

x	4	0
y	0	4

On putting $(0, 0)$ in the inequality $x + y \leq 4$, we get

$$0 + 0 \leq 4, \text{(which is true)}$$

So, the half plane is towards the origin.
Also, $x \geq 0, y \geq 0$, so the region lies in the Ist quadrant.
The graphical representation of the above system of inequations is given below

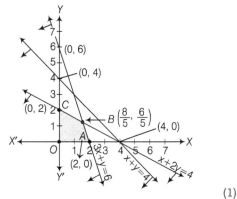

(1)

Clearly, the feasible region is $OABCO$.
The intersection point of lines (i) and (ii) is $B\left(\dfrac{8}{5}, \dfrac{6}{5}\right)$.
Thus, the corner points are

$$O(0, 0), A(2, 0), B\left(\dfrac{8}{5}, \dfrac{6}{5}\right), C(0, 2).$$

(1)

The values of Z at corner points are as follows

Corner points	$Z = 2x + 5y$
$O(0, 0)$	$Z = 0 + 0 = 0$
$A(2, 0)$	$Z = 2 \times 2 + 5 \times 0 = 4$
$B\left(\dfrac{8}{5}, \dfrac{6}{5}\right)$	$Z = 2 \times \dfrac{8}{5} + 5 \times \dfrac{6}{5} = \dfrac{46}{5} = 9.2$
$C(0, 2)$	$Z = 2 \times 0 + 5 \times 2 = 10$ (maximum)

Hence, the maximum value of Z is 10.   (1)

35. Given differential equation is
$$(x^3 + x^2 + x + 1)\frac{dy}{dx} = 2x^2 + x$$
$$\Rightarrow \qquad \frac{dy}{dx} = \frac{2x^2 + x}{x^3 + x^2 + x + 1}$$

It is a variable separable type differential equation.
$$\therefore \qquad dy = \frac{2x^2 + x}{x^3 + x^2 + x + 1}dx$$

On integrating both sides, we get
$$\int dy = \int \frac{2x^2 + x}{x^3 + x^2 + x + 1}dx$$
$$\Rightarrow \qquad y = \int \frac{2x^2 + x}{x^2(x + 1) + 1(x + 1)}dx$$
$$\Rightarrow \qquad y = \int \frac{2x^2 + x}{(x + 1)(x^2 + 1)}dx \qquad \dots\text{(i) (1)}$$

Using partial fraction

let $\dfrac{2x^2 + x}{(x + 1)(x^2 + 1)} = \dfrac{A}{x + 1} + \dfrac{Bx + C}{x^2 + 1}$ $\dots\text{(ii)}$

$$\Rightarrow \frac{2x^2 + x}{(x + 1)(x^2 + 1)} = \frac{A(x^2 + 1) + (Bx + C)(x + 1)}{(x + 1)(x^2 + 1)}$$
$$\Rightarrow \quad 2x^2 + x = A(x^2 + 1) + (Bx + C)(x + 1)$$
$$\Rightarrow \quad 2x^2 + x = A(x^2 + 1) + B(x^2 + x) + C(x + 1)$$
$$\Rightarrow \quad 2x^2 + x = (A + B)x^2 + A + (B + C)x + C \quad \text{(1)}$$

On comparing the coefficients of x^2, x and constant terms from both sides, we get
$$A + B = 2, \quad B + C = 1$$
and $\quad A + C = 0 \Rightarrow A = -C$
On solving above equations, we get
$$A = \frac{1}{2}, B = \frac{3}{2} \text{ and } C = -\frac{1}{2} \qquad \text{(1)}$$
On substituting the values of A, B and C in Eq. (ii), we get
$$\frac{2x^2 + x}{(x + 1)(x^2 + 1)} = \frac{\frac{1}{2}}{x + 1} + \frac{\frac{3}{2}x - \frac{1}{2}}{x^2 + 1}$$
On integrating both sides, we get
$$\int \frac{2x^2 + x}{(x + 1)(x^2 + 1)}dx = \frac{1}{2}\int \frac{dx}{x + 1}$$
$$+ \frac{3}{2}\int \frac{x}{x^2 + 1}dx - \frac{1}{2}\int \frac{dx}{x^2 + 1}$$

$$\Rightarrow y = \frac{1}{2}\log|x + 1| + I_1 - \frac{1}{2}\tan^{-1}x + C_2 \qquad \dots\text{(iii) (1)}$$
[from Eq. (i)]

where, $I_1 = \dfrac{3}{2}\displaystyle\int \dfrac{x}{x^2 + 1}dx$

Put $x^2 + 1 = t \Rightarrow 2xdx = dt \Rightarrow xdx = \dfrac{dt}{2}$

$\therefore \qquad I_1 = \dfrac{3}{4}\displaystyle\int \dfrac{dt}{t} = \dfrac{3}{4}\log|t| + C_1 = \dfrac{3}{4}\log|x^2 + 1| + C_1$

On putting the value of I_1 in Eq. (iii), we get
$$y = \frac{1}{2}\log|x + 1| + \frac{3}{4}\log|x^2 + 1| - \frac{1}{2}\tan^{-1}x + C$$
[where, $C = C_1 + C_2$]
which is the required solution.   (1)

36. (i) $\because (1, 1), (2, 2), (3, 3) \in R$
$\Rightarrow R$ is reflexive on A.
Now, $(1, 2) \in R$ but $(2, 1) \notin R$
$\Rightarrow R$ is not symmetric on A.
Now, $(2, 3) \in R$ and $(3, 1) \in R$ but $(2, 1) \notin R$
$\Rightarrow R$ is not transitive on A.

(ii) $\because (1, 1) (2, 2)$ and $(3, 3)$ are not in R.
$\Rightarrow R$ is not reflexive on A.
$\because (1, 2) \in R \Rightarrow (2, 1) \in R$ and $(1, 3) \in R$.
$\Rightarrow (3, 1) \in R$
$\therefore R$ is symmetric.
$\because (1, 2) \in R$ and $(2, 1) \in R$ but $(1, 1) \notin R$
$\therefore R$ is not transitive on A.

(iii) Given, $R = \{(x, y) : y = x + 5 \text{ and } x < 4\}$,
where $x, y \in N$
$\therefore R = \{(1, 6), (2, 7), (3, 8)\}$
$\because (1, 1), (2, 2)$ and $(3, 3)$ are not in R.
So, R is not reflexive.
Now, $(1, 6) \in R$ but $(6, 1) \notin R$
$\Rightarrow R$ is not symmetric.
Now, $(1, 6) \in R$ and there is no order pair in R which has 6 as the first element.
Similar is the case for $(2, 7)$ and $(3, 8)$
$\Rightarrow R$ is not transitive.

Or

Given, $R = \{(a, b) : 2 \text{ divides } (a - b)\}$
and $Z = $ Set of integers.

Reflexive Let $a \in Z$ be any arbitrary element.
Now, if $(a, a) \in R$, then 2 divides $a - a$, which is true.
So, R is reflexive.

Symmetric Let $a, b \in Z$, such that $(a, b) \in R$
2 divides $(a - b)$
$\Rightarrow$ 2 divides $[-(a - b)]$
$\Rightarrow$ 2 divides $(b - a) \Rightarrow (b, a) \in R$
So, R is symmetric.

Transitive Let $a, b, c \in Z$, such that $(a, b) \in R$ and $(b, c) \in R$
$\Rightarrow a - b$ and $b - c$ both are divisible by 2.

$\Rightarrow a - b + b - c$ is divisible by 2.

$\Rightarrow (a - c)$ is divisible by $2 \Rightarrow (a, c) \in R$

So, R is transitive.

Thus, R is reflexive, symmetric and transitive.

Hence, R is an equivalence relation.

37. (i) $\cos^{-1} x$ is always continuous in its domain, $x \in [-1, 1]$.

(ii) Given function, $f(x) = \begin{cases} 3x, & \text{for } x \leq 0 \\ 0, & \text{for } x > 0 \end{cases}$

Continuity at $x = 0$,

$\text{LHL} = \lim\limits_{x \to 0^-} f(x) = \lim\limits_{h \to 0} f(0 - h) = \lim\limits_{h \to 0} 3(0 - h)$

$\qquad = \lim\limits_{h \to 0} -3h = -3 \times 0 = 0$

$\text{RHL} = \lim\limits_{x \to 0^+} f(x) = \lim\limits_{h \to 0} f(0 + h) = \lim\limits_{h \to 0} 0 = 0$

and value of the function at $x = 0$,

$\qquad f(0) = 3 \times 0 = 0$

$\because \text{LHL} = \text{RHL} = f(0)$

$\therefore$ The given function $f(x)$ is continuous at $x = 0$.

(iii) Given function, $f(x) = |x - 2|, x \in R$

$\qquad f(x) = \begin{cases} -(x - 2), & \text{for } x \leq 2 \\ +(x - 2), & \text{for } x > 2 \end{cases}$

$\qquad f(x) = \begin{cases} 2 - x, & x \leq 2 \\ x - 2, & x > 2 \end{cases}$

Continuity at $x = 2$,

$\text{LHL} = \lim\limits_{x \to 2^-} f(x) = \lim\limits_{h \to 0} f(2 - h) = \lim\limits_{h \to 0} 2 - (2 - h)$

$\qquad = \lim\limits_{h \to 0} h = 0$

$\text{RHL} = \lim\limits_{x \to 2^+} f(x) = \lim\limits_{h \to 0} f(2 + h)$

$\qquad = \lim\limits_{h \to 0} \{(2 + h) - 2\}$

$\qquad = \lim\limits_{h \to 0} h = 0$

and value of function at $x = 2$,

$\qquad f(2) = 2 - 2 = 0$

$\because \text{LHL} = \text{RHL} = f(2)$

$\therefore f(x)$ is continuous at $x = 2$.

Or

Given function, $f(x) = |\cos 2x|$

At $x = \dfrac{\pi}{4}$,

$\qquad f\left(\dfrac{\pi}{4}\right) = \left|\cos \dfrac{\pi}{2}\right| = |0| = 0$

$\Rightarrow f(x)$ exists at $x = \dfrac{\pi}{4}$

Continuity at $x = \dfrac{\pi}{4}$,

$\text{LHL} = \lim\limits_{x \to \frac{\pi}{4}^-} = \lim\limits_{h \to 0} f\left(\dfrac{\pi}{4} - h\right)$

$\qquad = \lim\limits_{h \to 0} \left|\cos\left(\dfrac{\pi}{2} - 2h\right)\right|$

$\qquad = \lim\limits_{h \to 0} |\sin 2h| = |\sin 0| = 0$

$\text{RHL} = \lim\limits_{x \to \frac{\pi}{4}^+} = \lim\limits_{h \to 0} f\left(\dfrac{\pi}{4} + h\right)$

$\qquad = \lim\limits_{h \to 0} \left|\cos\left(\dfrac{\pi}{2} + 2h\right)\right|$

$\qquad = \lim\limits_{h \to 0} |-\sin 2h| = \lim\limits_{h \to 0} |-\sin 0| = 0$

$\because \text{LHL} = \text{RHL} = f\left(\dfrac{\pi}{4}\right)$

$\therefore$ The given function is continuous at $x = \dfrac{\pi}{4}$.

38. Let

$A = $ The event that question has some error

$E_1 = $ The event that question is solved by Ravi

$E_2 = $ The event that question is solved by Mohit

$E_3 = $ The event that question is solved by Sonia

Then, we have

$\qquad P(E_1) = \dfrac{30}{100}, P(E_2) = \dfrac{25}{100}, P(E_3) = \dfrac{45}{100}$

$\qquad P(A/E_1) = \dfrac{1}{100}, P(A/E_2) = \dfrac{1.2}{100}$

and $P(A/E_3) = \dfrac{2}{100}$

(i) Required probability $= P(A)$

$\qquad = \sum\limits_{i=1}^{3} P(E_i) P(A/E_i)$

$\qquad = P(E_1) P(A/E_1) + P(E_2) P(A/E_2)$
$\qquad \qquad \qquad \qquad \qquad + P(E_3) P(A/E_3)$

$\qquad = \dfrac{30}{100} \times \dfrac{1}{100} + \dfrac{25}{100} \times \dfrac{1.2}{100} + \dfrac{45}{100} \times \dfrac{2}{100}$

$\qquad = 0.003 + 0.003 + 0.009 = 0.015$

(ii) Required probability $= 1 - P(E_1/A)$

$\qquad = 1 - \left[\dfrac{P(E_1) P(A/E_1)}{P(E_1)P(A/E_1) + P(E_2) P(A/E_2)} \right.$
$\qquad \qquad \qquad \qquad \left. + P(E_3) P(A/E_3)\right]$

$\qquad = 1 - \left[\dfrac{\dfrac{30}{100} \times \dfrac{1}{100}}{\dfrac{30}{100} \times \dfrac{1}{100} + \dfrac{25}{100} \times \dfrac{1.2}{100} + \dfrac{45}{100} \times \dfrac{2}{100}}\right]$

$\qquad = 1 - \dfrac{0.003}{0.015} = 1 - 0.2 = 0.8$

SAMPLE QUESTION PAPER 7

MATHEMATICS

Time : 3 hrs   Max. Marks : 80

General Instructions

1. This question paper contains - five sections A, B, C, D and E. Each section is compulsory. However, there are internal choices in some questions.
2. Section A has 18 MCQ's and 02 Assertion-Reason based questions of 1 mark each.
3. Section B has 5 Very Short Answer (VSA) type questions of 2 marks each.
4. Section C has 6 Short Answer (SA) type questions of 3 marks each.
5. Section D has 4 Long Answer (LA) type questions of 5 marks each.
6. Section E has 3 source based/case based/passage based/integrated units of assessment (4 marks each) with sub parts.

Section A

(Multiple Choice Questions) Each question carries 1 mark

1. The value of the expression $|\vec{a} \times \vec{b}|^2 + |\vec{a} \cdot \vec{b}|^2$ is

   (a) $|\vec{a}|^2 |\vec{b}|$
   (b) $|\vec{a}|^2 |\vec{b}|^2$
   (c) $|\vec{a}||\vec{b}|^2$
   (d) $|\vec{a}||\vec{b}|$

2. The domain of the function $\cos^{-1}(2x - 1)$ belongs to

   (a) [0, 1]
   (b) (0, 1)
   (c) (0, 1]
   (d) [0, 1)

3. If $\vec{a}$ and $\vec{b}$ are two vectors such that $|\vec{a} + \vec{b}| = |\vec{a}|$, then $(2\vec{a} + \vec{b}) \cdot \vec{b}$ equals

   (a) 0
   (b) 1
   (c) $\vec{a}$
   (d) $\vec{b}$

4. Consider the set A containing n elements. Then, the total number of injective functions from A on itself is

   (a) $\left(\dfrac{n}{2}\right)!$ (b) $n!$ (c) $(n-1)!$ (d) $(n+1)!$

5. The relation R on the set $A = \{1, 2, 3\}$ given by $R = \{(1, 2), (2, 1)\}$ is

   (a) reflexive   (b) not reflexive
   (c) not symmetric   (d) None of these

6. The total number of functions from the set $A = \{1, 2, 3, 4\}$ to the set $B = \{a, b, c\}$ is

   (a) 80   (b) 81   (c) 90   (d) 50

7. The value of $\tan^{-1}\left[2\sin\left(2\cos^{-1}\dfrac{\sqrt{3}}{2}\right)\right]$ is

   (a) $\dfrac{\pi}{3}$ (b) $\dfrac{2\pi}{3}$ (c) $-\dfrac{\pi}{3}$ (d) $\dfrac{\pi}{6}$

8. If a line makes angles $\dfrac{\pi}{2}, \dfrac{3\pi}{4}$ and $\dfrac{\pi}{4}$ with X, Y and Z-axes, respectively, then the direction cosines are

   (a) $\pm\left(0, -\dfrac{1}{\sqrt{2}}, \dfrac{1}{\sqrt{2}}\right)$ (b) $\left(0, \dfrac{1}{\sqrt{2}}, \dfrac{3}{\sqrt{2}}\right)$

   (c) $\pm\left(0, \dfrac{1}{\sqrt{2}}, \dfrac{1}{\sqrt{2}}\right)$ (d) $\pm\left(\dfrac{1}{\sqrt{2}}, \dfrac{1}{\sqrt{2}}, \dfrac{1}{\sqrt{2}}\right)$

9. If $\vec{a} = 7\hat{i} + \hat{j} - 4\hat{k}$ and $\vec{b} = 2\hat{i} + 6\hat{j} + 3\hat{k}$, then the projection of $\vec{a}$ on $\vec{b}$ is

   (a) $\dfrac{8}{5}$ (b) $\dfrac{8}{7}$ (c) $\dfrac{7}{8}$ (d) $\dfrac{6}{5}$

10. The area of a parallelogram whose adjacent sides are represented by the vectors $2\hat{i} - 3\hat{k}$ and $4\hat{j} + 2\hat{k}$ is (in sq units)

    (a) $\sqrt{14}$ (b) $3\sqrt{14}$ (c) $4\sqrt{14}$ (d) $2\sqrt{15}$

11. For any two vectors $\vec{a}$ and $\vec{b}$, if $\vec{a} \perp \vec{b}$, then the value of $\vec{a} \cdot \vec{b}$ is

    (a) 1   (b) 0   (c) -1 (d) 2

12. If $\vec{a} = x\hat{i} + 2\hat{j} - z\hat{k}$ and $\vec{b} = 3\hat{i} - y\hat{j} + \hat{k}$ are two equal vectors, then the value of $x + y + z$ is

    (a) 1   (b) 2   (c) 0   (d) -1

13. The magnitude of vector $3\hat{i} - 4\hat{j} + 5\hat{k}$ is

    (a) $2\sqrt{5}$ (b) $5\sqrt{2}$ (c) 25   (d) 50

14. Cartesian equation of the line passing through the points $(1, 2, 3)$ and $(5, 4, 6)$ is given by

    (a) $\dfrac{x-1}{4} = \dfrac{y-2}{2} = \dfrac{z-3}{3}$ (b) $\dfrac{x-1}{-4} = \dfrac{y-2}{2} = \dfrac{z-3}{3}$

    (c) $\dfrac{x+1}{4} = \dfrac{y+2}{2} = \dfrac{z+3}{3}$ (d) $\dfrac{x-1}{4} = \dfrac{y-2}{2} = \dfrac{z+3}{3}$

15. For any vector $\vec{a}$, $(\vec{a} \cdot \hat{i})\hat{i} + (\vec{a} \cdot \hat{j})\hat{j} + (\vec{a} \cdot \hat{k})\hat{k}$ equals

    (a) $2\vec{a}$ (b) $3\vec{a}$ (c) $\vec{0}$ (d) $\vec{a}$

16. Vector equation of the line $\dfrac{x-4}{3} = \dfrac{y+1}{2} = \dfrac{3-z}{4}$ is given by

    (a) $\vec{r} = (4\hat{i} - \hat{j} + 3\hat{k}) + \lambda(3\hat{i} + 2\hat{j} + 4\hat{k})$

    (b) $\vec{r} = (4\hat{i} - \hat{j} + 3\hat{k}) + \lambda(3\hat{i} + 2\hat{j} - 4\hat{k})$

    (c) $\vec{r} = (4\hat{i} + \hat{j} - 3\hat{k}) + \lambda(3\hat{i} + 2\hat{j} - 4\hat{k})$

    (d) $\vec{r} = (4\hat{i} + \hat{j} - \hat{k}) + \lambda(3\hat{i} - 2\hat{j} - 4\hat{k})$

17. If A and B are two independent events such that $P(A) = \dfrac{1}{3}$ and $P(B) = \dfrac{1}{4}$, then $P(A' \cap B')$ equals

    (a) 1   (b) $\dfrac{1}{2}$ (c) 0   (d) $\dfrac{2}{3}$

18. If $\vec{a} = \hat{i} - \hat{j} + \hat{k}$ and $\vec{b} = \hat{i} + \hat{j} - \hat{k}$, then the value of $\vec{a} \cdot \vec{b}$ is

    (a) 0   (b) 1
    (c) -1 (d) 2

Assertion-Reason Based Questions

In the following questions, a statement of Assertion (A) is followed by a statement of Reason (R). Choose the correct answer out of the following choices.

   (a) Both A and R are true and R is the correct explanation of A
   (b) Both A and R are true but R is not the correct explanation of A
   (c) A is true but R is false
   (d) A is false but R is true

19. **Assertion (A)** The $f : R \to R$ given by $f(x) = [x] + x$ is one-one onto.

    Reason (R) A function is said to be one-one and onto, if each element has unique image and range of $f(x)$ is equal to codomain of $f(x)$.

20. Assertion (A) Let a relation R defined from set B to B such that $B = \{1, 2, 3, 4\}$ and $R = \{1, 1), (2, 2), (3, 3), (1, 3), (3, 1)\}$, then R is transitive.

Reason (R) A relation R in set A is called transitive, if $(a, b) \in R$ and $(b, c) \in R$ $\Rightarrow (a, c) \in R, \ \forall \ a, b, c \in A$

Section B

(This section comprises of very short answer type questions (VSA) of 2 marks each)

21. Check if the relation R in the set A of real numbers defined as $R = \{(a, b) : a < b\}$ is
(i) symmetric   (ii) transitive.

Or

Check whether the relation R defined on the set $A = \{1, 2, 3, 4, 5, 6\}$ as $R = \{(a, b) : b = a + 1\}$ is reflexive, symmetric or transitive.

22. Show that the function $f(x) = 4x^3 - 18x^2 + 27x - 7$ is always increasing on R.

23. Find the value of $\int \sin x \cdot \log \cos x \, dx$.

Or

Find $\int \dfrac{3 - 5 \sin x}{\cos^2 x} \, dx$.

24. If a line makes angles α, β and γ with the coordinate axes, then prove that
$$\cos 2\alpha + \cos 2\beta + \cos 2\gamma = -1.$$

25. Evaluate the integral $\displaystyle\int_0^{2\pi} \dfrac{1}{1 + e^{\sin x}} dx$.

Section C

(This section comprises of short answer type questions (SA) of 3 marks each)

26. If $y = \sin^{-1}\left(\dfrac{\sqrt{1+x} + \sqrt{1-x}}{2}\right)$, then show that $\dfrac{dy}{dx} = \dfrac{-1}{2\sqrt{1-x^2}}$.

27. A telephone company in a town has 500 subscribers on its list and collects fixed charge of ₹300 per subscriber per year. The company proposes to increase the annual subscription and it is believed that for every increase of ₹ 1, one subscriber will discontinue the service. What increase will bring maximum profit?

Or Prove that the function f defined by $f(x) = x^2 - x + 1$ is neither increasing nor decreasing in $(-1, 1)$. Hence, find the intervals in which $f(x)$ is

(i) strictly increasing.

(ii) strictly decreasing.

28. Evaluate $\int \dfrac{\sin x + \cos x}{9 + 16 \sin 2x} \, dx$.

Or

Evaluate $\int \dfrac{x^2 + 1}{(x-1)^2 \, (x+3)} \, dx$.

29. A coin is biased so that the head is three times as likely to occur as tail. If the coin is tossed twice, find the probability distribution of number of tails. Hence, find the mean of the number of tails.

Or

Suppose that 5 men out of 100 and 25 women out of 1000 are good orators. Assuming that there are equal number of men and women, find the probability of choosing a good orator.

30. Find the intervals in which the function $f(x) = (x-1)^3 \, (x-2)^2$ is

(i) increasing.   (ii) decreasing.

31. Find $I = \int \dfrac{2 \cos x}{(1 - \sin x)(1 + \sin^2 x)} \, dx$.

Section D

(This section comprises of long answer type questions (LA) of 5 marks each)

32. If $A = \begin{bmatrix} 1 & 3 & 2 \\ 2 & 0 & -1 \\ 1 & 2 & 3 \end{bmatrix}$, then show that

$A^3 - 4A^2 - 3A + 11I = O$.

Hence find A^{-1}.

33. The sum of three numbers is 6. If we multiply third number by 3 and add second number to it, we get 11. By adding first and third numbers, we get double of the second number. Represent it algebraically and find the numbers using matrix method.

Or If $A = \begin{bmatrix} 1 & 1 & 1 \\ 1 & 1 & 1 \\ 1 & 1 & 1 \end{bmatrix}$, prove that

$A^n = \begin{bmatrix} 3^{n-1} & 3^{n-1} & 3^{n-1} \\ 3^{n-1} & 3^{n-1} & 3^{n-1} \\ 3^{n-1} & 3^{n-1} & 3^{n-1} \end{bmatrix}, n \in N.$

34. Solve the following LPP graphically

Minimize $Z = 5x + 10y$,

Subject to the constraints

$x + 2y \le 120, x + y \ge 60, x - 2y \ge 0$

and $x, y \ge 0$

Or

Solve the following LPP graphically
Maximize and minimize $Z = 3x + 5y$
Subject to the constraints

$3x - 4y + 12 \ge 0,$

$2x - y + 2 \ge 0,$

$2x + 3y - 12 \ge 0,$

$0 \le x \le 4,$

and $y \ge 2$

35. Evaluate $\int \dfrac{1}{\cos^4 x + \sin^4 x} \, dx$.

Section E

(This section comprises of 3 case-study/ passage-based questions of 4 marks each with two sub-parts. First two case study questions have three sub-parts (i), (ii), (iii) of marks 1, 1, 2 respectively. The third case study question has two sub-parts of 2 marks each)

36. An architect designs a garden in society. The garden is in the shape rectangle inscribed in a circle of radius 10m as shown in given figure.

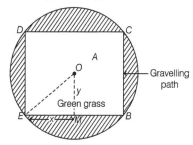

On the basis of above information, answer the following questions.

(i) If 2x and 2y represents the length and breadth of the rectangular part, then find the relation between the variables.

(ii) Find the area of the green grass A expressed as a function of x.

(iii) Show that the area A is maximum, when $x = 5\sqrt{2}$

Or If the area A is maximum, when $x = 5\sqrt{2}$, then find the maximum area and area of gravelling path.

37. In a school, teacher asks a question to three students Ravi, Mohit, Sonia.

The probability of solving the question by Ravi, Mohit, Sonia are 30%, 25% and 45% respectively. The probability of making error by Ravi, Mohit and Sonia are 1%, 1.2% and 2%, respectively.

On the basis of above information, answer the following questions.

(i) Find the conditional probability that an error is committed in solving question given that question is solved by Sonia.

(ii) Find the probability that Sonia solved the question and committed an error.

(iii) Find the total probability of committing an error in solving the question.

Or

If the solution of question is checked by teacher and has some error, then find the probability that the question is not solved by Ravi.

38. An architect designs a building for a multi-national company. The floor consists of a rectangular region with semi-circular ends having a perimeter of 200 m as shown below

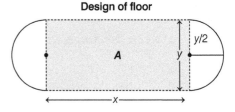
Design of floor

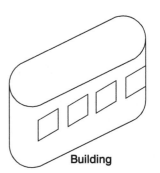
Building

On the basis of above information, answer the following questions.

(i) Find the maximum value of area A.

(ii) The CEO of the multi-national company is interested in maximizing the area of the whole floor including the semi-circular ends. For this to happen, find the value of x.

SOLUTIONS

1. (b) We have, $|\vec{a} \times \vec{b}|^2 + |\vec{a} \cdot \vec{b}|^2$

$$= |\vec{a}|^2 |\vec{b}|^2 \sin^2\theta + |\vec{a}|^2 |\vec{b}|^2 \cos^2\theta$$

$$= |\vec{a}|^2 |\vec{b}|^2 (\sin^2\theta + \cos^2\theta)$$

$$= |\vec{a}|^2 |\vec{b}|^2$$

2. (a) We have, $f(x) = \cos^{-1}(2x - 1)$

$\therefore \qquad -1 \le 2x - 1 \le 1$

$\Rightarrow \qquad 0 \le 2x \le 2$

$\Rightarrow \qquad 0 \le x \le 1$

$\therefore \qquad x \in [0, 1]$

3. (a) Given, $|\vec{a} + \vec{b}| = |\vec{a}|$

On squaring both sides, we get

$$|\vec{a} + \vec{b}|^2 = |\vec{a}|^2$$

$\Rightarrow |\vec{a}|^2 + 2\vec{a} \cdot \vec{b} + |\vec{b}|^2 = |\vec{a}|^2$

$\Rightarrow \qquad 2\vec{a} \cdot \vec{b} + \vec{b} \cdot \vec{b} = 0 \qquad [\because |\vec{x}|^2 = \vec{x} \cdot \vec{x}]$

$\Rightarrow \qquad (2\vec{a} + \vec{b}) \cdot \vec{b} = 0$

4. (b) Number of injective functions from A on A

$$= {}^nP_n = n!$$

5. (b) We have, $(1, 1), (2, 2), (3, 3) \notin R$.

So, R is not reflexive.

6. (b) If A and B are two sets having m and n elements respectively, then total number of functions from A to B is n^m.

$\therefore$ Total number of functions from A to B

$$= (3)^4 \qquad [\because m = 4, n = 3]$$

$$= 81$$

7. (a) Given, $\tan^{-1}\left[2\sin\left(2\cos^{-1}\dfrac{\sqrt{3}}{2}\right)\right]$

$$= \tan^{-1}\left[2\sin\left(2 \times \dfrac{\pi}{6}\right)\right]$$

$$= \tan^{-1}\left(2\sin\dfrac{\pi}{3}\right)$$

$$= \tan^{-1}\left(2 \times \dfrac{\sqrt{3}}{2}\right) = \tan^{-1}\sqrt{3} = \dfrac{\pi}{3}$$

8. (a) The direction cosines are $\pm\left(\cos\dfrac{\pi}{2}, \cos\dfrac{3\pi}{4}, \cos\dfrac{\pi}{4}\right)$.

i.e. $\pm\left(0, \dfrac{-1}{\sqrt{2}}, \dfrac{1}{\sqrt{2}}\right)$.

9. (b) Given, vectors are $\vec{a} = 7\hat{i} + \hat{j} - 4\hat{k}$

and $\vec{b} = 2\hat{i} + 6\hat{j} + 3\hat{k}$

Now, the projection of $\vec{a}$ on $\vec{b} = \dfrac{\vec{a}\cdot\vec{b}}{|\vec{b}|}$

$= \dfrac{(7\hat{i} + \hat{j} - 4\hat{k})\cdot(2\hat{i} + 6\hat{j} + 3\hat{k})}{\sqrt{2^2 + 6^2 + 3^2}}$

$= \dfrac{14 + 6 - 12}{\sqrt{49}} = \dfrac{8}{7}$

10. (c) Let adjacent sides of a parallelogram be

$\vec{a} = 2\hat{i} - 3\hat{k}$ and $\vec{b} = 4\hat{j} + 2\hat{k}$.

$\therefore$ Area of parallelogram $= |\vec{a} \times \vec{b}|$

$= |(2\hat{i} - 3\hat{k}) \times (4\hat{j} + 2\hat{k})|$

$= \begin{vmatrix} \hat{i} & \hat{j} & \hat{k} \\ 2 & 0 & -3 \\ 0 & 4 & 2 \end{vmatrix} = |\hat{i}(0 + 12) - \hat{j}(4 + 0) + \hat{k}(8 - 0)|$

$= |12\hat{i} - 4\hat{j} + 8\hat{k}|$

$= \sqrt{12^2 + (-4)^2 + (8)^2} = \sqrt{144 + 16 + 64}$

$= \sqrt{224} = 4\sqrt{14}$ sq units

11. (b) If $\vec{a} \perp \vec{b}$, then $\vec{a} \cdot \vec{b} = 0$

12. (c) Given, $\vec{a} = \vec{b}$

$\Rightarrow \quad x\hat{i} + 2\hat{j} - z\hat{k} = 3\hat{i} - y\hat{j} + \hat{k}$

$\Rightarrow \quad\quad x = 3, y = -2, z = -1$

$\therefore \quad\quad x + y + z = 3 - 2 - 1 = 0$

13. (b) Let $\vec{r} = 3\hat{i} - 4\hat{j} + 5\hat{k}$

On comparing with $\vec{r} = x\hat{i} + y\hat{j} + z\hat{k}$, we get

$x = 3, y = -4$ and $z = 5$

Then, magnitude of vector,

$|\vec{r}| = |3\hat{i} - 4\hat{j} + 5\hat{k}| = \sqrt{(3)^2 + (-4)^2 + (5)^2}$

$= \sqrt{9 + 16 + 25} = \sqrt{50} = 5\sqrt{2}$

14. (a) $\because$ Required cartesian equation of a line passing through $(1, 2, 3)$ and $(5, 4, 6)$ is given by

$\dfrac{x - 1}{5 - 1} = \dfrac{y - 2}{4 - 2} = \dfrac{z - 3}{6 - 3}$

$\Rightarrow \quad \dfrac{x - 1}{4} = \dfrac{y - 2}{2} = \dfrac{z - 3}{3}$

15. (d) Let $\vec{a} = x\hat{i} + y\hat{j} + z\hat{k}$

Now, $\vec{a} \cdot \hat{i} = (x\hat{i} + y\hat{j} + z\hat{k}) \cdot \hat{i} = x$

Similarly, $\vec{a} \cdot \hat{j} = y$ and $\vec{a} \cdot \hat{k} = z$

$\therefore (\vec{a} \cdot \hat{i})\hat{i} + (\vec{a} \cdot \hat{j})\hat{j} + (\vec{a} \cdot \hat{k})\hat{k} = x\hat{i} + y\hat{j} + z\hat{k} = \vec{a}$

16. (b) Given, equation can be re-written as

$\dfrac{x - 4}{3} = \dfrac{y - (-1)}{2} = \dfrac{z - 3}{-4}$

The line passes through the point $(4, -1, 3)$ and direction ratios of the line are $3, 2, -4$

$\therefore$ Required vector equation of the given line is

$\vec{r} = (4\hat{i} - \hat{j} + 3\hat{k}) + \lambda(3\hat{i} + 2\hat{j} - 4\hat{k})$

17. (b) We have, $P(A) = \dfrac{1}{3} \Rightarrow P(A') = 1 - \dfrac{1}{3} = \dfrac{2}{3}$

and $P(B) = \dfrac{1}{4} \Rightarrow P(B') = 1 - \dfrac{1}{4} = \dfrac{3}{4}$

Now, $P(A' \cap B') = P(A') \cdot P(B')$

$= \dfrac{2}{3} \times \dfrac{3}{4} = \dfrac{1}{2}$

18. (c) Given, $\vec{a} = \hat{i} - \hat{j} + \hat{k}$ and $\vec{b} = \hat{i} + \hat{j} - \hat{k}$

Then, $\vec{a} \cdot \vec{b} = (\hat{i} - \hat{j} + \hat{k})(\hat{i} + \hat{j} - \hat{k})$

$= 1 \times 1 + (-1) \times 1 + 1 \times (-1) = 1 - 1 - 1 = -1$

19. (a) **Assertion** Since, greatest integer $[x]$ gives only integer value.

But $f(x) = [x] + x$ gives all real values and there is no repeated value of $f(x)$ for any value of x.

$\therefore f(x)$ is one-one and onto.

Hence, Assertion is true.

Reason is also true and it is the correct explanation of Assertion.

20. (a) **Assertion** We have, $B = \{1, 2, 3, 4\}$

and $R = \{(1, 1), (2, 2), (3, 3), (1, 3), (3, 1)\}$

Here, $(1, 3), (3, 1) \in R$

$\Rightarrow \quad\quad (1, 1) \in R$

$\therefore R$ is transitive.

Hence, Assertion is true.

Reason is also true and it is the correct explanation of Assertion.

21. Given, $A =$ Set of real numbers and $R = \{(a, b) : a < b\}$

(i) **Symmetric** Let $(a, b) \in R$, then $a < b$ but $b \not< a$

$\Rightarrow (b, a) \notin R$.

e.g. $4 < 5$ but $5 \not< 4$

So, R is not symmetric (1)

(ii) **Transitive** Let $(a, b), (b, c) \in R$, then

$(a, b) \in R \Rightarrow a < b$ ...(i)

$(b, c) \in R \Rightarrow b < c$ ...(ii)

From Eqs. (i) and (ii), we get $a < c$

$\Rightarrow (a, c) \in R$

So, R is transitive. (1)

Or

The relation R on set $A = \{1, 2, 3, 4, 5, 6\}$ is defined as $(a, b) \in R$ iff $b = a + 1$.

Therefore, $R = \{(1, 2), (2, 3), (3, 4), (4, 5), (5, 6)\}$ (1/2)

Clearly, $(a, a) \notin R$ for any $a \in A$. So, R is not reflexive on A.

We observe that $(1, 2) \in R$ but $(2, 1) \notin R$.

So, R is not symmetric.   (1)

We also observe that $(1, 2) \in R$ and $(2, 3) \in R$ but $(1, 3) \notin R$. So, R is not transitive.   (1/2)

22. We have, $f(x) = 4x^3 - 18x^2 + 27x - 7$

On differentiating both sides w.r.t. x, we get
$$f'(x) = 12x^2 - 36x + 27$$
$$\Rightarrow \quad f'(x) = 3(4x^2 - 12x + 9)$$
$$\Rightarrow \quad f'(x) = 3(2x - 3)^2 \quad (1)$$
$$\Rightarrow \quad f'(x) \geq 0$$
$$\Rightarrow \text{For any } x \in R, (2x - 3)^2 \geq 0$$

Since, a perfect square number cannot be negative.

$\therefore$ Given, function $f(x)$ is an increasing function on R.   (1)

23. $\displaystyle\int \sin x \cdot \log \cos x \, dx$

Put $\cos x = t \Rightarrow -\sin x \, dx = dt$

$\therefore -\displaystyle\int \log t \, dt \Rightarrow -\int (\log t) \cdot 1 \, dt$

$$\Rightarrow -\left[\log t \int 1 dt - \int \left\{\frac{d}{dt}(\log t) \int 1 dt\right\} dt\right] \quad (1)$$

$$\Rightarrow -\left[(\log t) \cdot t - \int \frac{1}{t} \cdot t \, dt\right]$$

$$\Rightarrow -[t \cdot \log t - \int 1 \, dt]$$

$$\Rightarrow -[t \cdot \log t - t] + C \Rightarrow -t \cdot \log t + t + C$$

$$\Rightarrow -\cos x \log \cos x + \cos x + C \quad (1)$$

Or

Let $I = \displaystyle\int \frac{3 - 5\sin x}{\cos^2 x} dx = \int \left(\frac{3}{\cos^2 x} - \frac{5\sin x}{\cos^2 x}\right) dx \quad (1)$

$= 3\displaystyle\int \sec^2 x \, dx - 5\int \sec x \tan x \, dx$

$$\left[\because \cos x = \frac{1}{\sec x}, \frac{\sin x}{\cos x} = \tan x\right]$$

$= 3\tan x - 5\sec x + C \quad (1)$

24. We know that a line makes angles α, β and γ with the coordinate axes, then
$$\cos^2 \alpha + \cos^2 \beta + \cos^2 \gamma = 1 \quad (1/2)$$

Now, $\cos 2\alpha + \cos 2\beta + \cos 2\gamma$
$$= 2\cos^2 \alpha - 1 + 2\cos^2 \beta - 1 + 2\cos^2 \gamma - 1$$
$$[\because \cos 2\theta = 2\cos^2 \theta - 1] \quad (1/2)$$
$$= 2(\cos^2 \alpha + \cos^2 \beta + \cos^2 \gamma) - 3$$
$$= 2(1) - 3 = 2 - 3 = -1 = \text{RHS} \quad \textbf{Hence proved.} \quad (1)$$

25. We have, $I = \displaystyle\int_0^{2\pi} \frac{dx}{1 + e^{\sin x}}$ ...(i)

$I = \displaystyle\int_0^{2\pi} \frac{dx}{1 + e^{\sin(2\pi - x)}}$

$$\left[\because \int_0^a f(x) \, dx = \int_0^a f(a - x) \, dx\right] \quad (1/2)$$

$I = \displaystyle\int_0^{2\pi} \frac{dx}{1 + e^{-\sin x}} = \int_0^{2\pi} \frac{e^{\sin x}}{1 + e^{\sin x}} dx$ ...(ii)
$$(1/2)$$

On adding Eqs. (i) and (ii), we get

$$\Rightarrow \quad 2I = \int_0^{2\pi} \frac{1}{1 + e^{\sin x}} + \frac{e^{\sin x}}{1 + e^{\sin x}} dx$$

$$\Rightarrow \quad 2I = \int_0^{2\pi} \frac{1 + e^{\sin x}}{1 + e^{\sin x}} dx = \int_0^{2\pi} 1 \, dx$$
$$(1/2)$$

$$\Rightarrow \quad 2I = [x]_0^{2\pi} = [2\pi - 0] = 2\pi \Rightarrow I = \pi \quad (1/2)$$

26. We have, $y = \sin^{-1}\left(\dfrac{\sqrt{1 + x} + \sqrt{1 - x}}{2}\right)$

Put $x = \sin\theta$, we get
$$y = \sin^{-1}\left(\frac{\sqrt{1 + \sin\theta} + \sqrt{1 - \sin\theta}}{2}\right)$$

$$\Rightarrow \quad y = \sin^{-1}\left[\frac{\begin{bmatrix}\cos\theta/2 + \sin\theta/2 + \cos\theta/2\\ -\sin\theta/2\end{bmatrix}}{2}\right]$$

$$[\because 1 \pm \sin\theta = (\cos\theta/2 \pm \sin\theta/2)^2]$$

$$\Rightarrow \quad y = \sin^{-1}\left[\frac{2\cos\theta/2}{2}\right] \quad (1)$$

$$\Rightarrow \quad y = \sin^{-1}(\cos\theta/2) = \sin^{-1}\left(\frac{\pi}{2} - \sin\frac{\theta}{2}\right)$$

$$\Rightarrow \quad y = \sin^{-1}\frac{\pi}{2} - \frac{\theta}{2} \Rightarrow y = \sin^{-1}\frac{\pi}{2} - \frac{1}{2}\sin^{-1} x$$

$$[\because \text{put } \theta = \sin^{-1} x]$$

On differentiating w.r.t. x we get
$$\frac{dy}{dx} = -\frac{1}{2\sqrt{1 - x^2}} \quad \textbf{Hence proved.} \quad (2)$$

27. Let the company increases the annual subscription fee by ₹ x. Then, x subscribers will discontinue the service.   (1)

$\therefore$ Total revenue of company after the increment is given by $R(x) = (500 - x)(300 + x)$
$$= 500 \times 300 + 500x - 300x - x^2$$
$$= 15 \times 10^4 + 200x - x^2$$
$$= -x^2 + 200x + 150000$$

On differentiating both sides w.r.t. x, we get
$$R'(x) = -2x + 200 \quad \text{...(i)}$$

For maxima or minima, put $R'(x) = 0$
$$\Rightarrow \quad -2x + 200 = 0 \Rightarrow x = 100 \quad (1)$$

Again, differentiating Eq. (i) w.r.t. x, we get

$$R''(x) = -2$$

$$\Rightarrow \quad R''(100) = -2 < 0$$

So, $R(x)$ is maximum when $x = 100$.

Hence, the company should increase the subscription fee by ₹100, so that it has maximum profit. (1)

Or

Given, function is $f(x) = x^2 - x + 1$.

On differentiating both sides w.r.t. x, we get

$$f'(x) = 2x - 1$$

On putting $f'(x) = 0 \Rightarrow 2x - 1 = 0 \Rightarrow x = \dfrac{1}{2}$ (1)

Now, we find intervals in which $f(x)$ is strictly increasing or strictly decreasing.

Interval	$f'(x) = (2x-1)$	Sign of $f'(x)$
$x < \dfrac{1}{2}$	$(-)$	$-$ve
$x > \dfrac{1}{2}$	$(+)$	$+$ve

(1)

Here, $f(x)$ is strictly increasing on $\left(\dfrac{1}{2}, \infty\right)$ and $f(x)$ is strictly decreasing on $\left(-\infty, \dfrac{1}{2}\right)$.

$\Rightarrow f(x)$ is strictly increasing on $\left(\dfrac{1}{2}, 1\right)$ and $f(x)$ is strictly decreasing on $\left(-1, \dfrac{1}{2}\right)$

$\therefore f'(x)$ does not have same sign throughout the interval $(-1, 1)$.

Thus, $f(x)$ is neither increasing nor decreasing in $(-1, 1)$. (1)

28. Let $I = \displaystyle\int \dfrac{\sin x + \cos x}{9 + 16\sin 2x}\, dx$

$$= \int \dfrac{\sin x + \cos x}{9 + 16[1 - (\sin x - \cos x)^2]}\, dx$$

$$\begin{bmatrix} \because \sin 2\theta = 2\sin\theta\cos\theta = 2\sin\theta\cos\theta - 1 + 1 \\ = 2\sin\theta\cos\theta - (\cos^2\theta + \sin^2\theta) + 1 \\ = 1 - (\sin\theta - \cos\theta)^2 \end{bmatrix}$$

$$= \int \dfrac{(\sin x + \cos x)}{25 - 16(\sin x - \cos x)^2}\, dx \qquad (1)$$

Put $t = \sin x - \cos x \Rightarrow dt = (\cos x + \sin x)\, dx$

$\therefore$

$$I = \int \dfrac{dt}{25 - 16t^2} = \dfrac{1}{16}\int \dfrac{dt}{\left(\dfrac{5}{4}\right)^2 - t^2} \qquad (1)$$

$$= \dfrac{1}{16} \cdot \dfrac{1}{2} \cdot \dfrac{4}{5} \log \left| \dfrac{\dfrac{5}{4} + t}{\dfrac{5}{4} - t} \right| + C$$

$$\left[\because \int \dfrac{1}{a^2 - x^2}\, dx = \dfrac{1}{2a} \log \left| \dfrac{a + x}{a - x} \right| + C \right]$$

$$= \dfrac{1}{40} \log \left| \dfrac{5 + 4(\sin x - \cos x)}{5 - 4(\sin x - \cos x)} \right| + C$$

$$[\because \text{put } t = \sin x - \cos x] \quad (1)$$

Or

Let $I = \displaystyle\int \dfrac{x^2 + 1}{(x-1)^2 (x+3)}\, dx$

Again, let $\dfrac{x^2 + 1}{(x-1)^2 (x+3)} = \dfrac{A}{x-1} + \dfrac{B}{(x-1)^2} + \dfrac{C}{x+3}$ ...(i)

$\Rightarrow x^2 + 1 = A(x-1)(x+3) + B(x+3) + C(x-1)^2$ ...(ii)

On putting $x = 1$ in Eq. (ii), we get

$$2 = 4B \Rightarrow B = \dfrac{1}{2}$$

On putting $x = -3$ in Eq. (ii), we get

$$10 = 16C \Rightarrow C = \dfrac{10}{16} = \dfrac{5}{8} \qquad (1)$$

On equating coefficient of x^2 from both sides of Eq. (ii), we get

$$1 = A + C$$

$$\Rightarrow \quad A = 1 - C = 1 - \dfrac{5}{8} = \dfrac{3}{8}$$

Now, on substituting the values of A, B and C in Eq. (i), we get

$$\dfrac{x^2 + 1}{(x-1)^2 (x+3)} = \dfrac{3}{8} \cdot \dfrac{1}{(x-1)} + \dfrac{1}{2} \cdot \dfrac{1}{(x-1)^2} + \dfrac{5}{8} \cdot \dfrac{1}{(x+3)} \quad (1)$$

On integrating both sides, we get

$$\int \dfrac{x^2 + 1}{(x-1)^2 (x+3)}\, dx = \int \left[\dfrac{3}{8} \dfrac{1}{(x-1)} + \dfrac{1}{2} \dfrac{1}{(x-1)^2} + \dfrac{5}{8} \dfrac{1}{(x+3)} \right] dx$$

$$\therefore I = \dfrac{3}{8}\int \dfrac{1}{(x-1)}\, dx + \dfrac{1}{2}\int \dfrac{1}{(x-1)^2}\, dx + \dfrac{5}{8}\int \dfrac{1}{(x+3)}\, dx$$

$$= \dfrac{3}{8} \log|x-1| - \dfrac{1}{2(x-1)} + \dfrac{5}{8}\log|x+3| + C \qquad (1)$$

29. Let X be the random variable which denotes the number of tails when a biased coin is tossed twice.

So, X may have values 0, 1 or 2.

Since, the coin is biased in which head is 3 times as likely to occur as a tail.

$$\therefore \quad P(H) = \dfrac{3}{4} \text{ and } P(T) = \dfrac{1}{4}$$

$$P(X = 0) = P(HH) = P(H) \cdot P(H) = \left(\dfrac{3}{4}\right)^2 = \dfrac{9}{16} \quad (1/2)$$

$$P(X = 1) = P \text{ (one tail and one head)}$$

$$= P(HT, TH) = P(HT) + P(TH)$$

$$= P(H) \cdot P(T) + P(T) \cdot P(H)$$

$$= \dfrac{3}{4} \times \dfrac{1}{4} + \dfrac{1}{4} \times \dfrac{3}{4}$$

$$= \dfrac{3}{16} + \dfrac{3}{16} = \dfrac{6}{16} = \dfrac{3}{8} \qquad (1/2)$$

$P(X = 2) = P(\text{two tails}) = P(TT) = P(T) \cdot P(T)$

$$= \left(\frac{1}{4}\right)^2 = \frac{1}{16}$$ (1/2)

Therefore, the required probability distribution is as follows

X	0	1	2
P(X)	9/16	3/8	1/16

(1/2)

Now, mean $= \Sigma X P(X)$

$$= 0 \times \frac{9}{16} + 1 \times \frac{3}{8} + 2 \times \frac{1}{16}$$

$$= 0 + \frac{3}{8} + \frac{1}{8} = \frac{4}{8} = \frac{1}{2}$$ (1)

Or

Let E_1 be the event that selected person is men's and E_2 be the event that selected person is women, E_1 and E_2 are mutually exclusive and exhaustive event moreover $P(E_1) = P(E_2) = \frac{1}{2}$.

Let E be the event that selected person is good orator.

$\therefore P(E / E_1) = \frac{5}{100} = \frac{1}{20}$ and $P(E / E_2) = \frac{25}{1000} = \frac{1}{40}$ (1)

The probability of choosing a good orator,

$P(E) = P(E_1) \times P(E / E_1) + P(E_2) \times P(E / E_2)$

$$= \frac{1}{2} \times \frac{1}{20} + \frac{1}{2} \times \frac{1}{40} = \frac{2+1}{2 \times 40} = \frac{3}{80}$$ (2)

30. Given, $f(x) = (x - 1)^3 (x - 2)^2$

On differentiating both sides w.r.t. x, we get

$$f'(x) = (x-1)^3 \cdot \frac{d}{dx}(x-2)^2 + (x-2)^2 \cdot \frac{d}{dx}(x-1)^3$$

$$\left[\because \frac{d}{dx}(uv) = u\frac{dv}{dx} + v\frac{du}{dx}\right]$$

$\Rightarrow f'(x) = (x-1)^3 \cdot 2(x-2) + (x-2)^2 \cdot 3(x-1)^2$

$$= (x-1)^2 (x-2)[2(x-1) + 3(x-2)]$$

$$= (x-1)^2 (x-2)(2x-2 + 3x - 6)$$

$\Rightarrow f'(x) = (x-1)^2(x-2)(5x - 8)$

Now, put $f'(x) = 0 \Rightarrow (x-1)^2 (x-2)(5x-8) = 0$

Either $(x - 1)^2 = 0$ or $x - 2 = 0$ or $5x - 8 = 0$

$\therefore \qquad x = 1, \frac{8}{5}, 2$ (1)

Now, we find intervals and check in which interval $f(x)$ is strictly increasing and strictly decreasing.

Interval	$f'(x)$ $= (x-1)^2(x-2)(5x-8)$	Sign of $f'(x)$
$x < 1$	$(+)(-)(-)$	+ve
$1 < x < \frac{8}{5}$	$(+)(-)(-)$	+ve
$\frac{8}{5} < x < 2$	$(+)(-)(+)$	−ve
$x > 2$	$(+)(+)(+)$	+ve

(1)

We know that a function $f(x)$ is said to be an strictly increasing function, if $f'(x) > 0$ and strictly decreasing, if $f'(x) < 0$.

So, the given function $f(x)$ is increasing on the intervals $(-\infty, 1), \left(1, \frac{8}{5}\right)$ and $(2, \infty)$ and decreasing on $\left(\frac{8}{5}, 2\right)$.

Since, $f(x)$ is a polynomial function, so it is continuous at $x = 1, \frac{8}{5}, 2$.

Hence, $f(x)$ is

(i) increasing on intervals $\left(-\infty, \frac{8}{5}\right]$ and $[2, \infty)$.

(ii) decreasing on interval $\left[\frac{8}{5}, 2\right]$. (1)

31. Let $I = \int \frac{2\cos x}{(1-\sin x)(1+\sin^2 x)} dx$

Put $\sin x = t$, then $\cos x \, dx = dt$

$\therefore \qquad I = \int \frac{2 dt}{(1-t)(1+t^2)}$ ...(i)

Now, let $\frac{2}{(1-t)(1+t^2)} = \frac{A}{1-t} + \frac{Bt+C}{1+t^2}$

$\Rightarrow \qquad 2 = (1+t^2)A + (1-t)(Bt + C)$

$\Rightarrow \qquad 2 = (1+t^2)A + (Bt + C - Bt^2 - Ct)$

$\Rightarrow \qquad 2 = t^2(A-B) + t(B-C) + (A+C)$ (1)

On comparing the coefficients of like powers of t, we get

$$A - B = 0; B - C = 0 \text{ and } A + C = 2$$

$\Rightarrow \qquad A = B; B = C \text{ and } A + C = 2$

$\Rightarrow \qquad A = B = C = 1$

$\therefore \frac{2}{(1-t)(1+t^2)} = \frac{1}{1-t} + \frac{1+t}{1+t^2}$

Now, from Eq. (i), we get

$I = \int\left(\frac{1}{1-t} + \frac{1+t}{1+t^2}\right) dt$

$$= \int \frac{dt}{1-t} + \int \frac{1}{1+t^2} dt + \frac{1}{2}\int \frac{2t}{1+t^2} dt$$

$$= \frac{\log|1-t|}{(-1)} + \tan^{-1}t + \frac{1}{2}\log|1+t^2| + C$$ (1)

$$= \frac{1}{2}\log|1+\sin^2 x| - \log|1-\sin x| + \tan^{-1}(\sin x) + C$$

[putting $t = \sin x$]

$$= \tan^{-1}(\sin x) + \log\left|\frac{\sqrt{1+\sin^2 x}}{1-\sin x}\right| + C$$ (1)

$$\left[\because \log m - \log n = \log\left(\frac{m}{n}\right) \text{ and } n\log m = \log m^n\right]$$

32. We have, $A = \begin{bmatrix} 1 & 3 & 2 \\ 2 & 0 & -1 \\ 1 & 2 & 3 \end{bmatrix}$

Now, $A^2 = A \cdot A = \begin{bmatrix} 1 & 3 & 2 \\ 2 & 0 & -1 \\ 1 & 2 & 3 \end{bmatrix}\begin{bmatrix} 1 & 3 & 2 \\ 2 & 0 & -1 \\ 1 & 2 & 3 \end{bmatrix}$

$= \begin{bmatrix} 1+6+2 & 3+0+4 & 2-3+6 \\ 2+0-1 & 6+0-2 & 4+0-3 \\ 1+4+3 & 3+0+6 & 2-2+9 \end{bmatrix}$

$= \begin{bmatrix} 9 & 7 & 5 \\ 1 & 4 & 1 \\ 8 & 9 & 9 \end{bmatrix}$ (1)

and $A^3 = A^2 \cdot A = \begin{bmatrix} 9 & 7 & 5 \\ 1 & 4 & 1 \\ 8 & 9 & 9 \end{bmatrix}\begin{bmatrix} 1 & 3 & 2 \\ 2 & 0 & -1 \\ 1 & 2 & 3 \end{bmatrix}$

$= \begin{bmatrix} 9+14+5 & 27+0+10 & 18-7+15 \\ 1+8+1 & 3+0+2 & 2-4+3 \\ 8+18+9 & 24+0+18 & 16-9+27 \end{bmatrix}$

$= \begin{bmatrix} 28 & 37 & 26 \\ 10 & 5 & 1 \\ 35 & 42 & 34 \end{bmatrix}$ (1)

Now consider, LHS $= A^3 - 4A^2 - 3A + 11I$

$= \begin{bmatrix} 28 & 37 & 26 \\ 10 & 5 & 1 \\ 35 & 42 & 34 \end{bmatrix} - 4\begin{bmatrix} 9 & 7 & 5 \\ 1 & 4 & 1 \\ 8 & 9 & 9 \end{bmatrix}$

$\qquad - 3\begin{bmatrix} 1 & 3 & 2 \\ 2 & 0 & -1 \\ 1 & 2 & 3 \end{bmatrix} + 11\begin{bmatrix} 1 & 0 & 0 \\ 0 & 1 & 0 \\ 0 & 0 & 1 \end{bmatrix}$

$= \begin{bmatrix} 28-36-3+11 & 37-28-9+0 & 26-20-6+0 \\ 10-4-6+0 & 5-16+0+11 & 1-4+3+0 \\ 35-32-3+0 & 42-36-6+0 & 34-36-9+11 \end{bmatrix}$

$= \begin{bmatrix} 0 & 0 & 0 \\ 0 & 0 & 0 \\ 0 & 0 & 0 \end{bmatrix} = 0 = $ RHS   (1)

Now, $A^3 - 4A^2 - 3A + 11I = O$

Pre-multiplying by A^{-1}, we get

$A^{-1}A^3 - 4A^{-1}A^2 - 3A^{-1}A + 11A^{-1} = O$

$\Rightarrow \qquad A^2 - 4A - 3I + 11A^{-1} = O \quad [\because A^{-1}A = I]$

$\Rightarrow 11A^{-1} = 3I + 4A - A^2$ (1)

$\Rightarrow 11A^{-1} = \begin{bmatrix} 3 & 0 & 0 \\ 0 & 3 & 0 \\ 0 & 0 & 3 \end{bmatrix} + 4\begin{bmatrix} 1 & 3 & 2 \\ 2 & 0 & -1 \\ 1 & 2 & 3 \end{bmatrix} - \begin{bmatrix} 9 & 7 & 5 \\ 1 & 4 & 1 \\ 8 & 9 & 9 \end{bmatrix}$

$\Rightarrow 11A^{-1} = \begin{bmatrix} 3 & 0 & 0 \\ 0 & 3 & 0 \\ 0 & 0 & 3 \end{bmatrix} + \begin{bmatrix} 4 & 12 & 8 \\ 8 & 0 & -4 \\ 4 & 8 & 12 \end{bmatrix} - \begin{bmatrix} 9 & 7 & 5 \\ 1 & 4 & 1 \\ 8 & 9 & 9 \end{bmatrix}$

$\Rightarrow 11A^{-1} = \begin{bmatrix} -2 & 5 & 3 \\ 7 & -1 & -5 \\ -4 & -1 & 6 \end{bmatrix} \Rightarrow A^{-1} = \frac{1}{11}\begin{bmatrix} -2 & 5 & 3 \\ 7 & -1 & -5 \\ -4 & -1 & 6 \end{bmatrix}$ (1)

33. Let the first, second and third number be x, y and z, respectively. Then, according to given conditions, we have $\quad x + y + z = 6,\ y + 3z = 11$

and $\qquad x + z = 2y$ or $x - 2y + z = 0$

This system of equation can be written in matrix form as

$\begin{bmatrix} 1 & 1 & 1 \\ 0 & 1 & 3 \\ 1 & -2 & 1 \end{bmatrix}\begin{bmatrix} x \\ y \\ z \end{bmatrix} = \begin{bmatrix} 6 \\ 11 \\ 0 \end{bmatrix}$

or $AX = B$, where

$A = \begin{bmatrix} 1 & 1 & 1 \\ 0 & 1 & 3 \\ 1 & -2 & 1 \end{bmatrix}, X = \begin{bmatrix} x \\ y \\ z \end{bmatrix}$ and $B = \begin{bmatrix} 6 \\ 11 \\ 0 \end{bmatrix}$ (1)

Now consider, $|A| = \begin{vmatrix} 1 & 1 & 1 \\ 0 & 1 & 3 \\ 1 & -2 & 1 \end{vmatrix}$

$= 1(1+6) - 1(0-3) + 1(0-1)$

$= 7 + 3 - 1 = 9 \neq 0$

$\therefore\ A^{-1}$ exists.   (1)

Now, let us find the cofactor of elements of $|A|$.

Clearly, $C_{11} = (-1)^{1+1}\begin{vmatrix} 1 & 3 \\ -2 & 1 \end{vmatrix} = 7,$

$C_{12} = (-1)^{1+2}\begin{vmatrix} 0 & 3 \\ 1 & 1 \end{vmatrix} = 3$

$C_{13} = (-1)^{1+3}\begin{vmatrix} 0 & 1 \\ 1 & -2 \end{vmatrix} = -1, C_{21} = (-1)^{2+1}\begin{vmatrix} 1 & 1 \\ -2 & 1 \end{vmatrix} = -3,$

$C_{22} = (-1)^{2+2}\begin{vmatrix} 1 & 1 \\ 1 & 1 \end{vmatrix} = 0, C_{23} = (-1)^{2+3}\begin{vmatrix} 1 & 1 \\ 1 & -2 \end{vmatrix} = 3,$

$C_{31} = (-1)^{3+1}\begin{vmatrix} 1 & 1 \\ 1 & 3 \end{vmatrix} = 2, C_{32} = (-1)^{3+2}\begin{vmatrix} 1 & 1 \\ 0 & 3 \end{vmatrix} = -3$

and $C_{33} = (-1)^{3+3}\begin{vmatrix} 1 & 1 \\ 0 & 1 \end{vmatrix} = 1$ (1)

$\therefore\ \text{adj}(A) = \begin{bmatrix} C_{11} & C_{12} & C_{13} \\ C_{21} & C_{22} & C_{23} \\ C_{31} & C_{32} & C_{33} \end{bmatrix}^T = \begin{bmatrix} C_{11} & C_{21} & C_{31} \\ C_{12} & C_{22} & C_{32} \\ C_{13} & C_{23} & C_{33} \end{bmatrix}$

$\Rightarrow \text{adj}(A) = \begin{bmatrix} 7 & -3 & 2 \\ 3 & 0 & -3 \\ -1 & 3 & 1 \end{bmatrix}$

and $A^{-1} = \frac{1}{9}\begin{bmatrix} 7 & -3 & 2 \\ 3 & 0 & -3 \\ -1 & 3 & 1 \end{bmatrix} \quad \left[\because A^{-1} = \frac{\text{adj}(A)}{|A|}\right]$ (1)

Now, as $X = A^{-1}B$ $[\because AX = B]$

$\therefore \qquad \begin{bmatrix} x \\ y \\ z \end{bmatrix} = \frac{1}{9}\begin{bmatrix} 7 & -3 & 2 \\ 3 & 0 & -3 \\ -1 & 3 & 1 \end{bmatrix}\begin{bmatrix} 6 \\ 11 \\ 0 \end{bmatrix}$

$\Rightarrow \qquad \begin{bmatrix} x \\ y \\ z \end{bmatrix} = \frac{1}{9}\begin{bmatrix} 42-33+0 \\ 18+0+0 \\ -6+33+0 \end{bmatrix} = \frac{1}{9}\begin{bmatrix} 9 \\ 18 \\ 27 \end{bmatrix} = \begin{bmatrix} 1 \\ 2 \\ 3 \end{bmatrix}$

Hence, $x = 1$, $y = 2$ and $z = 3$.   (1)

Or

Given $A = \begin{bmatrix} 1 & 1 & 1 \\ 1 & 1 & 1 \\ 1 & 1 & 1 \end{bmatrix}$

To prove $A^n = \begin{bmatrix} 3^{n-1} & 3^{n-1} & 3^{n-1} \\ 3^{n-1} & 3^{n-1} & 3^{n-1} \\ 3^{n-1} & 3^{n-1} & 3^{n-1} \end{bmatrix}, n \in N$

Proof We shall prove this statement by using principle of mathematical induction.

Now, let $P(n)$ be the given statement,

i.e. $P(n): A^n = \begin{bmatrix} 3^{n-1} & 3^{n-1} & 3^{n-1} \\ 3^{n-1} & 3^{n-1} & 3^{n-1} \\ 3^{n-1} & 3^{n-1} & 3^{n-1} \end{bmatrix}$ (1)

For $n = 1$, we have

$P(1): A^1 = \begin{bmatrix} 3^{1-1} & 3^{1-1} & 3^{1-1} \\ 3^{1-1} & 3^{1-1} & 3^{1-1} \\ 3^{1-1} & 3^{1-1} & 3^{1-1} \end{bmatrix}$

$= \begin{bmatrix} 3^0 & 3^0 & 3^0 \\ 3^0 & 3^0 & 3^0 \\ 3^0 & 3^0 & 3^0 \end{bmatrix}$

$= \begin{bmatrix} 1 & 1 & 1 \\ 1 & 1 & 1 \\ 1 & 1 & 1 \end{bmatrix} = A$

∴ Statement is true for $n = 1$. (1)

Now, let us assume that statement is true for $n = k$, we have

$P(k): A^k = \begin{bmatrix} 3^{k-1} & 3^{k-1} & 3^{k-1} \\ 3^{k-1} & 3^{k-1} & 3^{k-1} \\ 3^{k-1} & 3^{k-1} & 3^{k-1} \end{bmatrix}$ ...(i) (1)

Now, we shall prove the statement for $n = k + 1$, we have

to show, $P(k + 1): A^{k+1} = \begin{bmatrix} 3^k & 3^k & 3^k \\ 3^k & 3^k & 3^k \\ 3^k & 3^k & 3^k \end{bmatrix}$

Consider, LHS $= A^{k+1} = A^k \cdot A$

$= \begin{bmatrix} 3^{k-1} & 3^{k-1} & 3^{k-1} \\ 3^{k-1} & 3^{k-1} & 3^{k-1} \\ 3^{k-1} & 3^{k-1} & 3^{k-1} \end{bmatrix} \begin{bmatrix} 1 & 1 & 1 \\ 1 & 1 & 1 \\ 1 & 1 & 1 \end{bmatrix}$

[using Eq. (i)] (1)

$= \begin{bmatrix} 3 \cdot 3^{k-1} & 3 \cdot 3^{k-1} & 3 \cdot 3^{k-1} \\ 3 \cdot 3^{k-1} & 3 \cdot 3^{k-1} & 3 \cdot 3^{k-1} \\ 3 \cdot 3^{k-1} & 3 \cdot 3^{k-1} & 3 \cdot 3^{k-1} \end{bmatrix}$

$= \begin{bmatrix} 3^k & 3^k & 3^k \\ 3^k & 3^k & 3^k \\ 3^k & 3^k & 3^k \end{bmatrix}$ = RHS

∴ Statement is true for $n = k + 1$.

Hence, by principle of mathematical induction, statement is true for all n, where $n \in N$. (1)

34. Our problem is to minimize

$Z = 5x + 10y$ ... (i)

Subject to the constraints

$x + 2y \le 120$ ...(ii)

$x + y \ge 60$ ...(iii)

$x - 2y \ge 0$ ...(iv)

and $x, y \ge 0$

Table for line $x + 2y = 120$ is

x	0	120
y	60	0

(1)

Put $(0, 0)$ in the inequality $x + 2y \le 120$, we get

$0 + 2 \times 0 \le 120$

⇒ $0 \le 120$ (which is true)

So, the half plane is towards the origin. Secondly, draw the graph of the line $x + y = 60$

x	0	60
y	60	0

(1)

On putting $(0, 0)$ in the inequality $x + y \ge 60$, we get

$0 + 0 \ge 60 \Rightarrow 0 \ge 60$ (which is false)

So, the half plane is away from the origin.

Thirdly, draw the graph of the line $x - 2y = 0$.

x	0	10
y	0	5

On putting $(5, 0)$ in the inequality $x - 2y \ge 0$, we get

$5 - 2 \times 0 \ge 0$

⇒ $5 \ge 0$ (which is true)

Thus, the half plane is towards the X-axis.

Since, $x, y \ge 0$

∴ The feasible region lies in the first quadrant. (1)

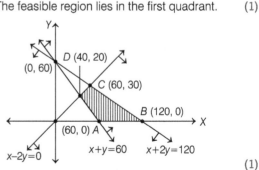

(1)

Clearly, feasible region is *ABCDA*.

On solving equations $x - 2y = 0$ and $x + y = 60$, we get $D(40, 20)$ and on solving equations $x - 2y = 0$ and $x + 2y = 120$, we get $C(60, 30)$. The corner points of the feasible region are $A(60, 0)$, $B(120, 0)$, $C(60, 30)$ and $D(40, 20)$.

The values of Z at these points are as follows

Corner points	Value of $Z = 5x + 10y$
A (60, 0)	300 (Minimum)
B (120, 0)	600
C (60, 30)	600
D (40, 20)	400

Clearly, the minimum value of Z is 300 at the point
(60, 0). (1)

Or

The given LPP can be rewritten as

Maximize or minimize $Z = 3x + 5y$

Subject to the constraints

$$3x - 4y \geq -12 \qquad \ldots(i)$$
$$2x - y \geq -2 \qquad \ldots(ii)$$
$$2x + 3y \geq 12 \qquad \ldots(iii)$$
$$x \leq 4 \qquad \ldots(iv)$$
$$y \geq 2 \qquad \ldots(v)$$
and $$x \geq 0 \qquad \ldots(vi)$$

Converting the inequations into equations, we obtain
the following equations $3x - 4y = -12, 2x - y = -2$,
$2x + 3y = 12$, $x = 4$, $y = 2$ and $x = 0$. (1)

Table for line $3x - 4y = -12$ is

x	0	−4
y	3	0

So, line passes through the points (0, 3) and (−4, 0).

Putting (0, 0) in the inequality $3x - 4y \geq -12$, we get

$$3 \times 0 - 4 \times 0 \geq -12$$
$$\Rightarrow \qquad 0 \geq -12 \text{ (which is true)}$$

So, the half plane is towards the origin.

Table for line $2x - y = -2$ is

x	0	−1
y	2	0

So, line passes through the points (0, 2) and (−1, 0).

On putting (0, 0) in the inequality $2x - y \geq -2$, we get

$$2 \times 0 - 0 \geq -2$$
$$\Rightarrow \qquad 0 \geq -2 \text{ (which is true)}$$

So, the half plane is towards the origin.

Table for line $2x + 3y = 12$ is

x	0	6
y	4	0

So, the line passes through the points (0, 4) and (6, 0).

On putting (0, 0) in the inequality $2x + 3y \geq 12$, we get

$$2 \times 0 + 3 \times 0 \geq 12$$
$$\Rightarrow \qquad 0 \geq 12 \text{ (which is false)}$$

So, the half plane is away from the origin. (1)

Draw the graph of the lines $x = 4$ and $y = 2$, which is
perpendicular to X and Y-axes.

Putting (0, 0) in the inequality $x \leq 4$, we get

$$0 \leq 4 \text{ (which is true)}$$

So, the half plane is towards the origin.

Putting (0, 0) in the inequality $y \geq 2$, we get

$$0 \geq 2 \text{ (which is false)}$$

So, the half plane is away from the origin.

The shaded region P_1, P_2, P_3, P_4, P_5 shown in figure
represents the feasible region of the given LPP.

The corner points of the feasible region are $P_1(3, 2)$,
$P_2(4, 2)$, $P_3(4, 6)$, $P_4\left(\dfrac{4}{5}, \dfrac{18}{5}\right)$ and $P_5\left(\dfrac{3}{4}, \dfrac{7}{2}\right)$. (1)

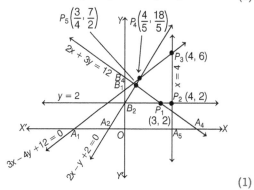

(1)

The value of the objective function at these points are
given in the following table

Corner points	Value of the objective function $Z = 3x + 5y$
$P_1(3, 2)$	$Z = 3 \times 3 + 5 \times 2 = 19$ (Minimum)
$P_2(4, 2)$	$Z = 3 \times 4 + 2 \times 5 = 22$
$P_3(4, 6)$	$Z = 3 \times 4 + 5 \times 6 = 42$ (Maximum)
$P_4\left(\dfrac{4}{5}, \dfrac{18}{5}\right)$	$Z = 3 \times \dfrac{4}{5} + 5 \times \dfrac{18}{5} = \dfrac{102}{5}$
$P_5\left(\dfrac{3}{4}, \dfrac{7}{2}\right)$	$Z = 3 \times \dfrac{3}{4} + 5 \times \dfrac{7}{2} = \dfrac{79}{4}$

Clearly, Z assumes its minimum value 19 at $x = 3$ and
$y = 2$. The maximum value of Z is 42 at $x = 4$ and $y = 6$. (1)

35. Let $I = \displaystyle\int \dfrac{1}{\cos^4 x + \sin^4 x} dx$

On dividing numerator and denominator by $\cos^4 x$ in
RHS, we get

$$I = \int \dfrac{\sec^4 x}{1 + \tan^4 x} dx$$

$$= \int \dfrac{(\sec^2 x)(\sec^2 x)}{1 + (\tan^2 x)^2} dx$$

$$= \int \dfrac{\sec^2 x (1 + \tan^2 x)}{1 + (\tan^2 x)^2} dx$$

On putting $\tan x = t \Rightarrow \sec^2 x \, dx = dt$

$$\therefore \qquad I = \int \frac{1+t^2}{1+t^4} \, dt \qquad (1)$$

Again, dividing numerator and denominator by t^2 in RHS, we get

$$I = \int \frac{1 + \dfrac{1}{t^2}}{t^2 + \dfrac{1}{t^2} + 2 - 2} \, dt = \int \frac{1 + \dfrac{1}{t^2}}{\left(t - \dfrac{1}{t}\right)^2 + 2} \, dt$$

Put $\qquad t - \dfrac{1}{t} = u$

$$\Rightarrow \qquad \left(1 + \frac{1}{t^2}\right) dt = du \qquad (2)$$

Then, $I = \int \dfrac{du}{u^2 + (\sqrt{2})^2}$

$$= \frac{1}{\sqrt{2}} \tan^{-1}\left(\frac{u}{\sqrt{2}}\right) + C$$

$$\left[\because \int \frac{dx}{x^2 + a^2} = \frac{1}{a} \tan^{-1}\left(\frac{x}{a}\right) + C\right]$$

$$= \frac{1}{\sqrt{2}} \tan^{-1}\left(\frac{t - \dfrac{1}{t}}{\sqrt{2}}\right) + C \quad \left[\text{putting } u = t - \frac{1}{t}\right]$$

$$= \frac{1}{\sqrt{2}} \tan^{-1}\left(\frac{t^2 - 1}{\sqrt{2}t}\right) + C$$

$$\therefore \quad I = \frac{1}{\sqrt{2}} \tan^{-1}\left(\frac{\tan^2 x - 1}{\sqrt{2} \tan x}\right) + C \quad [\because \text{put } t = \tan x]$$
$$(2)$$

36. (i) In $\triangle OEM$, we have $OE^2 = AM^2 + OM^2$

$$\Rightarrow \qquad 10^2 = x^2 + y^2$$

$$\Rightarrow \qquad x^2 + y^2 = 100 \qquad \ldots(i)$$

(ii) The area of green grass, $A = EB \times BC$

$$= (2x)(2y)$$
$$= 4xy$$
$$= 4x\sqrt{100 - x^2} \text{ m}^2 \text{ [from Eq. (i)]}$$

(iii) We have,

$$A = 4x\sqrt{100 - x^2}$$

$$\Rightarrow \quad \frac{dA}{dx} = 4\left[\sqrt{100 - x^2} + \frac{x}{2\sqrt{100 - x^2}}(-2x)\right]$$

$$= 4\left[\frac{100 - 2x^2}{\sqrt{100 - x^2}}\right]$$

For maximum, $\dfrac{dA}{dx} = 0$

$$\Rightarrow \quad 4\left[\frac{100 - 2x^2}{\sqrt{100 - x^2}}\right] = 0$$

$$\Rightarrow \quad 100 - 2x^2 = 0 \Rightarrow 100 = 2x^2$$

$$\Rightarrow \qquad x = \pm 5\sqrt{2} \Rightarrow x = 5\sqrt{2}$$
$$[\because x \text{ cannot be negative}]$$

Now, $\dfrac{d^2A}{dx^2} =$

$$4 \frac{\left[-4x\sqrt{100 - x^2} - (100 - 2x^2) \dfrac{1}{2\sqrt{100 - x^2}}(-2x)\right]}{(100 - x^2)}$$

$$= 4\frac{[-4x(100 - x^2) + (100x - 2x^3)]}{(100 - x^2)^{3/2}}$$

$$= 4\frac{[-300x + 2x^3]}{(100 - x^2)^{3/2}}$$

$$\therefore \quad \left(\frac{d^2A}{dx^2}\right)_{x = 5\sqrt{2}} = -\text{ive}$$

Thus, A is maximum when $x = 5\sqrt{2}$

$$Or$$

$$A_{max} = 4x\sqrt{100 - x^2}$$

$$= 4 \times 5\sqrt{2}\sqrt{100 - 50} \qquad [\because x = 5\sqrt{2}]$$

$$= 20\sqrt{2} \times 5\sqrt{2}$$

$$= 200 \text{ m}^2$$

The length of rectangle when A is maximum $= 2x$

$$= 2 \times 5\sqrt{2} = 10\sqrt{2} \text{ m}$$

$$\Rightarrow \quad y^2 = 100 - x^2 = 100 - 50 = 50 \qquad [\because x = 5\sqrt{2}]$$

$$\Rightarrow \quad y = 5\sqrt{2}$$

$$\Rightarrow \quad 2y = 10\sqrt{2} \text{ m}$$

$$\therefore \text{ Area of rectangle} = (2x)(2y) = 200 \text{ m}^2$$

Now, area of gravelling path

$$= \text{Area of circle} - \text{Area of rectangle}$$

$$= \pi(10)^2 - 200 = 100\pi - 200$$

$$= 100(\pi - 2) \text{ m}^2$$

37. Let

A : The event that question has some error

E_1 : The event that question is solved by Ravi

E_2 : The event that question is solved by Mohit

E_3 : The event that question is solved by Sonia

Then, we have

$$P(E_1) = \frac{30}{100}, P(E_2) = \frac{25}{100}, P(E_3) = \frac{45}{100}$$

and $P(A/E_1) = \dfrac{1}{100}, P(A/E_2) = \dfrac{1.2}{100}, P(A/E_3) = \dfrac{2}{100}$

(i) Required probability $= P(A/E_3) = \dfrac{2}{100} = 0.02$

(ii) Required probability $= P(E_3 \cap A) = P(A \cap E_3)$

$$= P(E_3) P(A/E_3)$$

$$= \frac{45}{100} \times \frac{2}{100}$$

$$= \frac{90}{10000}$$

$$= 0.009$$

(iii) Required probability = $P(A)$

$$= \sum_{i=1}^{3} P(E_i)\, P(A/E_i)$$

$$= P(E_1)\, P(A/E_1) + P(E_2)P(A/E_2) + P(E_3)\, P(A/E_3)$$

$$= \frac{30}{100} \times \frac{1}{100} + \frac{25}{100} \times \frac{1.2}{100} + \frac{45}{100} \times \frac{2}{100}$$

$$= 0.003 + 0.003 + 0.009 = 0.015$$

Or

Required probability = $P(\bar{E_1}/A)$

$$= 1 - P(E_1/A)$$

$$= 1 - \left[\frac{P(E_1)\, P(A/E_1)}{P(E_1)P(A/E_1) + P(E_2)\, P(A/E_2) + P(E_3)\, P(A/E_3)} \right]$$

$$= 1 - \left[\frac{\dfrac{30}{100} \times \dfrac{1}{100}}{\dfrac{30}{100} \times \dfrac{1}{100} + \dfrac{25}{100} \times \dfrac{1.2}{100} + \dfrac{45}{100} \times \dfrac{2}{100}} \right]$$

$$= 1 - \frac{0.003}{0.015} = 1 - 0.2 = 0.8$$

38. (i) From the figure, it is clear that perimeter of floor

$$= 200 \text{ m}$$

$$\Rightarrow 2 \times \pi\left(\frac{y}{2}\right) + 2x = 200 \Rightarrow \pi y + 2x = 200 \qquad ...(i)$$

From figure, we have

Area, $A = x \times y = xy = x\left[\dfrac{200 - 2x}{\pi}\right]$ [from Eq. (i)]

$$= \frac{1}{\pi} 2x(100 - x) = \frac{2}{\pi}(100x - x^2)$$

$$\therefore \quad \frac{dA}{dx} = \frac{2}{\pi}(100 - 2x)$$

$$\Rightarrow \frac{d^2A}{dx^2} = \frac{2}{\pi}(-2) = -\frac{4}{\pi}$$

For maximum, $\dfrac{dA}{dx} = 0 \Rightarrow \dfrac{2}{\pi}(100 - 2x) = 0$

$$\Rightarrow \qquad\qquad x = 50$$

Now, at $x = 50$, $\dfrac{d^2A}{dx^2} = -\dfrac{4}{\pi}$

$\therefore A$ is maximum at $x = 50$

So, maximum value of

$$A = \frac{2}{\pi}\{100 \times 50 - (50)^2\} = \frac{2}{\pi}(5000 - 2500)$$

$$= \frac{2}{\pi} \times 2500 = \frac{5000}{\pi} \text{ m}^2$$

(ii) Let B be the area of whole floor. Then,

$$B = 2 \times \frac{1}{2} \pi \left(\frac{y}{2}\right)^2 + xy = \frac{\pi}{4}y^2 + xy$$

$$= \frac{\pi}{4}\left(\frac{200 - 2x}{\pi}\right)^2 + x\left(\frac{200 - 2x}{\pi}\right) \quad \text{[from Eq. (i)]}$$

$$= \frac{1}{4\pi}(200 - 2x)^2 + \frac{x}{\pi}(200 - 2x)$$

$$= \frac{200 - 2x}{\pi}\left[\frac{200 - 2x}{4} + x\right]$$

$$= \frac{200 - 2x}{\pi}\left(\frac{200 - 2x + 4x}{4}\right)$$

$$= \frac{200 - 2x}{\pi}\left(\frac{200 + 2x}{4}\right)$$

$$= \left(\frac{40000 - 4x^2}{4x}\right)$$

$$\Rightarrow \quad \frac{dB}{dx} = \frac{1}{4\pi}(-8x)$$

and $\dfrac{d^2B}{dx^2} = -\dfrac{8}{4\pi}$

For maximum, $\dfrac{dB}{dx} = 0$

$$\Rightarrow \qquad -\frac{8}{4\pi}x = 0 \Rightarrow x = 0$$

At $x = 0$, $\dfrac{d^2B}{dx^2} = -\dfrac{8}{4\pi}$

$\therefore B$ is maximum at $x = 0$.

SAMPLE QUESTION PAPER 8

MATHEMATICS

Time : 3 hrs   Max. Marks : 80

General Instructions

1. This question paper contains - five sections A, B, C, D and E. Each section is compulsory. However, there are internal choices in some questions.
2. Section A has 18 MCQ's and 02 Assertion-Reason based questions of 1 mark each.
3. Section B has 5 Very Short Answer (VSA) type questions of 2 marks each.
4. Section C has 6 Short Answer (SA) type questions of 3 marks each.
5. Section D has 4 Long Answer (LA) type questions of 5 marks each.
6. Section E has 3 source based/case based/passage based/integrated units of assessment (4 marks each) with sub parts.

Section A

(Multiple Choice Questions) Each question carries 1 mark

1. The value of projection of the line joining the points (3, 4, 5) and (4, 6, 3) on the line joining the points $(-1, 2, 4)$ and (1, 0, 5) is
   (a) $\dfrac{4}{3}$ (b) $\dfrac{3}{4}$ (c) $\dfrac{1}{3}$ (d) $\dfrac{2}{3}$

2. If $A + B = \begin{bmatrix} 1 & 0 \\ 1 & 1 \end{bmatrix}$ and $A - 2B = \begin{bmatrix} -1 & 1 \\ 0 & -1 \end{bmatrix}$, then A is equal to
   (a) $\begin{bmatrix} 1/3 & 1/3 \\ 2/3 & 1/3 \end{bmatrix}$ (b) $\begin{bmatrix} 1/3 & 2/3 \\ 1/3 & 1/3 \end{bmatrix}$ (c) $\begin{bmatrix} 1/2 & 3/2 \\ 5/2 & 5/2 \end{bmatrix}$ (d) $\begin{bmatrix} 1 & 1 \\ 1/3 & 2/3 \end{bmatrix}$

3. The area of the parallelogram determined by the vectors $\hat{i} + 2\hat{j} + 3\hat{k}$ and $3\hat{i} - 2\hat{j} + \hat{k}$ is (in sq units)
   (a) 8   (b) $8\sqrt{3}$ (c) $8\sqrt{5}$ (d) 3

4. The total number of possible matrices of order 3×3 with each entry 2 or 0 is
   (a) 256   (b) 512   (c) 18   (d) 9

5. The magnitude of greater diagonal of parallelogram whose sides are $\hat{i} + \hat{j} - 2\hat{k}$ and $-2\hat{i} + 3\hat{j} + 4\hat{k}$, is
   (a) $\sqrt{21}$ (b) $\sqrt{31}$ (c) 21   (d) 31

6. If A is a matrix of order 2×3 and B is a matrix of order 3×5, then the order of matrix $(AB)'$ or $(AB)^T$ is
   (a) 2×5 (b) 5×2 (c) 3×5 (d) 5×3

7. The value of $\hat{i} \cdot (\hat{j} \times \hat{k}) + \hat{j} \cdot (\hat{i} \times \hat{k}) + \hat{k} \cdot (\hat{i} \times \hat{j})$ is equal to
   (a) 0   (b) -1 (c) 1   (d) 2

8. If $X + \begin{bmatrix} 4 & 6 \\ -3 & 7 \end{bmatrix} = \begin{bmatrix} 3 & -6 \\ 5 & -8 \end{bmatrix}$, then matrix X is
   (a) $\begin{bmatrix} -1 & -12 \\ 8 & -15 \end{bmatrix}$ (b) $\begin{bmatrix} 1 & -12 \\ -8 & -15 \end{bmatrix}$
   (c) $\begin{bmatrix} -1 & -1 \\ 0 & 0 \end{bmatrix}$ (b) $\begin{bmatrix} 7 & 0 \\ 2 & -1 \end{bmatrix}$

9. If $\vec{a} = 4\hat{i} - \hat{j} + \hat{k}$ and $\vec{b} = 2\hat{i} - 2\hat{j} + \hat{k}$, then $|\vec{a} - \vec{b}|$ is equal to
   (a) $\sqrt{3}$ (b) $\sqrt{5}$ (c) 5   (d) 3

10. The element a_{23} of a 3×3 matrix $A = [a_{ij}]$, whose elements a_{ij} are given by $a_{ij} = \dfrac{|i - j|}{2}$ is
    (a) 1   (b) 0   (c) $\dfrac{1}{2}$ (d) $-\dfrac{1}{2}$

11. If $A = \begin{bmatrix} 3 & -4 \\ 1 & -1 \end{bmatrix}$, then A^{-1} is equal to
    (a) $\begin{bmatrix} -1 & 4 \\ -1 & 3 \end{bmatrix}$ (b) $\begin{bmatrix} 1 & 4 \\ -1 & 3 \end{bmatrix}$
    (c) $\begin{bmatrix} 1 & -4 \\ 1 & -3 \end{bmatrix}$ (b) $\begin{bmatrix} 1 & 4 \\ 3 & -1 \end{bmatrix}$

12. If A_{ij} is the cofactor of the element a_{ij} of the determinant $\begin{vmatrix} 2 & -3 & 5 \\ 6 & 0 & 4 \\ 1 & 5 & -7 \end{vmatrix}$, then the value of $a_{32} \cdot A_{32}$ is
    (a) 100   (b) 225
    (c) 110   (d) 150

13. If A is a matrix of order 3×3 such that $|A| = 4$ and B is another matrix of same order such that $B = A^3$, then $|B|$ is equal to
    (a) 64   (b) 16   (c) 256   (d) 1024

14. All the vectors of magnitude $10\sqrt{3}$ that are perpendicular to the plane of $\hat{i} + 2\hat{j} + \hat{k}$ and $-\hat{i} + 3\hat{j} + 4\hat{k}$ is
    (a) $\pm(10\hat{i} - 10\hat{j} + 10\hat{k})$ (b) $\pm(10\hat{i} + 10\hat{j} - 10\hat{k})$
    (c) $\pm(5\hat{i} - 5\hat{j} + 5\hat{k})$ (d) $\pm(\hat{i} + \hat{j} - \hat{k})$

15. If $\vec{a}$ is a unit vector such that $\vec{a} \times \hat{i} = \hat{j}$, then $\vec{a} \cdot \hat{i}$ is equal to
    (a) 1   (b) 0   (c) -1 (d) $\hat{i}$

16. The angle between the vectors $\vec{a} \times \vec{b}$ and $\vec{b} \times \vec{a}$ is
    (a) $-\dfrac{\pi}{2}$ (b) π (c) $\dfrac{\pi}{2}$ (d) $\dfrac{3\pi}{2}$

17. If $\vec{a}$ and $\vec{b}$ are two vectors such that $\vec{a} \cdot \vec{b} = 6$, $|\vec{a}| = 3$ and $|\vec{b}| = 4$, then the projection of $\vec{a}$ on $\vec{b}$ is
    (a) $\dfrac{1}{2}$ (b) $\dfrac{3}{2}$ (c) $\dfrac{5}{2}$ (d) -1

18. If $\vec{b}$ is a unit vector such that $(\vec{a} + \vec{b}) \cdot (\vec{a} - \vec{b}) = 8$, then $|\vec{a}|$ is equal to
    (a) 1   (b) 2   (c) 3   (d) 4

Assertion-Reason Based Questions

In the following questions, a statement of Assertion (A) is followed by a statement of Reason (R). Choose the correct answer out of the following choices.

    (a) Both A and R are true and R is the correct explanation of A
    (b) Both A and R are true but R is not the correct explanation of A
    (c) A is true but R is false
    (d) A is false but R is true

19. **Assertion (A)** If $A = \begin{bmatrix} 3 & 1 \\ -5 & x \end{bmatrix}$, then $(-A)$ is given by $\begin{bmatrix} -3 & -1 \\ 5 & -x \end{bmatrix}$.

    Reason (R) The negative of a matrix is given by $-A$ and is defined as $-A = (-1)A$.

20. Assertion (A) If $A = \begin{bmatrix} 1 & 2 \\ 5 & -1 \end{bmatrix}$, then $|A| = -11$.

Reason (R) If $A = \begin{bmatrix} a_{11} & a_{12} \\ a_{21} & a_{22} \end{bmatrix}$, then $|A| = a_{11}a_{22} - a_{21}a_{12}$.

Section B

(This section comprises of very short answer type questions (VSA) of 2 marks each)

21. Show that the function
$f(x) = 4x^3 - 18x^2 + 27x - 7$ has neither maxima nor minima.

Or Show that the function $f(x) = \dfrac{x}{3} + \dfrac{3}{x}$
decreases in the intervals $(-3, 0) \cup (0, 3)$.

22. If $\operatorname{cosec}^{-1} x + \operatorname{cosec}^{-1} y + \operatorname{cosec}^{-1} z = \dfrac{-3\pi}{2}$,
find the value of $\dfrac{x}{y} + \dfrac{y}{z} + \dfrac{z}{x}$.

23. Find $[P(B/A) + P(A/B)]$, if $P(A) = \dfrac{3}{10}$,
$P(B) = \dfrac{2}{5}$ and $P(A \cup B) = \dfrac{3}{5}$.

Or

Three distinct numbers are chosen randomly from the first 50 natural numbers. Find the probability that all the three numbers are divisible by both 2 and 3.

24. Evaluate $\displaystyle\int \dfrac{x-3}{(x-1)^3} e^x dx$.

25. Three cards are drawn successively without replacement from a pack of 52 well-shuffled cards. What is the probability that first two cards are king and the third card drawn is an ace?

Section C

(This section comprises of short answer type questions (SA) of 3 marks each)

26. If $x, y, z \in [-1, 1]$ such that
$\sin^{-1} x + \sin^{-1} y + \sin^{-1} z = -\dfrac{3\pi}{2}$, find the value of $x^2 + y^2 + z^2$.

27. Show that the function $f : R \to R$ defined by $f(x) = 2x^3 - 5$, is a bijective function.

Or

If R_1 and R_2 be two equivalence relations on a set A, prove that $R_1 \cap R_2$ is also an equivalence relation on A.

28. If $x\sqrt{1+y} + y\sqrt{1+x} = 0, (x \neq y)$, then prove
that $\dfrac{dy}{dx} = -\dfrac{1}{(1+x)^2}$.

Or If $y = e^x \sin x$, then prove that
$$\dfrac{d^2 y}{dx^2} - 2\dfrac{dy}{dx} + 2y = 0$$

29. Evaluate $\displaystyle\int \dfrac{1}{3x^2 + 5x + 7} dx$.

Or Evaluate $\displaystyle\int \dfrac{xe^x}{(x+1)^2} dx$.

30. If $\vec{a}$ and $\vec{b}$ are unit vectors, then find the angle between $\vec{a}$ and $\vec{b}$, given that $(\sqrt{3}\,\vec{a} - \vec{b})$ is a unit vector.

31. Find all the points of local maxima and local minima of $f(x) = -x + 2\sin x$ on $[0, 2\pi]$. Also, find local maximum and minimum values.

Section D

(This section comprises of long answer type questions (LA) of 5 marks each)

32. Find $\dfrac{dy}{dx}$, if $y = (\cos x)^x + (\sin x)^{1/x}$.

33. Find the particular solution of the differential equation

$$\frac{dy}{dx} = \frac{x(2\log x + 1)}{\sin y + y\cos y},$$

given that $y = \dfrac{\pi}{2}$, when $x = 1$.

Or

Solve the following differential equation

$$xy\log\left|\frac{y}{x}\right| dx + \left[y^2 - x^2\log\left|\frac{y}{x}\right|\right] dy = 0$$

34. Solve the LPP,

maximise, $Z = 0.08x + 0.10y$

Subject to the constraints, $x + y \le 12000$,

$x \ge 2000$, $y \ge 4000$, $x \ge 0$, $y \ge 0$.

Or

Solve the following LPP graphically:
Minimize and maximize $Z = 5x + 2y$
Subject to constraints

$-2x - 3y \le -6$, $x - 2y \le 2$, $3x + 2y \le 12$

$-3x + 2y \le 3$, $x, y \ge 0$

35. Show that $\displaystyle\int_0^{\pi/2} f(\sin 2x)\sin x\, dx$

$$= \sqrt{2}\int_0^{\pi/4} f(\cos 2x)\cos x\, dx.$$

Section E

(This section comprises of 3 case-study/ passage-based questions of 4 marks each with two sub-parts. First two case study questions have three sub-parts (i), (ii), (iii) of marks 1, 1, 2 respectively. The third case study question has two sub-parts of 2 marks each)

36. Let a cone is inscribed in a sphere of radius R. The height and radius of cone are h and r respectively.

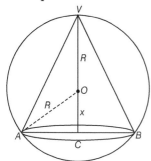

On the basis of above information, answer the following questions.

(i) Write the relation between r and R in terms of x

(ii) Write the volume V of the cone in terms of R and x.

(iii) Show that volume V of the cone is maximum when $x = \dfrac{R}{3}$.

Or If volume V of the cone is maximum at $x = \dfrac{R}{3}$, then find the maximum value of V and find the ratio of volume of cone and volume of sphere, when volume of cone is maximum.

37. A square piece of tin of side 24 cm is to be made into a box without top by cutting a square from each corner and folding up the flaps to form a box.

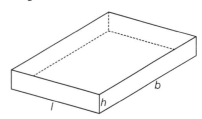

On the basis of above information, answer the following questions.

(i) Write the length, breadth and height of the box formed in terms of x.

(ii) Express volume V of the box in terms of x.

(iii) Show that volume of the box is maximum when $x = 4$ cm.

Or

If volume of the box is maximum at $x = 4$, then find the maximum value of volume of box. If rate of making the box is ₹5/cm², then find the cost of box when volume is maximum.

38. A can hit a target 4 times in 5 shots, B hit 3 times in 4 shots and C hit 2 times in 3 shots.

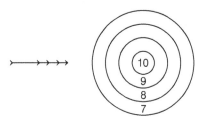

On the basis of above information, answer the following questions.

(i) Find P(any two of A, B and C will hit the target).

(ii) Find P(none of them will hit the target) and P(B and C may hit and A may not).

SOLUTIONS

1. (a) The direction ratios of the line joining $P(-1, 2, 4)$ and $Q(1, 0, 5)$ are proportional to $(2, -2, 1)$, i.e. $2\hat{i} - 2\hat{j} + \hat{k}$. and the direction ratio of the line joining $A(3, 4, 5)$ and $B(4, 6, 3)$ are proportional to $(1, 2, -2)$, i.e. $\hat{i} + 2\hat{j} - 2\hat{k}$.

Thus, the projection of line $\overrightarrow{AB}$ on $\overrightarrow{PQ}$ is

$$\frac{(\hat{i} + 2\hat{j} - 2\hat{k}) \cdot (2\hat{i} - 2\hat{j} + \hat{k})}{|2\hat{i} - 2\hat{j} + \hat{k}|} = \frac{1 \times 2 - 2 \times 2 - 2 \times 1}{\sqrt{2^2 + (-2)^2 + (1)^2}}$$

$$= \left|\frac{2 - 4 - 2}{3}\right| = \frac{4}{3}$$

2. (a) We have, $A + B = \begin{bmatrix} 1 & 0 \\ 1 & 1 \end{bmatrix} \Rightarrow B = \begin{bmatrix} 1 & 0 \\ 1 & 1 \end{bmatrix} - A$

$\because \quad A - 2B = \begin{bmatrix} -1 & 1 \\ 0 & -1 \end{bmatrix}$

$\therefore \quad A - 2\left(\begin{bmatrix} 1 & 0 \\ 1 & 1 \end{bmatrix} - A\right) = \begin{bmatrix} -1 & 1 \\ 0 & -1 \end{bmatrix}$

$\Rightarrow \quad 3A = \begin{bmatrix} -1 & 1 \\ 0 & -1 \end{bmatrix} + 2\begin{bmatrix} 1 & 0 \\ 1 & 1 \end{bmatrix} = \begin{bmatrix} 1 & 1 \\ 2 & 1 \end{bmatrix}$

$\therefore \quad A = \frac{1}{3}\begin{bmatrix} 1 & 1 \\ 2 & 1 \end{bmatrix} = \begin{bmatrix} 1/3 & 1/3 \\ 2/3 & 1/3 \end{bmatrix}$

3. (b) Let $\vec{a} = \hat{i} + 2\hat{j} + 3\hat{k}$ and $\vec{b} = 3\hat{i} - 2\hat{j} + \hat{k}$

Then, $\vec{a} \times \vec{b} = \begin{vmatrix} \hat{i} & \hat{j} & \hat{k} \\ 1 & 2 & 3 \\ 3 & -2 & 1 \end{vmatrix}$

$= \hat{i}(2 + 6) - \hat{j}(1 - 9) + \hat{k}(-2 - 6)$

$= 8\hat{i} + 8\hat{j} - 8\hat{k}$

$\therefore$ Area of parallelogram whose adjacent sides are $\vec{a}$ and $\vec{b}$,

$A = |\vec{a} \times \vec{b}| = \sqrt{8^2 + 8^2 + (-8)^2} = 8\sqrt{3}$ sq units

4. (b) Order of 3×3 matrix contains 9 elements. Each element can be selected in 2 ways (it can be either 2 or 0).

$\therefore$ Total number of possible matrices of order 3×3 with each entry 2 or 0 is 2^9, i.e. 512.

5. (a) Let $\vec{a} = \hat{i} + \hat{j} - 2\hat{k}$ and $\vec{b} = -2\hat{i} + 3\hat{j} + 4\hat{k}$

$\therefore$ Diagonal of parallelogram

$= \vec{a} + \vec{b} = (\hat{i} + \hat{j} - 2\hat{k}) + (-2\hat{i} + 3\hat{j} + 4\hat{k})$

$= -\hat{i} + 4\hat{j} + 2\hat{k}$

$\therefore |\vec{a} + \vec{b}| = \sqrt{(-1)^2 + (4)^2 + (2)^2} = \sqrt{1 + 16 + 4} = \sqrt{21}$

6. (b) Given, A is a matrix of order 2×3 and B is a matrix of order 3×5, therefore the product AB is a matrix of order 2×5.

Then, the order of matrix $(AB)'$ or $(AB)^T$ is 5×2.

7. (c) We have,

$\hat{i} \cdot (\hat{j} \times \hat{k}) + \hat{j} \cdot (\hat{i} \times \hat{k}) + \hat{k} \cdot (\hat{i} \times \hat{j}) = \hat{i} \cdot \hat{i} + \hat{j} \cdot (-\hat{j}) + \hat{k} \cdot \hat{k}$

$[\because \hat{i} \times \hat{j} = \hat{k}, \hat{j} \times \hat{k} = \hat{i}, \hat{i} \times \hat{k} = -\hat{j}, \vec{a} \times \vec{b} = -\vec{b} \times \vec{a}]$

$= 1 - 1 + 1 \qquad [\because \hat{i} \cdot \hat{i} = \hat{j} \cdot \hat{j} = \hat{k} \cdot \hat{k} = 1]$

$= 1$

8. (a) Let $A = \begin{bmatrix} 4 & 6 \\ -3 & 7 \end{bmatrix}$ and $B = \begin{bmatrix} 3 & -6 \\ 5 & -8 \end{bmatrix}$

Then, the given matrix equation is $X + A = B$.

$\therefore X + A = B$

$\Rightarrow X = B + (-A)$

$= \begin{bmatrix} 3 & -6 \\ 5 & -8 \end{bmatrix} + \begin{bmatrix} -4 & -6 \\ 3 & -7 \end{bmatrix} = \begin{bmatrix} 3-4 & -6-6 \\ 5+3 & -8-7 \end{bmatrix} = \begin{bmatrix} -1 & -12 \\ 8 & -15 \end{bmatrix}$

$\therefore \quad X = \begin{bmatrix} -1 & -12 \\ 8 & -15 \end{bmatrix}$

9. (b) We have, $\vec{a} = 4\hat{i} - \hat{j} + \hat{k}$ and $\vec{b} = 2\hat{i} - 2\hat{j} + \hat{k}$

$\therefore \quad \vec{a} - \vec{b} = (4\hat{i} - \hat{j} + \hat{k}) - (2\hat{i} - 2\hat{j} + \hat{k})$

$\qquad \qquad = 2\hat{i} + \hat{j}$

$\therefore |\vec{a} - \vec{b}| = \sqrt{(2)^2 + (1)^2 + (0)^2} = \sqrt{5}$

10. (c) Given, $A = [a_{ij}]_{3 \times 3}$

where, $a_{ij} = \dfrac{|i - j|}{2}$

Now, $a_{23} = \dfrac{|2 - 3|}{2} = \dfrac{|-1|}{2} = \dfrac{1}{2}$

11. (a) Given $A = \begin{bmatrix} 3 & -4 \\ 1 & -1 \end{bmatrix}$, then

$|A| = \begin{vmatrix} 3 & -4 \\ 1 & -1 \end{vmatrix} = -3 + 4 = 1 \neq 0$

So, A is not singular matrix and A^{-1} exists.
Now, cofactors of each element of $|A|$ are

$A_{11} = -1, A_{12} = -(1) = -1$

$A_{21} = -(-4) = 4, A_{22} = 3$

Now, $\text{adj } A = \begin{bmatrix} -1 & 4 \\ -1 & 3 \end{bmatrix}$

$A^{-1} = \dfrac{1}{|A|} \text{adj}(A) = \dfrac{1}{1}\begin{bmatrix} -1 & 4 \\ -1 & 3 \end{bmatrix}$

12. (c) Let $\Delta = \begin{vmatrix} 2 & -3 & 5 \\ 6 & 0 & 4 \\ 1 & 5 & -7 \end{vmatrix}$

Here, $a_{32} = 5$
Given, A_{ij} is the cofactor of the element a_{ij} of A.

$\therefore \qquad A_{32} = (-1)^{3+2}\begin{vmatrix} 2 & 5 \\ 6 & 4 \end{vmatrix} = -1(8 - 30) = 22$

$\Rightarrow a_{32} \cdot A_{32} = 5 \times 22 = 110$

13. (a) We have, $B = A^3$

$\Rightarrow \qquad |B| = |A^3| \Rightarrow |B| = |A|^3$

$\Rightarrow \qquad |B| = 4^3 \Rightarrow |B| = 64$

14. (a) Let $\vec{b}_1 = \hat{i} + 2\hat{j} + \hat{k}$ and $\vec{b}_2 = -\hat{i} + 3\hat{j} + 4\hat{k}$

Then, $\vec{b}_1 \times \vec{b}_2 = \begin{vmatrix} \hat{i} & \hat{j} & \hat{k} \\ 1 & 2 & 1 \\ -1 & 3 & 4 \end{vmatrix}$

$= \hat{i}(8 - 3) - \hat{j}(4 + 1) + \hat{k}(3 + 2)$

$= \hat{i}(5) - \hat{j}(5) + \hat{k}(5) = \vec{c} \text{ (say)}$

$\Rightarrow |\vec{b}_1 \times \vec{b}_2| = \sqrt{(5)^2 + (5)^2 + (5)^2} = 5\sqrt{3}$

Now, $\hat{c} = \dfrac{\vec{b}_1 \times \vec{b}_2}{|\vec{b}_1 \times \vec{b}_2|} = \dfrac{\hat{i}}{\sqrt{3}} - \dfrac{\hat{j}}{\sqrt{3}} + \dfrac{\hat{k}}{\sqrt{3}}$

Hence, required vector $= \pm(10\sqrt{3}\,\hat{c})$

$\qquad \qquad = \pm(10\hat{i} - 10\hat{j} + 10\hat{k})$

15. (b) We have, $|\vec{a}| = 1, \vec{a} \times \hat{i} = \hat{j}$

$\therefore \qquad \qquad \vec{a} = \hat{k}$

So, $\qquad \vec{a} \cdot \hat{i} = \hat{k} \cdot \hat{i} = 0$

16. (b) We know that $\vec{b} \times \vec{a} = -(\vec{a} \times \vec{b})$

So, angle between $\vec{a} \times \vec{b}$ and $\vec{b} \times \vec{a}$ is π.

17. (b) We have, $\vec{a} \cdot \vec{b} = 6, |\vec{a}| = 3$ and $|\vec{b}| = 4$

$\therefore$ Projection of $\vec{a}$ on $\vec{b} = \dfrac{\vec{a} \cdot \vec{b}}{|\vec{b}|} = \dfrac{6}{4} = \dfrac{3}{2}$

18. (c) We have, $(\vec{a} + \vec{b}) \cdot (\vec{a} - \vec{b}) = 8$

$\Rightarrow \qquad \qquad |\vec{a}|^2 - |\vec{b}|^2 = 8$

$\Rightarrow \qquad \qquad |\vec{a}|^2 = 8 + 1 \qquad [\because |\vec{b}| = 1]$

$\Rightarrow \qquad \qquad |\vec{a}|^2 = 9$

$\Rightarrow \qquad \qquad |\vec{a}| = 3$

19. (a) We define $-A = (-1)A$.

If $A = \begin{bmatrix} 3 & 1 \\ -5 & x \end{bmatrix}$,

then $-A$ is given by

$-A = (-1)A = (-1)\begin{bmatrix} 3 & 1 \\ -5 & x \end{bmatrix} = \begin{bmatrix} -3 & -1 \\ 5 & -x \end{bmatrix}$

20. (a) We have, $A = \begin{bmatrix} 1 & 2 \\ 5 & -1 \end{bmatrix}$

$\therefore \qquad \qquad |A| = \begin{vmatrix} 1 & 2 \\ 5 & -1 \end{vmatrix}$

$\qquad \qquad = 1(-1) - 5(2) = -1 - 10 = -11$

21. We have, $f(x) = 4x^3 - 18x^2 + 27x - 7$

$f'(x) = 12x^2 - 36x + 27$

$f'(x) = 3(4x^2 - 12x + 9)$

$\qquad = 3(2x - 3)^2$

Put $f'(x) = 0$

$\Rightarrow \qquad 3(2x - 3)^2 = 0$

$\Rightarrow \qquad (2x - 3)^2 = 0$

$\Rightarrow \qquad \qquad x = \dfrac{3}{2} \text{ (critical point)} \qquad (1)$

Since, $f'(x) > 0$ for all $x < \dfrac{3}{2}$ and for all $x > \dfrac{3}{2}$.

Hence, $x = \dfrac{3}{2}$ is a point of inflexion.

i.e. $f(x)$ has neither a point of maxima nor a point of minima. $\qquad (1)$

Or

Given, $f(x) = \dfrac{x}{3} + \dfrac{3}{x}$

$\Rightarrow \quad f'(x) = \dfrac{1}{3} - \dfrac{3}{x^2}$

$\Rightarrow \quad f'(x) = \dfrac{x^2 - 9}{3x^2}$ (1)

When $x \in (-3, 0) \cup (0, 3)$

$\qquad f'(x) < 0$ (1)

$\therefore f(x)$ is decreasing function in $(-3, 0) \cup (0, 3)$.

22. We know that the minimum value of $\text{cosec}^{-1} x$ is $\dfrac{-\pi}{2}$

which is attained at $x = -1$.

$\therefore \quad \text{cosec}^{-1} x + \text{cosec}^{-1} y + \text{cosec}^{-1} z = \dfrac{-3\pi}{2}$

$\Rightarrow \quad \text{cosec}^{-1} x + \text{cosec}^{-1} y + \text{cosec}^{-1} z$

$\qquad = \left(\dfrac{-\pi}{2}\right) + \left(\dfrac{-\pi}{2}\right) + \left(\dfrac{-\pi}{2}\right)$

$\Rightarrow \quad \text{cosec}^{-1} x = \text{cosec}^{-1} y = \text{cosec}^{-1} z = \dfrac{-\pi}{2}$ (1)

$\Rightarrow \quad x = y = z = \text{cosec}\left(\dfrac{-\pi}{2}\right) = -1$

$\therefore \quad \dfrac{x}{y} + \dfrac{y}{z} + \dfrac{z}{x} = \dfrac{(-1)}{(-1)} + \dfrac{(-1)}{(-1)} + \dfrac{(-1)}{(-1)}$

$\qquad = 1 + 1 + 1 = 3$ (1)

23. We have, $P(A) = \dfrac{3}{10}, P(B) = \dfrac{2}{5}$ and $P(A \cup B) = \dfrac{3}{5}$

We know that

$\qquad P(A \cup B) = P(A) + P(B) - P(A \cap B)$

$\Rightarrow \quad \dfrac{3}{5} = \dfrac{3}{10} + \dfrac{2}{5} - P(A \cap B)$

$\Rightarrow \quad P(A \cap B) = \dfrac{3}{10} + \dfrac{2}{5} - \dfrac{3}{5} = \dfrac{1}{10}$ (1)

Now, $[P(B / A) + P(A / B)] = \dfrac{P(A \cap B)}{P(A)} + \dfrac{P(A \cap B)}{P(B)}$

$\qquad = \dfrac{\frac{1}{10}}{3/10} + \dfrac{\frac{1}{10}}{2/5} = \dfrac{1}{3} + \dfrac{1}{4} = \dfrac{7}{12}$ (1)

Or

Three distinct numbers are chosen from first 50 natural numbers is $^{50}C_3$.

Total numbers which is divisible by 2 and 3 from first 50 natural numbers is

$\{6, 12, 18, 24, 30, 36, 42, 48\} = 8$ (1)

$\therefore$ Required probability $= \dfrac{^8C_3}{^{50}C_3}$

$\qquad = \dfrac{8 \times 7 \times 6}{50 \times 49 \times 48} = \dfrac{1}{350}$ (1)

24. Let $I = \displaystyle\int \dfrac{(x-3)}{(x-1)^3} e^x dx = \int \dfrac{e^x (x - 1 - 2)}{(x-1)^3} dx$

$\qquad = \displaystyle\int e^x \left\{ \dfrac{(x-1)}{(x-1)^3} - \dfrac{2}{(x-1)^3} \right\} dx$

$\qquad = \displaystyle\int e^x \left\{ \dfrac{1}{(x-1)^2} - \dfrac{2}{(x-1)^3} \right\} dx$

$\qquad = \displaystyle\int e^x \cdot \{f(x) + f'(x)\}\, dx,$ (1)

where $f(x) = \dfrac{1}{(x-1)^2}$ and $f'(x) = \dfrac{-2}{(x-1)^3}$

$\qquad = e^x \cdot f(x) + C = e^x \cdot \dfrac{1}{(x-1)^2} + C = \dfrac{e^x}{(x-1)^2} + C$ (1)

25. Since, there are 52 cards in a pack.

$\therefore \qquad n(S) = 52$

Let $A =$ event that the card drawn is king and $B =$ event that the card drawn is an ace.

Now, $\qquad P(A) = \dfrac{4}{52}$

$P\left(\dfrac{A}{A}\right) =$ Probability of drawing second king when one king has already been drawn

$\qquad = \dfrac{3}{51}$

$\qquad \qquad$ [$\because$ remaining cards are $(52 - 1) = 51$]

$P(B/AA) =$ Probability of drawing third card to be an ace when two kings have already been drawn

$\qquad = \dfrac{4}{50}$ (1)

Now, probability of getting first two cards are king and third card is an ace

$\qquad = P(A \cap A \cap B) = P(A) \cdot P\left(\dfrac{A}{A}\right) \cdot P\left(\dfrac{B}{AA}\right)$

$\qquad \qquad$ [by multiplication theorem]

$\qquad = \dfrac{4}{52} \times \dfrac{3}{51} \times \dfrac{4}{50} = \dfrac{2}{5525}$ (1)

26. We know that the minimum value of $\sin^{-1} x$ for $x \in [-1, 1]$ is $-\pi/2$.

$\therefore \sin^{-1} x \geq -\dfrac{\pi}{2}, \sin^{-1} y \geq -\dfrac{\pi}{2}, \sin^{-1} z \geq -\dfrac{\pi}{2} \forall$

$\qquad \qquad \qquad \qquad \qquad x, y, z \in [-1, 1]$ (1)

$\Rightarrow \sin^{-1} x + \sin^{-1} y + \sin^{-1} z \geq \left(-\dfrac{\pi}{2}\right)$

$\qquad \qquad \qquad \qquad \qquad + \left(-\dfrac{\pi}{2}\right) + \left(-\dfrac{\pi}{2}\right)$

$\Rightarrow \sin^{-1} x + \sin^{-1} y + \sin^{-1} z \geq -\dfrac{3\pi}{2}$

$\therefore \sin^{-1} x + \sin^{-1} y + \sin^{-1} z = -\dfrac{3\pi}{2}$ (1)

$\Rightarrow \sin^{-1} x = \sin^{-1} y = \sin^{-1} z = -\dfrac{\pi}{2}$

$\Rightarrow \quad x = y = z = \sin\left(-\dfrac{\pi}{2}\right)$

$\Rightarrow \quad x = y = z = -1$

Hence, $x^2 + y^2 + z^2 = (-1)^2 + (-1)^2 + (-1)^2 = 3$ (1)

27. Given, $f : R \to R$ defined by $f(x) = 2x^3 - 5$

For one-one (injective)

Let $\qquad f(x_1) = f(x_2), \ \forall x_1, x_2 \in R$

$\Rightarrow \qquad 2x_1^3 - 5 = 2x_2^3 - 5$

$\Rightarrow \qquad 2x_1^3 = 2x_2^3$

$\Rightarrow \qquad x_1^3 = x_2^3$

$\Rightarrow \qquad x_1 = x_2$

Thus, $\qquad f(x_1) = f(x_2) \Rightarrow x_1 = x_2$

So, f is one-one (injective). (1)

For onto (surjective)

Let y be an arbitrary element of R (codomain), then

$\qquad\qquad f(x) = y$

$\Rightarrow \qquad 2x^3 - 5 = y$

$\Rightarrow \qquad 2x^3 = y + 5$

$\Rightarrow \qquad x^3 = \dfrac{y + 5}{2}$

$\Rightarrow \qquad x = \left(\dfrac{y + 5}{2}\right)^{1/3}$

Clearly, $x \in R$ (domain), $\forall y \in R$ (codomain). (1)

Thus, for each $y \in R$ (codomain) there exists

$x = \left(\dfrac{y + 5}{2}\right)^{1/3} \in R$ (domain) such that

$f(x) = f\left[\left(\dfrac{y + 5}{2}\right)^{1/3}\right] = 2\left\{\left(\dfrac{y + 5}{2}\right)^{1/3}\right\}^3 - 5$

$= 2\left\{\left(\dfrac{y + 5}{2}\right)\right\} - 5 = y + 5 - 5 = y$

This shows that every element in the codomain has its pre-image in the domain.

So, f is onto (or f is surjective).

Thus, f is both one-one and onto (or both injective and surjective). Hence, f is bijective. **Hence proved.** (1)

Or

Let R_1 and R_2 be two equivalence relations on a set A.

Then, $R_1 \subseteq A \times A, R_2 \subseteq A \times A \Rightarrow (R_1 \cap R_2) \subseteq A \times A$.

So, $(R_1 \cap R_2)$ is a relation on A.

This relation on A satisfies the following properties.

(i) **Reflexivity** R_1 is reflexive and R_2 is reflexive

$\Rightarrow (a, a) \in R_1$ and $(a, a) \in R_2$ for all $a \in A$

$\Rightarrow (a, a) \in R_1 \cap R_2$ for all $a \in A$

$\Rightarrow R_1 \cap R_2$ is reflexive. (1)

(ii) **Symmetry** Let (a, b) be an arbitrary element of $R_1 \cap R_2$. Then,

$\qquad (a, b) \in R_1 \cap R_2$

$\Rightarrow (a, b) \in R_1$ and $(a, b) \in R_2$

$\Rightarrow (b, a) \in R_1$ and $(b, a) \in R_2$

$\qquad [\because R_1$ is symmetric and R_2 is symmetric$]$

$\Rightarrow (b, a) \in R_1 \cap R_2$

This shows that $R_1 \cap R_2$ is symmetric. (1)

(iii) **Transitivity** Let $(a, b) \in R_1 \cap R_2$ and $(b, c) \in R_1 \cap R_2$

$\Rightarrow (a, b) \in R_1, (a, b) \in R_2$ and $(b, c) \in R_1, (b, c) \in R_2$

$\Rightarrow \{(a, b) \in R_1, (b, c) \in R_1\}$,

and $\{(a, b) \in R_2, (b, c) \in R_2\}$

$\Rightarrow \{a, c\} \in R_1$ and $(a, c) \in R_2$

$\qquad [\because R_1$ is transitive and R_2 is transitive$]$

$\Rightarrow (a, c) \in R_1 \cap R_2$

This shows that $(R_1 \cap R_2)$ is transitive.

Thus, $R_1 \cap R_2$ is reflexive, symmetric and transitive.

Hence, $R_1 \cap R_2$ is an equivalence relation. (1)

28. To prove $\dfrac{dy}{dx} = -\dfrac{1}{(1 + x)^2}$

Given equation is $x\sqrt{1 + y} + y\sqrt{1 + x} = 0$,

where $x \neq y$, we first convert the given equation into $y = f(x)$ form.

Clearly, $x\sqrt{1 + y} = -y\sqrt{1 + x}$

On squaring both sides, we get

$\qquad\qquad x^2(1 + y) = y^2(1 + x)$

$\Rightarrow \qquad x^2 + x^2 y = y^2 + y^2 x$

$\Rightarrow \qquad x^2 - y^2 = y^2 x - x^2 y$

$\Rightarrow \qquad (x - y)(x + y) = -xy(x - y)$

$\qquad\qquad [\because a^2 - b^2 = (a - b)(a + b)]$

$\Rightarrow \qquad (x - y)(x + y) + xy(x - y) = 0$ (1)

$\Rightarrow \qquad (x - y)(x + y + xy) = 0$

$\therefore$ Either $\quad x - y = 0$ or $x + y + xy = 0$

Now, $\qquad x - y = 0 \Rightarrow x = y$

But it is given that $x \neq y$.

So, it is a contradiction.

$\therefore \qquad x - y = 0$ is rejected.

Now consider, $y + xy + x = 0$

$\Rightarrow \quad y(1 + x) = -x \Rightarrow y = \dfrac{-x}{1 + x}$ ...(i) (1)

On differentiating both sides w.r.t. x, we get

$\dfrac{dy}{dx} = \dfrac{(1 + x) \times \dfrac{d}{dx}(-x) - (-x) \times \dfrac{d}{dx}(1 + x)}{(1 + x)^2}$

[by using quotient rule of derivative]

$\Rightarrow \dfrac{dy}{dx} = \dfrac{(1 + x)(-1) + x(1)}{(1 + x)^2}$

$\Rightarrow \dfrac{dy}{dx} = \dfrac{-1 - x + x}{(1 + x)^2}$

$\therefore \dfrac{dy}{dx} = \dfrac{-1}{(1 + x)^2}$ (1)

Hence proved.

Or

We have, $y = e^x \sin x$ ...(i)

On differentiating both the sides of Eq. (i), we get

$$\frac{dy}{dx} = e^x \cos x + \sin x\, e^x$$

$\Rightarrow \qquad \frac{dy}{dx} = e^x(\cos x + \sin x)$ ...(ii) (1)

Again, differentiating both sides w.r.t. x, we get

$$\frac{d^2y}{dx^2} = e^x(-\sin x + \cos x) + e^x(\cos x + \sin x)$$

$\Rightarrow \qquad \frac{d^2y}{dx^2} = 2e^x \cos x$ ...(iii) (1)

Now,

To prove, $\dfrac{d^2y}{dx^2} - \dfrac{2dy}{dx} + 2y = 0$

$\text{LHS} = \dfrac{d^2y}{dx^2} - 2\dfrac{dy}{dx} + 2y$

$\quad = 2e^x \cos x - 2[e^x(\cos x + \sin x)] + 2[e^x \sin x]$

$\quad = 2e^x \cos x - 2e^x \cos x - 2e^x \sin x + 2e^x \sin x$

$\quad = 0$

$\quad = \text{RHS}$ **Hence proved.** (1)

29. Let $I = \displaystyle\int \frac{1}{3x^2 + 5x + 7} dx = \int \frac{dx}{3\left(x^2 + \dfrac{5x}{3} + \dfrac{7}{3}\right)}$

$= \dfrac{1}{3} \displaystyle\int \dfrac{dx}{x^2 + \dfrac{5x}{3} + \dfrac{7}{3}}$

$= \dfrac{1}{3} \displaystyle\int \dfrac{dx}{x^2 + \dfrac{5x}{3} + \dfrac{7}{3} + \dfrac{25}{36} - \dfrac{25}{36}}$

$= \dfrac{1}{3} \displaystyle\int \dfrac{dx}{\left(x + \dfrac{5}{6}\right)^2 + \left(\dfrac{7}{3} - \dfrac{25}{36}\right)}$ (1)

$= \dfrac{1}{3} \displaystyle\int \dfrac{dx}{\left(x + \dfrac{5}{6}\right)^2 + \left(\dfrac{84 - 25}{36}\right)}$

$= \dfrac{1}{3} \displaystyle\int \dfrac{dx}{\left(x + \dfrac{5}{6}\right)^2 + \left(\dfrac{\sqrt{59}}{6}\right)^2}$

$= \dfrac{1}{3} \cdot \dfrac{6}{\sqrt{59}} \tan^{-1}\left(\dfrac{x + \dfrac{5}{6}}{\dfrac{\sqrt{59}}{6}}\right) + C$

$\qquad\qquad \left[\because \displaystyle\int \dfrac{dx}{a^2 + x^2} = \dfrac{1}{a}\tan^{-1}\dfrac{x}{a}\right]$

$\therefore \quad I = \dfrac{2}{\sqrt{59}} \tan^{-1}\left(\dfrac{6x + 5}{\sqrt{59}}\right) + C$ (2)

Or

Let $I = \displaystyle\int \frac{xe^x}{(x+1)^2} dx = \int \frac{(x + 1 - 1)e^x}{(x+1)^2} dx$

$= \displaystyle\int \left[\frac{x+1}{(x+1)^2} - \frac{1}{(x+1)^2}\right] e^x dx$

$= \displaystyle\int \left[\frac{1}{x+1} - \frac{1}{(x+1)^2}\right] e^x dx$ (1)

Now consider, $f(x) = \dfrac{1}{1+x}$, then $f'(x) = \dfrac{-1}{(1+x)^2}$.

Thus, the given integrand is of the form

$$\int e^x\{f(x) + f'(x)\}\, dx.$$

Hence, $I = \dfrac{e^x}{x+1} + c$ $[\because \displaystyle\int e^x\{f(x) + f'(x)\}dx = e^x f(x)]$ (2)

30. Given, $\vec{a}$ and $\vec{b}$ are two unit vectors, then $|\vec{a}| = |\vec{b}| = 1$.

Also, $(\sqrt{3}\vec{a} - \vec{b})$ is a unit vector.

$\therefore \qquad |\sqrt{3}\vec{a} - \vec{b}| = 1$

$\Rightarrow \qquad |\sqrt{3}\vec{a} - \vec{b}|^2 = 1^2$

$\Rightarrow \quad (\sqrt{3}\vec{a} - \vec{b})\cdot(\sqrt{3}\vec{a} - \vec{b}) = 1$ $[\because |\vec{a}|^2 = \vec{a}\cdot\vec{a}]$

$\Rightarrow 3(\vec{a}\cdot\vec{a}) - \sqrt{3}(\vec{a}\cdot\vec{b}) - \sqrt{3}(\vec{b}\cdot\vec{a}) + \vec{b}\cdot\vec{b} = 1$

$\Rightarrow 3|\vec{a}|^2 - \sqrt{3}|\vec{a}||\vec{b}|\cos\theta$

$\qquad - \sqrt{3}|\vec{b}||\vec{a}|\cos\theta + |\vec{b}|^2 = 1$ (1)

where, θ is the angle between $\vec{a}$ and $\vec{b}$.

$\Rightarrow 3 \times 1 - \sqrt{3} \times 1 \times 1 \times \cos\theta - \sqrt{3} \times 1 \times 1 \times \cos\theta + 1 = 1$ (1)

$\Rightarrow \qquad\qquad 3 = 2\sqrt{3}\cos\theta$

$\Rightarrow \qquad\qquad \cos\theta = \dfrac{3}{2\sqrt{3}}$

$\Rightarrow \qquad\qquad \cos\theta = \dfrac{\sqrt{3}}{2} \Rightarrow \theta = \dfrac{\pi}{6}$

Hence, the required angle between $\vec{a}$ and $\vec{b}$ is $\dfrac{\pi}{6}$.   (1)

31. We have, $f(x) = -x + 2\sin x$

On differentiating both sides w.r.t. x, we get

$\qquad f'(x) = -1 + 2\cos x$ ...(i)

For local maxima and local minima, put $f'(x) = 0$

$\Rightarrow -1 + 2\cos x = 0 \Rightarrow \cos x = \dfrac{1}{2}$

$\Rightarrow \quad x = 2n\pi \pm \dfrac{\pi}{3} \Rightarrow x = \dfrac{\pi}{3}, \dfrac{5\pi}{3} \in [0, 2\pi]$ (1)

On differentiating both sides of Eq. (i) w.r.t. x, we get

$\qquad f''(x) = -2\sin x$

At $x = \pi/3$, $f''\left(\dfrac{\pi}{3}\right) = -2\sin\dfrac{\pi}{3} = -\sqrt{3} < 0$

$\therefore \; x = \dfrac{\pi}{3}$ is a point of local maxima.

At $x = \dfrac{5\pi}{3}, f''\left(\dfrac{5\pi}{3}\right) = -2\sin\dfrac{5\pi}{3} = \sqrt{3} > 0$

$\therefore$ $x = \dfrac{5\pi}{3}$ is a point of local minima.

Hence, the points of local maxima is $\dfrac{\pi}{3}$ and local minima is $\dfrac{5\pi}{3}$. (1)

On putting $x = \dfrac{\pi}{3}$ in $f(x)$, we get

$$f\left(\dfrac{\pi}{3}\right) = -\dfrac{\pi}{3} + 2\sin\dfrac{\pi}{3}$$

$$= -\dfrac{\pi}{3} + 2 \times \dfrac{\sqrt{3}}{2} = \dfrac{-\pi}{3} + \sqrt{3}$$

which is the required local maximum value.

On putting $x = \dfrac{5\pi}{3}$ in $f(x)$, we get

$$f\left(\dfrac{5\pi}{3}\right) = -\dfrac{5\pi}{3} + 2\sin\dfrac{5\pi}{3}$$

$$= \dfrac{-5\pi}{3} + 2 \times \left(\dfrac{-\sqrt{3}}{2}\right) = \dfrac{-5\pi}{3} - \sqrt{3}$$

which is the required local minimum value. (1)

32. Given, $y = (\cos x)^x + (\sin x)^{1/x}$

Let $u = (\cos x)^x$ and $v = (\sin x)^{1/x}$

Then, given equation becomes

$$y = u + v$$

On differentiating both sides w.r.t. x, we get

$\Rightarrow \qquad \dfrac{dy}{dx} = \dfrac{du}{dx} + \dfrac{dv}{dx}$ ...(i)(1)

Consider, $u = (\cos x)^x$

On taking log both sides, we get

$$\log u = \log (\cos x)^x$$

$\Rightarrow \qquad \log u = x \log (\cos x)$

$[\because \log m^n = n \log m]$ (1)

On differentiating both sides w.r.t. x, we get

$$\dfrac{1}{u}\dfrac{du}{dx} = x \cdot \dfrac{d}{dx}\log (\cos x) + \log (\cos x) \cdot \dfrac{d}{dx}(x)$$

[by using product rule of derivative]

$\Rightarrow \dfrac{1}{u}\dfrac{du}{dx} = x \cdot \dfrac{1}{\cos x}(-\sin x) + \log \cos x \cdot 1$

$\Rightarrow \dfrac{1}{u}\dfrac{du}{dx} = -x \tan x + \log (\cos x)$

$\Rightarrow \dfrac{du}{dx} = u\,[-x \tan x + \log \cos x]$

$\Rightarrow \dfrac{du}{dx} = (\cos x)^x[-x \tan x + \log \cos x]$ ...(ii) (1)

Now, consider $v = (\sin x)^{1/x}$

On taking log both sides, we get

$$\log v = \log (\sin x)^{1/x}$$

$\Rightarrow \qquad \log v = \dfrac{1}{x}\log \sin x$

$[\because \log m^n = n \log m]$

On differentiating both sides w.r.t. x, we get

$$\dfrac{1}{v}\dfrac{dv}{dx} = \dfrac{1}{x}\cdot\dfrac{d}{dx}(\log \sin x) + \log \sin x \cdot \dfrac{d}{dx}\left(\dfrac{1}{x}\right)$$

$\Rightarrow \dfrac{1}{v}\dfrac{dv}{dx} = \dfrac{1}{x}\cdot\dfrac{1}{\sin x}\cdot\cos x + \log \sin x\left(-\dfrac{1}{x^2}\right)$

$\Rightarrow \dfrac{1}{v}\dfrac{dv}{dx} = \dfrac{\cot x}{x} - \dfrac{\log (\sin x)}{x^2}$

$\Rightarrow \dfrac{dv}{dx} = v\left(\dfrac{\cot x}{x} - \dfrac{\log (\sin x)}{x^2}\right)$

$\Rightarrow \dfrac{dv}{dx} = (\sin x)^{1/x}\left[\dfrac{\cot x}{x} - \dfrac{\log (\sin x)}{x^2}\right]$ ...(iii) (1)

Now, from Eqs. (i), (ii) and (iii), we get

$$\dfrac{dy}{dx} = (\cos x)^x\,[-x \tan x + \log \cos x]$$

$$+ (\sin x)^{1/x}\left[\dfrac{\cot x}{x} - \dfrac{\log (\sin x)}{x^2}\right](1)$$

33. Given, differential equation is

$$\dfrac{dy}{dx} = \dfrac{x(2\log x + 1)}{\sin y + y\cos y}$$

On separating the variables, we get

$(\sin y + y\cos y)dy = (2x\log x + x)dx$ (1)

On integrating both sides, we get

$$\int (\sin y + y\cos y)dy = \int (2x\log x + x)dx$$

$$\int \sin y\, dy + \int y\cos y\, dy = 2\int x\log x\, dx + \int x\, dx$$

$$\Rightarrow \; -\cos y + [y\cdot\sin y - \int 1\cdot\sin y\, dy]$$

$$= 2\left[\log x \cdot \dfrac{x^2}{2} - \int \dfrac{1}{x}\cdot\dfrac{x^2}{2}dx\right] + \dfrac{x^2}{2}$$ (1)

$\Rightarrow -\cos y + y\sin y + \cos y = x^2 \cdot \log x - \int x\, dx + \dfrac{x^2}{2}$

$\Rightarrow \qquad y\sin y = x^2\log x - \dfrac{x^2}{2} + \dfrac{x^2}{2} + C$

$\Rightarrow \qquad y\sin y = x^2\log x + C$ ...(i)

Since, it is given that $y = \dfrac{\pi}{2}$, when $x = 1$. (1)

$\therefore$ From Eq. (i), we get

$$\dfrac{\pi}{2}\cdot\sin\dfrac{\pi}{2} = (1)^2 \cdot \log(1) + C$$

$\Rightarrow \quad \dfrac{\pi}{2} \times (1) = 1 \times 0 + C \quad \left[\because \sin\dfrac{\pi}{2} = 1 \text{ and } \log 1 = 0\right]$

$\Rightarrow \qquad C = \dfrac{\pi}{2}$

Hence, the required particular solution is

$$y\sin y = x^2\log x + \dfrac{\pi}{2}.$$ (2)

Or

Given differential equation is

$$xy \log\left|\frac{y}{x}\right| dx + \left[y^2 - x^2\log\left|\frac{y}{x}\right|\right] dy = 0$$

$$xy \log\left|\frac{y}{x}\right| dx = \left[x^2\log\left|\frac{y}{x}\right| - y^2\right] dy$$

$$\Rightarrow \quad \frac{dy}{dx} = \frac{xy \log\left|\frac{y}{x}\right|}{x^2\log\left|\frac{y}{x}\right| - y^2} = \frac{\frac{y}{x}\log\left|\frac{y}{x}\right|}{\log\left|\frac{y}{x}\right| - \frac{y^2}{x^2}} \quad \dots\text{(i)}$$

which is a homogeneous differential equation as $\frac{dy}{dx} = F\left(\frac{y}{x}\right)$.   (1)

On putting $y = vx \Rightarrow \frac{dy}{dx} = v + x\frac{dv}{dx}$ in Eq. (i), we get

$$v + x\frac{dv}{dx} = \frac{v \log|v|}{\log|v| - v^2}$$

$$\Rightarrow \quad x\frac{dv}{dx} = \frac{v \log|v|}{\log|v| - v^2} - v$$

$$\Rightarrow \quad x\frac{dv}{dx} = \frac{v \log|v| - v \log|v| + v^3}{\log|v| - v^2}$$

$$\Rightarrow \quad x\frac{dv}{dx} = \frac{v^3}{\log|v| - v^2}$$

$$\Rightarrow \quad \frac{\log|v| - v^2}{v^3}dv = \frac{dx}{x} \qquad (1)$$

On integrating both sides, we get

$$\int \frac{\log|v| - v^2}{v^3}dv = \int \frac{dx}{x}$$

$$\Rightarrow \quad \int \frac{\log|v|}{v^3}dv - \int \frac{1}{v}dv = \int \frac{dx}{x}$$

$$\Rightarrow \quad \underset{\text{II}}{\int (v)^{-3}} \underset{\text{I}}{\log|v|}dv - \log|v| = \log|x| + C_1 \qquad (1)$$

Using integration by parts, we get

$$\log|v| \int v^{-3}dv - \int\left[\frac{d}{dv}(\log|v|)\cdot\int v^{-3}dv\right]dv$$

$$= \log|v| + \log|x| + C_1$$

$$\Rightarrow \frac{v^{-2}}{-2}\log|v| - \int \frac{1}{v}\frac{v^{-2}}{(-2)}dv = \log|v| + \log|x| + C_1$$

$$\Rightarrow \frac{-1}{2v^2}\log|v| + \frac{1}{2}\int v^{-3}dv = \log|v| + \log|x| + C_1$$

$$\Rightarrow \frac{-1}{2v^2}\log|v| + \frac{1}{2}\cdot\frac{v^{-2}}{(-2)} = \log|v| + \log|x| + C_1$$

$$\Rightarrow \frac{-1}{2v^2}\log|v| - \frac{1}{4v^2} = \log|vx| + C_1$$

$$[\because \log m + \log n = \log mn]$$

$$\Rightarrow \quad \frac{-1}{2}\cdot\frac{x^2}{y^2}\log\left|\frac{y}{x}\right| - \frac{1}{4}\cdot\frac{x^2}{y^2} = \log\left|\frac{y}{x}\cdot x\right| + C_1 \quad (1)$$

$$\left[\text{putting } v = \frac{y}{x}\right]$$

$$\Rightarrow \quad \frac{-x^2}{2y^2}\log\left|\frac{y}{x}\right| - \frac{x^2}{4y^2} = \log|y| + C_1$$

$$\Rightarrow \quad \frac{-x^2}{y^2}\left[\frac{\log\left|\frac{y}{x}\right|}{2} + \frac{1}{4}\right] = \log|y| + C_1$$

$$\Rightarrow \quad \frac{x^2}{4y^2}\left[2\log\left|\frac{y}{x}\right| + 1\right] + \log|y| = -C_1$$

$$\therefore x^2\left[2\log\left|\frac{y}{x}\right| + 1\right] + 4y^2\log|y| = 4y^2C,$$

where $C = -C_1$

which is the required solution.   (1)

34. The linear programming problem is

Maximise $Z = 0.08x + 0.10y$

Subject to the constraints

$$x + y \le 12000, x \ge 2000, y \ge 4000$$

and $x \ge 0, y \ge 0$

Consider the constraints as equations, we get

$$x + y = 12000 \qquad \dots\text{(i)}$$
$$x = 2000 \qquad \dots\text{(ii)}$$
$$y = 4000 \qquad \dots\text{(iii)}$$

and $x, y = 0$

Table for $x + y = 12000$ is   (1)

x	0	12000
y	12000	0

So, line passes through the points (0, 12000) and (12000, 0).

On putting (0, 0) in the inequality $x + y \le 12000$, we get

$$0 + 0 \le 12000 \Rightarrow 0 \le 12000 \text{ [true]}$$

∴ The shaded region is towards the origin.   (1)

∵ Line $x = 2000$ is parallel to Y-axis.

On putting (1000, 0) in the inequality $x \ge 2000$, we get

$$1000 \ge 2000 \text{ [false]}$$

∴ The shaded region is at the right side of the line.

∵ Line $y = 4000$ is parallel to X-axis.

On putting (0, 6000) in the inequality $y \ge 4000$, we get

$$6000 \ge 4000 \text{ [true]}$$

∴ The shaded region is above the line.

The intersection point of lines (ii) and (iii), (i) and (iii), (i) and (ii) are respectively,

$A(2000, 4000)$, $B(8000, 4000)$ and $C(2000, 10000)$.   (1)

Now, plot the graph of the system of inequalities. The shaded portion ABC represents the feasible region which is bounded.

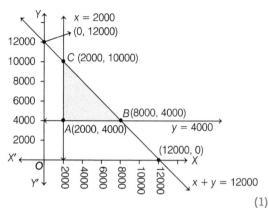

And the coordinates of the corner points are

$A(2000, 4000)$, $B(8000, 4000)$ and $C(2000, 10000)$, respectively.

Now, the values of Z at each corner point are given below

Corner points	$Z = 0.08x + 0.10y$
$A(2000, 4000)$	$Z = 0.08\,(2000) + 0.10\,(4000)$ $= 160 + 400 = 560$
$B(8000, 4000)$	$Z = 0.08\,(8000) + 0.10\,(4000)$ $= 640 + 400 = 1040$
$C(2000, 10000)$	$Z = 0.08\,(2000) + 0.10\,(10000)$ $= 160 + 1000 = 1160$ (maximum)

$\therefore$ Maximum value of Z is 1160 at $(2000, 10000)$. (1)

Or

Converting the given inequations into equations, we get

$2x + 3y = 6$, $x - 2y = 2$, $3x + 2y = 12$, $-3x + 2y = 3$, $x = 0$ and $y = 0$

Region represented by $-2x - 3y \le -6$: The line $-2x - 3y = -6$ or $2x + 3y = 6$ cuts OX and OY at $A_1(3, 0)$ and $B_1(0, 2)$ respectively. Join these points to obtain the line $2x + 3y = 6$.

Since $O(0, 0)$ does not satisfy the inequation $-2x - 3y \le -6$. So, the region represented by $-2x - 3y \le -6$ is that part of XOY-plane which does not contain the origin. (1)

Region represented by $x - 2y \le 2$: The line $x - 2y = 2$ meets the coordinate axes at $A_2(2, 0)$ and $B_2(0, -1)$. Join these points to obtain $x - 2y = 2$. Since, $(0, 0)$ satisfies the inequation $x - 2y \le 2$, so the region containing the origin represents the solution set of this inequation.

Region represented by $3x + 2y \le 12$: The line $3x + 2y \le 12$ intersects OX and OY at A_3 $(4, 0)$ and $B_3(0, 6)$. Join these points to obtain the line $3x + 2y = 12$. Clearly, $(0, 0)$ satisfies the inequation $3x + 2y \le 12$. So, the region containing the origin represents the solution set of the given inequation. (1)

Region represented by $-3x + 2y \le 3$: The line $-3x + 2y = 3$ intersects OX and OY at $A_4(-1, 0)$ and $B_4\left(0, \dfrac{3}{2}\right)$. Join these points to obtain the line $-3x + 2y = 3$. Clearly, $(0, 0)$ satisfies the inequation. So, the region containing the origin represents the solution set of the given inequation.

Region represented by $x \ge 0$, $y \ge 0$. Clearly, XOY quadrant represents the solution set of these two inequations. (1)

The shaded region shown in figure represents the common solution set of the above inequations. This region is the feasible region of the given LPP.

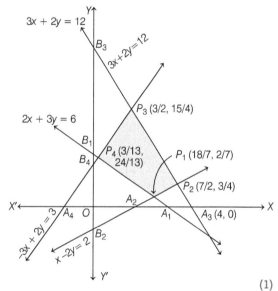

(1)

The coordinates of the corner points (vertices) of the shaded feasible region $P_1\,P_2\,P_3\,P_4$ are $P_1\left(\dfrac{18}{7}, \dfrac{2}{7}\right)$, $P_2\left(\dfrac{7}{2}, \dfrac{3}{4}\right)$, $P_3\left(\dfrac{3}{2}, \dfrac{15}{4}\right)$ and $P_4\left(\dfrac{3}{13}, \dfrac{24}{13}\right)$. These points have been obtained by solving the equations of the corresponding intersecting lines, simultaneously.

The values of the objective function at these points are given in the following table

Corner points	Value of the objective function $Z = 5x + 2y$
$P_1\left(\dfrac{18}{7}, \dfrac{2}{7}\right)$	$Z = 5 \times \dfrac{18}{7} + 2 \times \dfrac{2}{7} = \dfrac{94}{7}$
$P_2\left(\dfrac{7}{2}, \dfrac{3}{4}\right)$	$Z = 5 \times \dfrac{7}{2} + 2 \times \dfrac{3}{4} = 19$
$P_3\left(\dfrac{3}{2}, \dfrac{15}{4}\right)$	$Z = 5 \times \dfrac{3}{2} + 2 \times \dfrac{15}{4} = 15$
$P_4\left(\dfrac{3}{13}, \dfrac{24}{13}\right)$	$Z = 5 \times \dfrac{3}{13} + 2 \times \dfrac{24}{13} = \dfrac{63}{13}$

So, minimum value of Z is $\dfrac{63}{13}$ at $\left(\dfrac{3}{13}, \dfrac{24}{13}\right)$. (1)

35. Let $I = \int_0^{\pi/2} f(\sin 2x) \sin x \, dx$ ...(i)

$\Rightarrow I = \int_0^{\pi/2} f\left\{\sin 2\left(\dfrac{\pi}{2} - x\right)\right\} \sin\left(\dfrac{\pi}{2} - x\right) dx$

$$\left[\because \int_a^b f(x)\,dx = \int_a^b f(a + b - x)\,dx\right]$$

$\Rightarrow I = \int_0^{\pi/2} f\{\sin(\pi - 2x)\} \cos x \, dx$

$\Rightarrow I = \int_0^{\pi/2} f(\sin 2x) \cos x \, dx$ ...(ii) (1)

On adding Eqs. (i) and (ii), we get

$2I = \int_0^{\pi/2} f(\sin 2x) \cdot (\sin x + \cos x) \, dx$

$\Rightarrow 2I = 2\int_0^{\pi/4} f(\sin 2x) \cdot (\sin x + \cos x) \, dx$

$$\left[\because \int_0^{2a} f(x)\,dx = \int_0^a 2f(x)\,dx, \text{if} f(2a - x) = f(x)\right]$$

$\Rightarrow 2I = 2\sqrt{2} \int_0^{\pi/4} f(\sin 2x)\left(\dfrac{1}{\sqrt{2}} \sin x + \dfrac{1}{\sqrt{2}} \cos x\right) dx$ (1)

$\Rightarrow 2I = 2\sqrt{2} \int_0^{\pi/4} f(\sin 2x)$
$\left(\cos\dfrac{\pi}{4}\sin x + \sin\dfrac{\pi}{4}\cos x\right) dx$

$\Rightarrow 2I = 2\sqrt{2} \int_0^{\pi/4} f(\sin 2x) \sin\left(x + \dfrac{\pi}{4}\right) dx$

$$[\because \sin A\cos B + \cos A\sin B = \sin(A + B)] \text{ (1)}$$

$\Rightarrow 2I = 2\sqrt{2} \int_0^{\pi/4} f\left\{\sin 2\left(\dfrac{\pi}{4} - x\right)\right\} \sin\left(\dfrac{\pi}{4} - x + \dfrac{\pi}{4}\right) dx$

$$\left[\because \int_a^b f(x)\,dx = \int_a^b f(a + b - x)\,dx\right]$$

$\Rightarrow 2I = 2\sqrt{2} \int_0^{\pi/4} f\left\{\sin\left(\dfrac{\pi}{2} - 2x\right)\right\} \sin\left(\dfrac{\pi}{2} - x\right) dx$

$\Rightarrow 2I = 2\sqrt{2} \int_0^{\pi/4} f(\cos 2x) \cos x \, dx$

$$\left[\because \sin\left(\dfrac{\pi}{2} - \theta\right) = \cos\theta\right]$$

$\Rightarrow I = \sqrt{2} \int_0^{\pi/4} f(\cos 2x) \cos x \, dx$

$\therefore \int_0^{\pi/2} f(\sin 2x) \sin x \, dx = \sqrt{2} \int_0^{\pi/4} f(\cos 2x) \cos x \, dx$

Hence proved. (2)

36. (i) In ΔOAC, we have
$$OC^2 + AC^2 = OA^2$$

$\Rightarrow \qquad x^2 + r^2 = R^2 \Rightarrow r = \sqrt{R^2 - x^2}$

(ii) Volume of cone, $V = \dfrac{1}{3}\pi r^2 h$

$= \dfrac{1}{3}\pi(R^2 - x^2)(R + x)$

$= \dfrac{1}{3}\pi(R + x)^2(R - x)$

(iii) We have, $V = \dfrac{1}{3}\pi(R + x)^2(R - x)$

$\Rightarrow \qquad \dfrac{dv}{dx} = \dfrac{1}{3}\pi[2(R + x)(R - x) - (R + x)^2]$

$= \dfrac{1}{3}\pi[(R + x)(2R - 2x - R - x)]$

$= \dfrac{1}{3}\pi[(R + x)(R - 3x)]$

For maximum value $\dfrac{dV}{dx} = 0$

$\Rightarrow \quad \dfrac{1}{3}\pi(R + x)(R - 3x) = 0 \Rightarrow x = \dfrac{R}{3}$ $[\because R + x \neq 0]$

Again, $\dfrac{d^2V}{dx^2} = \dfrac{1}{3}\pi[R - 3x - 3(R + x)]$

$= \dfrac{1}{3}\pi[R - 3x - 3R - 3x]$

$= \dfrac{1}{3}\pi[-2R - 6x]$

$= \dfrac{-2}{3}\pi[R + x]$

$\dfrac{d^2V}{dx^2}\bigg|_{x=\frac{R}{3}} = \dfrac{-2}{3}\pi\left[R + \dfrac{R}{3}\right] < 0$

$\therefore \quad \dfrac{d^2V}{dx^2}\bigg|_{x=\frac{R}{3}} < 0$

So, V is maximum at $x = \dfrac{R}{3}$

Or

$\because$ Volume of the cone, $V = \dfrac{1}{3}\pi(R + x)^2(R - x)$

$\therefore$ Maximum volume $= \dfrac{1}{3}\pi\left[R + \dfrac{R}{3}\right]^2\left[R - \dfrac{R}{3}\right] = \dfrac{32\pi}{81}R^3$

Now, when volume is maximum,

$$r = \sqrt{R^2 - x^2} = \sqrt{R^2 - \dfrac{R^2}{9}} = \dfrac{2\sqrt{2}}{3}R$$

and $h = R + x = R + \dfrac{R}{3} = \dfrac{4R}{3}$

$\therefore$ Required ratio $= \dfrac{\dfrac{32\pi}{81}R^3}{\dfrac{4}{3}\pi R^3} = \dfrac{8}{27}$

37. (i)

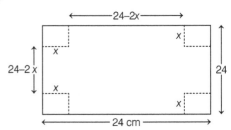

From figure it is clear that

Length of box $= 24 - 2x$

Breadth of box $= 24 - 2x$

Height of box $= x$

(ii) Volume of box, $V =$ length $\times$ breadth $\times$ height

$$= (24 - 2x)(24 - 2x)(x)$$

$$= x(24 - 2x)^2$$

(iii) We have,

$$V = x(24 - 2x)^2$$

$\therefore \quad \dfrac{dV}{dx} = (24 - 2x)^2 + 2x(24 - 2x)(-2)$

$$= (24 - 2x)[24 - 2x - 4x]$$

$$= (24 - 2x)(24 - 6x)$$

$$= 6(24 - 2x)(4 - x)$$

For maximum,

$$\dfrac{dV}{dx} = 0$$

$\Rightarrow \quad 6(24 - 2x)(4 - x) = 0$

$\Rightarrow \quad x = 4$ and $x = 12$

Again, $\dfrac{d^2V}{dx^2} = 6[-2(4 - x) + (24 - 2x)(-1)]$

$$= 6[-8 + 2x - 24 + 2x] = 6[4x - 32]$$

$\therefore \left.\dfrac{d^2V}{dx^2}\right|_{x=4} < 0$ and $\left.\dfrac{d^2V}{dx^2}\right|_{x=12} > 0$

So, V is maximum at $x = 4$

Or

$\because$ Volume of box, $V = x(24 - 2x)^2$

$\therefore \quad V_{\max} = x(24 - 2x)^2$

$$= 4(24 - 8)^2 = 4 \times 16^2 = 1024 \, \text{cm}^3$$

Length of box $= 24 - 2x = 24 - 2 \times 4 = 16 \, \text{cm}$,

Breadth of box $= 24 - 2x = 24 - 2 \times 4 = 16 \, \text{cm}$

and height of box $= 4 \, \text{cm}$

$\therefore$ Surface area of box $= 2(l + b)h + lb$

$$= 2(16 + 16) \times 4 + 16 \times 16$$

$$= 256 + 256 = 512 \, \text{cm}^2$$

$\therefore$ Total cost of making the box $= 512 \times 5 = ₹ \, 2560$

38. Consider the following events,

$E = A$ hits the target,

$F = B$ hits the target

and $G = C$ hits the target

(i) $\therefore$ Required probability $= P$ (any two of

A, B and C will hit the target)

$= P[(E \cap F \cap \overline{G}) \cup (\overline{E} \cap F \cap G) \cup (E \cap \overline{F} \cap G)]$

$= P(E \cap F \cap \overline{G}) + P(\overline{E} \cap F \cap G) + P(E \cap \overline{F} \cap G)$

$= P(E) P(F) P(\overline{G}) + P(\overline{E}) P(F) P(G) + P(E) P(\overline{F}) P(G)$

$= \dfrac{4}{5} \times \dfrac{3}{4} \times \dfrac{1}{3} + \dfrac{1}{5} \times \dfrac{3}{4} \times \dfrac{2}{3} + \dfrac{4}{5} \times \dfrac{1}{4} \times \dfrac{2}{3} = \dfrac{13}{30}$

$$[\because P(\overline{X}) = 1 - P(X)]$$

(ii) $\therefore$ Required probability

$= P$(none of A, B and C will hit the target)

$= P(\overline{E} \cap \overline{F} \cap \overline{G}) = P(\overline{E}) P(\overline{F}) P(\overline{G})$

$= \dfrac{1}{5} \times \dfrac{1}{4} \times \dfrac{1}{3} = \dfrac{1}{60} \qquad [\because P(\overline{X}) = 1 - P(X)]$

and $P(B$ and C may hit and A may not$)$

$= P(\overline{E} \cap F \cap G) = P(\overline{E}) P(F) P(G)$

$$[\because E, F \text{ and } G \text{ are independent events}]$$

$= \left(1 - \dfrac{4}{5}\right) \times \dfrac{3}{4} \times \dfrac{2}{3} = \dfrac{1}{5} \times \dfrac{3}{4} \times \dfrac{2}{3} = \dfrac{1}{10}$

SAMPLE QUESTION PAPER 9

MATHEMATICS

Time : 3 hrs   Max. Marks : 80

General Instructions

1. This question paper contains - five sections A, B, C, D and E. Each section is compulsory. However, there are internal choices in some questions.
2. Section A has 18 MCQ's and 02 Assertion-Reason based questions of 1 mark each.
3. Section B has 5 Very Short Answer (VSA) type questions of 2 marks each.
4. Section C has 6 Short Answer (SA) type questions of 3 marks each.
5. Section D has 4 Long Answer (LA) type questions of 5 marks each.
6. Section E has 3 source based/case based/passage based/integrated units of assessment (4 marks each) with sub parts.

Section A

(Multiple Choice Questions) Each question carries 1 mark

1. $\int_1^e \log x \, dx$ is equal to

(a) 1   (b) 2   (c) 3   (d) 4

2. If the lines $\dfrac{x-3}{1} = \dfrac{y-2}{5} = \dfrac{z+1}{\lambda}$ and $\dfrac{x-1}{6} = \dfrac{y+1}{-2} = \dfrac{z+6}{4}$ are perpendicular, then λ is equal to

(a) 1   (b) 2   (c) 3   (d) 4

3. Vector equation of the line $\dfrac{3-x}{-1} = \dfrac{y+2}{-3} = \dfrac{2-z}{1}$ is

(a) $\vec{r} = (3\hat{i} - 2\hat{j} + 2\hat{k}) + \lambda(\hat{i} - 3\hat{j} - \hat{k})$ (b) $\vec{r} = (3\hat{i} + 2\hat{j} - 2\hat{k}) + \lambda(\hat{i} + 3\hat{j} + \hat{k})$

(c) $\vec{r} = (3\hat{i} + 2\hat{j} + 2\hat{k}) + \lambda(\hat{i} - 3\hat{j} - \hat{k})$ (d) $\vec{r} = (\hat{i} + \hat{j} + \hat{k}) + \lambda(\hat{i} - 3\hat{j} - \hat{k})$

4. $\int \dfrac{\sin^6 x}{\cos^8 x}\,dx$ is equal to

(a) $\dfrac{\tan^6 x}{6} + C$

(b) $\dfrac{\tan^7 x}{7} + C$

(c) $\dfrac{\tan^5 x}{5} + C$

(d) $\dfrac{\cot^7 x}{7} + C$

5. If angle between the lines

$\dfrac{x+1}{3} = \dfrac{y+5}{-2} = \dfrac{z-1}{3}$ and

$\dfrac{1-x}{2} = \dfrac{2-y}{1} = \dfrac{1+z}{-1}$ is given by

$\cos\theta = \dfrac{a}{b\sqrt{33}}$, then $a+b$ is equal to

(a) 5 (b) 7 (c) 2 (d) 9

6. The cartesian equation of the line which passes through the point $(-2, 4, -5)$ and is parallel to the line $\dfrac{x+3}{3} = \dfrac{4-y}{5} = \dfrac{z+8}{6}$ is given by

(a) $\dfrac{x+2}{3} = \dfrac{y-4}{-5} = \dfrac{z+5}{6}$

(b) $\dfrac{x+2}{3} = \dfrac{y+4}{5} = \dfrac{z-5}{6}$

(c) $\dfrac{x-1}{3} = \dfrac{y-4}{5} = \dfrac{z+5}{6}$

(d) $\dfrac{x+2}{3} = \dfrac{y+4}{-5} = \dfrac{z+5}{-6}$

7. If A is a matrix of order 3 such that $A(\text{adj } A) = 10I$. Then, the value of $|\text{adj } A|$ is

(a) 10 (b) 100 (c) 110 (d) 5

8. Let $\vec{a} = \hat{i} - 2\hat{j} + 3\hat{k}$. If $\vec{b}$ is a vector such that $\vec{a} \cdot \vec{b} = |\vec{b}|^2$ and $|\vec{a} - \vec{b}| = \sqrt{7}$, then $|\vec{b}|$ is equal to

(a) 7 (b) 14 (c) $\sqrt{7}$ (d) 21

9. The value of λ if the vectors $2\hat{i} + \lambda\hat{j} + 3\hat{k}$ and $3\hat{i} + 2\hat{j} - 4\hat{k}$ are perpendicular to each other is

(a) 1 (b) 2 (c) 3 (d) 4

10. If a line makes angles $90°$, $135°$, $45°$ with the X, Y and Z-axes respectively, then its direction consines are

(a) $0, \dfrac{-1}{\sqrt{2}}, \dfrac{1}{\sqrt{2}}$

(b) $0, \dfrac{1}{\sqrt{3}}, \dfrac{-1}{\sqrt{3}}$

(c) $\dfrac{1}{\sqrt{2}}, \dfrac{1}{\sqrt{2}}, \dfrac{1}{\sqrt{2}}$

(d) $1, 1, 0$

11. If $\vec{a}$ and $\vec{b}$ are two unit vectors such that $\vec{a} + \vec{b}$ is also a unit vector, then the angle between $\vec{a}$ and $\vec{b}$ is

(a) π (b) $\dfrac{\pi}{2}$ (c) $\dfrac{\pi}{3}$ (d) $\dfrac{2\pi}{3}$

12. If A is skew-symmetric matrix, then A^2 is
(a) symmetric matrix
(b) skew-symmetric matrix
(c) null matrix
(d) None

13. The projection of $(\vec{b} + \vec{c})$ on $\vec{a}$, where $\vec{a} = 2\hat{i} - 2\hat{j} + \hat{k}$, $\vec{b} = \hat{i} + 2\hat{j} - 2\hat{k}$ and $\vec{c} = 2\hat{i} - \hat{j} + 4\hat{k}$ is

(a) 1 (b) 2
(c) 3 (d) 4

14. If $\vec{a}$ is a non-zero vector of magnitude $|\vec{a}|$ and λ is a non-zero scalar, $\lambda \vec{a}$ is unit vector, then the value of $|\vec{a}|$ is

(a) $\dfrac{1}{|\lambda|}$ (b) $|\lambda|$ (c) -1 (d) $\dfrac{2}{|\lambda|}$

15. The direction cosines of the line passing through the two points $(-2, 4, -5)$ and $(1, 2, 3)$ are

(a) $\dfrac{3}{\sqrt{77}}, \dfrac{-2}{\sqrt{77}}, \dfrac{3}{\sqrt{77}}$

(b) $\dfrac{3}{\sqrt{77}}, \dfrac{-2}{\sqrt{77}}, \dfrac{8}{\sqrt{77}}$

(c) $\dfrac{2}{\sqrt{83}}, \dfrac{-1}{\sqrt{83}}, \dfrac{5}{\sqrt{77}}$

(d) $\dfrac{1}{\sqrt{2}}, \dfrac{-1}{\sqrt{2}}, \dfrac{3}{\sqrt{2}}$

16. If $|\vec{a}| = 2$, $|\vec{b}| = 5$ and $\vec{a} \cdot \vec{b} = 2$, then $|\vec{a} - \vec{b}|$ is equal to

(a) 1 (b) 5 (c) -1 (d) 4

17. For any two vectors $\vec{a}$ and $\vec{b}$, $(\vec{a} \times \vec{b}) \cdot \vec{b}$ is equal to

(a) 1 (b) 0 (c) -1 (d) 2

18. The value of $\hat{i} \times (\hat{j} + \hat{k}) + \hat{j} \times (\hat{k} + \hat{i}) + \hat{k} \times (\hat{i} + \hat{j})$ is

(a) 1 (b) -1 (c) 0 (d) 2

Assertion-Reason Based Questions

In the following questions, a statement of Assertion (A) is followed by a statement of Reason (R). Choose the correct answer out of the following choices.

(a) Both A and R are true and R is the correct explanation of A
(b) Both A and R are true but R is not the correct explanation of A
(c) A is true but R is false
(d) A is false but R is true

19. Let R be any relation in the set A of human beings in a town at a particular time.

Assertion (A) If $R = \{(x, y) : x \text{ is wife of } y\}$, then R is reflexive.

Reason (R) If $R = \{(x, y) : x \text{ is father of } y\}$, then R is neither reflexive nor symmetric nor transitive.

20. Assertion (A) If $A = \begin{bmatrix} 2 & 4 \\ 3 & 2 \end{bmatrix}$ and $C = \begin{bmatrix} -2 & 5 \\ 3 & 4 \end{bmatrix}$, then $3A - C = \begin{bmatrix} 8 & 7 \\ 6 & 2 \end{bmatrix}$.

Reason (R) If the matrices A and B are of same order, say $m \times n$, satisfy the commutative law, then $A + B = B + A$.

Section B

(This section comprises of very short answer type questions (VSA) of 2 marks each)

21. Find the domain of $\sec^{-1}(2x + 1)$.

Or

Which is greater, $\tan 1$ or $\tan^{-1} 1$?

22. Find the value of $\cos^{-1}\left(\dfrac{1}{2}\right) + 2\sin^{-1}\left(\dfrac{1}{2}\right)$.

23. Evaluate $\displaystyle\int_{-\pi}^{\pi} (1 - x^2)\sin x \cos^2 x \, dx$.

Or Evaluate $\displaystyle\int_{-1}^{2} \dfrac{|x|}{x} \, dx$.

24. If A and B are square matrices such that $B = -A^{-1}BA$, then find the value of $(A + B)^2$.

25. Solve the differential equation $\cos\left(\dfrac{dy}{dx}\right) = a, \, (a \in R)$.

Section C

(This section comprises of short answer type questions (SA) of 3 marks each)

26. Find the value of a, if the function $f(x)$ defined by $f(x) = \begin{cases} 2x - 1, & x < 2 \\ a, & x = 2 \text{ is} \\ x + 1, & x > 2 \end{cases}$ continuous at $x = 2$.

27. If $\cos^{-1} x + \cos^{-1} y + \cos^{-1} z = \pi$, then prove that $x^2 + y^2 + z^2 + 2xyz = 1$

Or Find the domain of function $f(x) = \cos^{-1}(x^2 - 4)$.

28. Examine the continuity of

$$f(x) = \begin{cases} \dfrac{\log x - \log 2}{x - 2}, & x > 2 \\ \dfrac{1}{2}, & x = 2 \text{ at } x = 2. \\ 2\left(\dfrac{x - 2}{x^2 - 4}\right), & x < 2 \end{cases}$$

Or

If $x^y = e^{x - y}$, prove that $\dfrac{dy}{dx} = \dfrac{\log x}{(1 + \log x)^2}$

29. Evaluate $\displaystyle\int \dfrac{dx}{\sin(x - a) \cdot \cos(x - b)}$.

Or

Evaluate $\displaystyle\int \dfrac{xe^{2x}}{(1 + 2x)^2} \, dx$.

30. Sketch the graph of $y = |x + 3|$ and evaluate the area under the curve $y = |x + 3|$ above X-axis and between $x = -6$ to $x = 0$.

31. Solve the differential equation $(x - y)(dx + dy) = dx - dy, \, y(0) = -1$.

Section D

(This section comprises of long answer type questions (LA) of 5 marks each)

32. For $x > 0$, let $f(x) = \int_1^x \dfrac{\log_e t}{1+t}\, dt$. Find the function $f(x) + f\left(\dfrac{1}{x}\right)$ and show that $f(e) + f\left(\dfrac{1}{e}\right) = \dfrac{1}{2}$.

33. Find A^{-1}, if $A = \begin{bmatrix} 0 & 1 & 1 \\ 1 & 0 & 1 \\ 1 & 1 & 0 \end{bmatrix}$ and show that $A^{-1} = \dfrac{A^2 - 3I}{2}$.

Or

If $A = \begin{bmatrix} 1 & -1 & 1 \\ 2 & 1 & -3 \\ 1 & 1 & 1 \end{bmatrix}$, find A^{-1} and hence solve the system of linear equation

$$x + 2y + z = 4,$$
$$-x + y + z = 0,$$
$$x - 3y + z = 2.$$

34. Solve the LPP

Objective function $Z = 3x + 3.5y$ (maximise), subject to constraints are

$$x + 2y \geq 240$$
$$3x + 1.5y \geq 270$$
$$1.5x + 2y \leq 310$$
$$x \geq 0, y \geq 0$$

Or

Solve the following LPP by graphical method minimise $Z = 20x + 10y$

Subject to constraints are

$$x + 2y \leq 40,$$
$$3x + y \geq 30$$
$$4x + 3y \geq 60$$

and $\qquad x, y \geq 0$

35. Solve the following differential equation.

$$\sqrt{1 + x^2 + y^2 + x^2 y^2} + xy \dfrac{dy}{dx} = 0$$

Section E

(This section comprises of 3 case-study/ passage-based questions of 4 marks each with two sub-parts. First two case study questions have three sub-parts (i), (ii), (iii) of marks 1, 1, 2 respectively. The third case study question has two sub-parts of 2 marks each)

36. In a bolt factory, machines A, B and C manufacture respectively 25%, 35% and 40% of the total bolts. Of their output 5%, 4% and 2% are respectively defective bolts.

On the basis of above information, answer the following questions

(i) Find the probability that bolt drawn is defective given that bolt is manufactured by B.

(ii) Find the probability that bolt drawn is defective given that bolt is manufactured by C.

(iii) Find the probability that, if drawn bolt is defective, then it is manufactured by B.

Or

If drawn bolt is defective, then find the probability that it is not manufactured by C.

37. For a function $f(x)$, if $f(-x) = f(x)$, then $f(x)$ is an even function and $f(-x) = -f(x)$, then $f(x)$ is a odd function. Again, we have

$$\int_{-a}^{a} f(x)\, dx = \begin{cases} 2\displaystyle\int_0^a f(x)dx, & \text{if } f(x) \text{ is even} \\ 0, & \text{if } f(x) \text{ is odd} \end{cases}$$

On the basis of above information, answer the following questions

(i) Show that $f(x) = x^2 \sin x$ is an odd function.

(ii) Evaluate $\displaystyle\int_{-\pi}^{\pi} (x^2 \sin x)\, dx$.

(iii) Evaluate $\displaystyle\int_{-\pi}^{\pi} (x \sin x)\, dx$.

Or

Evaluate $\displaystyle\int_{-\pi/2}^{\pi/2} |\sin x|\, dx$.

38. In a test, you either guesses or copies or knows the answer to a multiple choice question with four choice.

The probability that you make a guess is $\dfrac{1}{3}$, you copies the answer is $\dfrac{1}{6}$. The probability that your answer is correct, given that you guess it, is $\dfrac{1}{8}$ and also the probability that your answer is correct, given that you copied it is $\dfrac{1}{4}$.

On the basis of above information, answer the following questions

(i) Find the probability that you knows the answer given that you correctly answered it.

(ii) Find the total probability of correctly answered the question.

SOLUTIONS

1. (a) Let $I = \displaystyle\int_1^e \underset{II}{1} \cdot \underset{I}{\log x}\, dx$

$= [\log x \cdot x]_1^e - \displaystyle\int_1^e x \cdot \dfrac{1}{x}\, dx$

$= (e \log e - \log 1) - \displaystyle\int_1^e 1\, dx$

$= e - [x]_1^e = e - (e - 1) = 1$

2. (a) Given lines are

$\dfrac{x-3}{1} = \dfrac{y-2}{5} = \dfrac{z+1}{\lambda}$ ...(i)

$\dfrac{x-1}{6} = \dfrac{y+1}{-2} = \dfrac{z+6}{4}$ ...(ii)

$\because$ Lines (i) and (ii) are perpendicular.

$\therefore \quad 1(6) + 5(-2) + \lambda(4) = 0$

$\Rightarrow \qquad 6 - 10 + 4\lambda = 0$

$\Rightarrow \qquad\qquad 4\lambda = 10 - 6 = 4$

$\Rightarrow \qquad\qquad \lambda = 1$

3. (a) Given equation of line can be rewritten as

$\dfrac{x-3}{1} = \dfrac{y-(-2)}{-3} = \dfrac{z-2}{-1}$

$\Rightarrow \quad (x, y, z) \equiv (3, -2, 2)$

and $\quad (a, b, c) = (1, -3, -1)$

$\therefore$ Required vector equation of line is given by

$\vec{r} = (3\hat{i} - 2\hat{j} + 2\hat{k}) + \lambda(\hat{i} - 3\hat{j} - \hat{k})$

4. (b) Let $I = \displaystyle\int \dfrac{\sin^6 x}{\cos^8 x}\, dx = \int \tan^6 x \sec^2 x\, dx$

Put $\tan x = t$

$\therefore \sec^2 x\, dx = dt$

$\therefore \qquad I = \displaystyle\int t^6 dt = \dfrac{t^7}{7} + C$

$= \dfrac{\tan^7 x}{7} + C$ $\qquad [\because t = \tan x]$

5. (d) Given lines are

$\dfrac{x+1}{3} = \dfrac{y+5}{-2} = \dfrac{z-1}{3}$ ...(i)

and $\quad \dfrac{1-x}{2} = \dfrac{2-y}{1} = \dfrac{1+z}{-1}$ ...(ii)

Now, angle between line (i) and line (ii) is given by

$\cos\theta = \left(\dfrac{|3(-2) + (-2)(-1) + 3(-1)|}{\sqrt{9+4+9}\,\sqrt{4+1+1}} \right)$

$\Rightarrow \quad \cos\theta = \dfrac{7}{\sqrt{132}} \Rightarrow \cos\theta = \dfrac{7}{2\sqrt{33}}$

$\Rightarrow \qquad a = 7 \text{ and } b = 2$

$\therefore \qquad a + b = 7 + 2 = 9$

6. (a) Given lines is parallel to the line

$\dfrac{x+3}{3} = \dfrac{4-y}{5} = \dfrac{z+8}{6}$ ...(i)

or $\qquad \dfrac{x+3}{3} = \dfrac{y-4}{-5} = \dfrac{z+8}{6}$

$\therefore$ Direction ratios of the line are 3, −5 and 6 also the given line passes through the point $(-2, 4, -5)$

$\therefore$ Required cartesian of the line is given by

$\dfrac{x+2}{3} = \dfrac{y-4}{-5} = \dfrac{z+5}{6}$

7. (b) We have, $A \cdot (\text{adj } A) = 10I$

We know that $A(\text{adj } A) = |A|I$

$\therefore$ $\quad\quad\quad |A| = 10$

Also, we know that $|\text{adj } A| = |A|^{3-1}$

$\therefore$ $\quad\quad\quad |\text{adj } A| = (10)^2 = 100$

8. (c) We have, $\vec{a} = \hat{i} - 2\hat{j} + 3\hat{k}$

Now, $|\vec{a}| = \sqrt{1+4+9} = \sqrt{14}$

Also, $\quad\quad |\vec{a} - \vec{b}| = \sqrt{7}$

$\Rightarrow \quad\quad |\vec{a} - \vec{b}|^2 = 7$

$\Rightarrow \quad (\vec{a} - \vec{b}) \cdot (\vec{a} - \vec{b}) = 7$

$\Rightarrow |\vec{a}|^2 + |\vec{b}|^2 - 2\vec{a} \cdot \vec{b} = 7$

$\Rightarrow \quad 14 + |\vec{b}|^2 - 2|\vec{b}|^2 = 7$ $[\because$ given $\vec{a} \cdot \vec{b} = |\vec{b}|^2]$

$\Rightarrow \quad\quad |\vec{b}|^2 = 7 \Rightarrow |\vec{b}| = \sqrt{7}$

9. (c) We have,

$(2\hat{i} + \lambda\hat{j} + 3\hat{k})$ and $(3\hat{i} + 2\hat{j} - 4\hat{k})$ are perpendicular.

$\therefore (2\hat{i} + \lambda\hat{j} + 3\hat{k}) \cdot (3\hat{i} + 2\hat{j} - 4\hat{k}) = 0$

$\Rightarrow \quad\quad\quad 6 + 2\lambda - 12 = 0$

$\Rightarrow \quad\quad\quad\quad 2\lambda = 6$

$\Rightarrow \quad\quad\quad\quad \lambda = 3$

10. (a) Let direction cosines of the line be l, m and n.

Given, $\alpha = 90°, \beta = 135°$ and $\gamma = 45°$

Then, $\quad l = \cos\alpha = \cos 90° = 0$,

$\quad\quad m = \cos\beta = \cos 135° = \dfrac{-1}{\sqrt{2}}$

and $\quad n = \cos\gamma = \cos 45° = \dfrac{1}{\sqrt{2}}$

Hence, the direction cosines of a line are

$0, \dfrac{-1}{\sqrt{2}}$ and $\dfrac{1}{\sqrt{2}}$.

11. (d) Given, $|\vec{a}| = 1, |\vec{b}| = 1$ and $|\vec{a} + \vec{b}| = 1$

Now, $|\vec{a} + \vec{b}|^2 = (\vec{a} + \vec{b}) \cdot (\vec{a} + \vec{b})$

$\quad\quad\quad\quad = \vec{a} \cdot \vec{a} + \vec{b} \cdot \vec{a} + \vec{a} \cdot \vec{b} + \vec{b} \cdot \vec{b}$

$\Rightarrow |\vec{a} + \vec{b}|^2 = |\vec{a}|^2 + 2\vec{a} \cdot \vec{b} + |\vec{b}|^2$

$\quad\quad\quad [\because \vec{a} \cdot \vec{b} = \vec{b} \cdot \vec{a}$ and $\vec{x} \cdot \vec{x} = |\vec{x}|^2]$

$\Rightarrow \quad\quad 1 = 1 + 2\vec{a} \cdot \vec{b} + 1$ [given]

$\Rightarrow \quad\quad 2\vec{a} \cdot \vec{b} = -1$

$\Rightarrow |\vec{a}||\vec{b}|\cos\theta = -\dfrac{1}{2}$ $[\because \vec{a} \cdot \vec{b} = |\vec{a}||\vec{b}|\cos\theta]$

$\Rightarrow \quad\quad \cos\theta = -\dfrac{1}{2}$ $[\because |\vec{a}| = |\vec{b}| = 1]$

$\Rightarrow \quad\quad \cos\theta = \cos\dfrac{2\pi}{3} \Rightarrow \theta = \dfrac{2\pi}{3}$

Hence, the angle between $\vec{a}$ and $\vec{b}$ is $\dfrac{2\pi}{3}$.

12. (a) $(A^2)' = (A')^2 = (-A)^2 = A^2$ $[\because A' = -A]$

Hence, A^2 is symmetric matrix.

13. (b) We have, $\vec{a} = 2\hat{i} - 2\hat{j} + \hat{k}, \vec{b} = \hat{i} + 2\hat{j} - 2\hat{k}$ and

$\vec{c} = 2\hat{i} - \hat{j} + 4\hat{k}$

Consider, $(\vec{b} + \vec{c}) = (\hat{i} + 2\hat{j} - 2\hat{k}) + (2\hat{i} - \hat{j} + 4\hat{k})$

$\quad\quad\quad\quad = 3\hat{i} + \hat{j} + 2\hat{k}$

Now, the projection of $\vec{b} + \vec{c}$ on $\vec{a}$ is given by

$\dfrac{(\vec{b} + \vec{c}) \cdot \vec{a}}{|\vec{a}|} = \dfrac{(3\hat{i} + \hat{j} + 2\hat{k}) \cdot (2\hat{i} - 2\hat{j} + \hat{k})}{\sqrt{2^2 + (-2)^2 + (1)^2}}$

$\quad\quad\quad\quad = \dfrac{6 - 2 + 2}{\sqrt{4 + 4 + 1}} = \dfrac{6}{3} = 2$

14. (a) Vector λa is a unit vector.

$\therefore \quad\quad |\lambda \vec{a}| = 1 \Rightarrow |\lambda||\vec{a}| = 1$

$\therefore \quad\quad |\vec{a}| = \dfrac{1}{|\lambda|}$

15. (b) Let $(x_1, y_1, z_1) \equiv (-2, 4, -5)$ and $(x_2, y_2, z_2) \equiv (1, 2, 3)$

DR's of the line are

$\quad\quad 1 - (-2), 2 - 4, 3 - (-5) = 3, -2, 8$

$\quad\quad [\because$ DR's of the line are $x_2 - x_1, y_2 - y_1$ and $z_2 - z_1]$

$\therefore$ DC's are

$\dfrac{3}{\sqrt{(3)^2 + (-2)^2 + (8)^2}}, \dfrac{-2}{\sqrt{(3)^2 + (-2)^2 + (8)^2}},$

$\quad\quad\quad\quad\quad\quad \dfrac{8}{\sqrt{(3)^2 + (-2)^2 + (8)^2}}$

$= \dfrac{3}{\sqrt{9 + 4 + 64}}, \dfrac{-2}{\sqrt{9 + 4 + 64}}, \dfrac{8}{\sqrt{9 + 4 + 64}}$

$= \dfrac{3}{\sqrt{77}}, \dfrac{-2}{\sqrt{77}}, \dfrac{8}{\sqrt{77}}$

16. (b) We have,

$|\vec{a} - \vec{b}|^2 = (\vec{a} - \vec{b}) \cdot (\vec{a} - \vec{b})$

$\quad\quad\quad = |\vec{a}|^2 - 2\vec{a} \cdot \vec{b} + |\vec{b}|^2$

$\quad\quad\quad = (2)^2 - 2 \times 2 + (5)^2$

$\quad\quad\quad [$ given, $|\vec{a}| = 2, |\vec{b}| = 5$ and $|\vec{a} \cdot \vec{b}| = 2]$

$\quad\quad\quad = 4 - 4 + 25 = 25$

$\therefore \quad |\vec{a} - \vec{b}| = 5$

17. (b) We known that $\vec{a} \times \vec{b}$ is perpendicular to both $\vec{a}$

and $\vec{b}$

$\therefore (\vec{a} \times \vec{b}) \cdot \vec{b} = 0$

18. (c) We have,

$\hat{i} \times (\hat{j} + \hat{k}) + \hat{j} \times (\hat{k} + \hat{i}) + \hat{k} \times (\hat{i} + \hat{j})$

$= \hat{i} \times \hat{j} + \hat{i} \times \hat{k} + \hat{j} \times \hat{k} + \hat{j} \times \hat{i} + \hat{k} \times \hat{i} + \hat{k} \times \hat{j}$

$= \hat{k} - \hat{j} + \hat{i} - \hat{k} + \hat{j} - \hat{i} = 0$

19. (d) **Assertion** Here R is not reflexive: as x cannot be wife of x.

Hence, Assertion is false.

Reason Here, R is not reflexive; as x cannot be father of x, for any x. R is not symmetric as if x is father of y, then y cannot be father of x. R is not transitive as if x is father of y and y is father of z, then x is grandfather (not father) of z.

Hence, Reason is true.

20. (b) **Assertion** Given, $A = \begin{bmatrix} 2 & 4 \\ 3 & 2 \end{bmatrix}$ and $C = \begin{bmatrix} -2 & 5 \\ 3 & 4 \end{bmatrix}$

Then, $3A - C = 3\begin{bmatrix} 2 & 4 \\ 3 & 2 \end{bmatrix} - \begin{bmatrix} -2 & 5 \\ 3 & 4 \end{bmatrix}$

$= \begin{bmatrix} 6 & 12 \\ 9 & 6 \end{bmatrix} - \begin{bmatrix} -2 & 5 \\ 3 & 4 \end{bmatrix}$

$= \begin{bmatrix} 6-(-2) & 12-5 \\ 9-3 & 6-4 \end{bmatrix} = \begin{bmatrix} 8 & 7 \\ 6 & 2 \end{bmatrix}$

Hence, both Assertion and Reason are true but Reason is not the correct explanation of Assertion.

21. The domain of $\sec^{-1}(x)$ is $(-\infty, -1] \cup [1, \infty)$. Therefore, $\sec^{-1}(2x+1)$ will be defined for inequality

$2x + 1 \geq 1 \text{ or } 2x + 1 \leq -1$ (1)

$\Rightarrow \quad 2x \geq 0 \text{ or } 2x \leq -2$

$\Rightarrow \quad x \geq 0 \text{ or } x \leq -1$

$\Rightarrow \quad x \in (-\infty, -1] \cup [0, \infty)$

So, domain of $\sec^{-1}(2x + 1)$ is $(-\infty, -1] \cup [0, \infty)$. (1)

Or

We know that

$\tan^{-1}(1) = \dfrac{\pi}{4}$ and $1 > \dfrac{\pi}{4}$

Now, $\qquad 1 > \dfrac{\pi}{4}$

$\Rightarrow \qquad \tan 1 > \tan \dfrac{\pi}{4}$ (1)

$\Rightarrow \qquad \tan 1 > 1$

$\Rightarrow \qquad \tan 1 > 1 > \dfrac{\pi}{4} \Rightarrow \tan 1 > \dfrac{\pi}{4}$

$\Rightarrow \qquad \tan 1 > \tan^{-1}(1) \qquad \left[\because \tan^{-1}(1) = \dfrac{\pi}{4} \right]$

So, $\tan 1$ is greater than $\tan^{-1}(1)$. (1)

22. Let $\cos^{-1}\left(\dfrac{1}{2}\right) = x$

$\Rightarrow \qquad \cos x = \dfrac{1}{2} = \cos \dfrac{\pi}{3}$

$\Rightarrow \qquad x = \dfrac{\pi}{3} \in [0, \pi]$

$[\because$ principal value branch of $\cos^{-1}$ is $[0, \pi]]$

Again, let $\sin^{-1}\left(\dfrac{1}{2}\right) = y$

$\Rightarrow \qquad \sin y = \dfrac{1}{2} = \sin \dfrac{\pi}{6}$ (1)

$\Rightarrow \qquad y = \dfrac{\pi}{6} \in \left[-\dfrac{\pi}{2}, \dfrac{\pi}{2} \right]$

$\left[\because \text{ principal value branch of } \sin^{-1} \text{ is } \left[-\dfrac{\pi}{2}, \dfrac{\pi}{2} \right] \right]$

$\therefore \; \cos^{-1}\left(\dfrac{1}{2}\right) + 2\sin^{-1}\left(\dfrac{1}{2}\right) = \dfrac{\pi}{3} + 2 \cdot \dfrac{\pi}{6} = \dfrac{\pi}{3} + \dfrac{\pi}{3} = \dfrac{2\pi}{3}$ (1)

23. Let $I = \int_{-\pi}^{\pi} (1 - x^2) \sin x \cos^2 x \, dx$

Again, let $f(x) = (1 - x^2) \sin x \cos^2 x$

$\therefore \; f(-x) = [1 - (-x)^2] \sin(-x) \cos^2(-x)$

$= (1 - x^2)(-\sin x)\cos^2 x$ (1)

$= -(1 - x^2) \sin x \cos^2 x = -f(x)$

$\therefore f(x)$ is odd function

$\therefore \quad I = 0 \quad \left[\because \int_{-a}^{a} f(x)\,dx = 0, \text{ if } f(x) \text{ is odd function} \right]$ (1)

Or

Let $I = \int_{-1}^{2} \dfrac{|x|}{x} dx = \int_{-1}^{0} \dfrac{|x|}{x} dx + \int_{0}^{2} \dfrac{|x|}{x} dx$

$= \int_{-1}^{0} \dfrac{-x}{x} dx + \int_{0}^{2} \dfrac{x}{x} dx \quad \left[\because |x| = \begin{cases} -x, & x < 0 \\ x, & x \geq 0 \end{cases} \right]$ (1)

$= \int_{-1}^{0} -1 \, dx + \int_{0}^{2} 1 \, dx = [-x]_{-1}^{0} + [x]_{0}^{2}$

$= [0 - (1)] + [2 - 0] = -1 + 2 = 1$ (1)

24. We have, $B = -A^{-1}BA$

$\Rightarrow \qquad AB = -A(A^{-1}BA) = -(AA^{-1})(BA)$

$= -(I)(BA) = -BA$ (1)

$\Rightarrow AB + BA = 0$

Now, $(A + B)^2 = (A + B)(A + B)$

$= A^2 + AB + BA + B^2$

$= A^2 + 0 + B^2 \qquad [\because AB = -BA]$

$= A^2 + B^2$ (1)

25. Given equation is $\cos\left(\dfrac{dy}{dx}\right) = a$

which can be rewritten as $\dfrac{dy}{dx} = \cos^{-1} a$

$\Rightarrow \qquad dy = \cos^{-1} a \, dx$ (1)

$\Rightarrow \qquad \int dy = \int \cos^{-1} a \, dx$

$\Rightarrow \qquad y = \cos^{-1} a \cdot x + C$

which is the required solution. (1)

26. Given, $f(x) = \begin{cases} 2x-1, & x<2 \\ a, & x=2 \\ x+1, & x>2 \end{cases}$

$\because f(x)$ is continuous at $x=2$.

$\therefore \quad \lim\limits_{x \to 2^-} f(x) = \lim\limits_{x \to 2^+} f(x) = f(2)$ ...(i) **(1)**

Now, $\lim\limits_{x \to 2^-} f(x) = \lim\limits_{x \to 2^-} (2x-1) = \lim\limits_{h \to 0} [2(2-h)-1] = 3$

$\lim\limits_{x \to 2^+} f(x) = \lim\limits_{x \to 2^+} (x+1) = \lim\limits_{h \to 0} [(2+h)+1] = 3$ **(1)**

and $f(2) = a$

From Eq. (i), we have

$3 = 3 = a \Rightarrow a = 3$ **(1)**

27. Let $\cos^{-1} x = \alpha$, $\cos^{-1} y = \beta$ and $\cos^{-1} z = \gamma$

$\Rightarrow \cos\alpha = x, \cos\beta = y$ and $\cos\gamma = z$

Since, $\alpha + \beta + \gamma = \pi$

$\therefore \qquad \alpha + \beta = \pi - \gamma$

Now, $\cos(\alpha + \beta) = \cos(\pi - \gamma)$

$\Rightarrow \quad \cos\alpha\cos\beta - \sin\alpha\sin\beta = -\cos\gamma$ **(1)**

$\Rightarrow \quad xy - \sqrt{1-x^2}\sqrt{1-y^2} = -z$

$\Rightarrow \qquad xy + z = \sqrt{1-x^2}\sqrt{1-y^2}$

$\Rightarrow \quad x^2y^2 + z^2 + 2xyz = 1 - x^2 - y^2 + x^2y^2$

[squaring on both sides]

$\Rightarrow \quad x^2 + y^2 + z^2 + 2xyz = 1$ **Hence proved. (2)**

Or

We know that domain of $\cos^{-1} x$ is $[-1, 1]$.

So, $f(x) = \cos^{-1}(x^2 - 4)$ will be defined.

When $\quad -1 \le x^2 - 4 \le 1$

$\Rightarrow \quad -1 + 4 \le x^2 - 4 + 4 \le 1 + 4 \Rightarrow 3 \le x^2 \le 5$ **(1)**

Now, when $x^2 \ge 3$

$\Rightarrow \qquad x^2 - 3 \ge 0$

$\Rightarrow \qquad (x - \sqrt3)(x + \sqrt3) \ge 0$

(1)

$\therefore \qquad x \in (-\infty, -\sqrt3] \cup [\sqrt3, \infty)$ ...(i)

When $x^2 \le 5$

$\Rightarrow \quad x^2 - 5 \le 0 \Rightarrow (x - \sqrt5)(x + \sqrt5) \le 0$

$\therefore \qquad x \in [-\sqrt5, \sqrt5]$ ...(ii)

From Eqs. (i) and (ii), we get

$x \in [-\sqrt5, -\sqrt3] \cup [\sqrt3, \sqrt5]$

So, domain of $\cos^{-1}(x^2 - 4)$ is $[-\sqrt5, -\sqrt3] \cup [\sqrt3, \sqrt5]$.

(1)

28. At $x=2$, LHL $= \lim\limits_{x \to 2^-} f(x)$

$= \lim\limits_{h \to 0} f(2-h) = \lim\limits_{h \to 0} \dfrac{2\{(2-h)-2\}}{\{(2-h)^2 - 4\}}$

[$\because$ putting $x = 2 - h$ when $x \to 2^-$, then $h \to 0$]

$= \lim\limits_{h \to 0} \dfrac{-2h}{4 + h^2 - 4h - 4} = \lim\limits_{h \to 0} \dfrac{-2}{h-4} = \dfrac12$ **(1)**

and RHL $= \lim\limits_{x \to 2^+} f(x)$

$= \lim\limits_{h \to 0} f(2+h) = \lim\limits_{h \to 0} \dfrac{\log(2+h) - \log 2}{2 + h - 2}$

[$\because$ putting $x = 2 + h$ when $x \to 2^+$, then $h \to 0$] **(1)**

$= \lim\limits_{h \to 0} \dfrac{\log\left(1 + \dfrac{h}{2}\right)}{h}$ $\left[\because \log m - \log n = \log\dfrac{m}{n}\right]$

$= \lim\limits_{h \to 0} \dfrac{\log\left(1 + \dfrac{h}{2}\right)}{2\left(\dfrac{h}{2}\right)} = \dfrac12$ $\left[\because \lim\limits_{x \to 0} \dfrac{\log(1+x)}{x} = 1\right]$

Also, $\quad f(2) = \dfrac12$

Thus, $\quad$ LHL $=$ RHL $= f(2)$

$\therefore f(x)$ is continuous at $x = 2$. **(1)**

Or

We have, $x^y = e^{x-y} \Rightarrow y\log x = x - y$ $[\because \log e = 1]$

$\Rightarrow y(\log x + 1) = x \Rightarrow y = \dfrac{x}{\log x + 1}$ **(1)**

$\therefore \quad \dfrac{dy}{dx} = \dfrac{(\log x + 1)\cdot 1 - x\left(\dfrac1x + 0\right)}{(\log x + 1)^2} = \dfrac{\log x}{(\log x + 1)^2}$ **(2)**

29. Let $I = \displaystyle\int \dfrac{dx}{\sin(x-a)\cdot\cos(x-b)}$

$= \dfrac{1}{\cos(b-a)} \displaystyle\int \dfrac{\cos[(x-a)-(x-b)]}{\sin(x-a)\cdot\cos(x-b)} dx$

[multiplying numerator and denominator by $\cos(b-a)$]

$= \dfrac{1}{\cos(b-a)} \displaystyle\int \dfrac{\begin{bmatrix} \cos(x-a)\cos(x-b) \\ + \sin(x-a)\sin(x-b) \end{bmatrix}}{\sin(x-a)\cdot\cos(x-b)} dx$ **(1)**

[$\because \cos(A-B) = \cos A\cos B + \sin A\sin B$]

$= \dfrac{1}{\cos(b-a)} \left\{ \displaystyle\int \left[\dfrac{\cos(x-a)\cos(x-b)}{\sin(x-a)\cos(x-b)}\right] dx \right.$

$\left. + \displaystyle\int \left[\dfrac{\sin(x-a)\sin(x-b)}{\sin(x-a)\cos(x-b)}\right] dx \right\}$

$= \dfrac{1}{\cos(b-a)} \left[\displaystyle\int \cot(x-a)\,dx + \displaystyle\int \tan(x-b)\,dx\right]$ **(1)**

$= \dfrac{1}{\cos(b-a)} [\log|\sin(x-a)| - \log|\cos(x-b)|] + C$

[$\because \int \cot x\,dx = \log|\sin x| + C, \int \tan x\,dx = -\log|\cos x| + C$]

$$= \frac{1}{\cos(b-a)} \log \left| \frac{\sin(x-a)}{\cos(x-b)} \right| + C$$

$$\left[\because \log m - \log n = \log \frac{m}{n} \right] \quad (1)$$

Or

Let $I = \int \frac{xe^{2x}}{(1+2x)^2} \, dx$

Put $2x = t \Rightarrow 2 = \frac{dt}{dx} \Rightarrow dx = \frac{dt}{2}$

$$\therefore \quad I = \int \frac{\frac{t}{2}e^t}{(1+t)^2} \frac{dt}{2} = \frac{1}{4} \int \frac{te^t}{(1+t)^2} \, dt$$

$$= \frac{1}{4} \int \frac{(1+t-1)e^t}{(1+t)^2} \, dt$$

$$= \frac{1}{4} \int e^t \left[\frac{(1+t)}{(1+t)^2} - \frac{1}{(1+t)^2} \right] dt$$

$$= \frac{1}{4} \int e^t \left[\frac{1}{(1+t)} - \frac{1}{(1+t)^2} \right] dt \quad (1)$$

$$= \frac{1}{4} e^t \cdot \frac{1}{1+t} + C$$

$$\left[\because \int e^t [f(t) + f'(t)] dt = e^t f(t) + C \right]$$

$$\therefore \quad I = \frac{e^{2x}}{4(1+2x)} + C \qquad [\text{putting } t = 2x] \ (2)$$

30. First, we sketch the graph of
$$y = |x + 3|$$

$$\therefore \quad y = |x + 3| = \begin{cases} x + 3, & \text{if } x + 3 \geq 0 \\ -(x + 3), & \text{if } x + 3 < 0 \end{cases}$$

$$\Rightarrow \quad y = |x + 3| = \begin{cases} x + 3, & \text{if } x \geq -3 \\ -x - 3, & \text{if } x < -3 \end{cases}$$

So, we have $y = x + 3$ for $x \geq -3$ and $y = -x - 3$ for $x < -3$.

A sketch of $y = |x + 3|$ is shown below

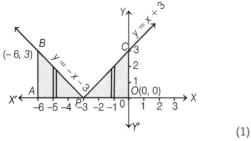

(1)

Here, $y = x + 3$ is the straight line which cuts X and Y-axes at $(-3, 0)$ and $(0, 3)$, respectively.

Thus, $y = x + 3$ for $x \geq -3$ represents the part of line which lies on the right side of $x = -3$.

Similarly, $y = -x - 3$, $x < -3$ represents the part of line $y = -x - 3$, which lies on left side of $x = -3$.

Clearly, required area

= Area of region $ABPA$ + Area of region $PCOP$

$$= \int_{-6}^{-3} (-x - 3) \, dx + \int_{-3}^{0} (x + 3) \, dx$$

$$= \left[-\frac{x^2}{2} - 3x \right]_{-6}^{-3} + \left[\frac{x^2}{2} + 3x \right]_{-3}^{0}$$

$$= \left[\left(-\frac{9}{2} + 9 \right) - (-18 + 18) \right] + \left[0 - \left(\frac{9}{2} - 9 \right) \right]$$

$$= \left(-\frac{9}{2} - \frac{9}{2} \right) + (9 + 9) = 18 - 9 = 9 \text{ sq units} \qquad (2)$$

31. The given differential equation is
$$(x - y)(dx + dy) = dx - dy$$

$$\Rightarrow \quad (x - y - 1) \, dx = -(x - y + 1) \, dy$$

$$\Rightarrow \quad \frac{dy}{dx} = -\frac{x - y - 1}{x - y + 1} \qquad \ldots(i)$$

Let $x - y = v$.

Then, $1 - \frac{dy}{dx} = \frac{dv}{dx} \Rightarrow \frac{dy}{dx} = 1 - \frac{dv}{dx}$ (1)

On putting $x - y = v$ and $\frac{dy}{dx} = 1 - \frac{dv}{dx}$ in Eq. (i), we get

$$1 - \frac{dv}{dx} = -\frac{v - 1}{v + 1}$$

$$\Rightarrow \quad \frac{dv}{dx} = \frac{v - 1}{v + 1} + 1$$

$$\Rightarrow \quad \frac{dv}{dx} = \frac{2v}{v + 1}$$

$$\Rightarrow \quad \frac{v + 1}{v} \, dv = 2 \, dx$$

$$\Rightarrow \quad \left(1 + \frac{1}{v} \right) dv = 2 \, dx$$

$$\Rightarrow \quad \int \left(1 + \frac{1}{v} \right) dv = 2 \int dx$$

$$\Rightarrow \quad v + \log |v| = 2x + C$$

$$\Rightarrow \quad x - y + \log |x - y| = 2x + C$$

$$\Rightarrow \quad \log |x - y| = x + y + C \qquad \ldots(ii) \quad (1)$$

It is given that $y(0) = -1$, i.e. when $x = 0, y = -1$.

On putting $x = 0$ and $y = -1$ in Eq. (ii), we get

$$\log 1 = -1 + C$$

$$\Rightarrow \quad C = 1 \qquad [\because \log 1 = 0]$$

On putting $C = 1$ in Eq. (ii), we get

$$\log |x - y| = x + y + 1 \Rightarrow |x - y| = e^{x + y + 1}$$

$$\Rightarrow \quad x - y = \pm e^{x + y + 1} \qquad (1)$$

32. Given, $f(x) = \int_1^x \frac{\log_e t}{1 + t} \, dt \qquad \ldots(i)$

Then, $f\left(\frac{1}{x} \right) = \int_1^{1/x} \frac{\log_e t}{1 + t} \, dt$

Put $t = \frac{1}{u} \Rightarrow dt = -\frac{1}{u^2} \, du$

Also, if $t = 1$, then $u = 1$ and if $t = \dfrac{1}{x}$, then $u = x$ (1)

$$\therefore \; f\left(\frac{1}{x}\right) = \int_1^x \frac{\log_e \frac{1}{u}}{1 + \frac{1}{u}} \times \frac{(-1)}{u^2}\, du = \int_1^x \frac{\log_e u}{(1+u)u}\, du$$

$$\left[\because \log_e \frac{1}{u} = \log_e 1 - \log_e u = 0 - \log_e u \right]$$

$$= \int_1^x \frac{\log_e t}{(1+t)t}\, dt \quad \text{[replacing } u \text{ by } t\text{] ...(ii)} \;(1)$$

On adding Eqs. (i) and (ii), we get

$$f(x) + f\left(\frac{1}{x}\right) = \int_1^x \left\{ \frac{\log_e t}{1+t} + \frac{\log_e t}{(1+t)t} \right\} dt$$

$$= \int_1^x \frac{x \log_e t}{1+t}\left(\frac{1+t}{t}\right) dt$$

$$= \int_1^x \frac{x \log_e t}{t}\, dt \quad \text{...(iii)} \;(1)$$

Again, put $v = \log_e t \;\Rightarrow\; \dfrac{1}{t}\,dt = dv$

Also, if $t = x$, then $v = \log_e x$ and if $t = 1$, then $v = 0$
Then, from Eq. (iii), we get

$$f(x) + f\left(\frac{1}{x}\right) = \int_0^{\log_e x} v\, dv = \left[\frac{v^2}{2}\right]_0^{\log_e x} = \frac{1}{2}[\log_e x]^2 - 0$$

At $x = e$, $f(e) + f\left(\dfrac{1}{e}\right) = \dfrac{1}{2}(\log_e e)^2 = \dfrac{1}{2}$

$$[\because \log_a a = 1] \; \textbf{Hence proved.} \;(2)$$

33. We have, $A = \begin{bmatrix} 0 & 1 & 1 \\ 1 & 0 & 1 \\ 1 & 1 & 0 \end{bmatrix}$

Clearly, $|A| = \begin{vmatrix} 0 & 1 & 1 \\ 1 & 0 & 1 \\ 1 & 1 & 0 \end{vmatrix} = 0 - 1(0-1) + 1(1-0) = 2 \neq 0$

$\therefore \; A^{-1}$ exists.   (1)
Now, let us evaluate the cofactors of elements of $|A|$.

Clearly, $C_{11} = (-1)^{1+1}\begin{vmatrix} 0 & 1 \\ 1 & 0 \end{vmatrix} = -1$

$C_{21} = (-1)^{2+1}\begin{vmatrix} 1 & 1 \\ 1 & 0 \end{vmatrix} = 1, \; C_{31} = (-1)^{3+1}\begin{vmatrix} 1 & 1 \\ 0 & 1 \end{vmatrix} = 1,$

$C_{12} = (-1)^{1+2}\begin{vmatrix} 1 & 1 \\ 1 & 0 \end{vmatrix} = 1, \; C_{22} = (-1)^{2+2}\begin{vmatrix} 0 & 1 \\ 1 & 0 \end{vmatrix} = -1,$

$C_{32} = (-1)^{3+2}\begin{vmatrix} 0 & 1 \\ 1 & 1 \end{vmatrix} = 1, \; C_{13} = (-1)^{1+3}\begin{vmatrix} 1 & 0 \\ 1 & 1 \end{vmatrix} = 1,$

$C_{23} = (-1)^{2+3}\begin{vmatrix} 0 & 1 \\ 1 & 1 \end{vmatrix} = 1 \text{ and } C_{33} = (-1)^{3+3}\begin{vmatrix} 0 & 1 \\ 1 & 0 \end{vmatrix} = -1$ (1)

$$\therefore \; \text{adj}\,(A) = \begin{bmatrix} C_{11} & C_{12} & C_{13} \\ C_{21} & C_{22} & C_{23} \\ C_{31} & C_{32} & C_{33} \end{bmatrix}^T = \begin{bmatrix} C_{11} & C_{21} & C_{31} \\ C_{12} & C_{22} & C_{32} \\ C_{13} & C_{23} & C_{33} \end{bmatrix}$$

$$= \begin{bmatrix} -1 & 1 & 1 \\ 1 & -1 & 1 \\ 1 & 1 & -1 \end{bmatrix}$$

Thus, $A^{-1} = \dfrac{1}{|A|}\,\text{adj}\,(A) = \dfrac{1}{2}\begin{bmatrix} -1 & 1 & 1 \\ 1 & -1 & 1 \\ 1 & 1 & -1 \end{bmatrix}$ (1)

Now consider,

$$A^2 - 3I = \left(\begin{bmatrix} 0 & 1 & 1 \\ 1 & 0 & 1 \\ 1 & 1 & 0 \end{bmatrix}\begin{bmatrix} 0 & 1 & 1 \\ 1 & 0 & 1 \\ 1 & 1 & 0 \end{bmatrix}\right) - 3\begin{bmatrix} 1 & 0 & 0 \\ 0 & 1 & 0 \\ 0 & 0 & 1 \end{bmatrix}$$

$$= \begin{bmatrix} 2 & 1 & 1 \\ 1 & 2 & 1 \\ 1 & 1 & 2 \end{bmatrix} - \begin{bmatrix} 3 & 0 & 0 \\ 0 & 3 & 0 \\ 0 & 0 & 3 \end{bmatrix}$$

$$= \begin{bmatrix} -1 & 1 & 1 \\ 1 & -1 & 1 \\ 1 & 1 & -1 \end{bmatrix} = 2A^{-1}$$

Hence, $A^{-1} = \dfrac{A^2 - 3I}{2}$ **Hence proved.** (2)

Or

We have, $A = \begin{bmatrix} 1 & -1 & 1 \\ 2 & 1 & -3 \\ 1 & 1 & 1 \end{bmatrix}$

Clearly, $|A| = \begin{vmatrix} 1 & -1 & 1 \\ 2 & 1 & -3 \\ 1 & 1 & 1 \end{vmatrix}$

$$= 1(1+3) + 1(2+3) + 1(2-1)$$
$$= 4 + 5 + 1 = 10 \neq 0$$

$\therefore \; A^{-1}$ exist.   (1)
Now, let us find the cofactors C_{ij} of elements a_{ij} in A.

Clearly, $C_{11} = (-1)^{1+1}\begin{vmatrix} 1 & -3 \\ 1 & 1 \end{vmatrix} = 4,$

$C_{12} = (-1)^{2+1}\begin{vmatrix} 2 & -3 \\ 1 & 1 \end{vmatrix} = -5, \; C_{13} = (-1)^{1+3}\begin{vmatrix} 2 & 1 \\ 1 & 1 \end{vmatrix} = 1,$

$C_{21} = (-1)^{2+1}\begin{vmatrix} -1 & 1 \\ 1 & 1 \end{vmatrix} = 2, \; C_{22} = (-1)^{2+2}\begin{vmatrix} 1 & 1 \\ 1 & 1 \end{vmatrix} = 0,$

$C_{23} = (-1)^{2+3}\begin{vmatrix} 1 & -1 \\ 1 & 1 \end{vmatrix} = -2, \; C_{31} = (-1)^{3+1}\begin{vmatrix} -1 & 1 \\ 1 & -3 \end{vmatrix} = 2,$

$C_{32} = (-1)^{3+2}\begin{vmatrix} 1 & 1 \\ 2 & -3 \end{vmatrix} = 5, \; C_{33} = (-1)^{3+3}\begin{vmatrix} 1 & -1 \\ 2 & 1 \end{vmatrix} = 3$ (1)

$$\therefore \; \text{adj}(A) = \begin{bmatrix} C_{11} & C_{12} & C_{13} \\ C_{21} & C_{22} & C_{23} \\ C_{31} & C_{32} & C_{33} \end{bmatrix}^T = \begin{bmatrix} C_{11} & C_{21} & C_{31} \\ C_{12} & C_{22} & C_{32} \\ C_{13} & C_{23} & C_{33} \end{bmatrix}$$

$$\Rightarrow \; \text{adj}(A) = \begin{bmatrix} 4 & 2 & 2 \\ -5 & 0 & 5 \\ 1 & -2 & 3 \end{bmatrix}$$

$$\Rightarrow \; A^{-1} = \frac{1}{|A|}\text{adj}(A) = \frac{1}{10}\begin{bmatrix} 4 & 2 & 2 \\ -5 & 0 & 5 \\ 1 & -2 & 3 \end{bmatrix} \quad \text{...(i)} \;(1)$$

Now, let us solve the given system of linear equations which can be written in matrix form as

$$\begin{bmatrix} 1 & 2 & 1 \\ -1 & 1 & 1 \\ 1 & -3 & 1 \end{bmatrix}\begin{bmatrix} x \\ y \\ z \end{bmatrix} = \begin{bmatrix} 4 \\ 0 \\ 2 \end{bmatrix}$$

$\therefore A^T X = B$, where $X = \begin{bmatrix} x \\ y \\ z \end{bmatrix}$ and $B = \begin{bmatrix} 4 \\ 0 \\ 2 \end{bmatrix}$ (1)

Since, $|A^T| = |A| = 10 \neq 0$. So, the given system of equations is consistent and have a unique solution given by $X = (A^T)^{-1} B = (A^{-1})^T B$

$\Rightarrow \begin{bmatrix} x \\ y \\ z \end{bmatrix} = \frac{1}{10}\begin{bmatrix} 4 & 2 & 2 \\ -5 & 0 & 5 \\ 1 & -2 & 3 \end{bmatrix}^T \begin{bmatrix} 4 \\ 0 \\ 2 \end{bmatrix} = \frac{1}{10}\begin{bmatrix} 4 & -5 & 1 \\ 2 & 0 & -2 \\ 2 & 5 & 3 \end{bmatrix}\begin{bmatrix} 4 \\ 0 \\ 2 \end{bmatrix}$

$= \frac{1}{10}\begin{bmatrix} 18 \\ 4 \\ 14 \end{bmatrix} = \begin{bmatrix} 9/5 \\ 2/5 \\ 7/5 \end{bmatrix}$

$\Rightarrow x = \frac{9}{5}, y = \frac{2}{5}$ and $z = \frac{7}{5}$,

which is the required solution. (1)

34. Our problem is to maximise $Z = 3x + 3.5y$

Subject to the constraints $x + 2y \geq 240$

$3x + 1.5y \geq 270$

$1.5x + 2y \leq 310$

and $x \geq 0, y \geq 0$

Consider the above inequality as equation, we get

$x + 2y = 240$ ...(i)
$3x + 1.5y = 270$ ...(ii)
$1.5x + 2y = 310$ ...(iii)

and $x = 0, y = 0$ ...(iv)

Table for the line $x + 2y = 240$ is

x	0	240
y	120	0

So, line $x + 2y = 240$ passes through the points (0, 120) and (240, 0). On putting (0, 0) in the inequality $x + 2y \geq 240$, we get $0 + 2 \times 0 \geq 240$

$\Rightarrow$ $0 \geq 240$ (false) (1)

So, the half plane is away from the origin.

Table for the line $3x + 1.5y = 270$

x	0	90
y	180	0

So, line $3x + 1.5y = 270$ passes through the points (0, 180) and (90, 0).

On putting (0, 0) in the inequality $3x + 1.5y \geq 270$, we get $3 \times 0 + 1.5 \times 0 \geq 270$

$\Rightarrow$ $0 \geq 270$ (false) (1)

So, the half plane is away from the origin.

Table for the line $1.5x + 2y = 310$ is

x	0	620/3
y	155	0

So, line $1.5x + 2y = 310$ passes through the points (0, 155) and $\left(\frac{620}{3}, 0\right)$.

On putting (0, 0) in the inequality $1.5x + 2y \leq 310$, we get

$1.5 \times 0 + 2 \times 0 \leq 310 \Rightarrow 0 \leq 310$ (true)

So, the half plane is towards the origin. (1)

The intersection point of lines (ii) and (iii) is $B(20, 140)$, of lines (iii) and (i) is $A(140, 50)$, of lines (i) and (ii) is $C(40, 100)$. Since, $x, y \geq 0$

So, the feasible region lies in the first quadrant.

On plotting the graph, we get the feasible region $CABC$, whose corner points are $C(40, 100)$, $A(140, 50)$ and $B(20, 140)$.

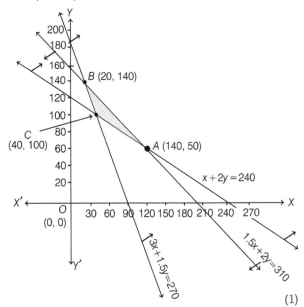

(1)

Now, the values of Z at these points are as follows

Corner points	$Z = 3x + 3.5y$
$A(140, 50)$	$Z = 3 \times 140 + 3.5 \times 50 = 595$ (maximum)
$B(20, 140)$	$Z = 3 \times 20 + 3.5 \times 140 = 550$
$C(40, 100)$	$Z = 3 \times 40 + 3.5 \times 100 = 470$

The maximum value of Z is 595 and it is occur at $A(140, 50)$. (1)

Or

Converting the given inequations into equations, we obtain the following equations

$x + 2y = 40, 3x + y = 30, 4x + 3y = 60, x = 0$ and $y = 0$

Region represented by $x + 2y \leq 40$; The line $x + 2y = 40$ meets the coordinate axes at A_1 (40, 0) and B_1 (0, 20) respectively. Join these points to obtain the line $x + 2y = 40$.

Clearly, (0, 0) satisfies the inequation $x + 2y \leq 40$.

So, the region in *XY*-plane that contains the origin represents the solution set of the given inequation. Region represented by $3x + y \geq 30$: The line $3x + y = 30$ meets *X* and *Y*-axes at A_2 (10, 0) and B_2 (0, 30) respectively. Join these points to obtain this line. We find that the point *O* (0, 0) does not satisfy the inequation $3x + y \geq 30$. So, that region in *xy*-plane which does not contain the origin is the solution set of this inequation. (1)

Region represented by $4x + 3y \geq 60$: The line $4x + 3y = 60$ meets *X* and *Y*-axes at A_3 (15, 0) and B_1 (0, 20) respectively. Join these points to obtain the line $4x + 3y = 60$. We observe that the point *O* (0, 0) does not satisfy the inequation $4x + 3y \geq 60$. So, the region not containing the origin in *XY*-plane represents the solution set of the given inequation.

Region represented by $x \geq 0, y \geq 0$: Clearly, the region represented by the non-negativity restrictions $x \geq 0$ and $y \geq 0$ is the first quadrant in *XY*-plane. (1)

The shaded region $A_3 A_1 QP$ in figure represents the common region of the regions represented by the above inequations. This region expresents the feasible region of the given LPP.

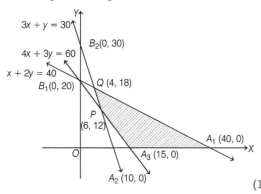

(1)

The coordinates of the corner points of the shaded feasible region are A_3 (15, 0), A_1 (40, 0), Q (4, 18) and P (6, 12). These points have been obtained by solving the equations of the corresponding intersecting lines, simultaneously.

The values of the objective function at these points are given in the following table

Corner points	Value of the objective function $Z = 20x + 10y$
A_3 (15, 0)	$Z = 20 \times 15 + 10 \times 0 = 300$
A_1 (40, 0)	$Z = 20 \times 40 + 10 \times 0 = 800$
Q (4, 18)	$Z = 20 \times 4 + 10 \times 18 = 260$
P (6, 12)	$Z = 20 \times 6 + 10 \times 12 = 240$

Out of these values of *Z*, the minimum value is 240 which is attained at point P (6, 12). Hence, $x = 6, y = 12$ is the optimal solution of the given LPP and the optimal value of *Z* is 240. (2)

35. Given differential equation is
$$\sqrt{1 + x^2 + y^2 + x^2 y^2} + xy\frac{dy}{dx} = 0$$

$$\Rightarrow \quad \sqrt{1(1 + x^2) + y^2(1 + x^2)} = -xy\frac{dy}{dx}$$

$$\Rightarrow \quad \sqrt{(1 + x^2)(1 + y^2)} = -xy\frac{dy}{dx}$$

$$\Rightarrow \quad \sqrt{1 + x^2} \cdot \sqrt{1 + y^2} = -xy\frac{dy}{dx}$$

$$\Rightarrow \quad \frac{y}{\sqrt{1 + y^2}}dy = -\frac{\sqrt{1 + x^2}}{x}dx \quad (1)$$

On integrating both sides, we get

$$\int \frac{y}{\sqrt{1 + y^2}}dy = -\int \frac{\sqrt{1 + x^2}}{x^2} \cdot x\, dx$$

On putting $1 + y^2 = t$ and $1 + x^2 = u^2$

$$\Rightarrow \quad 2y\, dy = dt \text{ and } 2x\, dx = 2u\, du$$

$$\Rightarrow \quad y\, dy = \frac{dt}{2} \text{ and } x\, dx = u\, du$$

$$\therefore \quad \frac{1}{2}\int \frac{dt}{\sqrt{t}} = -\int \frac{u}{u^2 - 1} \cdot u\, du \quad (1)$$

$$\Rightarrow \quad \frac{1}{2}\int t^{-1/2}dt = -\int \frac{u^2}{u^2 - 1}du$$

$$\Rightarrow \quad \frac{1}{2}\frac{t^{1/2}}{1/2} = -\int \frac{(u^2 - 1 + 1)}{u^2 - 1}du$$

$$\Rightarrow \quad t^{1/2} = -\int \frac{u^2 - 1}{u^2 - 1}du - \int \frac{1}{u^2 - 1}du$$

$$\Rightarrow \quad \sqrt{1 + y^2} = -\int du - \int \frac{1}{u^2 - (1)^2}du \quad (1)$$

$$[\text{putting } t = 1 + y^2]$$

$$\Rightarrow \quad \sqrt{1 + y^2} = -u - \frac{1}{2}\log\left|\frac{u - 1}{u + 1}\right| + C$$

$$\left[\because \int \frac{dx}{x^2 - a^2} = \frac{1}{2a}\log\left|\frac{x - a}{x + a}\right|\right]$$

$$\therefore \quad \sqrt{1 + y^2} = -\sqrt{1 + x^2} - \frac{1}{2}\log\left|\frac{\sqrt{1 + x^2} - 1}{\sqrt{1 + x^2} + 1}\right| + C$$

$$[\text{putting } u = \sqrt{1 + x^2}]$$

which is the required solution. (2)

36. We have,
$$P(E_1) = \frac{25}{100}, P(E_2) = \frac{35}{100}, P(E_3) = \frac{40}{100}$$

$$P(F/E_1) = \frac{5}{100}, P(F/E_2) = \frac{4}{100}, P(F/E_3) = \frac{2}{100}$$

(i) Required probability $= P(F/E_2) = \frac{4}{100} = 0.04$

(ii) Required probability $= P(F/E_3) = \frac{2}{100} = 0.02$

(iii) Required probability $= P(E_2/F)$

$$= \frac{P(E_2)\,P(F/E_2)}{P(E_1)P(F/E_1) + P(E_2)P(F/E_2) + P(E_3)\,P(F/E_3)}$$

$$= \frac{\dfrac{35}{100} \times \dfrac{4}{100}}{\dfrac{25}{100} \times \dfrac{5}{100} + \dfrac{35}{100} \times \dfrac{4}{100} + \dfrac{40}{100} \times \dfrac{2}{100}}$$

$$= \frac{140}{125 + 140 + 80} = \frac{140}{345} = \frac{28}{69}$$

Or

Required probability

$$= 1 - P(E_3/F)$$

$$= 1 - \left[\frac{P(E_3)\,P(F/E_3)}{\substack{P(E_1)P(F/E_3) + P(E_2)\,P(F/E_2) \\ \hspace{2.5em} + P(E_3)\,P(F/E_3)}} \right]$$

$$= 1 - \left[\frac{\dfrac{40}{100} \times \dfrac{2}{100}}{\dfrac{25}{100} \times \dfrac{5}{100} + \dfrac{35}{100} \times \dfrac{4}{100} + \dfrac{40}{100} \times \dfrac{2}{100}} \right]$$

$$= 1 - \frac{80}{125 + 140 + 80} = 1 - \frac{140}{345} = \frac{205}{345} = \frac{41}{69}$$

37. (i) We have, $f(x) = x^2 \sin x$

$$\Rightarrow f(-x) = (-x)^2 \sin(-x) = -x^2 \sin x = -f(x)$$

$\therefore f(x)$ is odd function.

(ii) Since $f(x)$ is odd function, then $\displaystyle\int_{-\pi}^{\pi} f(x)\,dx = 0$.

(iii) We have, $g(x) = x \sin x$

$\therefore g(-x) = (-x)\sin(-x) = x\sin x = g(x)$

$\therefore g(x)$ is even function.

$$\therefore \int_{-\pi}^{\pi} x \sin x\,dx = 2\int_{0}^{\pi} x \sin x\,dx$$

$$= 2\left[[x(-\cos x)]_0^\pi - \int_0^\pi (-\cos x)\cdot 1\,dx \right]$$

$$= 2\,[[-x\cos x]_0^\pi + [\sin x]_0^\pi]$$

$$= 2\,[-\pi\cos\pi] = 2\pi$$

Or

We have, $h(x) = |\sin x|$

$h(-x) = |\sin(-x)| = |-\sin x| = |\sin x| = h(x)$

$\therefore h(x)$ is even function.

$$\therefore \int_{-\pi/2}^{\pi/2} |\sin x|\,dx = 2\int_{0}^{\pi/2} |\sin x|\,dx$$

$$= 2\int_{0}^{\pi/2} \sin x\,dx = 2\,[-\cos x]_0^{\pi/2}$$

$$= 2\left[-\cos\frac{\pi}{2} + \cos 0 \right] = 2$$

38. Let E_1, E_2, E_3 and A be the events defined as follows

$E_1 =$ You guess the answer

$E_2 =$ You copies the answer

$E_3 =$ You knows the answer

$A =$ You answers correctly

Clearly, $P(E_1) = \dfrac{1}{3}$ and $P(E_2) = \dfrac{1}{6}$

(i) Since, E_1, E_2 and E_3 are mutually exclusive and exhaustive events.

$$\therefore \quad P(E_1) + P(E_2) + P(E_3) = 1$$

$$\Rightarrow \quad P(E_3) = 1 - P(E_1) - P(E_2)$$

$$= 1 - \frac{1}{3} - \frac{1}{6}$$

$$= \frac{3}{6} = \frac{1}{2}$$

$$P\left(\frac{A}{E_1}\right) = \frac{1}{8},\ P\left(\frac{A}{E_2}\right) = \frac{1}{4}\ \text{and}\ P\left(\frac{A}{E_3}\right) = 1$$

$$\therefore \text{Required probability} = P\left(\frac{E_3}{A}\right)$$

$$= \frac{P(E_3)\,P\left(\dfrac{A}{E_3}\right)}{P(E_1)\,P\left(\dfrac{A}{E_1}\right) + P(E_2)\,P\left(\dfrac{A}{E_2}\right) + P(E_3)\,P\left(\dfrac{A}{E_3}\right)}$$

$$= \frac{\dfrac{1}{2}}{\dfrac{1}{24} + \dfrac{1}{24} + \dfrac{1}{2}} = \frac{12}{14} = \frac{6}{7}$$

(ii) Required probability $= P(A)$

$$= \sum_{i=1}^{3} P(E_i)\,P\left(\frac{A}{E_i}\right)$$

$$= P(E_1)\,P\left(\frac{A}{E_1}\right) + P(E_2)\,P\left(\frac{A}{E_2}\right) + P(E_3)\,P\left(\frac{A}{E_3}\right)$$

$$= \frac{1}{3} \times \frac{1}{8} + \frac{1}{6} \times \frac{1}{4} + \frac{1}{2} \times 1$$

$$= \frac{1}{24} + \frac{1}{24} + \frac{1}{2}$$

$$= \frac{1 + 1 + 12}{24} = \frac{14}{24} = \frac{7}{12}$$

SAMPLE QUESTION PAPER 10

MATHEMATICS

Time : 3 hrs   Max. Marks : 80

General Instructions

1. This question paper contains - five sections A, B, C, D and E. Each section is compulsory. However, there are internal choices in some questions.
2. Section A has 18 MCQ's and 02 Assertion-Reason based questions of 1 mark each.
3. Section B has 5 Very Short Answer (VSA) type questions of 2 marks each.
4. Section C has 6 Short Answer (SA) type questions of 3 marks each.
5. Section D has 4 Long Answer (LA) type questions of 5 marks each.
6. Section E has 3 source based/case based/passage based/integrated units of assessment (4 marks each) with sub parts.

Section A

(Multiple Choice Questions) Each question carries 1 mark

1. If $f(x) = x\,|x|$, then $f'(x)$ is equal to

(a) x^2 　　　　(b) $2x$ 　　　　(c) $2|x|$ 　　　　(d) 1

2. The function $f : R \to R$ given by $f(x) = \cos x$ for all $x \in R$ is

(a) one-one 　　(b) not one-one 　　(c) bijective 　　(d) None

3. The angle between the unit vectors $\hat{a}$ and $\hat{b}$, given that $|\hat{a} + \hat{b}| = 1$ is

(a) $\dfrac{\pi}{3}$ 　　(b) $\dfrac{\pi}{2}$ 　　(c) $\dfrac{2\pi}{3}$ 　　(d) $-\dfrac{\pi}{3}$

4. If order and degree of the differential equation $\left(\dfrac{dy}{dx}\right)^4 + 3x\,\dfrac{d^2y}{dx^2} = 0$ is m and n respectively, then $m - n$ is equal to

(a) 1 　　　　(b) 2 　　　　(c) 3 　　　　(d) 0

5. The value of $x\,dy + (x-1)dx = 0$ is

(a) $y = \log x - x + C$ (b) $y = \log x + x + C$

(c) $y = -\log x + C$ (d) $y = -\log x - x + C$

6. If $A \equiv (2, 3, 1)$ and $B \equiv (5, 4, 2)$, then direction ratios of $\overrightarrow{AB}$ are

(a) $-3, 1, 1$ (b) $3, 1, 1$

(c) $5, 4, 2$ (d) $3, 0, 1$

7. Let $R = \{(a, a^3): a$ is the prime number less than $5\}$ be a relation, then the range of R is

(a) $\{2, 3\}$ (b) $\{8, 27\}$

(c) $\{2\}$ (d) $\{2, 3, 8, 27\}$

8. If a matrix A is both symmetric and skew-symmetric, then A is

(a) null matrix   (b) identity matrix

(c) diagonal matrix   (d) None

9. The value of $\tan\left[\dfrac{1}{2}\cos^{-1}\left(\dfrac{\sqrt{5}}{3}\right)\right]$ is

(a) $\dfrac{3+\sqrt{5}}{2}$ (b) $\dfrac{3-\sqrt{5}}{2}$

(c) $\dfrac{-3+\sqrt{5}}{2}$ (d) $\dfrac{-3-\sqrt{5}}{2}$

10. If $f(x) = 2|x| + 3\,|\sin x| + 6$, then the right hand derivative of $f(x)$ at $x = 0$ is

(a) 1   (b) 5   (c) 3   (d) 4

11. If $xy^2 = ax^2 + bxy + y^2$, then $\dfrac{dy}{dx}$ is equal to

(a) $\dfrac{2x^2 + axy + y^2}{x^2 + y^2 + 2xy}$ (b) $\dfrac{ax + by - xy}{xy + x^2 + y^2}$

(c) $\dfrac{2ax + by - y^2}{2xy - bx - 2y}$ (d) $\dfrac{2ax + by + y^2}{2xy + bx + 2y}$

12. The value of $\displaystyle\int \sin^5\left(\dfrac{x}{2}\right)\cdot\cos\left(\dfrac{x}{2}\right)dx$ is

(a) $\dfrac{1}{3}\left(\sin^6\dfrac{x}{2}\right) + C$ (b) $\left(\sin^6\dfrac{x}{2}\right) + C$

(c) $\dfrac{1}{3}\left(\cos^6\dfrac{x}{2}\right) + C$ (d) $\left(\cos^6\dfrac{x}{2}\right) + C$

13. $\displaystyle\int \dfrac{1}{x(1+x^2)}\,dx$ is equal to

(a) $\dfrac{1}{2}\log\left|\dfrac{x^2+1}{x^2}\right| + C$ (b) $\dfrac{1}{2}\log\left|\dfrac{x^2}{x^2+1}\right| + C$

(c) $-\dfrac{1}{2}\log\left|\dfrac{x^2}{x^2+1}\right| + C$ (d) $\dfrac{1}{2}\log\left|\dfrac{x^2+1}{x+1}\right| + C$

14. The value of $\tan^{-1}\left\{\tan\dfrac{15\pi}{4}\right\}$ is

(a) $\dfrac{\pi}{4}$ (b) $\dfrac{3\pi}{4}$ (c) $-\dfrac{\pi}{4}$ (d) π

15. If $[x]$ denotes the greatest integer function, then $\displaystyle\int_0^{3/2} [x^2]\,dx$ is equal to

(a) $\sqrt{2} - 2$ (b) $2 - \sqrt{2}$

(c) $\sqrt{2}$ (d) $\sqrt{2} + 2$

16. If A is symmetric matrix, then $B'AB$ is

(a) symmetric matrix

(b) skew symmetric matrix

(c) scalar matrix

(d) none

17. A unit vector in the direction opposite to $-\dfrac{3}{4}\hat{j}$ is

(a) $\hat{i}$ (b) $\hat{j}$ (c) $\hat{k}$ (d) $-\hat{i}$

18. The area of the triangle whose two sides are represented by the vectors $2\hat{i}$ and $-3\hat{j}$ is

(a) 6 sq units   (b) 3 sq units

(c) 2 sq units   (d) 1 sq unit

Assertion-Reason Based Questions

In the following questions, a statement of Assertion (A) is followed by a statement of Reason (R). Choose the correct answer out of the following choices.

(a) Both A and R are true and R is the correct explanation of A

(b) Both A and R are true but R is not the correct explanation of A

(c) A is true but R is false

(d) A is false but R is true

19. **Assertion (A)** If $A = \begin{bmatrix} 2 & 4 \\ 3 & 2 \end{bmatrix}$ and $B = \begin{bmatrix} 1 & 3 \\ -2 & 5 \end{bmatrix}$, then $A + B = \begin{bmatrix} 3 & 7 \\ 1 & 7 \end{bmatrix}$.

Reason (R) Two different matrices can be added only if they are of same order.

20. **Assertion (A)** Let $f: R \to R$ be defined by $f(x) = x^2 + 1$. Then, pre-images of 17 are ± 4.

Reason (R) A function $f: A \to B$ is called a one-one function, if distinct elements of A have distinct images in B.

Section B

(This section comprises of very short answer type questions (VSA) of 2 marks each)

21. If $A = \begin{bmatrix} 2 & 3 \\ -1 & 2 \end{bmatrix}$, find $A^2 - 4A + I$.

Or

If $A = \begin{bmatrix} 1 & 0 \\ -1 & 7 \end{bmatrix}$ and $I = \begin{bmatrix} 1 & 0 \\ 0 & 1 \end{bmatrix}$, then find K so that $A^2 = 8A + KI$.

22. Find the value of k for which

$$f(x) = \begin{cases} kx + 5, & \text{when } x \leq 2 \\ x - 1, & \text{when } x > 2 \end{cases}$$

is continuous at $x = 2$.

23. Evaluate $\int \dfrac{1}{\sqrt{9 + 8x - x^2}}\, dx$

Or

Evaluate $\int x \log x\, dx$

24. Show that the function $x + \dfrac{1}{x}$ is increasing for $x > 1$.

25. Find $|\vec{a} \times \vec{b}|$, if $\vec{a} = 2\hat{i} + \hat{j} + 3\hat{k}$ and $\vec{b} = 3\hat{i} + 5\hat{j} - 2\hat{k}$.

Section C

(This section comprises of short answer type questions (SA) of 3 marks each)

26. Show that the function $f : R \to R$ defined by $f(x) = \dfrac{3x - 1}{2}, x \in R$ is one-one and onto functions.

27. If $y = x^x$, then prove that

$$\frac{d^2y}{dx^2} - \frac{1}{y}\left(\frac{dy}{dx}\right)^2 - \frac{y}{x} = 0$$

Or If $y = \dfrac{\sin^{-1} x}{\sqrt{1 - x^2}}$, then show that

$$(1 - x^2)\frac{d^2y}{dx^2} - 3x\frac{dy}{dx} - y = 0.$$

28. Evaluate $\int (\sqrt{\tan x} + \sqrt{\cot x})\, dx$.

Or

Evaluate $\int e^x \left(\dfrac{1 + \sin x}{1 + \cos x}\right) dx$.

29. Find the particular solution of the differential equation $(1 + e^{2x})\, dy + (1 + y^2) e^x\, dx = 0$, given that $y = 1$, when $x = 0$.

Or Solve the following differential equation $y^2\, dx + (x^2 - xy + y^2)\, dy = 0$.

30. Find whether the following function is differentiable at $x = 1$ and $x = 2$ or not.

$$f(x) = \begin{cases} x, & x < 1 \\ 2 - x, & 1 \leq x \leq 2 \\ -2 + 3x - x^2, & x > 2 \end{cases}$$

31. Find the value of c for which the vectors $\vec{a} = (c \log_2 x)\hat{i} - 6\hat{j} + 3\hat{k}$ and $\vec{b} = (\log_2 x)\hat{i} + 2\hat{j} + (2c \log_2 x)\hat{k}$ make an obtuse angle for any $x \in (0, \infty)$.

Section D

(This section comprises of long answer type questions (LA) of 5 marks each)

32. Show that area of the parallelogram, whose diagonals are given by $\vec{a}$ and $\vec{b}$ is $\dfrac{|\vec{a} \times \vec{b}|}{2}$. Also, find the area of the parallelogram, whose diagonals are $2\hat{i} - \hat{j} + \hat{k}$ and $\hat{i} + 3\hat{j} - \hat{k}$.

33. If $A = \begin{bmatrix} 0 & -\tan \alpha/2 \\ \tan \alpha/2 & 0 \end{bmatrix}$ and I is the identity matrix of order 2, show that

$$I + A = (I - A)\begin{bmatrix} \cos \alpha & -\sin \alpha \\ \sin \alpha & \cos \alpha \end{bmatrix}.$$

Or

Solve the following system of equations using matrix method.

$$x + y + z = 7000$$

$$10x + 16y + 17z = 110000$$

$$x - y = 0$$

34. Maximise $Z = 8x + 9y$ subject to the constraints given below

$$2x + 3y \leq 6$$
$$3x - 2y \leq 6$$
$$y \leq 1$$
$$x, y \geq 0.$$

Or

Solve minimise $Z = 5x + 7y$

Subject to constraints

$$2x + y \geq 8; \ x + 2y \geq 10$$

$$x, y \geq 0$$

35. Evaluate $\displaystyle\int_0^{2\pi} \dfrac{x \sin^{2n} x}{\sin^{2n} x + \cos^{2n} x} \, dx$.

Section E

(This section comprises of 3 case-study/ passage-based questions of 4 marks each with two sub-parts. First two case study questions have three sub-parts (i), (ii), (iii) of marks 1, 1, 2 respectively. The third case study question has two sub-parts of 2 marks each)

36. In a test, you either guess or copy or know the answer of a multiple choice question with four choices.

The probability that you make a guess is $\dfrac{1}{3}$, you copy the answer is $\dfrac{1}{6}$. The probability that your answer is correct, given that you guess it, is $\dfrac{1}{8}$ and also the probability that your answer is correct, given that you copy it is $\dfrac{1}{4}$.

On the basis of above information, answer the following questions.

(i) Find the probability that your answer is correct given that you guess the answer.

(ii) Find the probability that your answer is correct given that you know the answer.

(iii) Find the probability that you know the answer given that you correctly answered it.

Or

Find the total probability of correctly answering the question.

37. Consider the following curves
$$x^2 + y^2 \leq 1 \text{ and } x + y \geq 1$$
On the basis of above information, answer the following questions.

(i) Evaluate $\displaystyle\int (\sqrt{1 - x^2}) \, dx$

(ii) Write the expression to evaluate area of shaded region.

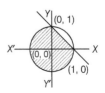

(iii) Find point of intersection of both curves and also write the formula for

$$\int \sqrt{a^2 - x^2}\, dx$$

Or Find the area of common region bounded by both curves

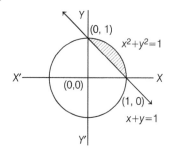

38. In a bolt factory, machines A, B and C manufactured respectively, 25%, 35% and 40% of the total bolts. Of their output 5%, 4% and 2% are respectively, defective bolts.

On the basis of above information, answer the following questions.

(i) Find the probability, if drawn bolt is defective, then it is manufactured by B.

(ii) If drawn bolt is defective, then find the probability that it is not manufactured by C.

SOLUTIONS

1. (c) Given, $f(x) = x|x|$

$$f(x) = \begin{cases} -x^2 & x < 0 \\ x^2 & x \geq 0 \end{cases}$$

$$f'(x) = \begin{cases} -2x & x < 0 \\ 2x & x \geq 0 \end{cases}$$

$\therefore$ $f'(x) = 2|x|$

2. (b) We know that $f(0) = \cos 0 = 1$ and $f(2\pi) = \cos 2\pi = 1$

So, different elements in R may have the same image. Hence, f is not one-one.

3. (c) We have, $|\hat{a} + \hat{b}| = 1$

Let θ be the angle between $\hat{a}$ and $\hat{b}$.

Now, $|\hat{a} + \hat{b}| = 1$

$\Rightarrow$ $|\hat{a} + \hat{b}|^2 = 1$

$\Rightarrow$ $(\hat{a} + \hat{b}) \cdot (\hat{a} + \hat{b}) = 1$

$\Rightarrow$ $|\hat{a}|^2 + |\hat{b}|^2 + 2\hat{a} \cdot \hat{b} = 1$

$\Rightarrow$ $1 + 1 + 2|\hat{a}||\hat{b}| \cos \theta = 1$ $[\because |\hat{a}| = |\hat{b}| = 1]$

$\Rightarrow$ $2 \cos \theta = -1$

$\Rightarrow$ $\cos \theta = -\dfrac{1}{2}$

$\Rightarrow$ $\theta = \pi - \dfrac{\pi}{3} = \dfrac{2\pi}{3}$

4. (a) We have, $\left(\dfrac{dy}{dx}\right)^4 + 3x\dfrac{d^2y}{dx^2} = 0$

$\therefore$ Order $= 2 \Rightarrow m = 2$

and degree $= 1 \Rightarrow n = 1$

$\therefore$ $m - n = 2 - 1 = 1$

5. (a) We have, $x\, dy + (x - 1)dx = 0$

$\Rightarrow$ $x\, dy = (1 - x)dx$

$\Rightarrow$ $dy = \left(\dfrac{1-x}{x}\right)dx$ ...(i)

On integrating both sides of Eq. (i), we get

$\Rightarrow$ $\int dy = \int \left(\dfrac{1-x}{x}\right)dx$

$\Rightarrow$ $\int dy = \int \dfrac{1}{x}dx - \int dx$

$\Rightarrow$ $y = \log x - x + C$

6. (b) Given $A \equiv (2, 3, 1)$

and $B \equiv (5, 4, 2)$

$\therefore$ Direction ratios of $\overrightarrow{AB}$ are

$(5 - 2), (4 - 3), (2 - 1)$

i.e.   3, 1, 1

7. (b) Given $R = \{(a, a^3) : a \text{ is prime number less than 5}\}$

$\Rightarrow$ $R = \{(2, 8), (3, 27)\}$

Hence, range of $R = \{8, 27\}$

8. (a) Null matrix

9. (b) We have, $\tan\left(\dfrac{1}{2}\cos^{-1}\left(\dfrac{\sqrt{5}}{3}\right)\right)$

Let $\cos^{-1}\left(\dfrac{\sqrt{5}}{3}\right) = x \Rightarrow \cos x = \dfrac{\sqrt{5}}{3}$

$\Rightarrow$ $\sin x = \sqrt{1 - \left(\dfrac{\sqrt{5}}{3}\right)^2} = \sqrt{1 - \dfrac{5}{9}} = \dfrac{2}{3}$

Now, $\tan\left(\dfrac{x}{2}\right) = \dfrac{1 - \cos x}{\sin x}$

$\Rightarrow$ $\tan\left(\dfrac{x}{2}\right) = \dfrac{1 - \dfrac{\sqrt{5}}{3}}{\dfrac{2}{3}} = \dfrac{3 - \sqrt{5}}{2}$

$\therefore$ $\tan\left(\dfrac{1}{2}\cos^{-1}\left(\dfrac{\sqrt{5}}{3}\right)\right) = \dfrac{3 - \sqrt{5}}{2}$

10. (b) We have, $f(x) = 2|x| + 3|\sin x| + 6$

RHD $f'(0) = \lim\limits_{h \to 0} \dfrac{f(0+h) - f(0)}{h}$

$= \lim\limits_{h \to 0} \dfrac{2|0+h| + 3\sin|0+h| + 6 - (2(0) + 3(0) + 6)}{h}$

$\Rightarrow \quad f'(0) = \lim\limits_{h \to 0} \dfrac{2|h| + 3|\sinh|}{h}$

$\Rightarrow \quad f'(0) = \lim\limits_{h \to 0} \dfrac{2h}{h} + \dfrac{3\sin h}{h}$

$\Rightarrow \quad f'(0) = 2 + 3 = 5$

11. (c) Given, $xy^2 = ax^2 + bxy + y^2$

On differentiating w.r.t. x, we get

$$x2y\dfrac{dy}{dx} + y^2 = 2ax + b\left(x\dfrac{dy}{dx} + y\right) + 2y\dfrac{dy}{dx}$$

$\Rightarrow \quad 2xy\dfrac{dy}{dx} + y^2 = 2ax + bx\dfrac{dy}{dx} + by + 2y\dfrac{dy}{dx}$

$\Rightarrow \dfrac{dy}{dx}(2xy - bx - 2y) = 2ax + by - y^2$

$\Rightarrow \quad \dfrac{dy}{dx} = \dfrac{2ax + by - y^2}{2xy - bx - 2y}$

12. (a) Let $I = \int \sin^5\left(\dfrac{x}{2}\right)\cos\left(\dfrac{x}{2}\right)dx$

Put $\sin\dfrac{x}{2} = t \Rightarrow \dfrac{1}{2}\cos\dfrac{x}{2}dx = dt$

$\therefore \qquad I = 2\int t^5 dt$

$\Rightarrow \qquad I = 2\dfrac{t^6}{6} + C$

$\Rightarrow \qquad I = \dfrac{1}{3}\left(\sin^6\dfrac{x}{2}\right) + C$

13. (b) Let $I = \int \dfrac{dx}{x(1+x^2)} \Rightarrow I = \int \dfrac{dx}{x^3\left(\dfrac{1}{x^2}+1\right)}$

Put $\dfrac{1}{x^2} + 1 = t \Rightarrow \dfrac{-2}{x^3}dx = dt$

$\therefore \qquad I = -\dfrac{1}{2}\int \dfrac{dt}{t} = -\dfrac{1}{2}\log|t| + C$

$\Rightarrow \qquad I = -\dfrac{1}{2}\log\left|\dfrac{1}{x^2}+1\right| + C$

$\Rightarrow \qquad I = -\dfrac{1}{2}\log\left|\dfrac{x^2+1}{x^2}\right| + C$

$\Rightarrow \qquad I = \dfrac{1}{2}\log\left|\dfrac{x^2}{x^2+1}\right| + C$

14. (c) We have,

$$\tan^{-1}\left\{\tan\dfrac{15\pi}{4}\right\} = \tan^{-1}\left\{\tan\left(4\pi - \dfrac{\pi}{4}\right)\right\}$$

$= \tan^{-1}\left\{-\tan\dfrac{\pi}{4}\right\}$

$\qquad\qquad [\because \tan(4\pi - \theta) = -\tan\theta]$

$= \tan^{-1}(-1)$

Now, let $\tan^{-1}(-1) = \theta$

$\Rightarrow \qquad \tan\theta = -1$

$\Rightarrow \qquad \tan\theta = -\tan\dfrac{\pi}{4}$

$\Rightarrow \qquad \tan\theta = \tan\left(\dfrac{-\pi}{4}\right) \quad [\because \tan(-\theta) = -\tan\theta]$

$\Rightarrow \qquad \theta = -\dfrac{\pi}{4} \qquad \left[\because \dfrac{-\pi}{4} \in \left(\dfrac{-\pi}{2}, \dfrac{\pi}{2}\right)\right]$

$\therefore \tan^{-1}\left\{\tan\dfrac{15\pi}{4}\right\} = \dfrac{-\pi}{4}$

15. (b) Let $\qquad I = \int\limits_0^{3/2} [x^2]dx$

$\Rightarrow \qquad I = \int\limits_0^1 0\,dx + \int\limits_1^{\sqrt{2}} dx + \int\limits_{\sqrt{2}}^{3/2} 2\,dx$

$\Rightarrow \qquad I = 0 + [x]_1^{\sqrt{2}} + [2x]_{\sqrt{2}}^{3/2}$

$\Rightarrow \qquad I = \sqrt{2} - 1 + 3 - 2\sqrt{2}$

$\Rightarrow \qquad I = \sqrt{2} + 2 - 2\sqrt{2}$ or $I = 2 - \sqrt{2}$

16. (a) $(B' AB)' = (AB)'(B')' = B' A' B = B' AB \qquad [\because A' = A]$

17. (b) Let $\vec{a} = -\dfrac{3}{4}\hat{j}$. So, any vector in the direction

opposite to $\vec{a}$ is given by $\vec{b} = -\vec{a} = \dfrac{3}{4}\hat{j}$

$\therefore \qquad \hat{b} = \dfrac{\vec{b}}{|\vec{b}|} = \dfrac{\dfrac{3}{4}\hat{j}}{\left(\dfrac{3}{4}\right)} = \hat{j}$

So, required vector is $\hat{j}$.

18. (b) Let $\vec{a} = 2\hat{i}$ and $\vec{b} = -3\hat{j}$

$\therefore$ Area of triangle $= \dfrac{1}{2}|\vec{a} \times \vec{b}| = \dfrac{1}{2}|(2\hat{i}) \times (-3\hat{j})|$

$= \dfrac{1}{2}|-6\hat{k}| \qquad [\because \hat{i} \times \hat{j} = \hat{k}]$

$= \dfrac{1}{2} \times 6 = 3$ sq units

19. (a) The given matrices are $A = \begin{bmatrix} 2 & 4 \\ 3 & 2 \end{bmatrix}$ and $B = \begin{bmatrix} 1 & 3 \\ -2 & 5 \end{bmatrix}$

Then, $A + B = \begin{bmatrix} 2 & 4 \\ 3 & 2 \end{bmatrix} + \begin{bmatrix} 1 & 3 \\ -2 & 5 \end{bmatrix}$

$= \begin{bmatrix} 2+1 & 4+3 \\ 3-2 & 2+5 \end{bmatrix} = \begin{bmatrix} 3 & 7 \\ 1 & 7 \end{bmatrix}$

Hence, Assertion is true. Reason is also true and it is the correct explanation of Assertion.

20. (b) **Assertion** Consider, $x^2 + 1 = 17$

$$\Rightarrow \qquad x^2 = 16 \Rightarrow x = \pm 4$$

Hence, pre-images of 17 are ± 4.

Hence, both Assertion and Reason are true but Reason is not the correct explanation of Assertion.

21. Given, $A = \begin{bmatrix} 2 & 3 \\ -1 & 2 \end{bmatrix}$

Now, $A^2 = \begin{bmatrix} 2 & 3 \\ -1 & 2 \end{bmatrix}\begin{bmatrix} 2 & 3 \\ -1 & 2 \end{bmatrix}$

$= \begin{bmatrix} 4-3 & 6+6 \\ -2-2 & -3+4 \end{bmatrix} = \begin{bmatrix} 1 & 12 \\ -4 & 1 \end{bmatrix}$ (1)

$\therefore \quad A^2 - 4A + I = \begin{bmatrix} 1 & 12 \\ -4 & 1 \end{bmatrix} - 4\begin{bmatrix} 2 & 3 \\ -1 & 2 \end{bmatrix} + \begin{bmatrix} 1 & 0 \\ 0 & 1 \end{bmatrix}$

$= \begin{bmatrix} 1 & 12 \\ -4 & 1 \end{bmatrix} - \begin{bmatrix} 8 & 12 \\ -4 & 8 \end{bmatrix} + \begin{bmatrix} 1 & 0 \\ 0 & 1 \end{bmatrix}$

$= \begin{bmatrix} 1-8+1 & 12-12+0 \\ -4+4+0 & 1-8+1 \end{bmatrix}$

$= \begin{bmatrix} -6 & 0 \\ 0 & -6 \end{bmatrix} = -6\begin{bmatrix} 1 & 0 \\ 0 & 1 \end{bmatrix} = -6I$ (1)

Or

We have, $A = \begin{bmatrix} 1 & 0 \\ -1 & 7 \end{bmatrix}$

$\therefore \quad A^2 = A \cdot A = \begin{bmatrix} 1 & 0 \\ -1 & 7 \end{bmatrix}\begin{bmatrix} 1 & 0 \\ -1 & 7 \end{bmatrix} = \begin{bmatrix} 1 & 0 \\ -8 & 49 \end{bmatrix}$

and $8A + KI = 8\begin{bmatrix} 1 & 0 \\ -1 & 7 \end{bmatrix} + K\begin{bmatrix} 1 & 0 \\ 0 & 1 \end{bmatrix}$

$= \begin{bmatrix} 8+K & 0 \\ -8 & 56+K \end{bmatrix}$ ...(i) (1)

$\because \qquad A^2 = 8A + KI$

$\Rightarrow \begin{bmatrix} 1 & 0 \\ -8 & 49 \end{bmatrix} = \begin{bmatrix} 8+K & 0 \\ -8 & 56+K \end{bmatrix}$

$\Rightarrow \qquad 1 = 8+K$ and $56 + K = 49$

$\Rightarrow \qquad K = -7$ ...(ii) (1)

22. At $x = 2$, $f(2) = k(2) + 5 = 2k + 5$

$\lim\limits_{x \to 2^+} f(x) = \lim\limits_{h \to 0} f(2+h)$

[put $x = 2 + h$ when $x \to 2^+$ then $h \to 0$]

$= \lim\limits_{h \to 0} [(2+h) - 1] = \lim\limits_{h \to 0} (1+h) = 1$

$\lim\limits_{x \to 2^-} f(x) = \lim\limits_{h \to 0} f(2-h)$

[put $x = 2 - h$ when $x \to 2^-$ then, $h \to 0$]

$= \lim\limits_{h \to 0} \{k(2-h) + 5\}$

$= \lim\limits_{h \to 0} \{2k + 5 - kh\} = 2k + 5$ (1)

$\because f(x)$ is continuous at $x = 2$.

So, LHL = RHL = $f(2)$

$\Rightarrow \qquad 2k + 5 = 1 \Rightarrow k = -\dfrac{4}{2} = -2$ (1)

23. Let $I = \int \dfrac{1}{\sqrt{9 + 8x - x^2}}\, dx$

$= \int \dfrac{1}{\sqrt{-[x^2 - 8x - 9]}}\, dx$

$= \int \dfrac{1}{\sqrt{-[(x-4)^2 - 16 - 9]}}\, dx$ (1)

$= \int \dfrac{1}{\sqrt{25 - (x-4)^2}}\, dx$

$= \int \dfrac{1}{\sqrt{(5)^2 - (x-4)^2}}$

$= \sin^{-1}\dfrac{x-4}{5} + C$ (1)

Or

Let $I = \int \underset{\text{II}}{x} \underset{\text{I}}{\log x}$

$= \log x \cdot \dfrac{x^2}{2} - \int \dfrac{x^2}{2} \cdot \dfrac{1}{x}\, dx$

[using integration by parts] (1)

$= \dfrac{1}{2} x^2 \log x - \dfrac{1}{2} \int x\, dx$

$= \dfrac{1}{2} x^2 \log x - \dfrac{x^2}{4} + C$

$= \dfrac{x^2}{2}\left[\log x - \dfrac{1}{2}\right] + C$ (1)

24. Let $f(x) = x + \dfrac{1}{x}$

$\therefore \quad f'(x) = 1 - \dfrac{1}{x^2} = \dfrac{x^2 - 1}{x^2}$ (1)

Now, we have $\qquad x > 1$

$\Rightarrow \qquad x^2 > 1$

$\Rightarrow \qquad x^2 - 1 > 0$

$\Rightarrow \qquad \dfrac{x^2 - 1}{x^2} > 0 \qquad [\because x > 1]$

$\Rightarrow \qquad f'(x) > 0$

Hence, $f(x)$ is increasing for $x > 1$. (1)

25. We have, $\vec{a} = 2\hat{i} + \hat{j} + 3\hat{k}$

and $\qquad \vec{b} = 3\hat{i} + 5\hat{j} - 2\hat{k}$

$\therefore \quad \vec{a} \times \vec{b} = \begin{vmatrix} \hat{i} & \hat{j} & \hat{k} \\ 2 & 1 & 3 \\ 3 & 5 & -2 \end{vmatrix}$

$= \hat{i}(-2 - 15) - \hat{j}(-4 - 9) + \hat{k}(10 - 3)$

$= -17\hat{i} + 13\hat{j} + 7\hat{k}$ (1)

$\therefore |\vec{a} \times \vec{b}| = \sqrt{(-17)^2 + (13)^2 + (7)^2}$

$= \sqrt{289 + 169 + 49} = \sqrt{507}$ (1)

26. Given, $f(x) = \dfrac{3x-1}{2}, x \in R$

For one-one Let $x_1, x_2 \in R$ such that $f(x_1) = f(x_2)$

$\Rightarrow \qquad \dfrac{3x_1-1}{2} = \dfrac{3x_2-1}{2}$

$\Rightarrow \qquad 3x_1 - 1 = 3x_2 - 1$

$\Rightarrow \qquad 3x_1 = 3x_2$

$\Rightarrow \qquad x_1 = x_2$

$\therefore$ f is one-one.   (1)

For onto Let $y \in R$, then $f(x) = y$

$\Rightarrow \qquad \dfrac{3x-1}{2} = y$

$\Rightarrow \qquad 3x - 1 = 2y$

$\Rightarrow \qquad 3x = 2y + 1$

$\Rightarrow \qquad x = \dfrac{2y+1}{3} \in R \qquad \ldots(i)$ (1)

Thus, for each $y \in R$, there exists $x = \dfrac{2y+1}{3} \in R$ such

that $f\left(\dfrac{2y+1}{3}\right) = y$

Hence, f is onto.

So, f is one-one and onto.   **Hence proved.** (1)

27. Given, $y = x^x$

On taking log both sides, we get

$$\log y = \log x^x$$

$\Rightarrow \qquad \log y = x \log x$ (1)

On differentiating both sides w.r.t. x, we get

$$\frac{1}{y}\frac{dy}{dx} = x \frac{d}{dx}(\log x) + \log x \frac{d}{dx}(x)$$

[by using product rule of derivative]

$\Rightarrow \qquad \dfrac{1}{y}\dfrac{dy}{dx} = x \times \dfrac{1}{x} + \log x \cdot 1$

$\Rightarrow \qquad \dfrac{1}{y}\dfrac{dy}{dx} = (1 + \log x)$

$\Rightarrow \qquad \dfrac{dy}{dx} = y(1 + \log x) \qquad \ldots(i)$ (1)

Again, differentiating both sides w.r.t. x, we get

$$\frac{d^2y}{dx^2} = y \frac{d}{dx}(1 + \log x) + (1 + \log x)\frac{dy}{dx}$$

[by using product rule of derivative]

$\Rightarrow \quad \dfrac{d^2y}{dx^2} = y \times \dfrac{1}{x} + (1 + \log x)\dfrac{dy}{dx}$

$\Rightarrow \quad \dfrac{d^2y}{dx^2} = \dfrac{y}{x} + (1 + \log x)\dfrac{dy}{dx}$

$\Rightarrow \quad \dfrac{d^2y}{dx^2} = \dfrac{y}{x} + \dfrac{1}{y}\left(\dfrac{dy}{dx}\right)\left(\dfrac{dy}{dx}\right)$ [using Eq. (i)]

$\therefore \qquad \dfrac{d^2y}{dx^2} - \dfrac{1}{y}\left(\dfrac{dy}{dx}\right)^2 - \dfrac{y}{x} = 0$ **Hence proved.** (1)

Or

Given, $y = \dfrac{\sin^{-1}x}{\sqrt{1-x^2}}$

On differentiating both sides w.r.t. x, we get

$$\frac{dy}{dx} = \frac{\sqrt{1-x^2} \times \frac{d}{dx}(\sin^{-1}x) - (\sin^{-1}x) \times \frac{d}{dx}\sqrt{1-x^2}}{(\sqrt{1-x^2})^2}$$

$$= \frac{\left[\sqrt{1-x^2} \times \frac{1}{\sqrt{1-x^2}} - \sin^{-1}x \cdot \frac{1}{2\sqrt{1-x^2}} \cdot \frac{d}{dx}(1-x^2)\right]}{(\sqrt{1-x^2})^2}$$

$$= \frac{\left[\sqrt{1-x^2} \cdot \frac{1}{\sqrt{1-x^2}} - (\sin^{-1}x) \cdot \frac{-2x}{2\sqrt{1-x^2}}\right]}{1-x^2}$$

$$= \frac{1 + \frac{x\sin^{-1}x}{\sqrt{1-x^2}}}{(1-x^2)}$$

$\Rightarrow \qquad \dfrac{dy}{dx} = \dfrac{1+xy}{1-x^2} \qquad \left[\because \dfrac{\sin^{-1}x}{\sqrt{1-x^2}} = y\right]$

$\Rightarrow (1-x^2)\dfrac{dy}{dx} = 1 + xy$ (1½)

On differentiating both sides of above equation w.r.t. x, we get

$$(1-x^2) \cdot \frac{d}{dx}\left(\frac{dy}{dx}\right) + \frac{dy}{dx} \cdot \frac{d}{dx}(1-x^2) = \frac{d}{dx}(1+xy)$$

[by using product rule of derivative]

$\Rightarrow \qquad (1-x^2)\dfrac{d^2y}{dx^2} + \dfrac{dy}{dx}(-2x) = x\dfrac{dy}{dx} + y \cdot 1$

$\Rightarrow (1-x^2)\dfrac{d^2y}{dx^2} - 2x\dfrac{dy}{dx} - x\dfrac{dy}{dx} - y = 0$

$\therefore \qquad (1-x^2)\dfrac{d^2y}{dx^2} - 3x\dfrac{dy}{dx} - y = 0$ (1½)

28. Let $I = \displaystyle\int (\sqrt{\tan x} + \sqrt{\cot x})\,dx = \int\left(\dfrac{\sqrt{\sin x}}{\sqrt{\cos x}} + \dfrac{\sqrt{\cos x}}{\sqrt{\sin x}}\right)dx$

$$\left[\because \tan\theta = \frac{\sin\theta}{\cos\theta} \text{ and } \cot\theta = \frac{\cos\theta}{\sin\theta}\right]$$

$$= \int \frac{\sin x + \cos x}{\sqrt{\sin x}\sqrt{\cos x}}\,dx = \int \frac{\sin x + \cos x}{\sqrt{\sin x \cos x}}\,dx$$

$$= \sqrt{2} \int \frac{\sin x + \cos x}{\sqrt{2\sin x \cos x}}\,dx$$

$$= \sqrt{2} \int \frac{\sin x + \cos x}{\sqrt{1 - (\sin x - \cos x)^2}}\,dx \qquad (1)$$

Put $\sin x - \cos x = t$

$\Rightarrow \quad (\cos x + \sin x)dx = dt$

$\therefore \qquad I = \sqrt{2} \displaystyle\int \frac{1}{\sqrt{1-t^2}}\,dt$

$$= \sqrt{2}\sin^{-1}(t) + C \left[\because \int \frac{1}{\sqrt{1-x^2}} dx = \sin^{-1}x + C \right]$$

$$= \sqrt{2}\sin^{-1}(\sin x - \cos x) + C \quad [\because t = \sin x - \cos x]$$

(2)

Or

Let $\quad I = \int e^x \left(\frac{1+\sin x}{1+\cos x} \right) dx$

$$= \int e^x \left[\frac{1+2\sin(x/2)\cos(x/2)}{2\cos^2(x/2)} \right] dx$$

$$\left[\because \sin\theta = 2\sin\frac{\theta}{2}\cos\frac{\theta}{2} \text{ and } 1+\cos\theta = 2\cos^2\frac{\theta}{2} \right]$$

$$= \int e^x \left[\frac{1}{2\cos^2(x/2)} + \frac{2\sin(x/2)\cos(x/2)}{2\cos^2(x/2)} \right] dx$$

$$= \int e^x \left[\frac{1}{2}\sec^2\left(\frac{x}{2}\right) + \tan\frac{x}{2} \right] dx \qquad (1)$$

Thus, we have integration of the form

$$\int e^x [f(x) + f'(x)] dx$$

Here, $f(x) = \tan\frac{x}{2} \Rightarrow f'(x) = \sec^2\frac{x}{2} \cdot \frac{1}{2} = \frac{1}{2}\sec^2\frac{x}{2}$

$\therefore \qquad I = e^x f(x) + C = e^x \tan\frac{x}{2} + C$

$$[\because \int e^x [f(x) + f'(x)] dx = e^x f(x) + C] \quad (2)$$

29. Given, differential equation is

$$(1+e^{2x})dy + (1+y^2)e^x dx = 0$$

$$\Rightarrow \qquad (1+e^{2x})dy = -(1+y^2)e^x dx$$

$$\Rightarrow \qquad \frac{dy}{1+y^2} = -\frac{e^x}{1+e^{2x}} dx \qquad (1)$$

On integrating both sides, we get

$$\int \frac{dy}{1+y^2} = -\int \frac{e^x}{1+e^{2x}} dx$$

Put $e^x = t \Rightarrow e^x dx = dt$

$$\therefore \qquad \int \frac{dy}{1+y^2} = -\int \frac{dt}{1+t^2}$$

$$\Rightarrow \qquad \tan^{-1}y = -\tan^{-1}t + C$$

$$\Rightarrow \quad \tan^{-1}y + \tan^{-1}e^x = C \qquad [\because t = e^x] \quad (1)$$

Now, it is given that $y = 1$, when $x = 0$.

$$\therefore \qquad \tan^{-1}(1) + \tan^{-1}(e^0) = C$$

$$\Rightarrow \qquad \tan^{-1}(1) + \tan^{-1}(1) = C \qquad [\because e^0 = 1]$$

$$\Rightarrow \qquad \frac{\pi}{4} + \frac{\pi}{4} = C$$

$$\Rightarrow \qquad C = 2 \times \frac{\pi}{4} = \frac{\pi}{2}$$

Hence, the required particular solution is

$$\tan^{-1}y + \tan^{-1}e^x = \frac{\pi}{2} \qquad (1)$$

Or

We have, $y^2 dx + (x^2 - xy + y^2)dy = 0$

$$\Rightarrow \qquad \frac{dy}{dx} = \frac{-y^2}{x^2 - xy + y^2} \qquad \qquad ...(i)$$

This is homogeneous differential equation.

Now, on putting $y = vx \Rightarrow \frac{dy}{dx} = v + x\frac{dv}{dx}$ in

Eq. (i), we get (1)

$$v + x\frac{dv}{dx} = \frac{-v^2 x^2}{x^2 - vx^2 + v^2 x^2}$$

$$\Rightarrow \qquad v + x\frac{dv}{dx} = \frac{-v^2}{1 - v + v^2}$$

$$\Rightarrow \qquad x\frac{dv}{dx} = \frac{-v^2}{1 - v + v^2} - v$$

$$\Rightarrow \qquad x\frac{dv}{dx} = \frac{-v - v^3}{1 - v + v^2}$$

$$\therefore \qquad \frac{1 - v + v^2}{v(1+v^2)}dv = -\frac{1}{x}dx \qquad (1)$$

On integrating both sides, we get

$$\int \frac{1+v^2}{v(1+v^2)}dv - \int \frac{v}{v(1+v^2)}dv = -\int \frac{1}{x}dx$$

$$\Rightarrow \qquad \int \frac{1}{v}dv - \int \frac{1}{1+v^2}dv = -\int \frac{1}{x}dx$$

$$\Rightarrow \qquad \log|v| - \tan^{-1}v = -\log|x| + \log C$$

$$\Rightarrow \qquad \log\left|\frac{vx}{C}\right| = \tan^{-1}v$$

$$\Rightarrow \qquad \left|\frac{vx}{C}\right| = e^{\tan^{-1}v}$$

$$\Rightarrow \qquad \left|\frac{y}{C}\right| = e^{\tan^{-1}(y/x)} \qquad [\because vx = y]$$

$$\therefore \qquad |y| = C e^{\tan^{-1}(y/x)},$$

(1)

which is the required solution.

30. Given, $f(x) = \begin{cases} x, & x < 1 \\ 2 - x, & 1 \le x \le 2 \\ -2 + 3x - x^2, & x > 2 \end{cases}$

Differentiability at $x = 1$

$$\text{LHD} = \lim_{h \to 0} \frac{f(1-h) - f(1)}{-h}$$

$$= \lim_{h \to 0} \frac{(1-h) - [2 - (1)]}{-h} = \lim_{h \to 0} \frac{-h}{-h} = 1$$

$$\text{RHD} = \lim_{h \to 0} \frac{f(1+h) - f(1)}{h}$$

$$= \lim_{h \to 0} \frac{2 - (1+h) - (2-1)}{h} = \lim_{h \to 0} \frac{-h}{h} = -1$$

$\because \qquad \text{LHD} \ne \text{RHD}$

So, $f(x)$ is not differentiable at $x = 1$. (1)

Differentiability at $x = 2$

$$\text{LHD} = \lim_{h \to 0} \frac{f(2 - h) - f(2)}{-h}$$

$$= \lim_{h \to 0} \frac{2 - (2 - h) - (2 - 2)}{-h}$$

$$= \lim_{h \to 0} \frac{h}{-h} = -1$$

$$\text{RHD} = \lim_{h \to 0} \frac{f(2 + h) - f(2)}{h}$$

$$= \lim_{h \to 0} \frac{-2 + 3(2 + h) - (2 + h)^2 - (2 - 2)}{h}$$

$$= \lim_{h \to 0} \frac{-2 + 6 + 3h - (4 + h^2 + 4h) - 0}{h}$$

$$= \lim_{h \to 0} \frac{-h^2 - h}{h}$$

$$= \lim_{h \to 0} \frac{-h(h + 1)}{h} = -(0 + 1) = -1 \qquad (1)$$

$\because$ LHD = RHD

So, $f(x)$ is differentiable at $x = 2$.

Hence, $f(x)$ is not differentiable at $x = 1$, but it differentiable at $x = 2$. $\qquad (1)$

31. Let θ be the angle between the vectors $\vec{a}$ and $\vec{b}$.

Then, $\cos \theta = \dfrac{\vec{a} \cdot \vec{b}}{|\vec{a}||\vec{b}|}$

For θ to be an obtuse angle, we must have

$\Rightarrow \quad \cos \theta < 0 \ \forall \ x \in (0, \infty)$

$\Rightarrow \dfrac{\vec{a} \cdot \vec{b}}{|\vec{a}||\vec{b}|} < 0 \ \forall \ x \in (0, \infty)$

$\Rightarrow \quad \vec{a} \cdot \vec{b} < 0 \ \forall \ x \in (0, \infty)$

$\Rightarrow \quad c(\log_2 x)^2 - 12 + 6c(\log_2 x) < 0 \ \forall \ x \in (0, \infty)$

$\Rightarrow \quad cy^2 + 6cy - 12 < 0 \ \forall \ y \in R, \qquad (1)$

where $y = \log_2 x \qquad [\because x > 0 \Rightarrow y = \log_2 x \in R]$

$\Rightarrow \quad c < 0$ and $36c^2 + 48c < 0$

$[\because ax^2 + bx + c < 0 \ \forall \ x \Rightarrow a < 0$

and discriminant < 0]

$\Rightarrow \quad c < 0$ and $c(3c + 4) < 0$

$\Rightarrow \quad c < 0$ and $-\dfrac{4}{3} < c < 0$

$\Rightarrow \quad c \in \left(\dfrac{-4}{3}, 0 \right) \qquad (2)$

32. Let $ABCD$ be a parallelogram such that $\overrightarrow{AC} = \vec{a}$ and $\overrightarrow{BD} = \vec{b}$. Also, let $\overrightarrow{AB} = \vec{p}$ and $\overrightarrow{AD} = \vec{q}$, then $\overrightarrow{BC} = \vec{q}$ and $\overrightarrow{DC} = \vec{p}$.

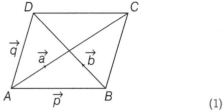

(1)

Now, by triangle law of addition, we get

$$\overrightarrow{AC} = \vec{p} + \vec{q} \Rightarrow \vec{a} = \vec{p} + \vec{q} \qquad \text{...(i)}$$

Similarly, $\overrightarrow{BD} = -\vec{p} + \vec{q} \Rightarrow \vec{b} = -\vec{p} + \vec{q} \qquad \text{...(ii)}$

On adding Eqs. (i) and (ii), we get

$$\vec{a} + \vec{b} = 2\vec{q} \Rightarrow \vec{q} = \frac{1}{2}(\vec{a} + \vec{b}) \qquad \text{...(iii)}$$

On subtracting Eq. (ii) from Eq. (i), we get

$$\vec{a} - \vec{b} = 2\vec{p} \Rightarrow \vec{p} = \frac{1}{2}(\vec{a} - \vec{b}) \qquad \text{...(iv)} \ (1)$$

Now, $\vec{p} \times \vec{q} = \dfrac{1}{4}\{(\vec{a} - \vec{b}) \times (\vec{a} + \vec{b})\}$

[using Eqs. (iii) and (iv)]

$$= \frac{1}{4}\{\vec{a} \times \vec{a} + \vec{a} \times \vec{b} - \vec{b} \times \vec{a} - \vec{b} \times \vec{b}\}$$

$$= \frac{1}{4}\{\vec{a} \times \vec{b} + \vec{a} \times \vec{b}\}$$

$$\begin{bmatrix} \because \vec{a} \times \vec{a} = \vec{b} \times \vec{b} = \vec{0} \\ \text{and } \vec{a} \times \vec{b} = -\vec{b} \times \vec{a} \end{bmatrix}$$

$$= \frac{1}{4} \times 2(\vec{a} \times \vec{b})$$

$$= \frac{1}{2}(\vec{a} \times \vec{b})$$

So, area of a parallelogram $ABCD = \dfrac{1}{2}|\vec{a} \times \vec{b}| \qquad (1)$

Hence proved.

Now, area of a parallelogram whose diagonals are $2\hat{i} - \hat{j} + \hat{k}$ and $\hat{i} + 3\hat{j} - \hat{k}$

$$= \frac{1}{2}|(2\hat{i} - \hat{j} + \hat{k}) \times (\hat{i} + 3\hat{j} - \hat{k})|$$

$$= \frac{1}{2} \begin{vmatrix} \hat{i} & \hat{j} & \hat{k} \\ 2 & -1 & 1 \\ 1 & 3 & -1 \end{vmatrix}$$

$$= \frac{1}{2}|\hat{i}(1 - 3) - \hat{j}(-2 - 1) + \hat{k}(6 + 1)|$$

$$= \frac{1}{2}|-2\hat{i} + 3\hat{j} + 7\hat{k}| = \frac{1}{2}\sqrt{(-2)^2 + (3)^2 + (7)^2}$$

$$= \frac{1}{2}\sqrt{4 + 9 + 49} = \frac{1}{2}\sqrt{62} \text{ sq units} \qquad (2)$$

33. LHS $= I + A$

$$= \begin{bmatrix} 1 & 0 \\ 0 & 1 \end{bmatrix} + \begin{bmatrix} 0 & -\tan\dfrac{\alpha}{2} \\ \tan\dfrac{\alpha}{2} & 0 \end{bmatrix} = \begin{bmatrix} 1 & -\tan\dfrac{\alpha}{2} \\ \tan\dfrac{\alpha}{2} & 1 \end{bmatrix}$$

(1)

RHS $= (I - A) \begin{bmatrix} \cos\alpha & -\sin\alpha \\ \sin\alpha & \cos\alpha \end{bmatrix}$

$$= \left\{ \begin{bmatrix} 1 & 0 \\ 0 & 1 \end{bmatrix} - \begin{bmatrix} 0 & -\tan\alpha/2 \\ \tan\alpha/2 & 0 \end{bmatrix} \right\} \begin{bmatrix} \cos\alpha & -\sin\alpha \\ \sin\alpha & \cos\alpha \end{bmatrix}$$

$$= \begin{bmatrix} 1-0 & 0+\tan\alpha/2 \\ -\tan\alpha/2 & 1-0 \end{bmatrix} \begin{bmatrix} \cos\alpha & -\sin\alpha \\ \sin\alpha & \cos\alpha \end{bmatrix}$$

(1)

$$= \begin{bmatrix} 1 & \tan\alpha/2 \\ -\tan\alpha/2 & 1 \end{bmatrix} \begin{bmatrix} \cos\alpha & -\sin\alpha \\ \sin\alpha & \cos\alpha \end{bmatrix}$$

$$= \begin{bmatrix} \cos\alpha + \tan\dfrac{\alpha}{2}\sin\alpha & -\sin\alpha + \tan\dfrac{\alpha}{2}\cos\alpha \\ -\tan\dfrac{\alpha}{2}\cos\alpha + \sin\alpha & \tan\dfrac{\alpha}{2}\sin\alpha + \cos\alpha \end{bmatrix}$$

[multiplying rows by columns]

$$= \begin{bmatrix} \dfrac{\cos\alpha \cos\dfrac{\alpha}{2} + \sin\dfrac{\alpha}{2}\sin\alpha}{\cos\dfrac{\alpha}{2}} & \dfrac{-\sin\alpha \cos\dfrac{\alpha}{2} + \sin\dfrac{\alpha}{2}\cos\alpha}{\cos\dfrac{\alpha}{2}} \\ \dfrac{-\sin\dfrac{\alpha}{2}\cos\alpha + \sin\alpha \cos\dfrac{\alpha}{2}}{\cos\dfrac{\alpha}{2}} & \dfrac{\sin\dfrac{\alpha}{2}\sin\alpha + \cos\alpha \cos\dfrac{\alpha}{2}}{\cos\dfrac{\alpha}{2}} \end{bmatrix}$$

(1)

$$= \begin{bmatrix} \dfrac{\cos\left(\alpha - \dfrac{\alpha}{2}\right)}{\cos\dfrac{\alpha}{2}} & \dfrac{\sin\left(\dfrac{\alpha}{2} - \alpha\right)}{\cos\dfrac{\alpha}{2}} \\ \dfrac{\sin\left(\alpha - \dfrac{\alpha}{2}\right)}{\cos\dfrac{\alpha}{2}} & \dfrac{\cos\left(\alpha - \dfrac{\alpha}{2}\right)}{\cos\dfrac{\alpha}{2}} \end{bmatrix}$$

$$\begin{bmatrix} \because \cos(A-B) = \cos A \cos B + \sin A \sin B \\ \text{and } \sin(A-B) = \sin A \cos B - \cos A \sin B \end{bmatrix}$$

$$= \begin{bmatrix} \dfrac{\cos\dfrac{\alpha}{2}}{\cos\dfrac{\alpha}{2}} & \dfrac{-\sin\dfrac{\alpha}{2}}{\cos\dfrac{\alpha}{2}} \\ \dfrac{\sin\dfrac{\alpha}{2}}{\cos\dfrac{\alpha}{2}} & \dfrac{\cos\dfrac{\alpha}{2}}{\cos\dfrac{\alpha}{2}} \end{bmatrix} = \begin{bmatrix} 1 & -\tan\dfrac{\alpha}{2} \\ \tan\dfrac{\alpha}{2} & 1 \end{bmatrix} = \text{LHS}$$

Hence proved. (2)

Or

We have the following system of equations

$$x + y + z = 7000 \qquad \text{...(i)}$$
$$\Rightarrow \quad 10x + 16y + 17z = 110000 \qquad \text{...(ii)}$$
and $$x - y = 0 \qquad \text{...(iii)}$$

This system of equations can be written in matrix from as $AX = B$

where, $A = \begin{bmatrix} 1 & 1 & 1 \\ 10 & 16 & 17 \\ 1 & -1 & 0 \end{bmatrix}$, $X = \begin{bmatrix} x \\ y \\ z \end{bmatrix}$ and $B = \begin{bmatrix} 7000 \\ 110000 \\ 0 \end{bmatrix}$

Here, $|A| = \begin{vmatrix} 1 & 1 & 1 \\ 10 & 16 & 17 \\ 1 & -1 & 0 \end{vmatrix}$

$$\Rightarrow \quad |A| = 1(0+17) - 1(0-17) + 1(-10-16)$$
$$= 17 + 17 - 26$$
$$= 8 \neq 0 \qquad (1)$$

So, A is non-singular matrix and its inverse exists.
Now, cofactors of elements of $|A|$ are

$$A_{11} = (-1)^2 \begin{vmatrix} 16 & 17 \\ -1 & 0 \end{vmatrix} = 1(0+17) = 17$$

$$A_{12} = (-1)^3 \begin{vmatrix} 10 & 17 \\ 1 & 0 \end{vmatrix} = -1(0-17) = 17$$

$$A_{13} = (-1)^4 \begin{vmatrix} 10 & 16 \\ 1 & -1 \end{vmatrix} = 1(-10-16) = -26$$

$$A_{21} = (-1)^3 \begin{vmatrix} 1 & 1 \\ -1 & 0 \end{vmatrix} = -1(0+1) = -1$$

$$A_{22} = (-1)^4 \begin{vmatrix} 1 & 1 \\ 1 & 0 \end{vmatrix} = 1(0-1) = -1$$

$$A_{23} = (-1)^5 \begin{vmatrix} 1 & 1 \\ 1 & -1 \end{vmatrix} = -1(-1-1) = 2$$

$$A_{31} = (-1)^4 \begin{vmatrix} 1 & 1 \\ 16 & 17 \end{vmatrix} = 1(17-16) = 1$$

$$A_{32} = (-1)^5 \begin{vmatrix} 1 & 1 \\ 10 & 17 \end{vmatrix} = -1(17-10) = -7$$

$$A_{33} = (-1)^6 \begin{vmatrix} 1 & 1 \\ 10 & 16 \end{vmatrix} = 1(16-10) = 6 \qquad (1)$$

$$\therefore \quad \text{adj}(A) = \begin{bmatrix} A_{11} & A_{12} & A_{13} \\ A_{21} & A_{22} & A_{23} \\ A_{31} & A_{32} & A_{33} \end{bmatrix}^T$$

$$= \begin{bmatrix} 17 & 17 & -26 \\ -1 & -1 & 2 \\ 1 & -7 & 6 \end{bmatrix}^T$$

$$= \begin{bmatrix} 17 & -1 & 1 \\ 17 & -1 & -7 \\ -26 & 2 & 6 \end{bmatrix}$$

Now, $A^{-1} = \dfrac{\text{adj}(A)}{|A|} = \dfrac{1}{8}\begin{bmatrix} 17 & -1 & 1 \\ 17 & -1 & -7 \\ -26 & 2 & 6 \end{bmatrix}$

(1)

and the solution of given system is given by

$$X = A^{-1} B.$$

$$\Rightarrow \quad \begin{bmatrix} x \\ y \\ z \end{bmatrix} = \frac{1}{8} \begin{bmatrix} 17 & -1 & 1 \\ 17 & -1 & -7 \\ -26 & 2 & 6 \end{bmatrix} \begin{bmatrix} 7000 \\ 110000 \\ 0 \end{bmatrix}$$

$$= \frac{1}{8} \begin{bmatrix} 119000 - 110000 + 0 \\ 119000 - 110000 + 0 \\ -182000 + 220000 + 0 \end{bmatrix}$$

$$= \frac{1}{8} \begin{bmatrix} 9000 \\ 9000 \\ 38000 \end{bmatrix} = \begin{bmatrix} 1125 \\ 1125 \\ 4750 \end{bmatrix}$$

On comparing the corresponding elements, we get

$$x = 1125, \ y = 1125, \ z = 4750. \hspace{2em} \textbf{(2)}$$

34. We have the following LPP,

Maximise $Z = 8x + 9y$

Subject to the constraints

$$2x + 3y \leq 6$$

$$3x - 2y \leq 6$$

$$y \leq 1 \text{ and } x, y \geq 0$$

Now, considering the inequations as equations, we get

$$2x + 3y = 6 \hspace{3em} \ldots\text{(i)}$$

$$3x - 2y = 6 \hspace{3em} \ldots\text{(ii)}$$

and $\hspace{4em} y = 1 \hspace{3em} \ldots\text{(iii)}$

Table for line $2x + 3y = 6$ is

x	3	0
y	0	2

So, it passes through the points, $(3, 0)$ and $(0, 2)$.
On putting $(0, 0)$ in the inequality $2x + 3y \leq 6$, we get

$$0 \leq 6 \text{ [which is true]} \hspace{2em} \textbf{(1)}$$

So, the half plane is towards the origin.

Table for line $3x - 2y = 6$ is

x	2	0
y	0	-3

So, it passes through the points $(2, 0)$ and $(0, -3)$.
On putting $(0, 0)$ in the inequality $3x - 2y \leq 6$, we get

$$0 \leq 6 \text{ [which is true]} \hspace{2em} \textbf{(1)}$$

So, the half plane is towards the origin.
The line $y = 1$ is perpendicular to Y-axis.
On putting $(0, 0)$ in the inequality $y \leq 1$, we get

$$0 \leq 1 \text{ [which is true]}$$

So, the half plane is towards the origin.
Also, $x \geq 0, y \geq 0$, so the feasible region lies in the first quadrant.

The point of intersection of Eqs. (i) and (ii) is $\left(\dfrac{30}{13}, \dfrac{6}{13}\right)$,

Eqs. (ii) and (iii) is $\left(\dfrac{8}{3}, 1\right)$ and Eqs. (i) and (iii) is $\left(\dfrac{3}{2}, 1\right)$.

$\hspace{20em}$ **(1)**

The graphical representation of the above system of inequations is given below

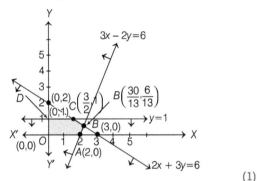

$\hspace{20em}$ **(1)**

Clearly, feasible region is $OABCDO$, whose corner points are $O(0, 0), A(2, 0), B\left(\dfrac{30}{13}, \dfrac{6}{13}\right), C\left(\dfrac{3}{2}, 1\right)$ and $D(0, 1)$.

The values of Z at corner points are as follows

Corner points	$Z = 8x + 9y$
$O(0, 0)$	$Z = 0 + 0 = 0$
$A(2, 0)$	$Z = 8 \times 2 + 0 = 16$
$B\left(\dfrac{30}{13}, \dfrac{6}{13}\right)$	$Z = 8 \times \dfrac{30}{13} + \dfrac{9 \times 6}{13}$ $= \dfrac{294}{13} = 22.62 \text{ (maximum)}$
$C\left(\dfrac{3}{2}, 1\right)$	$Z = 8 \times \dfrac{3}{2} + 9 = 21$
$D(0, 1)$	$Z = 0 + 9 \times 1 = 9$

In the table, we find that maximum value of Z is 22.62, when $x = \dfrac{30}{13}$ and $y = \dfrac{6}{13}$. $\hspace{3em}$ **(1)**

Or

To solve the LPP graphically, we first convert the inequations into equations to obtain the following lines.

$$2x + y = 8,$$

$$x + 2y = 10,$$

$$x = 0, y = 0$$

The line $2x + y = 8$ meets the coordinate axes at $A_1(4, 0)$ and $B_1(0, 8)$, join these points to obtain the line represented by $2x + y = 8$.

Clearly, $O(0, 0)$ does not satisfy the inequation $2x + y \geq 8$.

So, the region not containing the origin is represented by this inequation. $\hspace{3em}$ **(1)**

The line $x + 2y = 10$ meets the coordinate axes at A_2 (10, 0) and B_2(0, 5). Join these points to obtain the line represented by $x + 2y = 10$.

Clearly, O(0, 0) does not satisfy the inequation $x + 2y \geq 10$.

So, the region not containing the origin is represented by this inequation. Clearly, $x \geq 0$ and $y \geq 0$ respresent the first quadrant. (1)

Thus, the shaded region in figure is the feasible region of the LPP. The coordinates of the corner points of this region are A_2(10, 0), P(2, 4) and B_1(0, 8).

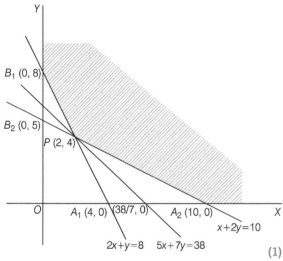

The point P(2, 4) is obtained by solving $2x + y = 8$ and $x + 2y = 10$ simultaneously. The values of the objective function $Z = 5x + 7y$ at the corner points of the feasible region are given in the following table

Point (x, y)	Value of the objective function $Z = 5x + 7y$
A_2(10, 0)	$Z = 5 \times 10 + 7 \times 0 = 50$
P(2, 4)	$Z = 5 \times 2 + 7 \times 4 = 38$
B_1(0, 8)	$Z = 5 \times 0 + 7 \times 8 = 56$

Clearly, Z is minimum at $x = 2$ and $y = 4$. (2)

35. Let $\quad I = \int_0^{2\pi} \dfrac{x \sin^{2n} x}{\sin^{2n} x + \cos^{2n} x} dx \quad$ ...(i)

Then, $I = \int_0^{2\pi} \dfrac{(2\pi - x) \sin^{2n} (2\pi - x)}{\sin^{2n} (2\pi - x) + \cos^{2n} (2\pi - x)} dx$

$\Rightarrow \quad I = \int_0^{2\pi} \dfrac{(2\pi - x) \sin^{2n} x}{\sin^{2n} x + \cos^{2n} x} dx \quad$ ...(ii) (1)

On adding Eqs. (i) and (ii), we get

$2I = \int_0^{2\pi} \dfrac{2\pi \sin^{2n} x}{\sin^{2n} x + \cos^{2n} x} dx$

$\Rightarrow \quad I = \pi \int_0^{2\pi} \dfrac{\sin^{2n} x}{\sin^{2n} x + \cos^{2n} x} dx$

$\Rightarrow \quad I = 2\pi \int_0^{\pi} \dfrac{\sin^{2n} x}{\sin^{2n} x + \cos^{2n} x} dx \quad$ (1)

$\left[\because \int_0^{2a} f(x) dx = 2 \int_0^{a} f(x), \text{ if } f(2a - x) = f(x) \right]$

$\Rightarrow \quad I = 4\pi \int_0^{\pi/2} \dfrac{\sin^{2n} x}{\sin^{2n} x + \cos^{2n} x} dx \quad$ ...(iii)

$\Rightarrow \quad I = 4\pi \int_0^{\pi/2} \dfrac{\sin^{2n} (\pi/2 - x)}{\sin^{2n} (\pi/2 - x) + \cos^{2n} (\pi/2 - x)} dx$

$\Rightarrow \quad I = 4\pi \int_0^{\pi/2} \dfrac{\cos^{2n} x}{\cos^{2n} x + \sin^{2n} x} dx \quad$ ...(iv) (1)

On adding Eqs. (iii) and (iv), we get

$2I = 4\pi \int_0^{\pi/2} \left[\dfrac{\sin^{2n} x}{\sin^{2n} x + \cos^{2n} x} + \dfrac{\cos^{2n} x}{\sin^{2n} x + \cos^{2n} x} \right] dx$

$= 4\pi \int_0^{\pi/2} 1 \, dx = 4\pi \times \dfrac{\pi}{2}$

$\therefore I = \pi^2$ (2)

36. Let E_1, E_2, E_3 and A be the events defined as follows

E_1 : You guess the answer

E_2 : You copy the answer

E_3 : You know the answer

A : You answer correctly

We have, $P(E_1) = \dfrac{1}{3}, P(E_2) = \dfrac{1}{6}$,

$P\left(\dfrac{A}{E_1}\right) = \dfrac{1}{8}$ and $P\left(\dfrac{A}{E_2}\right) = \dfrac{1}{4}$

Since, E_1, E_2, E_3 are mutually exclusive and exhaustive events

$\therefore \quad P(E_1) + P(E_2) + P(E_3) = 1$

$\Rightarrow \quad P(E_3) = 1 - P(E_1) - P(E_2)$

$= 1 - \dfrac{1}{3} - \dfrac{1}{6}$

$= \dfrac{3}{6} = \dfrac{1}{2}$

(i) Required probability $= P\left(\dfrac{A}{E_1}\right) = \dfrac{1}{8}$

(ii) Required probability $= P\left(\dfrac{A}{E_3}\right) = 1$

(iii) Required probability $= P\left(\dfrac{E_3}{A}\right)$

$= \dfrac{P(E_3) P\left(\dfrac{A}{E_3}\right)}{P(E_1) P\left(\dfrac{A}{E_1}\right) + P(E_2) P\left(\dfrac{A}{E_2}\right) + P(E_3) P\left(\dfrac{A}{E_3}\right)}$

$= \dfrac{\dfrac{1}{2}}{\dfrac{1}{24} + \dfrac{1}{24} + \dfrac{1}{2}} = \dfrac{12}{14} = \dfrac{6}{7}$

Or

Required probability = $P(A)$

$$= \sum_{i=1}^{3} P(E_i)\, P\!\left(\frac{A}{E_i}\right)$$

$$= P(E_1) P\!\left(\frac{A}{E_1}\right) + P(E_2) P\!\left(\frac{A}{E_2}\right) + P(E_3) P\!\left(\frac{A}{E_3}\right)$$

$$= \frac{1}{3}\times\frac{1}{8} + \frac{1}{6}\times\frac{1}{4} + \frac{1}{2}\times 1$$

$$= \frac{1}{24} + \frac{1}{24} + \frac{1}{2}$$

$$= \frac{1+1+12}{24}$$

$$= \frac{14}{24} = \frac{7}{12}$$

37. (i) Let $I = \int \sqrt{1-x^2}\, dx$

$$I = \frac{x}{2}\sqrt{1-x^2} + \frac{1}{2}\sin^{-1}x + C$$

(ii) Required expression is given by

$$\pi(1)^2 - \left[\int_0^1 \sqrt{1-x^2}\,dx - \int_0^1 (1-x)\,dx\right]$$

(iii) We have,

$x^2 + y^2 = 1$ and $x + y = 1$

$\Rightarrow \quad x^2 + (1-x)^2 = 1$

$\Rightarrow \quad x^2 + 1 + x^2 - 2x = 1$

$\Rightarrow \quad 2x^2 - 2x = 0$

$\Rightarrow \quad 2x(x-1) = 0$

$\Rightarrow \quad x = 0, 1$

when $\quad x = 0$

$\Rightarrow \quad y = 1$

and $\quad x = 1$

$\Rightarrow \quad y = 0$

∴ Point of intersection are $(1, 0)$ and $(0, 1)$.

Now, $\int \sqrt{a^2 - x^2}\,dx = \frac{x}{2}\sqrt{a^2-x^2} + \frac{a^2}{2}\sin^{-1}\frac{x}{a} + c$

Or

Required area $= \int_0^1 [\sqrt{1-x^2} - (1-x)]dx$

$$= \left[\frac{x}{2}\sqrt{1-x^2} + \frac{1}{2}\sin^{-1}x - x + \frac{x^2}{2}\right]_0^1$$

$$= 0 + \frac{1}{2}\sin^{-1}1 - 1 + \frac{1}{2} - 0$$

$$= \frac{\pi}{4} - \frac{1}{2}\ \text{sq units}$$

38. Consider the following events

$E_1 = $ Bolt is manufactured by machine A

$E_2 = $ Bolt is manufactured by machine B

$E_3 = $ Bolt is manufactured by machine C

$F = $ Drawn bolt is defective

We have, $P(E_1) = \dfrac{25}{100}$, $P(E_2) = \dfrac{35}{100}$,

$$P(E_3) = \frac{40}{100}\quad P(F/E_1) = \frac{5}{100},$$

$$P(F/E_2) = \frac{4}{100}\ \text{and}\ P(F/E_3) = \frac{2}{100}$$

(i) Required probability $= P(E_2/F)$

$$= \frac{P(E_2)\,P(F/E_2)}{P(E_1)P(F/E_1) + P(E_2)P(F/E_2) + P(E_3)P(F/E_3)}$$

$$= \frac{\dfrac{35}{100}\times\dfrac{4}{100}}{\dfrac{25}{100}\times\dfrac{5}{100} + \dfrac{35}{100}\times\dfrac{4}{100} + \dfrac{40}{100}\times\dfrac{2}{100}}$$

$$= \frac{140}{125 + 140 + 80}$$

$$= \frac{140}{345} = \frac{28}{69}$$

(ii) Required probability $= 1 - P(E_3/F)$

$$= 1 - \left[\frac{P(E_3)\,P(F/E_3)}{\begin{array}{c}P(E_1)P(F/E_1) + P(E_2)\,P(F/E_2)\\ + P(E_3)\,P(F/E_3)\end{array}}\right]$$

$$= 1 - \left[\frac{\dfrac{40}{100}\times\dfrac{2}{100}}{\dfrac{25}{100}\times\dfrac{5}{100} + \dfrac{35}{100}\times\dfrac{4}{100} + \dfrac{40}{100}\times\dfrac{2}{100}}\right]$$

$$= 1 - \frac{80}{125 + 140 + 80}$$

$$= 1 - \frac{80}{345}$$

$$= \frac{265}{345} = \frac{53}{69}$$

SAMPLE QUESTION PAPER 11

MATHEMATICS

Time : 3 hrs   Max. Marks : 80

General Instructions

1. This question paper contains - five sections A, B, C, D and E. Each section is compulsory. However, there are internal choices in some questions.
2. Section A has 18 MCQ's and 02 Assertion-Reason based questions of 1 mark each.
3. Section B has 5 Very Short Answer (VSA) type questions of 2 marks each.
4. Section C has 6 Short Answer (SA) type questions of 3 marks each.
5. Section D has 4 Long Answer (LA) type questions of 5 marks each.
6. Section E has 3 source based/case based/passage based/integrated units of assessment (4 marks each) with sub parts.

Section A

(Multiple Choice Questions) Each question carries 1 mark

1. If $A' = \begin{bmatrix} -2 & 3 \\ 1 & 2 \end{bmatrix}$ and $B = \begin{bmatrix} -1 & 0 \\ 1 & 2 \end{bmatrix}$, then the value of $[A + 2B]'$ is

(a) $\begin{bmatrix} -4 & 1 \\ 5 & 6 \end{bmatrix}$ (b) $\begin{bmatrix} -4 & 5 \\ 1 & 6 \end{bmatrix}$ (c) $\begin{bmatrix} -4 & 5 \\ 6 & 1 \end{bmatrix}$ (d) $\begin{bmatrix} -4 & 1 \\ 2 & 4 \end{bmatrix}$

2. The interval in which $y = x^2 e^{-x}$ is increasing with respect to x is

(a) [0, 2]   (b) (0, 2)   (c) [0, 2)   (d) (0, 2]

3. If the direction cosines of a line are $\left(\dfrac{1}{c}, \dfrac{1}{c}, \dfrac{1}{c} \right)$, then the value of c is

(a) $\pm \sqrt{3}$ (b) ± 1 (c) $\pm \dfrac{1}{\sqrt{3}}$ (d) ± 3

4. $\cos^{-1}\left(\dfrac{-\sqrt{3}}{2}\right)$ is equal to

(a) $\dfrac{\pi}{6}$ (b) $\dfrac{5\pi}{6}$ (c) $\dfrac{3\pi}{2}$ (d) $\dfrac{\pi}{3}$

5. If A and B are symmetric matrices of same order, then $(AB' - BA')$ is a
   (a) symmetric matrix
   (b) skew-symmetric matrix
   (c) identify matrix
   (d) null matrix

6. If $[2\,1\,3]\begin{bmatrix} -1 & 0 & -1 \\ -1 & 1 & 0 \\ 0 & 1 & 1 \end{bmatrix}\begin{bmatrix} 1 \\ 0 \\ -1 \end{bmatrix} = A$, then the
   order of matrix A is
   (a) 2×2 (b) 2×1 (c) 1×2 (d) 1×1

7. If A is a 3×3 non-singular matrix such that $AA^T = A^T A$ and $B = A^{-1}A^T$, then BB^T is
   (a) B (b) B^{-1} (c) I (d) A

8. The non-zero values of x satisfying the matrix equation

$$x\begin{bmatrix} 2x & 2 \\ 3 & x \end{bmatrix} + 2\begin{bmatrix} 8 & 5x \\ 4 & 4x \end{bmatrix} = 2\begin{bmatrix} x^2+8 & 24 \\ 10 & 6x \end{bmatrix}$$ is

   (a) 1   (b) 2   (c) 3   (d) 4

9. The function $f(x) = \sin x + \cos x\, x \in \left[0, \dfrac{\pi}{4}\right]$ is

   (a) increasing function
   (b) strictly increasing function
   (c) decreasing function
   (d) strictly decreasing function

10. $\int x^x (1 + \log x)\, dx$ is equal to

   (a) $-x^x + C$ (b) $x^x + C$
   (c) -1 (d) None of these

11. The maximum value of function $h(x) = \sin(2x) + 5$ is
   (a) 4   (b) 6   (c) 2   (d) 1

12. The minimum value of function $f(x) = |x + 2| - 1$ is
   (a) 1   (b) 0   (c) -1 (d) -2

13. If $\begin{bmatrix} 3y-x & -2x \\ 3 & 7 \end{bmatrix} = \begin{bmatrix} 5 & -2 \\ 3 & 7 \end{bmatrix}$, then the value
   of $x + y$ is
   (a) 1   (b) 2   (c) 5   (d) 3

14. The direction cosines of a line which makes equal angles with the coordinate axes are

   (a) $\pm\left(\dfrac{1}{\sqrt{2}}, \dfrac{1}{\sqrt{2}}, \dfrac{1}{\sqrt{2}}\right)$ (b) $\pm\left(\dfrac{1}{\sqrt{3}}, \dfrac{1}{\sqrt{3}}, \dfrac{1}{\sqrt{3}}\right)$
   (c) $\pm\left(\dfrac{1}{\sqrt{5}}, \dfrac{1}{\sqrt{5}}, \dfrac{1}{\sqrt{5}}\right)$ (d) $\pm(1, 1, 1)$

15. If two line $\vec{r} = \vec{a}_1 + \lambda \vec{b}_1$ and $\vec{r} = \vec{a}_2 + \mu \vec{b}_2$ are coplanar then the value of $(\vec{a}_2 - \vec{a}_1)\cdot(\vec{b}_1 \times \vec{b}_2)$ is
   (a) 1   (b) 2   (c) 0   (d) -1

16. For what value of a the vectors $2\hat{i} - 3\hat{j} + 4\hat{k}$ and $a\hat{i} + 6\hat{j} - 8\hat{k}$ are collinear?
   (a) 1   (b) 2   (c) -3 (d) -4

17. If $|\vec{a}| = 4$ and $-3 \le \lambda \le 2$, then the range of $|\lambda\, \vec{a}|$ is
   (a) $[2, 8]$ (b) $[-12, 8]$
   (c) $[-12, 8)$ (d) $(-12, 8)$

18. If A is a square matrix of order 3 such that $|\text{adj}\, A| = 64$. Then, the value of $|A|$ is
   (a) ± 8 (b) ± 4
   (c) ± 64 (d) 2

Assertion-Reason Based Questions

In the following questions, a statement of Assertion (A) is followed by a statement of Reason (R). Choose the correct answer out of the following choices.

   (a) Both A and R are true and R is the correct explanation of A.
   (b) Both A and R are true but R is not the correct explanation of A.
   (c) A is true but R is false.
   (d) A is false but R is true.

19. **Assertion (A)** The function $f : R \to R$ given by $f(x) = x^3$ is injective.

   Reason (R) The function $f : X \to Y$ is injective, if $f(x) = f(y) \Rightarrow x = y, \forall\, x, y \in X$.

20. **Assertion (A)** If $\begin{vmatrix} 2x & 5 \\ 8 & x \end{vmatrix} = \begin{vmatrix} 6 & -2 \\ 7 & 3 \end{vmatrix}$, then $= \pm 6$.

   Reason (R) If A and B are matrices of order 3 and $|A| = 4, |B| = 6$, then $|2AB| = 192$.

Section B

(This section comprises of very short answer type questions (VSA) of 2 marks each)

21. Show that all the positive integral powers of a symmetric matrix are symmetric.

Or If $A = \begin{bmatrix} 3 & 0 & -1 \\ 2 & 3 & 0 \\ 0 & 4 & 1 \end{bmatrix}$, then find $|\text{adj (adj }A)|$.

22. If $y = |x - x^2|$, then find $\dfrac{dy}{dx}$ at $x = 1$.

23. If $\vec{a} \times \vec{b} = \vec{c} \times \vec{d}$ and $\vec{a} \times \vec{c} = \vec{b} \times \vec{d}$, show that $\vec{a} - \vec{d}$ is parallel to $\vec{b} - \vec{c}$, where $\vec{a} \neq \vec{d}$ and $\vec{b} \neq \vec{c}$.

Or

If the points $A(-1, 3, 2), B(-4, 2, -2)$ and $C(5, 5, \lambda)$ are collinear, find the value of λ.

24. Let $\vec{a}, \vec{b}$ and $\vec{c}$ be three vectors such that $|\vec{a}| = 1, |\vec{b}| = 2$ and $|\vec{c}| = 3$. If the projection of $\vec{b}$ along $\vec{a}$ is equal to the projection of $\vec{c}$ along $\vec{a}$ and $\vec{b}$ and $\vec{c}$ are perpendicular to each other, find $|3\vec{a} - 2\vec{b} + 2\vec{c}|$.

25. Solve $\dfrac{dy}{dx} = \dfrac{1}{y^2 + \sin y}$.

Section C

(This section comprises of short answer type questions (SA) of 3 marks each)

26. Show that the function $f : R - (-1) \rightarrow R - \{1\}$ defined by $f(x) = \dfrac{x}{x+1}$ is bijective.

27. Show that $y = \log(1 + x) - \dfrac{2x}{2+x}$, $x > -1$ is an increasing function of x, throughout its domain.

Or

Find the intervals in which the function given by $f(x) = \sin x + \cos x, 0 \leq x \leq 2\pi$ is

(i) increasing.   (ii) decreasing.

28. Find the value of $\displaystyle\int \dfrac{\tan^2 x \sec^2 x}{1 - \tan^6 x} dx$.

Or

Find the value of $\displaystyle\int \sin x \cdot \log \cos x \, dx$.

29. If $f : R - \{2\} \rightarrow R - \{3\}$ is defined by $f(x) = \dfrac{3x+1}{x-2}$, where R is the set of real numbers, show that f is bijective.

Or

Check whether the relation R in the set Z of integers defined as $R = \{(a, b) : a + b$ is "divisible by 2"$\}$ is reflexive, symmetric or transitive. Write the equivalence class containing 0 i.e. [0].

30. Find the area bounded by the curve $x^2 + y^2 = a^2$ using integration.

31. Find the particular solution of the differential equation $\log\left(\dfrac{dy}{dx}\right) = 3x + 4y$, given that $y = 0$, when $x = 0$.

Section D

(This section comprises of long answer type questions (LA) of 5 marks each)

32. Solve $(x^3 - 3xy^2)\, dx = (y^3 - 3x^2 y)\, dy$.

33. Find the shortest distance between the lines

$$\frac{x-8}{3} = \frac{y+9}{-16} = \frac{z-10}{7} \text{ and}$$

$$\frac{x-15}{3} = \frac{y-29}{8} = \frac{5-z}{5}.$$

Or

If $\vec{a}$, $\vec{b}$ and $\vec{c}$ are three mutually perpendicular vectors of the same magnitude, then prove that $\vec{a} + \vec{b} + \vec{c}$ is equally inclined with the vectors $\vec{a}$, $\vec{b}$ and $\vec{c}$.

34. Solve the given LPP maximise $Z = 24x + 18y$. Subject to constraints $2x + 3y \leq 10$, $x \geq 0$, $y \geq 0$, $3x + 2y \leq 10$.

Or

Solve the given LPP

Maximise $(Z) = 100x + 120y$

Subject to constraints,

$$2x + 3y \leq 30$$

$$3x + y \leq 17$$

$$x \geq 0, \ y \geq 0$$

35. Prove that the radius of the right circular cylinder of greatest curved surface area which can be inscribed in a given cone is half of that of the cone.

Section E

(This section comprises of 3 case-study/ passage-based questions of 4 marks each with two sub-parts. First two case study questions have three sub-parts (i), (ii), (iii) of marks 1, 1, 2 respectively. The third case study question has two sub-parts of 2 marks each)

36. A random variable X has the following probability distribution

X	0	1	2	3	4	5	6	7
P(X)	0	k	$2k$	$2k$	$3k$	k^2	$2k^2$	$7k^2 + k$

On the basis of above information, answer the following questions.

(i) Find the value of $P(1 \leq x < 3)$ in terms of k.

(ii) Find the value of $P(0 \leq x \leq 4)$ in terms of k.

(iii) Find the value of k and then evaluate $P(x < 6)$.

Or

If $k = \dfrac{1}{10}$, evaluate $P(x \geq 6)$ and $P(0 < x < 5)$.

37. The sum of the surface area of a rectangular parallelopiped with sides x, $2x$ and $\dfrac{x}{3}$ and a sphere of radius y is given to be constant.

On the basis of above information, answer the following questions.

(i) If S is the constant, then find the relation between S, x and y.

(ii) If the combined volume is denoted by V, then find the relation between V, x and y.

(iii) Find the relation between x and y when the volume V is minimum.

Or If at $x = 3y$, volume V is minimum, then find the value of minimum volume and the value of S.

38. An insurance company believes that people can be divided into two classes: those who are accident prone and those who are not. The company's statistics show that an accident-prone person will have an accident at sometime within a fixed one-year period with probability 0.6, whereas this probability is 0.2 for a person who is not accident prone. The company knows that 20% of the population is accident prone.

On the basis of above information, answer the following questions.

(i) What is the probability that a new policyholder will have an accident within a year of purchasing a policy?

(ii) Suppose that a new policy holder has an accident within a year of purchasing a policy. What is the probability that he or she is accident prone?

Answers

1. (b) **2.** (b) **3.** (a) **4.** (b) **5.** (b)

6. (d) **7.** (c) **8.** (d) **9.** (a) **10.** (b)

11. (b) **12.** (c) **13.** (d) **14.** (b) **15.** (c)

16. (d) **17.** (b) **18.** (a) **19.** (a) **20.** (b)

21. Or 1

22. $\dfrac{dy}{dx}$ does not exist at $x = 1$

23. or 10

24. $\sqrt{61}$

25. $\dfrac{y^3}{3} - \cos y = x + C$

27. Or (i) $\left[0, \dfrac{\pi}{4}\right]$ and $\left[\dfrac{5\pi}{4}, 2\pi\right]$ (ii) $\left[\dfrac{\pi}{4}, \dfrac{5\pi}{4}\right]$

28. $\dfrac{1}{6}\log\left|\dfrac{1 + \tan^3 x}{1 - \tan^3 x}\right| + C$ Or $-\cos x \log \cos x + \cos x + C$

29. Or $\{..., -6, -4, -2, 0, 2, 4, 6, ...\}$

30. πa^2 sq units

31. $4e^{3x} + 3e^{-4y} - 7 = 0$

32. $x^2 - y^2 = (x^2 + y^2)^2 C^2$

33. 14 units.

34. The maximum value of Z is 84 at $\left(\dfrac{10}{3}, 0\right)$.

Or The maximum value of Z is 1260 at $(3, 8)$.

36. (i) $3k$ (ii) $8k$ (iii) $k = \dfrac{1}{10}$ and $P(x < 6) = \dfrac{81}{100}$

Or $P(x \geq 6) = \dfrac{19}{100}$ and $P(0 < x < 5) = \dfrac{4}{5}$.

37. (i) $S = 6x^2 + 4\pi y^2$ (ii) $V = \dfrac{4}{3}\pi y^3 + \dfrac{2}{3}x^3$

(iii) $x = 3y$ Or $V = \dfrac{2}{3}x^3\left(1 + \dfrac{2\pi}{27}\right)$ and $S = 2x^2\left[3 + \dfrac{2}{9}\pi\right]$.

38. (i) $\dfrac{7}{25}$ (ii) $\dfrac{3}{7}$

Scan this QR code from your mobile phone to get the explanations of this paper.

SAMPLE QUESTION PAPER 12

MATHEMATICS

Time : 3 hrs   Max. Marks : 80

General Instructions

1. This question paper contains - five sections A, B, C, D and E. Each section is compulsory. However, there are internal choices in some questions.
2. Section A has 18 MCQ's and 02 Assertion-Reason based questions of 1 mark each.
3. Section B has 5 Very Short Answer (VSA) type questions of 2 marks each.
4. Section C has 6 Short Answer (SA) type questions of 3 marks each.
5. Section D has 4 Long Answer (LA) type questions of 5 marks each.
6. Section E has 3 source based/case based/passage based/integrated units of assessment (4 marks each) with sub parts.

Section A

(Multiple Choice Questions) Each question carries 1 mark

1. If $\int_0^1 (3x^2 + 2x + k)\,dx = 0$, then the value of k is

(a) 2   (b) 0   (c) 1   (d) –2

2. The value of λ, if the vector $2\hat{i} + \lambda\hat{j} - 4\hat{k}$ and $2\hat{i} - \hat{j} + \hat{k}$ are perpendicular is

(a) 0   (b) 1   (c) 2   (d) –1

3. If a relation R on the set $\{1, 2, 3, 4\}$ be defined by $R = \{(x, y): y = 2x\}$, then R is

(a) reflexive
(b) symmetric
(c) transitive
(d) neither reflexive nor symmetric nor transitive

4. Set A has 4 elements and the set B has 5 elements. Then, the number of injective mappings that can be defined from A to B is

(a) 24   (b) 60   (c) 120   (d) 210

5. The domain of the function defined by $f(x) = \sin^{-1}\sqrt{x-1}$ is

(a) [1, 2]   (b) (1, 2)   (c) [1, 2)   (d) (1, 2]

6. An equivalence relation R in A divides it into equivalence classes A_1, A_2, A_3. Then, the value of $A_1 \cup A_2 \cup A_3$ and, $A_1 \cap A_2 \cap A_3$ is respectively

(a) A, ϕ (b) ϕ, A (c) A, A (d) ϕ, ϕ

7. The principal values of $\tan^{-1}(-\sqrt{3})$ and $\cos^{-1}\left(-\dfrac{1}{2}\right)$ are

(a) $-\dfrac{\pi}{3}$ and $-\dfrac{\pi}{3}$ (b) $\dfrac{2\pi}{3}$ and $\dfrac{2\pi}{3}$

(c) $-\dfrac{\pi}{3}$ and $\dfrac{2\pi}{3}$ (d) $\dfrac{2\pi}{3}$ and $-\dfrac{4\pi}{3}$

8. Which of the following is true?

(a) $*$ defined by $a*b = \dfrac{a+b}{2}$ is a binary operation on Z

(b) Subtraction is a binary operation on N.

(c) All binary commutative operations are associative

(d) $*$ defined by $a*b = \dfrac{a+b}{2}$ is a binary operation on Q

9. How many reflexive relations are possible in a set A whose $n(A) = 3$?

(a) 64   (b) 32   (c) 128   (d) 1024

10. Let $A = \begin{bmatrix} 200 & 50 \\ 10 & 2 \end{bmatrix}$ and $B = \begin{bmatrix} 50 & 40 \\ 2 & 3 \end{bmatrix}$, then $|AB|$ is equal to

(a) 460   (b) 2000

(c) 3000   (d) -7000

11. If $A = \begin{bmatrix} 1 & 0 \\ 1 & 1 \end{bmatrix}$, then A^3 is

(a) $\begin{bmatrix} 1 & 0 \\ 3 & 1 \end{bmatrix}$ (b) $\begin{bmatrix} 1 & 3 \\ 0 & 1 \end{bmatrix}$ (c) $\begin{bmatrix} 1 & 3 \\ 0 & 0 \end{bmatrix}$ (d) $\begin{bmatrix} 3 & 0 \\ 1 & 1 \end{bmatrix}$

12. If $x = t^2$ and $y = t^3$, then $\dfrac{d^2y}{dx^2}$ is

(a) $\dfrac{3t}{4}$ (b) $\dfrac{3}{t}$ (c) $\dfrac{3}{4t}$ (d) $\dfrac{4}{3t}$

13. $\int e^x(1 - \cot x + \cosec^2 x)\,dx$ is equal to

(a) $e^x(1 - \cot x) + C$ (b) $e^x(1 + \cot x) + C$

(c) $e^x(\cosec x) + C$ (d) $e^x \cot x + C$

14. $\int_{-\pi/2}^{\pi/2} x^2 \sin x \, dx$ is equal to

(a) 1   (b) 0   (c) -1 (d) 2

15. The area bounded by $y = x^2$, the X-axis and the lines $x = -1$ and $x = 1$ is

(a) $\dfrac{1}{3}$ sq unit   (b) $\dfrac{2}{3}$ sq unit

(c) 3 sq units   (d) 1 sq unit

16. How many arbitrary constants are there in the particular solution of the differential equation $\dfrac{dy}{dx} = -4xy^2$; $y(0) = 1$?

(a) 1   (b) 2

(c) 0   (d) 3

17. For what value of n is the following differential equation homogeneous

$$\frac{dy}{dx} = \frac{x^3 - y^n}{x^2 y + xy^2}?$$

(a) 1   (b) 2

(c) 3   (d) 4

18. $\int_0^2 [x]\,dx$ is equal to

(a) 0   (b) 1

(c) -1 (d) 2

Assertion-Reason Based Questions

In the following questions, a statement of Assertion (A) is followed by a statement of Reason (R). Choose the correct answer out of the following choices.

(a) Both A and R are true and R is the correct explanation of A

(b) Both A and R are true but R is not the correct explanation of A

(c) A is true but R is false

(d) A is false but R is true

19. Assertion (A) The function $f : R^* \to R^*$ defined by $f(x) = \dfrac{1}{x}$ is one-one and onto, where R^* is the set of all non-zero real numbers.

Reason (R) The function $g : N \to R^*$ defined by $f(x) = \dfrac{1}{x}$ is one-one and onto.

20. Assertion (A) If $\begin{bmatrix} xy & 4 \\ z+5 & x+y \end{bmatrix} = \begin{bmatrix} 4 & w \\ 0 & 4 \end{bmatrix}$, then $x = 2, y = 2, z = -5$ and $w = 4$.

Reason (R) Two matrices are equal, if their orders are same and their corresponding elements are equal.

Section B

(This section comprises of very short answer type questions (VSA) of 2 marks each)

21. If A is a square matrix of order 3 such that $A^2 = 2A$, then find the value of $|A|$.

Or

If $A = \begin{bmatrix} 3 & 1 \\ -1 & 2 \end{bmatrix}$, show that $A^2 - 5A + 7I = O$

Hence, find A^{-1}.

22. Find the value(s) of k, so that the following function is continuous at $x = 0$

$$f(x) = \begin{cases} \dfrac{1 - \cos kx}{x \sin x}, & \text{if } x \neq 0 \\ \dfrac{1}{2}, & \text{if } x = 0 \end{cases}$$

23. Find $\displaystyle\int \dfrac{1}{\cos^2 x (1 - \tan x)^2}\, dx$.

Or

Evaluate $\displaystyle\int_0^1 x(1 - x)^n\, dx$.

24. Find the area of the region bounded by the parabola $y^2 = 8x$ and the line $x = 2$.

25. Solve the following differential equation

$$\dfrac{dy}{dx} = x^3 \operatorname{cosec} y, \text{ given that } y(0) = 0.$$

Section C

(This section comprises of short answer type questions (SA) of 3 marks each)

26. Find the intervals in which the function f given by $f(x) = \tan x - 4x$, $x \in \left(0, \dfrac{\pi}{2}\right)$ is

(i) strictly increasing (ii) strictly decreasing

27. Prove that the greatest integer function defined by $f(x) = [x]$, $0 < x < 2$ is not differentiable at $x = 1$.

Or

If $x = a\sec\theta$, $y = b\tan\theta$, find $\dfrac{d^2 y}{dx^2}$ at $\theta = \dfrac{\pi}{6}$.

28. Find the area of the region bounded by the curves $x^2 + y^2 = 4$, $y = \sqrt{3}x$ and X-axis in the first quadrant.

Or

Find the area of the ellipse $x^2 + 9y^2 = 36$ using integration.

29. If $\vec{a} \neq \vec{0}$, $\vec{a} \cdot \vec{b} = \vec{a} \cdot \vec{c}$, $\vec{a} \times \vec{b} = \vec{a} \times \vec{c}$, then show that $\vec{b} = \vec{c}$.

Or

Find the shortest distance between the following lines

$$\vec{r} = (\hat{i} + \hat{j} - \hat{k}) + s(2\hat{i} + \hat{j} + \hat{k})$$

and $\vec{r} = (\hat{i} + \hat{j} + 2\hat{k}) + t(4\hat{i} + 2\hat{j} + 2\hat{k})$

30. Find the general solution of the following differential equation

$$x\, dy - (y + 2x^2)\, dx = 0.$$

31. Find $\displaystyle\int \dfrac{x^2 + 1}{(x^2 + 2)(x^2 + 3)}\, dx$.

Section D

(This section comprises of long answer type questions (LA) of 5 marks each)

32. Write the vector equations of following lines and hence find the distance between them

$$\frac{x-1}{2} = \frac{y-2}{3} = \frac{z+4}{6}, \quad \frac{x-3}{4} = \frac{y-3}{6} = \frac{z+5}{12}$$

33. If $A = \begin{bmatrix} 1 & 2 & 0 \\ -2 & -1 & -2 \\ 0 & -1 & 1 \end{bmatrix}$, find A^{-1}. Hence,

solve the system of equations;

$$x - 2y = 10$$
$$2x - y - z = 8$$
$$-2y + z = 7$$

Or

Evaluate the product AB, where

$$A = \begin{bmatrix} 1 & -1 & 0 \\ 2 & 3 & 4 \\ 0 & 1 & 2 \end{bmatrix} \text{ and } B = \begin{bmatrix} 2 & 2 & -4 \\ -4 & 2 & -4 \\ 2 & -1 & 5 \end{bmatrix}$$

Hence, solve the system of linear equations

$$x - y = 3$$
$$2x + 3y + 4z = 17$$
$$y + 2z = 7$$

34. Solve the following linear programming problem (LPP) graphically. Maximize $Z = x + 2y$. Subject to constraints,

$$x + 2y \geq 100$$
$$2x - y \leq 0$$
$$2x + y \leq 200$$
$$x, y \geq 0$$

Or

The corner points of the feasible region determined by the system of linear constraints are as shown below

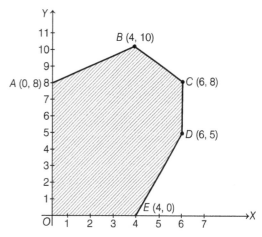

Answer each of the following

(i) Let $Z = 3x - 4y$ be the objective function. Find the maximum and minimum value of Z and also the corresponding points at which the maximum and minimum value occurs.

(ii) Let $Z = px + qy$, where $p, q > 0$ be the objective function. Find the condition on p and q so that the maximum value of Z occurs at $B(4, 10)$ and $C(6, 8)$. Also, mention the number of optimal solutions in this case.

35. If $\vec{a}$, $\vec{b}$ and $\vec{c}$ are three vectors, such that $|\vec{a}| = 3$, $|\vec{b}| = 4$ and $|\vec{c}| = 5$ and each one of these is perpendicular to the sum of other two, then find $|\vec{a} + \vec{b} + \vec{c}|$.

Section E

(This section comprises of 3 case-study/ passage-based questions of 4 marks each with two sub-parts. First two case study questions have three sub-parts (i), (ii), (iii) of marks 1, 1, 2 respectively. The third case study question has two sub-parts of 2 marks each)

36. The probability distribution function which shows the number of hours (X), a student study during lockdown period in a day, is given by

X	0	1	2
$P(X)$	$3C^3$	$4C - 10C^2$	$5C - 1$

where, $C > 0$.

On the basis of above information, answer the following questions.

(i) Find the value of $P(0 \le X < 2)$ in terms of C.

(ii) Find the value of C.

Or

If $C = \dfrac{1}{3}$, evaluate $P(X \ge 1)$ and $P(X = 2)$.

(iii) Find $P(X \ge 0)$.

37. A toy making company made a toy in which a cylinder is inscribed in a sphere. The height and radius of cylinder is H and R, respectively, while the radius of sphere is a.

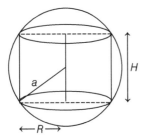

On the basis of above information, answer the following questions.

(i) Find the relation between R and H.

(ii) Find the value of volume of cylinder V in terms of H.

(iii) Find the value of H when V is maximum.

Or

If V is maximum at $H = \dfrac{2}{\sqrt{3}}\, a$, then find the maximum value of V.

38. A doctor is to visit a patient. From the past experience, it is known that the probabilities that he will come by train, bus, scooter or by other means of transport are respectively $\dfrac{3}{10}, \dfrac{1}{5}, \dfrac{1}{10}$ and $\dfrac{2}{5}$. The probability that he will be late are $\dfrac{1}{4}, \dfrac{1}{3}$ and $\dfrac{1}{12}$, if he comes by train, bus and scooter respectively, but if he comes by other means of transport, then he will not be late.

On the basis of above information, answer the following questions.

(i) Find the probability that doctor comes by train and he is late.

(ii) Find the probability that he is late and also find the probability that he comes by scooter given that he is late.

Answers

1. (d) 2. (a) 3. (d) 4. (c) 5. (a)

6. (a) 7. (c) 8. (d) 9. (a) 10. (d)

11. (a) 12. (c) 13. (a) 14. (b) 15. (b)

16. (c) 17. (c) 18. (b) 19. (c) 20. (a)

21. 0 and 8 Or $\dfrac{1}{7}\begin{bmatrix} 2 & -1 \\ 1 & 3 \end{bmatrix}$

22. ± 1

23. $\dfrac{1}{1-\tan x}+C$ Or $\dfrac{1}{(n+1)(n+2)}$

24. $\dfrac{32}{3}$ sq units

25. $\cos y = 1 - \dfrac{x^4}{4}$

26. (i) $\left(0, \dfrac{\pi}{3}\right)$ (ii) $\left(\dfrac{\pi}{3}, \dfrac{\pi}{2}\right)$

27. Or $\dfrac{-3\sqrt{3}b}{a^2}$

28. $\dfrac{2\pi}{3}$ sq units Or 12π sq units

29. $\dfrac{3\sqrt{5}}{\sqrt{6}}$ sq units

30. $y = 2x^2 + Cx$

31. $-\dfrac{1}{\sqrt{2}}\tan^{-1}\left(\dfrac{x}{\sqrt{2}}\right)+\dfrac{2}{\sqrt{3}}\tan^{-1}\left(\dfrac{x}{\sqrt{3}}\right)+C$

32. $\vec{r} = (\hat{i}+2\hat{j}-4\hat{k})+\lambda(2\hat{i}+3\hat{j}+6\hat{k})$

and $\vec{r} = (3\hat{i}+3\hat{j}-5\hat{k})+\mu(4\hat{i}+6\hat{j}+12\hat{k})$;

$\dfrac{\sqrt{293}}{7}$ units

33. $\begin{bmatrix} -3 & -2 & -4 \\ 2 & 1 & 2 \\ 2 & 1 & 3 \end{bmatrix}$; $x = 0, y = -5$ and $z = -3$

Or $\begin{bmatrix} 6 & 0 & 0 \\ 0 & 6 & 0 \\ 0 & 0 & 6 \end{bmatrix}$; $x = 2, y = -1, z = 4$

34. $Z = 400$ is maximum at $(0, 200)$

Or (i) $Z_{max} = 12$ at $(4, 0)$ and $Z_{min} = -32$ at $(0, 8)$

(ii) $p = q$; infinite

35. $5\sqrt{2}$

36. (i) $3C^3 + 4C - 10C^2$ (ii) $\dfrac{1}{3}$ Or $P(X \geq 1) = \dfrac{8}{9}, P(X = 2) = \dfrac{2}{3}$

(iii) 1

37. (i) $R^2 + \dfrac{H^2}{4} = a^2$ (ii) $\pi\left(a^2 H - \dfrac{H^3}{4}\right)$

(iii) $\dfrac{2}{\sqrt{3}}a$ Or $\dfrac{4}{3\sqrt{3}}\pi a^3$

38. (i) $\dfrac{3}{40}$ (ii) $\dfrac{1}{18}$

Scan this QR code from your mobile phone to get the explanations of this paper.

SAMPLE QUESTION PAPER 13

MATHEMATICS

Time : 3 hrs   Max. Marks : 80

General Instructions

1. This question paper contains - five sections A, B, C, D and E. Each section is compulsory. However, there are internal choices in some questions.
2. Section A has 18 MCQ's and 02 Assertion-Reason based questions of 1 mark each.
3. Section B has 5 Very Short Answer (VSA) type questions of 2 marks each.
4. Section C has 6 Short Answer (SA) type questions of 3 marks each.
5. Section D has 4 Long Answer (LA) type questions of 5 marks each.
6. Section E has 3 source based/case based/passage based/integrated units of assessment (4 marks each) with sub parts.

Section A

(Multiple Choice Questions) Each question carries 1 mark

1. $\cot^{-1}(-\sqrt{3}) + \tan^{-1}(1)$ is equal to

(a) $\dfrac{\pi}{12}$ (b) $\dfrac{13\pi}{12}$ (c) $\dfrac{13\pi}{2}$ (d) $\dfrac{\pi}{2}$

2. Let R be the relation in the set $\{1, 2, 3, 4\}$ given by $R = \{(1, 2), (2, 2), (1, 1), (4, 4), (1, 3), (3, 3), (3, 2)\}$. Then, R is

(a) reflexive but not transitive   (b) reflexive and transitive

(c) neither reflexive nor symmetric   (d) symmetric but not transitive

3. $\tan^{-1}\left(\sqrt{2}\sin\dfrac{3\pi}{4}\right)$ is equal to

(a) $\dfrac{\pi}{2}$ (b) $\dfrac{\pi}{6}$ (c) $\dfrac{\pi}{3}$ (d) $\dfrac{\pi}{4}$

4. Matrix X, if $X + \begin{bmatrix} 4 & 6 \\ -3 & 7 \end{bmatrix} = \begin{bmatrix} 3 & -6 \\ 5 & -8 \end{bmatrix}$ is

(a) $\begin{bmatrix} -1 & -12 \\ 8 & -15 \end{bmatrix}$ (b) $\begin{bmatrix} 1 & -12 \\ -8 & 15 \end{bmatrix}$

(c) $\begin{bmatrix} -1 & 8 \\ -12 & -15 \end{bmatrix}$ (d) $\begin{bmatrix} 1 & 1 \\ 0 & 0 \end{bmatrix}$

5. If $\cos^{-1}\alpha + \cos^{-1}\beta + \cos^{-1}\gamma = 3\pi$, then

evaluate $(\alpha^3 + \beta^3 + \gamma^3) - \left(\dfrac{1}{\alpha} + \dfrac{1}{\beta} + \dfrac{1}{\gamma}\right)$

(a) 1   (b) 0   (c) −1   (d) 2

6. If $A = \begin{bmatrix} \cos\theta & -\sin\theta \\ \sin\theta & \cos\theta \end{bmatrix}$, then find the value

of θ (where, $\theta \in \left(0, \dfrac{\pi}{2}\right)$) satisfying the

equation $A^T + A = I_2$.

(a) $\dfrac{\pi}{2}$ (b) $\dfrac{\pi}{6}$ (c) $\dfrac{\pi}{3}$ (d) π

7. If $f(x) = ax^2 + bx + c$, then

$f'(1) + f'(4) - f'(5)$ is equal to
(a) a (b) b (c) −1   (d) c

8. Find the point where, $f(x) = xe^x$ is minimum.

(a) 1   (b) −1   (c) 0   (d) 2

9. $\displaystyle\int_0^{\pi/2} x\sin x \, dx$ is equal to

(a) −1   (b) 1   (c) 2   (d) −3

10. If $y = 1 - x + \dfrac{x^2}{2!} - \dfrac{x^3}{3!} + \dfrac{x^4}{4!} \ldots \infty$, then

$\dfrac{d^2 y}{dx^2} - y$ is equal to

(a) 0   (b) −1   (c) x (d) x^2

11. $\displaystyle\int \dfrac{x^3}{x+1} \, dx$ is equal to

(a) $x + \dfrac{x^2}{2} - \dfrac{x^3}{3} - \log|1+x| + C$

(b) $x - \dfrac{x^2}{2} + \dfrac{x^3}{3} - \log|1+x| + C$

(c) $x + \log x + C$

(d) $x - \dfrac{x^3}{3} + \dfrac{x^4}{2} + \log|1+x| + C$

12. If $\{x\}$ is fractional part function, then

$\displaystyle\int_0^2 \{x\} \, dx$ is equal to

(a) 1   (b) 2   (c) −1   (d) 3

13. If the angle between the vectors $\hat{i} + \hat{k}$ and $\hat{i} - \hat{j} + \alpha\hat{k}$ is $\dfrac{\pi}{2}$, then the value of α is

(a) 1   (b) −1   (c) 0   (d) 2

14. If $\vec{a} = (\hat{i} + 3\hat{j} - 2\hat{k}) \times (-\hat{i} + 3\hat{k})$, then the value of $|\vec{a}|$ is

(a) 91   (b) $\sqrt{91}$
(c) 31   (d) $\sqrt{31}$

15. $\displaystyle\int_0^1 3^{x-[x]} \, dx$ is equal to

(a) $\dfrac{1}{\log 3}$ (b) $\dfrac{2}{\log 3}$

(c) $\dfrac{3}{\log 3}$ (d) $\dfrac{\log 3}{2}$

16. If $|\vec{a}| = 2, |\vec{b}| = 3$ and $\vec{a} \cdot \vec{b} = 3$, then the projection of $\vec{b}$ on $\vec{a}$ is

(a) $\dfrac{2}{3}$ (b) $\dfrac{3}{2}$ (c) $\dfrac{4}{5}$ (d) $\dfrac{5}{4}$

17. If the lines $\dfrac{x-1}{2} = \dfrac{2-y}{1} = \dfrac{z}{3}$ and $\dfrac{x+1}{5} = \dfrac{-y-2}{-3} = \dfrac{1-z}{\alpha}$ are perpendicular, then α is equal to

(a) 2   (b) $\dfrac{7}{3}$ (c) $\dfrac{1}{3}$ (d) $\dfrac{1}{7}$

18. If $|\vec{a} \times \vec{b}|^2 + (\vec{a} \cdot \vec{b})^2 = 144$ and $|\vec{a}| = 4$, then the value of $|\vec{b}|$ is

(a) 2   (b) 1   (c) 3   (d) 5

Assertion-Reason Based Questions

In the following questions, a statement of Assertion (A) is followed by a statement of Reason (R). Choose the correct answer out of the following choices.

(a) Both A and R are true and R is the correct explanation of A.
(b) Both A and R are true but R is not the correct explanation of A.
(c) A is true but R is false.
(d) A is false but R is true.

19. Assertion (A) Let A and B be sets. Then, the function $f : A \times B \to B \times A$ such that $f(a, b) = (b, a)$ is bijective.

Reason (R) A function f is said to be bijective, if it is both one-one and onto.

20. **Assertion (A)** If $A = \begin{bmatrix} 1 & 1 & -2 \\ 2 & 1 & -3 \\ 5 & 4 & -9 \end{bmatrix}$, then $|A| = 0$.

   Reason (R) $|\text{adj } A| = |A|^{n-1}$, where n is order of matrix.

Section B

(This section comprises of very short answer type questions (VSA) of 2 marks each)

21. If $xy = 1$, prove that $\dfrac{dy}{dx} + y^2 = 0$.

   Or

   If $y = x^{\sin x}$, find $\dfrac{dy}{dx}$.

22. Evaluate the determinant

   $\Delta = \begin{vmatrix} \log_3 512 & \log_4 3 \\ \log_3 8 & \log_4 9 \end{vmatrix}$.

23. Evaluate $\displaystyle\int \dfrac{1}{x(x^n + 1)} \, dx$.

Or

Solve $(x - 1)\dfrac{dy}{dx} = 2 \, xy$.

24. If $\vec{a} \times \vec{b} = \vec{c} \times \vec{d}$ and $\vec{a} \times \vec{c} = \vec{b} \times \vec{d}$, show that $\vec{a} - \vec{d}$ is parallel to $\vec{b} - \vec{c}$, where $\vec{a} \neq \vec{d}$ and $\vec{b} \neq \vec{c}$.

25. Two vectors $\vec{a}$ and $\vec{b}$, prove that the vector $|\vec{a}|\vec{b} + |\vec{b}|\vec{a}$ is orthogonal to the vector $|\vec{a}|\vec{b} - |\vec{b}|\vec{a}$.

Section C

(This section comprises of short answer type questions (SA) of 3 marks each)

26. If $(x - y)e^{\frac{x}{x-y}} = 0$, prove that $y\dfrac{dy}{dx} + x = 2y$.

27. Show that the relation R in the S at $A = \{x : x \in W, 0 \leq x \leq 12\}$ given by $R = \{(a, b) : |a - b| \text{ is multiple of } 4\}$ is an equivalence relation. Also, find the set of all elements related to 2.

   Or

   Show that the function $f : R \rightarrow \{x \in R : -1 < x < 1\}$ defined by $f(x) = \dfrac{x}{1 + |x|}$, $x \in R$ is one-one and onto function.

28. If $f(x) = \begin{cases} \dfrac{1 - \cos 4x}{x^2} & , \ x < 0 \\ a & , \ x = 0 \\ \dfrac{\sqrt{x}}{\sqrt{16 + \sqrt{x}} - 4} & , \ x > 0 \end{cases}$

   and f is continuous at $x = 0$, then find the value of a.

Or Show that the function $f(x) = |x + 1| + |x - 1|$, $\forall x \in R$, is not differentiable at the points $x = -1$ and $x = 1$.

29. If $y(t)$ is a solution of $(1 + t)\dfrac{dy}{dt} - ty = 1$ and $y(0) = -1$, then show that $y(1) = -\dfrac{1}{2}$.

Or It is given that the rate at which some bacteria multiply is proportional to the instantaneous number present. If the original number of bacteria doubles in two hours, in how many hours will it be five times?

30. A ladder 5 m long is leaning against a wall. Bottom of ladder is pulled along the ground away from wall at the rate of 2 m/s. How fast is the height on the wall decreasing, when the foot of ladder is 4 m away from the wall?

31. Evaluate $\displaystyle\int_0^{\pi} \log(1 + \cos x) \, dx$

Section D

(This section comprises of long answer type questions (LA) of 5 marks each)

32. Show that the lines

$\vec{r} = 3\hat{i} + 2\hat{j} - 4\hat{k} + \lambda(\hat{i} + 2\hat{j} + 2\hat{k})$ and

$\vec{r} = 5\hat{i} - 2\hat{j} + \mu(3\hat{i} + 2\hat{j} + 6\hat{k})$ are

intersecting. Hence, find their point of intersection.

33. Two farmers Hariom and Siyaram cultivates only three varieties of rice namely Basmati, Permal and Naura.

The sale (in ₹) of these varieties of rice by both the farmers in the month of September and October are given by the following matrices A and B.

September Sales (in ₹)

$$A = \begin{array}{c} \\ \end{array} \begin{array}{ccc} \text{Basmati} & \text{Permal} & \text{Naura} \\ \begin{bmatrix} 10000 & 20000 & 30000 \\ 50000 & 30000 & 10000 \end{bmatrix} & & \begin{array}{l} \text{Hariom} \\ \text{Siyaram} \end{array} \end{array}$$

October Sales (in ₹)

$$B = \begin{array}{c} \\ \end{array} \begin{array}{ccc} \text{Basmati} & \text{Permal} & \text{Naura} \\ \begin{bmatrix} 5000 & 10000 & 6000 \\ 20000 & 10000 & 10000 \end{bmatrix} & & \begin{array}{l} \text{Hariom} \\ \text{Siyaram} \end{array} \end{array}$$

(i) Find the combined sales in September and October for each farmer in each variety.

(ii) Find the decrease in sales from September to October.

(iii) If both farmers receive 2% profit on gross sales, then compute the profit for each farmer and for each variety sold in October.

Or Find the adjoint of the matrix

$$A = \begin{bmatrix} -1 & -2 & -2 \\ 2 & 1 & -2 \\ 2 & -2 & 1 \end{bmatrix} \text{ and}$$

hence show that $A(\text{adj } A) = |A| I_3$.

34. Solve the given LPP minimise $Z = 4x + 3y$

Subject to the constraints

$200x + 100y \geq 4000$, $x + 2y \geq 50$

$40x + 40y \geq 1400$, $x, y \geq 0$

Or Solve the given LPP maximize

$(Z) = 22x + 18y$

Subject to constraints, $x + y \leq 20$

$360x + 240y \leq 5760$

$x \geq 0$, $y \geq 0$

35. If $y = (x)^x + (\sin x)^x$, then find $\dfrac{dy}{dx}$.

Section E

(This section comprises of 3 case-study/ passage-based questions of 4 marks each with two sub-parts. First two case study questions have three sub-parts (i), (ii), (iii) of marks 1, 1, 2 respectively. The third case study question has two sub-parts of 2 marks each.)

36. Given three identical boxes I, II and III, each containing two coins. In box I both coins are gold coins, in box II both are silver coins and in box III there is one gold and one silver coin. A person chooses a box at random and takes out a coin.

On the basis of above information, answer the following questions.

(i) Find the probability of choosing one box and the probability of getting gold coin from III box.

(ii) Find the probability of choosing III box and getting gold coin.

(iii) Find total probability of drawing gold coin.

Or If drawn coin is of gold, then find the probability that other coin in box is also of gold.

37. A building has front gate of the shape as shown below.

It is in the shape of trapezium whose three sides other than base is 10 m. Height of the gate is h m.

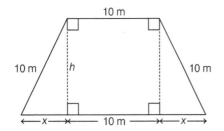

On the basis of above information, answer the following questions.

(i) Find the relation between x and h.

(ii) Express the area of gate A in terms of x.

(iii) Find the value of x when the area A is maximum.

Or If at $x = 5$ the area A is maximum, then find the value of h and the maximum value of A.

38. The random variable X has a probability distribution $P(X)$ of the following form, where k is some number:

$$P(X = x) = \begin{cases} k, & \text{if } x = 0 \\ 2k, & \text{if } x = 1 \\ 3k, & \text{if } x = 2 \\ 0, & \text{otherwise} \end{cases}$$

On the basis of above information, answer the following questions:

(i) Find the value of k, $P(X = 2)$ and $P(X > 2)$.

(ii) Find the value of $P(X < 2)$ and $P(0 < x < 2)$.

Answers

1. (b)	**2.** (b)	**3.** (d)	**4.** (a)	**5.** (b)
6. (c)	**7.** (b)	**8.** (b)	**9.** (b)	**10.** (a)
11. (b)	**12.** (a)	**13.** (b)	**14.** (b)	**15.** (b)
16. (b)	**17.** (b)	**18.** (c)	**19.** (a)	**20.** (b)

21. Or $x^{\sin x}\left[\cos x \log x + \dfrac{\sin x}{x}\right]$

22. $\dfrac{15}{2}$

23. $\dfrac{1}{n}\log\left|\dfrac{x^n}{x^n + 1}\right| + C$ Or $y = (x - 1)^2 Ae^{2x}$

27. $\{2, 6, 10\}$ **28.** $a = 8$

29. Or $\dfrac{\log 25}{\log 2}$ **30.** $\dfrac{8}{3}$ m/s

31. $-\pi \log_e 2$

32. $(-1, -6, -12)$

33. (i) Basmati Permal Naura
$$\begin{bmatrix} 15000 & 30000 & 36000 \\ 70000 & 40000 & 20000 \end{bmatrix}\begin{matrix} \text{Hariom} \\ \text{Siyaram} \end{matrix}$$

(ii) Basmati Permal Naura
$$\begin{bmatrix} 5000 & 10000 & 24000 \\ 30000 & 20000 & 0 \end{bmatrix}\begin{matrix} \text{Hariom} \\ \text{Siyaram} \end{matrix}$$

(iii) Basmati Permal Naura
$$\begin{bmatrix} 100 & 200 & 120 \\ 400 & 200 & 200 \end{bmatrix}\begin{matrix} \text{Hariom} \\ \text{Siyaram} \end{matrix}$$

Or adj $A = \begin{bmatrix} -3 & 6 & 6 \\ -6 & 3 & -6 \\ -6 & -6 & 3 \end{bmatrix}$

34. $Z_{\min} = 110$ at $(5, 30)$ Or $Z_{\max} = 392$ at $(8, 12)$

35. $\dfrac{dy}{dx} = x^x(1 + \log x) + (\sin x)^x(x\cot x + \log \sin x)$

36. (i) $\dfrac{1}{3}$ and $\dfrac{1}{2}$ (ii) $\dfrac{1}{6}$ (iii) $\dfrac{1}{2}$ Or $\dfrac{2}{3}$

37. (i) $x^2 + h^2 = 100$ (ii) $A = (10 + x)\sqrt{100 - x^2}$

(iii) $x = 5$ Or $h = 5\sqrt{3}$ m and $A = 75\sqrt{3}$ m^2

38. (i) $k = \dfrac{1}{6}$, $P(X = 2) = \dfrac{1}{2}$ and $P(X > 2) = 0$

(ii) $P(X < 2) = \dfrac{1}{2}$ adn $P(0 < X < 2) = \dfrac{1}{3}$

SAMPLE QUESTION PAPER 14

MATHEMATICS

Time : 3 hrs   Max. Marks : 80

General Instructions

1. This question paper contains - five sections A, B, C, D and E. Each section is compulsory. However, there are internal choices in some questions.
2. Section A has 18 MCQ's and 02 Assertion-Reason based questions of 1 mark each.
3. Section B has 5 Very Short Answer (VSA) type questions of 2 marks each.
4. Section C has 6 Short Answer (SA) type questions of 3 marks each.
5. Section D has 4 Long Answer (LA) type questions of 5 marks each.
6. Section E has 3 source based/case based/passage based/integrated units of assessment (4 marks each) with sub parts.

Section A

(Multiple Choice Questions) Each question carries 1 mark

1. If the vectors $\vec{a} = 2\hat{i} - 3\hat{j} + \hat{k}$ and $\vec{b} = \hat{j} + \lambda\hat{k}$ are perpendicular, then λ is
   (a) 4   (b) 3   (c) 2   (d) 1

2. $\begin{bmatrix} 2x+y & 4x \\ 5x-7 & 4x \end{bmatrix} = \begin{bmatrix} 7 & 7y-13 \\ y & x+6 \end{bmatrix}$, then the value of $x+y$ is
   (a) 1   (b) 2   (c) 4   (d) 5

3. If the relation R defined on the set $A = \{1, 2, 3, 4, 5, 6\}$ is $R = \{(a, b): b = a+1\}$, then R is
   (a) reflexive   (b) reflexive and symmetric
   (c) not reflexive   (d) reflexive but not transitive

4. $\cot\left(\dfrac{\pi}{3} - 2\cot^{-1}\left(\dfrac{1}{\sqrt{3}}\right)\right)$ is equal to

(a) $\dfrac{1}{\sqrt{3}}$ (b) $\dfrac{1}{\sqrt{2}}$ (c) 1   (d) $\dfrac{-1}{\sqrt{3}}$

5. For matrix $A = \begin{bmatrix} 1 & -2 \\ 3 & 5 \end{bmatrix}$, $(A')A$ is equal to

(a) $\begin{bmatrix} 10 & 13 \\ 13 & 29 \end{bmatrix}$ (b) $\begin{bmatrix} 10 & 13 \\ 29 & 13 \end{bmatrix}$

(c) $\begin{bmatrix} 13 & 29 \\ 10 & 13 \end{bmatrix}$ (d) $\begin{bmatrix} 1 & 10 \\ 1 & 10 \end{bmatrix}$

6. If $y = (1 + x^{1/6})(1 + x^{1/3})(1 - x^{1/6})$, then $\dfrac{dy}{dx}$ at $x = 1$ is equal to

(a) $\dfrac{2}{3}$ (b) $-\dfrac{2}{3}$

(c) 3   (d) $\dfrac{-4}{3}$

7. The additive inverse of the matrix

$$A = \begin{bmatrix} 2 & -5 & 0 \\ 4 & 3 & -1 \end{bmatrix} \text{ is}$$

(a) $\begin{bmatrix} 2 & -5 & 0 \\ 4 & 3 & -1 \end{bmatrix}$ (b) $\begin{bmatrix} -2 & 5 & 0 \\ -4 & -3 & 1 \end{bmatrix}$

(c) $\begin{bmatrix} -5 & -2 & 0 \\ 1 & 2 & 4 \end{bmatrix}$ (d) $\begin{bmatrix} -4 & -3 & 1 \\ -2 & 5 & 0 \end{bmatrix}$

8. If $\tan^{-1}(x^2 + y^2) = a$, then $\dfrac{dy}{dx}$ is equal to

(a) $\dfrac{x}{y}$ (b) $-\dfrac{x}{y}$ (c) $\dfrac{y}{x}$ (d) $-\dfrac{y}{x}$

9. If $f(x) = |\cos x|$, then $f'\left(\dfrac{\pi}{4}\right)$ is equal to

(a) $\dfrac{1}{\sqrt{2}}$ (b) $\dfrac{-1}{\sqrt{2}}$ (c) 1   (d) -1

10. The function $f(x) = (x^3 - 6x^2 + 12x - 18)$ is

(a) strictly increasing function
(b) increasing function
(c) decreasing function
(d) strictly decreasing function

11. $\int e^{ax}\{af(x) + f'(x)\}\, dx$ is equal to

(a) $e^{ax}f(x) + C$ (b) $ae^{ax}(x) + C$
(c) $e^{ax}f'(x) + C$ (d) $e^x f(ax) + C$

12. $\int_0^{\pi/2} \log \tan x \, dx$ is equal to

(a) 1   (b) -1
(c) 0   (d) 2

13. If $\vec{a} = \hat{i} + \hat{j} + 2\hat{k}$ and $\vec{b} = 3\hat{i} + 2\hat{j} - \hat{k}$, then the value of $(\vec{a} + 3\vec{b})\cdot(2\vec{a} - \vec{b})$ is

(a) 15   (b) 5
(c) -15 (d) 10

14. $\int \sin^2 \dfrac{x}{2}\, dx$ is equal to

(a) $\dfrac{x - \sin x}{2} + C$ (b) $\dfrac{x + \sin x}{2} + C$

(c) $\dfrac{\sin x - x}{2} + C$ (d) $\dfrac{x}{2} + \sin x + C$

15. Solve $(2y - 1)dx - (2x + 3)dy = 0$

(a) $(2x + 3)(2y - 1) = C$ (b) $\dfrac{2y - 1}{2x + 3} = C$

(c) $\dfrac{y - 1}{2x + 3} = C$ (d) $\dfrac{2y - 1}{x + 3} = C$

16. The degree of the differential equation

$$\left(\dfrac{d^2 y}{dx^2}\right)^2 + \left(\dfrac{dy}{dx}\right)^2 = x\sin\left(\dfrac{dy}{dx}\right) \text{ is}$$

(a) 1   (b) 2
(c) not defined   (d) 3

17. The projection of the vector $7\hat{i} + \hat{j} - 4\hat{k}$ on $2\hat{i} + 6\hat{j} + 3\hat{k}$ is

(a) $\dfrac{7}{8}$ (b) $\dfrac{8}{7}$ (c) $\dfrac{1}{7}$ (d) $\dfrac{1}{8}$

18. If A is a matrix of order 3×3 such that $|A| = 5$, then $|A(\text{adj } A)|$ is equal to

(a) 25   (b) 125   (c) 5   (d) $\dfrac{1}{125}$

Assertion-Reason Based Questions

In the following questions, a statement of Assertion (A) is followed by a statement of Reason (R). Choose the correct answer out of the following choices.

(a) Both A and R are true and R is the correct explanation of A.
(b) Both A and R are true but R is not the correct explanation of A.
(c) A is true but R is false.
(d) A is false but R is true.

19. If R is the relation in the set $A = \{1, 2, 3, 4, 5\}$ given by $R = \{(a, b) : |a - b| \text{ is even}\}$,

Assertion (A) R is an equivalence relation.

Reason (R) All elements of $\{1, 3, 5\}$ are related to all elements of $\{2, 4\}$.

20. **Assertion (A)** If $A = \begin{bmatrix} 2 & 3 & -1 \\ 1 & 4 & 2 \end{bmatrix}$ and $B = \begin{bmatrix} 2 & 3 \\ 4 & 5 \\ 2 & 1 \end{bmatrix}$, then AB and BA both are defined.

Reason (R) For the two matrices A and B, the product AB is defined, if number of columns in A is equal to the number of rows in B.

Section B

(This section comprises of very short answer type questions (VSA) of 2 marks each)

21. If $\vec{a}$ and $\vec{b}$ are unit vectors, then find the angle between $\vec{a}$ and $\vec{b}$, given that $(\sqrt{3}\,\vec{a} - \vec{b})$ is a unit vector.

    Or

    The x-coordinate of a point on the line joining the points $P(2, 2, 1)$ and $Q(5, 1, -2)$ is 4. Find its z-coordinate.

22. Find the values of λ and μ for which $(2\hat{i} + 6\hat{j} + 27\hat{k}) \times (\hat{i} + \lambda\hat{j} + \mu\hat{k}) = 0$.

23. If $y = x^{1/x}$, find $\dfrac{dy}{dx}$.

    Or

    If $x = a(\theta + \sin\theta)$, $y = a(1 - \cos\theta)$, find $\dfrac{dy}{dx}$.

24. Find the domain of the function
    $f(x) = \cos^{-1} x + \sin^{-1} 2x$.

25. Evaluate $\displaystyle\int \dfrac{x^2 - 1}{x^2 + 4}\, dx$.

Section C

(This section comprises of short answer type questions (SA) of 3 marks each)

26. Find the area of the region bounded by the curves $y^2 = 9x$ and $y = 3x$.

27. If $A = \{1, 2, 3, \ldots, 9\}$ and R is the relation in $A \times A$ defined by $(a, b) R(c, d)$, if $a + d = b + c$ for (a, b), (c, d) in $A \times A$. Prove that R is an equivalence relation. Also, obtain the equivalence class $[(2, 5)]$.

    Or

    If $f : X \to Y$ is a function. Define a relation R on X given by $R = \{(a, b) : f(a) = f(b)\}$. Show that R is an equivalence relation on X.

28. Evaluate $\displaystyle\int \dfrac{1 + x^2}{1 + x^4}\, dx$.

    Or

    Evaluate $\displaystyle\int x \cdot (\log x)^2\, dx$.

29. Find the particular solution of the differential equation

    $e^x \tan y\, dx + (2 - e^x)\sec^2 y\, dy = 0$,
    given that $y = \dfrac{\pi}{4}$ when $x = 0$.

    Or

    Find the particular solution of the differential equation

    $(3xy + y^2)\, dx + (x^2 + xy)\, dy = 0$,

    for $x = 1$, $y = 1$.

30. Let $\vec{a}, \vec{b}$ and $\vec{c}$ be three vectors such that $|\vec{a}| = 1, |\vec{b}| = 2$ and $|\vec{c}| = 3$. If the projection of $\vec{b}$ along $\vec{a}$ is equal to the projection of $\vec{c}$ along $\vec{a}$ and $\vec{b}, \vec{c}$ are perpendicular to each other, find $|3\vec{a} - 2\vec{b} + 2\vec{c}|$.

31. Find the area of the region bounded by the line $y = 3x + 2$, the X-axis and the ordinates $x = -1$ and $x = 1$.

Section D

(This section comprises of long answer type questions (LA) of 5 marks each)

32. Evaluate $\int \dfrac{x+1}{x(1+xe^x)^2} dx.$

33. Solve the following LPP maximise
$Z = 12x + 16y$ subject to constraints,
$x + y \le 1200,\ y \le \dfrac{x}{2},\ x \le 3y + 600\ x, y \ge 0$

Or

Solve the LPP maximise $(Z) = 40x + 50y$
Subject to constraints,
$$3x + y \le 9$$
$$x + 2y \le 8$$
$$x, y \ge 0$$

34. Solve the following system of equations by matrix method, where $x \ne 0,\ y \ne 0$ and $z \ne 0.$

$\dfrac{2}{x} - \dfrac{3}{y} + \dfrac{3}{z} = 10,\ \dfrac{1}{x} + \dfrac{1}{y} + \dfrac{1}{z} = 10$

and $\quad \dfrac{3}{x} - \dfrac{1}{y} + \dfrac{2}{z} = 13.$

Or

If $A = \begin{bmatrix} 1 & -1 \\ 2 & -1 \end{bmatrix},\ B = \begin{bmatrix} a & 1 \\ b & -1 \end{bmatrix}$
and $(A + B)^2 = A^2 + B^2$, then find the values of a and b.

35. For any two vectors $\vec{a}$ and $\vec{b}$, show that
$$(1 + |\vec{a}|^2)(1 + |\vec{b}|^2) = \{(1 - \vec{a} \cdot \vec{b})\}^2$$
$$+ |\vec{a} + \vec{b} + (\vec{a} \times \vec{b})|^2$$

Section E

(This section comprises of 3 case-study/ passage-based questions of 4 marks each with two sub-parts. First two case study questions have three sub-parts (i), (ii), (iii) of marks 1, 1, 2 respectively. The third case study question has two sub-parts of 2 marks each)

36. A random variable X has the following probability distribution:

X	0	1	2	3	4	5	6	7	8
P(X)	a	3a	5a	7a	9a	11a	13a	15a	17a

On the basis of above information, answer the following questions.

(i) Find the value of a.

(ii) Find $P(X = 4)$.

(iii) Find $P(X > 5)$ and $P(0 \le X \le 2)$.

Or

Find $(1 \le X \le 4)$ and $P(3 < X \le 6)$.

37. Consider the given equation $\dfrac{dy}{dx} + Py = Q$

The above equation is known as linear differential equation. Here, $IF = e^{\int Pdx}$ and solution is given by $y \cdot IF = \int Q \cdot IF\ dx + C$

Now consider the given equation
$$(1 + \sin x)\dfrac{dy}{dx} + y \cos x + x = 0$$

On the basis of above information, answer the following questions.

(i) Find the value of P and Q.

(ii) Find IF.

(iii) Find the general solution of the given equation.

Or

If $y(1 + \sin x) = -\dfrac{x^2}{2} + C$ and $y(0) = 1$, then find y and $y\left(\dfrac{\pi}{2}\right).$

38. An electronic assembly consists of two sub-systems say A and B as shown below.

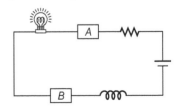

From previous testing procedures, the following probabilities are assumed to be known $P(A \text{ fails}) = 0.2$, $P(B \text{ fails alone}) = 0.15$, $P(A \text{ and } B \text{ fail}) = 0.15$.

On the basis of above information, answer the following questions.

(i) Find the probability $P(B \text{ fails})$ and the probability $P(A \text{ fails alone})$.

(ii) Find the probability $P(\text{whole system fail})$ and the probability $P(A \text{ fails}/B \text{ has failed})$.

Answers

1. (b) **2.** (d) **3.** (c) **4.** (d) **5.** (a)

6. (b) **7.** (b) **8.** (b) **9.** (b) **10.** (b)

11. (a) **12.** (c) **13.** (c) **14.** (a) **15.** (b)

16. (c) **17.** (b) **18.** (b) **19.** (c) **20.** (a)

21. $\dfrac{\pi}{6}$ *Or* -1

22. $\lambda = 3$ and $\mu = \dfrac{27}{2}$

23. $x^{1/x}\left(\dfrac{1-\log x}{x^2}\right)$ *Or* $\tan\dfrac{\theta}{2}$

24. $\left[-\dfrac{1}{2}, \dfrac{1}{2}\right]$

25. $x - \dfrac{5}{2}\tan^{-1}\left(\dfrac{x}{2}\right) + C$

26. $\dfrac{1}{2}$ sq untis

27. $\{(1,4), (2,5), (3,6), (4,7), (5,8), (6,9)\}$

28. $\dfrac{1}{\sqrt{2}}\tan^{-1}\left(\dfrac{x^2-1}{\sqrt{2}x}\right) + C$ *Or* $\dfrac{x^2}{2}(\log x)^2 - \dfrac{x^2}{2}\log x + \dfrac{x^2}{4} + C$

29. $\tan y = 2 - e^x$ *Or* $|y^2 + 2xy| = \dfrac{3}{x^2}$

30. $\sqrt{61}$

31. $\dfrac{13}{3}$ sq units

32. $\log(xe^x) - \log(1 + xe^x) + \dfrac{1}{1 + xe^x} + C$

33. Maximum $Z = 16000$ at $C(800, 400)$

Or Maximum $Z = 230$ at $E(2, 3)$

34. $x = \dfrac{1}{2}$, $y = \dfrac{1}{3}$ and $z = \dfrac{1}{5}$ *Or* $a = 1$ and $b = 4$

36. (i) $\dfrac{1}{81}$ (ii) $\dfrac{1}{9}$ (iii) $\dfrac{5}{9}, \dfrac{1}{9}$ *Or* $\dfrac{8}{27}, \dfrac{11}{27}$

37. (i) $P = \dfrac{\cos x}{1 + \sin x}$ and $Q = \dfrac{-x}{1 + \sin x}$

(ii) $1 + \sin x$

(iii) $y(1 + \sin x) = -\dfrac{x^2}{2} + C$ *Or* $\dfrac{8 - \pi^2}{16}$

38. (i) 0.30 and 0.05 (ii) 0.35 and 0.5

Scan this QR code from your mobile phone to get the explanations of this paper.

SAMPLE QUESTION PAPER 15

MATHEMATICS

Time : 3 hrs   Max. Marks : 80

General Instructions

1. This question paper contains - five sections A, B, C, D and E. Each section is compulsory. However, there are internal choices in some questions.
2. Section A has 18 MCQ's and 02 Assertion-Reason based questions of 1 mark each.
3. Section B has 5 Very Short Answer (VSA) type questions of 2 marks each.
4. Section C has 6 Short Answer (SA) type questions of 3 marks each.
5. Section D has 4 Long Answer (LA) type questions of 5 marks each.
6. Section E has 3 source based/case based/passage based/integrated units of assessment (4 marks each) with sub parts.

Section A

(Multiple Choice Questions) Each question carries 1 mark

1. If the angle between the vectors $5\hat{i} + 3\hat{j} + 4\hat{k}$ and $6\hat{i} - 8\hat{j} - \hat{k}$ is $\cos^{-1}\left(\dfrac{\sqrt{2}}{a\sqrt{b}}\right)$, then $a + b$ is equal to
   (a) 105   (b) 106   (c) 100   (d) 104

2. Evaluate $\displaystyle\int_{-1}^{2} \dfrac{|x|}{x}\, dx$
   (a) 2   (b) 3   (c) 1   (d) 4

3. If $x = \cos^{-1}\left(-\dfrac{1}{2}\right)$, then $x + \dfrac{\pi}{3}$ is equal to
   (a) $\dfrac{2\pi}{3}$ (b) π (c) 2π (d) 3π

4. If $A = \begin{bmatrix} x & 1 \\ -1 & -x \end{bmatrix}$ satisfies the equation $A^2 = O$, then the value of x is

(a) 1   (b) –1   (c) ±1   (d) $\pm\sqrt{2}$

5. If domain of the function $f(x) = \sin^{-1}\sqrt{x-1}$ is $[a, b]$, then $b - a$ is equal to

(a) 1   (b) 2   (c) 3   (d) 4

6. If $x = t^2$, $y = t^3$, then $\dfrac{d^2 y}{dx^2}$ is equal to

(a) $\dfrac{3}{4}t$ (b) $\dfrac{3}{2}t$ (c) $3t$ (d) $\dfrac{3t}{2}$

7. The function $f(x) = \begin{cases} \dfrac{\sin 3x}{x}, & x \neq 0 \\ \dfrac{k}{2}, & x = 0 \end{cases}$ is continuous at $x = 0$, then the value of k is

(a) 2   (b) 4   (c) 6   (d) 8

8. If $A = \begin{bmatrix} 4 & x+2 \\ 2x-3 & x+1 \end{bmatrix}$ is a symmetric matrix, then the value of x is

(a) 1   (b) 2   (c) 5   (d) 4

9. The value of a so that the sum of the squares of the roots of the equation $x^2 - (a-2)x - a + 1 = 0$ assure the least value is

(a) 1   (b) 2   (c) 3   (d) 4

10. Evaluate $\displaystyle\int \dfrac{e^{\tan^{-1} x}}{1+x^2}\, dx$

(a) $e^{-\tan^{-1} x} + C$ (b) $e^{\tan^{-1} x} + C$

(c) $e^{\cot^{-1} x} + C$ (d) $-e^{\tan^{-1} x} + C$

11. $\displaystyle\int_0^3 \dfrac{1}{x^2 + 9}\, dx$ is equal to

(a) $\dfrac{\pi}{6}$ (b) $\dfrac{\pi}{3}$ (c) $\dfrac{\pi}{12}$ (d) $\dfrac{\pi}{4}$

12. The angle between two vectors $\vec{a}$ and $\vec{b}$ with magnitudes $\sqrt{3}$ and 4, respectively such that $\vec{a} \cdot \vec{b} = 2\sqrt{3}$ is

(a) $\dfrac{\pi}{2}$ (b) $\dfrac{\pi}{4}$ (c) $\dfrac{\pi}{6}$ (d) $\dfrac{\pi}{3}$

13. If a line makes angles α, β and γ with the coordinate axes, then the value of $\sin^2 \alpha + \sin^2 \beta + \sin^2 \gamma$ is

(a) 1   (b) 2   (c) 3   (d) –1

14. The equation of line passing through the points $(-1, 2, 1)$ and $(3, 1, 4)$ is given by

(a) $\dfrac{x-1}{4} = \dfrac{y-2}{-1} = \dfrac{z-1}{3}$ (b) $\dfrac{x+1}{4} = \dfrac{y-2}{1} = \dfrac{z-1}{3}$

(c) $\dfrac{x+1}{4} = \dfrac{y-2}{-1} = \dfrac{z-1}{3}$ (d) $\dfrac{x+1}{3} = \dfrac{y+1}{4} = \dfrac{z-1}{2}$

15. The projection of the vector $\hat{i} - \hat{j}$ on the vector $\hat{i} + \hat{j}$ is

(a) 1   (b) 0   (c) –1   (d) 2

16. Given, $|\vec{a}| = 10$, $|\vec{b}| = 2$ and $\vec{a} \cdot \vec{b} = 12$, find $|\vec{a} \times \vec{b}|$.

(a) 256   (b) 16   (c) 225   (d) 15

17. The area of the parallelogram having adjacent sides $\vec{a}$ and $\vec{b}$ given by $2\hat{i} + \hat{j} + \hat{k}$ and $3\hat{i} + \hat{j} + 4\hat{k}$, respectively is

(a) 35 sq units   (b) $\sqrt{35}$ sq units

(c) 34 sq units   (d) $\sqrt{34}$ sq units

18. $\displaystyle\int_0^2 e^{[x]}\, dx$ is equal to

(a) e (b) $e+1$ (c) $e-1$ (d) $e-2$

Assertion-Reason Based Questions

In the following questions, a statement of Assertion (A) is followed by a statement of Reason (R). Choose the correct answer out of the following choices.

(a) Both A and R are true and R is the correct explanation of A.

(b) Both A and R are true but R is not the correct explanation of A.

(c) A is true but R is false.

(d) A is false but R is true.

19. Assertion (A) The modulus function $f : R \to R$ given by $f(x) = |x|$ is neither one-one nor onto.

Reason (R) The signum function $f : R \to R$ given by $f(x) = \begin{cases} 1, & x > 0 \\ 0, & x = 0 \\ -1, & x < 0 \end{cases}$ is bijective.

20. Let A and B be two symmetric matrices of order 3.

Assertion (A) $A(BA)$ and $(AB)A$ are symmetric matrices.

Reason (R) AB is symmetric matrix, if matrix multiplication of A with B is commutative.

Section B

(This section comprises of very short answer type questions (VSA) of 2 marks each)

21. Evaluate $\int_{0}^{\pi} \dfrac{e^{\cos x}}{e^{\cos x} + e^{-\cos x}} \, dx$

Or Evaluate $\int_{1}^{2} [3x] \, dx$.

22. Find a matrix A such that
$2A - 3B + 5C = 0$, where $B = \begin{bmatrix} -2 & 2 & 0 \\ 3 & 1 & 4 \end{bmatrix}$
and $C = \begin{bmatrix} 2 & 0 & -2 \\ 7 & 1 & 6 \end{bmatrix}$.

23. If $\vec{a} \times \vec{b} = \vec{a} \times \vec{c}, \vec{a} \neq 0$ and $\vec{b} \neq \vec{c}$, show that $\vec{b} = \vec{c} + t \vec{a}$ for some scalar t.

Or

If $\vec{a}, \vec{b}, \vec{c}$ are mutually perpendicular unit vectors, find $|2\vec{a} + \vec{b} + \vec{c}|$.

24. Show that $f(x) = x^{9} + 4x^{7} + 11$ is an increasing function for all $x \in R$.

25. Show that $(\vec{a} \times \vec{b})^{2} = |\vec{a}|^{2} |\vec{b}|^{2} - (\vec{a} \cdot \vec{b})^{2}$
$$= \begin{vmatrix} \vec{a} \cdot \vec{a} & \vec{a} \cdot \vec{b} \\ \vec{a} \cdot \vec{b} & \vec{b} \cdot \vec{b} \end{vmatrix}$$

Section C

(This section comprises of short answer type questions (SA) of 3 marks each)

26. If $e^{y}(x + 1) = 1$, then show that
$$\dfrac{d^{2}y}{dx^{2}} = \left(\dfrac{dy}{dx} \right)^{2}.$$

27. A man is moving away from a tower 41.6 m high at the rate of 2 m/sec. Find the rate at which the angle of elevation of the top of tower is changing, when he is at a distance of 30 m from the foot of the tower. Assume that the eye level of the man is 1.6 m from the ground.

Or

Find the area of region bounded by the curve $y^{2} = 4x$ and the line $x = 4$.

28. Evaluate $\int \dfrac{2x^{2} + 1}{x^{2}(x^{2} + 4)} dx$

Or

Find $\int \dfrac{(2x - 5e)^{2x}}{(2x - 3)^{3}} dx$

29. Evaluate $\int_{0}^{\pi/2} \log(\sin x) \, dx$.

Or Evaluate $\int \dfrac{\sin^{6} x + \cos^{6} x}{\sin^{2} x \cos^{2} x} dx$.

30. Solve the differential equation
$(x^{2} - yx^{2}) dy + (y^{2} + x^{2}y^{2}) dx = 0$, given that $y = 1$, when $x = 1$.

31. Find the vector $\vec{p}$ which is perpendicular to both $\vec{\alpha} = 4\hat{i} + 5\hat{j} - \hat{k}$ and $\vec{\beta} = \hat{i} - 4\hat{j} + 5\hat{k}$ and $\vec{p} \cdot \vec{q} = 21$, where $\vec{q} = 3\hat{i} + \hat{j} - \hat{k}$.

Section D

(This section comprises of long answer type questions (LA) of 5 marks each)

32. Consider $f: R^+ \to (-9, \infty)$ given by

$f(x) = 5x^2 + 6x - 9$. Prove that f is bijective (where, R^+ is the set of all positive real numbers).

33. If $A = \begin{bmatrix} \cos\alpha & -\sin\alpha & 0 \\ \sin\alpha & \cos\alpha & 0 \\ 0 & 0 & 1 \end{bmatrix}$, find adj A and

verify that $A\,(\text{adj}A) = (\text{adj } A)\,A = |A|I_3$.

Or If $A = \begin{vmatrix} 1 & 3 & 4 \\ 2 & 1 & 2 \\ 5 & 1 & 1 \end{vmatrix}$, find A^{-1}.

Hence solve the system of equations

$x + 3y + 4z = 8$

$2x + y + 2z = 5$

and $\quad 5x + y + z = 7$

34. Solve the given LPP:

Minimise $Z = 10x - 70y + 1900$

Subject to constraints $x, y \le 5$, $x + y \le 8$, $x + y \ge 4$ and $x, y \ge 0$.

Or

Solve the given LPP :

Maximize $Z = 4500x + 5000y$

Subject to constraints

$x + y \le 250$,

$5x + 8y \le 1400$,

and $\quad x, y \ge 0$

35. Evaluate

$$\int \frac{\sqrt{x^2 + 1}\,[\log|x^2 + 1| - 2\log|x|]}{x^4} \, dx.$$

Section E

(This section comprises of 3 case-study/passage-based questions of 4 marks each with two sub-parts. First two case study questions have three sub-parts (i), (ii), (iii) of marks 1, 1, 2 respectively. The third case study question has two sub-parts of 2 marks each)

36. The odds against a husband who is 45 yr old, living till he is 70 are 7 : 5 and the odds against his wife who is now 36, living till she is 61 are 5 : 3.

On the basis of above information, answer the following questions.

(i) Find the probabilities of husband living till 70 and wife living till 61.

(ii) Find the probability P(couple will be alive 25 yr hence).

(iii) Find the probability P(exactly one of them will be alive 25 yr hence).

Or

Find the probability P(none of them will be alive 25 yr hence) and probability P(atleast one of them will be alive 25 yr hence).

37. If $f(x)$ is a continuous function defined on $[a, b]$, then $\int_a^b f(x)\,dx = \int_a^b f(a + b - x)\,dx$

On the basis of above information, answer the following questions.

(i) Evaluate $\int_1^2 \frac{\sqrt{x}}{\sqrt{x} + \sqrt{3 - x}}\,dx$.

(ii) Evaluate $\int_{\frac{\pi}{6}}^{\frac{\pi}{3}} \log \tan x\,dx$.

(iii) Evaluate $\int_a^b \frac{x^{1/n}}{x^{1/n} + (a + b - x)^{1/n}}\,dx$.

Or

Evaluate $\int_a^b \frac{f(x)}{f(x) + f(a + b - x)}\,dx$.

38. A fair die is rolled. Consider the events $A = \{1, 3, 5\}$, $B = \{2, 3\}$ and $C = \{2, 3, 4, 5\}$.

On the basis of above information, answer the following questions.

(i) Find the probability $P(A/B)$ and $P(B/A)$.

(ii) Find the probability $P(A/C)$, $P(A \cap B / C)$ and $P(A \cup B / C)$.

Answers

1. (b)   **2.** (c)   **3.** (b)   **4.** (c)   **5.** (a)

6. (c)   **7.** (c)   **8.** (c)   **9.** (a)   **10.** (b)

11. (c)   **12.** (d)   **13.** (b)   **14.** (c)   **15.** (b)

16. (b)   **17.** (b)   **18.** (b)   **19.** (c)   **20.** (b)

21. $\dfrac{\pi}{2}$ Or 4

22. $A = \begin{bmatrix} -8 & 3 & 5 \\ -13 & -1 & -9 \end{bmatrix}$

23. Or $\sqrt{6}$

27. $-\dfrac{4}{125}$ rad/sec Or $\dfrac{64}{3}$ sq units

28. $-\dfrac{1}{4x} + \dfrac{7}{8} \tan^{-1}\left(\dfrac{x}{2}\right) + C$ Or $\dfrac{e^{2x}(2x-3)^{-2}}{2} + C$

29. $-\dfrac{\pi}{2}\log 2$ Or $\tan x - \cot x - 3x + C$

30. $\log|y| + \dfrac{1}{y} = -\dfrac{1}{x} + x + 1$

31. $\vec{p} = 7\hat{i} - 7\hat{j} - 7\hat{k}$

33. $\begin{vmatrix} \cos\alpha & \sin\alpha & 0 \\ -\sin\alpha & \cos\alpha & 0 \\ 0 & 0 & 1 \end{vmatrix}$

Or $A^{-1} = \begin{bmatrix} \dfrac{-1}{11} & \dfrac{1}{11} & \dfrac{2}{11} \\ \dfrac{8}{11} & \dfrac{-19}{11} & \dfrac{6}{11} \\ \dfrac{-3}{11} & \dfrac{14}{11} & \dfrac{-5}{11} \end{bmatrix}$; $x = 1$, $y = 1$ and $z = 1$

34. Minimum value of Z is 1550 at $(0, 5)$

Or Maximum value of Z is 1150000 at $(200, 50)$

35. $-\dfrac{1}{3}\left(1 + \dfrac{1}{x^2}\right)^{3/2} \left\{\log\left|1 + \dfrac{1}{x^2}\right| - \dfrac{2}{3}\right\} + C$

36. (i) $\dfrac{5}{12}$ and $\dfrac{3}{8}$ (ii) $\dfrac{5}{32}$ (iii) $\dfrac{23}{48}$ Or $\dfrac{61}{96}$

37. (i) $\dfrac{1}{2}$ (ii) 0 (iii) $\dfrac{b-a}{2}$ Or $\dfrac{b-a}{2}$

38. (i) $\dfrac{1}{2}$ and $\dfrac{1}{3}$ (ii) $\dfrac{1}{2}, \dfrac{1}{4}$ and $\dfrac{3}{4}$

LATEST CBSE
SAMPLE PAPER
&
ONE DAY
BEFORE EXAM

LATEST CBSE
SAMPLE PAPER

Issued by Central Board of Secondary Education (CBSE)

MATHEMATICS

Time : 3 hrs   Max. Marks : 80

General Instructions

1. This question paper contains - five sections A, B, C, D and E. Each section is compulsory. However, there are internal choices in some questions.
2. Section A has 18 MCQ's and 02 Assertion-Reason based questions of 1 mark each.
3. Section B has 5 Very Short Answer (VSA) type questions of 2 marks each.
4. Section C has 6 Short Answer (SA) type questions of 3 marks each.
5. Section D has 4 Long Answer (LA) type questions of 5 marks each.
6. Section E has 3 source based/case based/passage based/integrated units of assessment (4 marks each) with sub parts.

Section A

(Multiple Choice Questions) Each question carries 1 mark

1. If $A = [a_{ij}]$ is a skew-symmetric matrix of order n, then

   (a) $a_{ij} = \dfrac{1}{a_{ij}} \ \forall \ i, j$

   (b) $a_{ij} \neq 0 \ \forall \ i, j$

   (c) $a_{ij} = 0$, where $i = j$

   (d) $a_{ij} \neq 0$, where $i = j$

2. If A is a square matrix of order 3, $|A'| = -3$, then $|AA'|$ is equal to

   (a) 9

   (b) -9

   (c) 3

   (d) -3

3. The area of a triangle with vertices A, B, C is given by

   (a) $|\overrightarrow{AB} \times \overrightarrow{AC}|$

   (b) $\dfrac{1}{2}|\overrightarrow{AB} \times \overrightarrow{AC}|$

   (c) $\dfrac{1}{4}|\overrightarrow{AC} \times \overrightarrow{AB}|$

   (d) $\dfrac{1}{8}|\overrightarrow{AC} \times \overrightarrow{AB}|$

4. The value of k for which the function

$$f(x) = \begin{cases} \dfrac{1 - \cos 4x}{8x^2}, & \text{if } x \neq 0 \\ k, & \text{if } x = 0 \end{cases}$$ is continuous

at $x = 0$ is
(a) 0　　　(b) – 1　　　(c) 1　　　(d) 2

5. If $f'(x) = x + \dfrac{1}{x}$, then $f(x)$ is

(a) $x^2 + \log|x| + C$

(b) $\dfrac{x^2}{2} + \log|x| + C$

(c) $\dfrac{x}{2} + \log|x| + C$

(d) $\dfrac{x}{2} - \log|x| + C$

6. If m and n respectively, are the order and the degree of the differential equation $\dfrac{d}{dx}\left[\left(\dfrac{dy}{dx}\right)^4\right] = 0$, then $m + n$ is equal to

(a) 1　　　(b) 2　　　(c) 3　　　(d) 4

7. The solution set of the inequality $3x + 5y < 4$ is
(a) an open half-plane not containing the origin.
(b) an open half-plane containing the origin.
(c) the whole XY-plane not containing the line $3x + 5y = 4$.
(d) a closed half plane containing the origin.

8. The scalar projection of the vector $3\hat{i} - \hat{j} - 2\hat{k}$ on the vector $\hat{i} + 2\hat{j} - 3\hat{k}$ is

(a) $\dfrac{7}{\sqrt{14}}$　　(b) $\dfrac{7}{14}$　　(c) $\dfrac{6}{13}$　　(d) $\dfrac{7}{2}$

9. The value of $\displaystyle\int_2^3 \dfrac{x}{x^2 + 1}\, dx$ is

(a) $\log 4$　　　　　　(b) $\log \dfrac{3}{2}$

(c) $\dfrac{1}{2}\log 2$　　　　　(d) $\log \dfrac{9}{4}$

10. If A, B are non-singular square matrices of the same order, then $(AB^{-1})^{-1}$ is equal to
(a) $A^{-1}B$　　　　　(b) $A^{-1}B^{-1}$
(c) BA^{-1}　　　　　(d) AB

11. The corner points of the shaded unbounded feasible region of an LPP are $(0, 4)$, $(0.6, 1.6)$ and $(3, 0)$ as shown in the figure. The minimum value of the objective function $Z = 4x + 6y$ occurs at

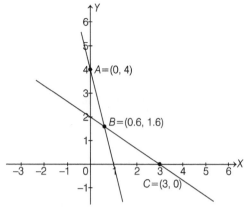

(a) $(0.6, 1.6)$ only
(b) $(3, 0)$ only
(c) $(0.6, 1.6)$ and $(3, 0)$ only
(d) at every point of the line-segment joining the points $(0.6, 1.6)$ and $(3, 0)$

12. If $\begin{vmatrix} 2 & 4 \\ 5 & 1 \end{vmatrix} = \begin{vmatrix} 2x & 4 \\ 6 & x \end{vmatrix}$, then the possible value(s) of x is/are
(a) 3　　　　　　　　　(b) $\sqrt{3}$
(c) $-\sqrt{3}$　　　　　　(d) $\sqrt{3}, -\sqrt{3}$

13. If A is a square matrix of order 3 and $|A| = 5$, then $|\text{adj } A|$ is equal to

(a) 5　　(b) 25　　(c) 125　　(d) $\dfrac{1}{5}$

14. Given two independent events A and B such that $P(A) = 0.3$, $P(B) = 0.6$ and $P(A' \cap B')$ is
(a) 0.9　　(b) 0.18　　(c) 0.28　　(d) 0.1

15. The general solution of the differential equation $y\,dx - x\,dy = 0$ is
(a) $xy = C$　　　　　(b) $x = Cy^2$
(c) $y = Cx$　　　　　(d) $y = Cx^2$

16. If $y = \sin^{-1} x$, then $(1 - x^2)y_2$ is equal to
(a) xy_1　　(b) xy　　(c) xy_2　　(d) x^2

17. If two vectors $\vec{a}$ and $\vec{b}$ are such that $|\vec{a}| = 2$, $|\vec{b}| = 3$ and $\vec{a} \cdot \vec{b} = 4$, then $|\vec{a} - 2\vec{b}|$ is equal to
(a) $\sqrt{2}$　　(b) $2\sqrt{6}$　　(c) 24　　(d) $2\sqrt{2}$

18. P is a point on the line joining the points $A(0, 5, -2)$ and $B(3, -1, 2)$. If the x-coordinate of P is 6, then its z-coordinate is
(a) 10　　(b) 6　　(c) – 6　　(d) – 10

Assertion-Reason Based Questions

In the following questions, a statement of Assertion (A) is followed by a statement of Reason (R). Choose the correct answer out of the following choices.

   (a) Both A and R are true and R is the correct explanation of A.

   (b) Both A and R are true but R is not the correct explanation of A.

   (c) A is true but R is false.

   (d) A is false but R is true.

19. Assertion (A) The domain of the function $\sec^{-1} 2x$ is $\left(-\infty, -\dfrac{1}{2}\right] \cup \left[\dfrac{1}{2}, \infty\right)$

Reason (R) $\sec^{-1}(-2) = -\dfrac{\pi}{4}$

20. Assertion (A) The acute angle between the line $\vec{r} = \hat{i} + \hat{j} + 2\hat{k} + \lambda(\hat{i} - \hat{j})$ and the X-axis is $\dfrac{\pi}{4}$

Reason(R) The acute angle θ between the lines

$$\vec{r} = x_1\hat{i} + y_1\hat{j} + z_1\hat{k} + \lambda(a_1\hat{i} + b_1\hat{j} + c_1\hat{k}) \text{ and}$$

$$\vec{r} = x_2\hat{i} + y_2\hat{j} + z_2\hat{k} + \mu(a_2\hat{i} + b_2\hat{j} + c_2\hat{k}) \text{ is}$$

given by

$$\cos\theta = \dfrac{|a_1 a_2 + b_1 b_2 + c_1 c_2|}{\sqrt{a_1^2 + b_1^2 + c_1^2}\,\sqrt{a_2^2 + b_2^2 + c_2^2}}$$

Section B

(This section comprises of very short answer type questions (VSA) of 2 marks each)

21. Find the value of $\sin^{-1}\left[\sin\left(\dfrac{13\pi}{7}\right)\right]$.

Or Prove that the function f is surjective, where $f : N \to N$ such that

$$f(n) = \begin{cases} \dfrac{n+1}{2}, & \text{if } n \text{ is odd} \\[2mm] \dfrac{n}{2}, & \text{if } n \text{ is even} \end{cases}$$

Is the function injective? Justify your answer.

22. A man 1.6 m tall walks at the rate of 0.3 m/sec away from a street light that is 4 m above the ground. At what rate is the tip of his shadow moving? At what rate is his shadow lengthening?

23. If $\vec{a} = \hat{i} - \hat{j} + 7\hat{k}$ and $\vec{b} = 5\hat{i} - \hat{j} + \lambda\hat{k}$, then find the value of λ so that the vectors $\vec{a} + \vec{b}$ and $\vec{a} - \vec{b}$ are orthogonal.

Or

Find the direction ratios and direction cosines of a line parallel to the line whose equations are $6x - 12 = 3y + 9 = 2z - 2$.

24. If $y\sqrt{1 - x^2} + x\sqrt{1 - y^2} = 1$, then prove that

$$\dfrac{dy}{dx} = -\sqrt{\dfrac{1 - y^2}{1 - x^2}}$$

25. Find $|\vec{x}|$, if $(\vec{x} - \vec{a}) \cdot (\vec{x} + \vec{a}) = 12$, where $\vec{a}$ is a unit vector.

Section C

(This section comprises of short answer type questions (SA) of 3 marks each)

26. Find $\displaystyle\int \dfrac{dx}{\sqrt{3 - 2x - x^2}}$.

27. Three friends go for coffee. They decide who will pay the bill, by each tossing a coin and then letting the "odd person" pay.There is no odd person, if all three tosses produce the same result. If there is no odd person in the first round, they make a second round of tosses and they continue to do so until there is an odd person.

What is the probability that exactly three rounds of tosses are made?

Or

Find the mean number of defective items in a sample of two items drawn one-by-one without replacement from an urn containing 6 items, which include 2 defective items.

Assume that the items are identical in shape and size.

28. Evaluate $\int_{\pi/6}^{\pi/3} \dfrac{dx}{1+\sqrt{\tan x}}$.

Or

Evaluate $\int_0^4 |x-1|\, dx$.

29. Solve the differential equation
$y\,dx + (x - y^2)\,dy = 0$.

Or

Solve the differential equation
$x\,dy - y\,dx = \sqrt{x^2 + y^2}\, dx$.

30. Solve the following linear programming problem graphically

Maximize $Z = 400x + 300y$ subject to
$x + y \le 200,\ x \le 40,\ x \ge 20,\ y \ge 0$.

31. Find $\int \dfrac{(x^3 + x + 1)}{(x^2 - 1)}\, dx$.

Section D

(This section comprises of long answer type questions (LA) of 5 marks each)

32. Make a rough sketch of the region
$\{(x, y): 0 \le y \le x^2,\ 0 \le y \le x,\ 0 \le x \le 2\}$ and find the area of the region using integration.

33. Define the relation R in the set $N \times N$ as follows

For $(a, b), (c, d) \in N \times N, (a, b)\,R(c, d)$, if $ad = bc$. Prove that R is an equivalence relation in $N \times N$.

Or

Given a non-empty set X, define the relation R in $P(X)$ as follows

For $A, B \in P(X), (A, B) \in R$ iff $A \subset B$. Prove that R is reflexive, transitive and not symmetric.

34. An insect is crawling along the line
$\vec{r} = 6\hat{i} + 2\hat{j} + 2\hat{k} + \lambda(\hat{i} - 2\hat{j} + 2\hat{k})$ and
another insect is crawling along the line
$\vec{r} = -4\hat{i} - \hat{k} + \mu(3\hat{i} - 2\hat{j} - 2\hat{k})$.

At what points on the lines should they reach so that the distance between them is the shortest? Find the shortest possible distance between them.

Or

The equations of motion of a rocket are $x = 2t,\ y = -4t,\ z = 4t$, where the time t is given in seconds, and the coordinates of a moving point in km. What is the path of the rocket? At what distances will the rocket be from the starting point $O(0, 0, 0)$ and from the following line in 10 sec?

$\vec{r} = 20\hat{i} - 10\hat{j} + 40\hat{k} + \mu(10\hat{i} - 20\hat{j} + 10\hat{k})$

35. If $A = \begin{bmatrix} 2 & -3 & 5 \\ 3 & 2 & -4 \\ 1 & 1 & -2 \end{bmatrix}$, find A^{-1}. Use A^{-1} to

solve the following system of equations
$2x - 3y + 5z = 11,\ 3x + 2y - 4z = -5$,
$x + y - 2z = -3$.

Section E

(This section comprises of 3 case-study/ passage-based questions of 4 marks each with two sub-parts. First two case study questions have three sub-parts (i), (ii), (iii) of marks 1, 1, 2 respectively. The third case study question has two sub-parts of 2 marks each)

36. Read the following passage and answer the questions given below.

The temperature of a person during an intestinal illness is given by

$f(x) = -0.1\,x^2 + mx + 98.6, \ 0 \le x \le 12, \ m$

being a constant, where $f(x)$ is the temperature in °F at x days.

(i) Is the function differentiable in the interval (0, 12)? Justify your answer.

(ii) If 6 is the critical point of the function, then find the value of the constant m.

(iii) Find the intervals in which the function is strictly increasing/strictly decreasing.

Or

Find the points of local maximum/local minimum, if any, in the interval (0, 12) as well as the points of absolute maximum/absolute minimum in the interval [0, 12].

Also, find the corresponding local maximum/local minimum and the absolute maximum/absolute minimum values of the function.

37. Read the following passage and answer the questions given below.

In an elliptical sport field the authority wants to design a rectangular soccer field with the maximum possible area. The sport field is given by the graph of $\dfrac{x^2}{a^2} + \dfrac{y^2}{b^2} = 1.$

(i) If the length and the breadth of the rectangular field be 2x and 2y respectively, then find the area function in terms of x.

(ii) Find the critical point of the function.

(iii) Use first derivative test to find the length 2x and width 2y of the soccer field (in terms of a and b) that maximize its area.

Or Use Second Derivative Test to find the length 2x and width 2y of the soccer field (in terms of a and b) that maximize its area.

38. Read the following passage and answer the questions given below.

There are two antiaircraft guns, named as *A* and *B*. The probabilities that the shell fired from them hits an airplane are 0.3 and 0.2, respectively. Both of them fired one shell at an airplane at the same time.

(i) What is the probability that the shell fired from exactly one of them hit the plane?

(ii) If it is known that the shell fired from exactly one of them hit the plane, then what is the probability that it was fired from *B*?

SOLUTIONS

1. (c) In a skew-symmetric matrix, the (i, j)th element is negative of the (j, i)th element

i.e. $\qquad a_{ij} = -a_{ji}$

For the element of ith row and ith column,

$$a_{ii} = -a_{ii}$$
$$\Rightarrow \qquad 2a_{ii} = 0$$
$$\Rightarrow \qquad a_{ii} = 0$$

Hence, the (i, i)th element $= 0$

2. (a) Given, A is a square matrix of order 3 and $|A'| = -3$

Now, $|AA'| = |A||A'|$ $\qquad [\because |AB| = |A||B|]$

$\qquad\quad = |A'||A'|$ $\qquad\quad [\because |A| = |A'|]$

$\qquad\quad = (-3)(-3)$

$\qquad\quad = 9$

3. (b) $\because$ The area of the parallelogram with adjacent sides $\overrightarrow{AB}$ and $\overrightarrow{AC}$ is given by $|\overrightarrow{AB} \times \overrightarrow{AC}|$.

Hence, the area of the triangle with vertices A, B, C is given by $\dfrac{1}{2}|\overrightarrow{AB} \times \overrightarrow{AC}|$.

4. (c) Given, $f(x) = \begin{cases} \dfrac{1-\cos 4x}{8x^2}, & \text{if } x \neq 0 \\ k, & \text{if } x = 0 \end{cases}$

The function $f(x)$ is continuous at $x = 0$

If $\lim\limits_{x \to 0} f(x) = f(0)$ $\qquad\qquad$ ...(i)

We have, $f(0) = k$ $\qquad\qquad$ ...(ii)

Now, $\lim\limits_{x \to 0} f(x) = \lim\limits_{x \to 0}\left(\dfrac{1-\cos 4x}{8x^2}\right)$

$\qquad\qquad = \lim\limits_{x \to 0}\left(\dfrac{2\sin^2 2x}{8x^2}\right)$

$\qquad\qquad = \lim\limits_{x \to 0}\left(\dfrac{\sin^2 2x}{4x^2}\right)$

$\qquad\qquad = \lim\limits_{x \to 0}\left(\dfrac{\sin 2x}{2x}\right)^2 = 1$ $\qquad$ ...(iii)

Now, from Eqs. (i), (ii) and (iii), we get

$$k = 1$$

5. (b) Given, $f'(x) = x + \dfrac{1}{x}$ $\qquad\qquad\qquad$ ...(i)

On integrating both sides of Eq. (i), we get

$$\int f'(x)\,dx = \int\left(x + \dfrac{1}{x}\right)dx$$
$$\Rightarrow \qquad f(x) = \int x\,dx + \int\dfrac{1}{x}\,dx$$
$$\Rightarrow \qquad f(x) = \dfrac{x^2}{2} + \log|x| + C$$

6. (c) Given, $\dfrac{d}{dx}\left[\left(\dfrac{dy}{dx}\right)\right]^4 = 0$

$$\Rightarrow \quad 4\left(\dfrac{dy}{dx}\right)^3 \dfrac{d}{dx}\left(\dfrac{dy}{dx}\right) = 0$$
$$\Rightarrow \quad 4\left(\dfrac{dy}{dx}\right)^3 \dfrac{d^2y}{dx^2} = 0 \qquad\qquad \text{...(i)}$$

From Eq (i), we get $m = 2$ and $n = 1$

$\therefore\ m + n = 2 + 1 = 3$

7. (b) Given, inequality is $3x + 5y < 4$ $\qquad$ ...(i)

On putting $(0, 0)$ in inequality (i), we get

$$3(0) + 5(0) < 4$$
$$\Rightarrow \qquad\qquad 0 < 4, \text{ which is true}$$

Hence, the given strict inequality represents an open half plane and it contains the origin as $(0, 0)$ satisfies it.

8. (a) Let $\vec{a} = 3\hat{i} - \hat{j} - 2\hat{k}$ and $\vec{b} = \hat{i} + 2\hat{j} - 3\hat{k}$ scalar projection of $\vec{a}$ on $\vec{b}$ is given by $\left(\dfrac{\vec{a}\cdot\vec{b}}{|\vec{b}|}\right)$.

$\therefore$ Required scalar projection is given by

$$\dfrac{(3\hat{i} - \hat{j} - 2\hat{k})\cdot(\hat{i} + 2\hat{j} - 3\hat{k})}{|\hat{i} + 2\hat{j} - 3\hat{k}|}$$
$$= \dfrac{3 - 2 + 6}{\sqrt{(1)^2 + (2)^2 + (-3)^2}} = \dfrac{7}{\sqrt{14}}$$

9. (c) Let $I = \displaystyle\int_2^3 \dfrac{x\,dx}{x^2 + 1}$

Let $x^2 + 1 = t$

$\Rightarrow\ 2x\,dx = dt$

$\Rightarrow\ x\,dx = \dfrac{dt}{2}$

Now, when $x = 2$, then $t = 5$

and when $x = 3$, then $t = 10$

$\therefore \qquad I = \dfrac{1}{2}\displaystyle\int_5^{10} \dfrac{dt}{t}$

$\Rightarrow \qquad I = \dfrac{1}{2}[\log t]_5^{10}$

$\qquad\qquad = \dfrac{1}{2}[\log 10 - \log 5]$

$\Rightarrow \qquad I = \dfrac{1}{2}\log\left(\dfrac{10}{5}\right) = \dfrac{1}{2}\log 2$

10. (c) Given, $|A| \neq 0$ and $|B| \neq 0$

Now, $(AB^{-1})^{-1} = (B^{-1})^{-1}A^{-1}$ $\qquad [\because (AB)^{-1} = B^{-1}A^{-1}]$

$\qquad\qquad\qquad = BA^{-1}$

11. (d)

Corner points	Value of $Z = 4x + 6y$
$A(0, 4)$	24
$B(0.6, 1.6)$	12 (Minimum)
$C(3, 0)$	12 (Minimum)

The minimum value of the objective function occurs at two adjacent corner points $(0.6, 1.6)$ and $(3, 0)$.

Now, on plotting $4x + 6y < 12$, we found there is no point in the half plane $4x + 6y < 12$ in common with the feasible region. So, the minimum value occurs at every point on the line-segment joining the points $(0.6, 1.6)$ and $(3, 0)$.

12. (d) We have, $\begin{vmatrix} 2 & 4 \\ 5 & 1 \end{vmatrix} = \begin{vmatrix} 2x & 4 \\ 6 & x \end{vmatrix}$

$\Rightarrow \quad 2(1) - 5(4) = 2x(x) - 6(4)$

$\Rightarrow \quad 2 - 20 = 2x^2 - 24$

$\Rightarrow \quad 2x^2 = -18 + 24 = 6$

$\Rightarrow \quad x^2 = 3$

$\Rightarrow \quad x = \pm \sqrt{3}$

i.e. $\quad x = \sqrt{3}, -\sqrt{3}$

13. (b) Given, A is a square matrix of order 3 i.e. $n = 3$ and $|A| = 5$.

Now, $|adj\ A| = |A|^{n-1}$ (where, n = order of the matrix)

$\Rightarrow \quad |adj\ A| = |A|^{3-1} = |A|^2 = (5)^2 = 25$

14. (c) Given, $P(A) = 0.3$ and $P(B) = 0.6$

Now, $P(A' \cap B') = P(A') \times P(B')$

[as A and B are independent events i.e. A' and B' are also independent events]

$\qquad = [1 - P(A)] \times [1 - P(B)]$

$\qquad = (1 - 0.3) \times (1 - 0.6)$

$\qquad = 0.7 \times 0.4$

$\qquad = 0.28$

15. (c) We have,

$\qquad\qquad ydx - xdy = 0$

$\Rightarrow \qquad\qquad xdy = ydx$

$\Rightarrow \qquad\qquad \dfrac{dy}{y} = \dfrac{dx}{x}$ ...(i)

On integrating both sides of Eq. (i), we get

$\qquad\qquad \int \dfrac{dy}{y} = \int \dfrac{dx}{x}$

$\Rightarrow \qquad \log|y| = \log|x| + \log C$

$\Rightarrow \qquad \log|y| = \log|x|C$

$\Rightarrow \qquad |y| = |x|C$

$\Rightarrow \qquad y = \pm Cx$

$\Rightarrow \qquad y = Cx$

16. (a) We have, $\quad y = \sin^{-1} x$

$\Rightarrow \qquad\qquad \dfrac{dy}{dx} = \dfrac{1}{\sqrt{1 - x^2}}$

$\Rightarrow \quad (\sqrt{1 - x^2}) \cdot \dfrac{dy}{dx} = 1$

Again, differentiating both sides w.r.t. x, we get

$(\sqrt{1 - x^2}) \dfrac{d}{dx}\left(\dfrac{dy}{dx}\right) + \dfrac{dy}{dx}\left(\dfrac{d}{dx}\sqrt{1 - x^2}\right) = 0$

$\Rightarrow \quad \sqrt{1 - x^2}\dfrac{d^2y}{dx^2} + \dfrac{dy}{dx}\left(\dfrac{-2x}{2\sqrt{1 - x^2}}\right) = 0$

$\Rightarrow \quad \sqrt{1 - x^2}\dfrac{d^2y}{dx^2} - \dfrac{x}{\sqrt{1 - x^2}}\left(\dfrac{dy}{dx}\right) = 0$

$\Rightarrow \quad (1 - x^2)\dfrac{d^2y}{dx^2} - x\left(\dfrac{dy}{dx}\right) = 0$

$\Rightarrow \quad (1 - x^2)\dfrac{d^2y}{dx^2} = x\dfrac{dy}{dx}$

or $\qquad (1 - x^2)y_2 = xy_1$

17. (b) Given, $|\vec{a}| = 2, |\vec{b}| = 3$ and $\vec{a} \cdot \vec{b} = 4$

Now, $|\vec{a} - 2\vec{b}|^2 = (\vec{a} - 2\vec{b}) \cdot (\vec{a} - 2\vec{b})$

$\Rightarrow \quad |\vec{a} - 2\vec{b}|^2 = \vec{a} \cdot \vec{a} - 2\vec{a} \cdot \vec{b} - 2\vec{b} \cdot \vec{a} + 4\vec{b} \cdot \vec{b}$

$\qquad\qquad = |\vec{a}|^2 - 4\vec{a} \cdot \vec{b} + 4|\vec{b}|^2$

$\qquad\qquad = (2)^2 - 4(4) + 4(3)^2$

$\qquad\qquad = 4 - 16 + 36 = 24$

$\Rightarrow \quad |\vec{a} - 2\vec{b}|^2 = 24$

$\Rightarrow \quad |\vec{a} - 2\vec{b}| = \sqrt{24} = 2\sqrt{6}$

18. (b) The line through the points $A(0, 5, -2)$ and $B(3, -1, 2)$ is given by $\dfrac{x - 0}{3 - 0} = \dfrac{y - 5}{-1 - 5} = \dfrac{z + 2}{2 + 2}$

$\Rightarrow \quad \dfrac{x}{3} = \dfrac{y - 5}{-6} = \dfrac{z + 2}{4}$

Let $\dfrac{x}{3} = \dfrac{y - 5}{-6} = \dfrac{z + 2}{4} = k$

(where, k is any arbitrary scalar)

Now, any point P on the above line is given by

$\qquad (3k, -6k + 5, 4k - 2)$

Given, x-coordinate of P is 6.

$\therefore \qquad\qquad 3k = 6 \Rightarrow k = 2$

Now, its z-coordinate is given by

$\qquad 4k - 2 = 4(2) - 2 = 8 - 2 = 6$

19. (c) $\because \sec^{-1} x$ is defined, if $x \le -1$ or $x \ge 1$

Hence, $\sec^{-1} 2x$ will be defined, if $x \le \dfrac{-1}{2}$ or $x \ge \dfrac{1}{2}$

Hence, Assertion is true.

Now, $\sec^{-1}(-2) = \pi - \sec^{-1}(2)$

$$= \pi - \frac{\pi}{3} = \frac{2\pi}{3} \neq \frac{-\pi}{4}$$

Hence, Reason is false.

20. (a) The equation of the X-axis may be written as $\vec{r} = t\hat{i}$

Now, the acute angle θ between the line

$$\vec{r} = \hat{i} + \hat{j} + 2\hat{k} + \lambda(\hat{i} - \hat{j}) \text{ and } \vec{r} = t\hat{i}$$

$$\cos\theta = \frac{|1 \times 1 + (-1) \times 0 + 0 \times 0|}{\sqrt{1^2 + (-1)^2 + 0^2}\sqrt{1^2 + 0^2 + 0^2}} = \frac{1}{\sqrt{2}}$$

$$\Rightarrow \theta = \frac{\pi}{4}$$

Hence, both Assertion and Reason are true and Reason is a correct explanation of Assertion.

21. $\sin^{-1}\left[\sin\left(\frac{13\pi}{7}\right)\right] = \sin^{-1}\left(\sin\left(2\pi - \frac{\pi}{7}\right)\right)$ (1)

$$= \sin^{-1}\left(\sin\left(\frac{-\pi}{7}\right)\right)$$

$$= \frac{-\pi}{7} \quad \left[\because \frac{-\pi}{7} \in \left[\frac{-\pi}{2}, \frac{\pi}{2}\right]\right] \text{(1)}$$

Or

Consider a natural number n in co-domain N.

Case 1 When n is odd.

Therefore, $n = 2r + 1$ for some $r \in N$.

Then, there exists $4r + 1 \in N$ such that

$$f(4r + 1) = \frac{4r + 1 + 1}{2} = 2r + 1.$$

Therefore, f is onto. (1)

Case II When n is even

Therefore, $n = 2r$ for some $r \in N$

Then, there exists $4r \in N$ such that $f(4r) = \frac{4r}{2} = 2r$.

Hence, f is surjective.

Now, it can be observed that

$$f(1) = \frac{1 + 1}{2} = \frac{2}{2} = 1 \text{ and } f(2) = \frac{2}{2} = 1$$

Here, $f(1) = f(2)$ but $1 \neq 2$

Hence, f is not injective. (1)

22. Let AB represent the height of the street light from the ground.

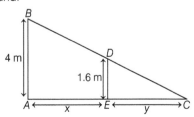

At any time t s, let the man represented as ED of height 1.6 m be at a distance of x m from AB and the length of his shadow EC be y m.

From similarity of $\triangle ABC$ and $\triangle EDC$, we have

$$\frac{4}{1.6} = \frac{x + y}{y} \Rightarrow 4y = 1.6x + 1.6y \Rightarrow 2.4y = 1.6x$$

$$\Rightarrow \qquad 3y = 2x \qquad \ldots(i) \text{ (1)}$$

Now, differentiating both sides of Eq. (i) w.r.t. t, we get

$$3\frac{dy}{dt} = 2\frac{dx}{dt} \Rightarrow \frac{dy}{dt} = \frac{2}{3} \times 0.3 \quad \left[\because \frac{dx}{dt} = 0.3\,\text{m/s}\right]$$

$$\Rightarrow \frac{dy}{dt} = 0.2$$

At any time t s, the tip of his shadow is at a distance of $(x + y)$ m from AB.

$\therefore$ The rate at which the tip of his shadow is moving

$$= \left(\frac{dx}{dt} + \frac{dy}{dt}\right) = (0.3 + 0.2) = 0.5\,\text{m/s}$$

The rate at which his shadow is lengthening

$$= \frac{dy}{dt} = 0.2 \text{ m/s} \tag{1}$$

23. Given, $\vec{a} = \hat{i} - \hat{j} + 7\hat{k}$ and $\vec{b} = 5\hat{i} - \hat{j} + \lambda\hat{k}$

Now, $\vec{a} + \vec{b} = 6\hat{i} - 2\hat{j} + (7 + \lambda)\hat{k}$

and $\vec{a} - \vec{b} = -4\hat{i} + (7 - \lambda)\hat{k}$

$\because (\vec{a} + \vec{b})$ and $(\vec{a} - \vec{b})$ are orthogonal. (1)

$\therefore \qquad\qquad (\vec{a} + \vec{b}) \cdot (\vec{a} - \vec{b}) = 0$

$\Rightarrow [6\hat{i} - 2\hat{j} + (7 + \lambda)\hat{k}] \cdot [-4\hat{i} + (7 - \lambda)\hat{k}] = 0$

$\Rightarrow \qquad\qquad -24 + 49 - \lambda^2 = 0$

$\Rightarrow \qquad\qquad \lambda^2 = 25$

$\Rightarrow \qquad\qquad \lambda = \pm 5 \qquad \text{(1)}$

Or

Given, line is $6x - 12 = 3y + 9 = 2z - 2$ which can be rewritten as

$$\frac{x - 2}{\left(\frac{1}{6}\right)} = \frac{y + 3}{\left(\frac{1}{3}\right)} = \frac{z - 1}{\left(\frac{1}{2}\right)} \qquad \ldots(i)$$

Hence, the required direction ratios of a line parallel to line (i) are $\left(\frac{1}{6}, \frac{1}{3}, \frac{1}{2}\right)$ or (1, 2, 3). (1)

Now, the required direction cosines are

$$\left(\frac{1}{\sqrt{(1)^2 + (2)^2 + (3)^2}}, \frac{2}{\sqrt{(1)^2 + (2)^2 + (3)^2}},\right.$$

$$\left.\frac{3}{\sqrt{(1)^2 + (2)^2 + (3)^2}}\right)$$

$$= \left(\frac{1}{\sqrt{1+4+9}}, \frac{2}{\sqrt{1+4+9}}, \frac{3}{\sqrt{1+4+9}} \right)$$

$$= \left(\frac{1}{\sqrt{14}}, \frac{2}{\sqrt{14}}, \frac{3}{\sqrt{14}} \right) \qquad (1)$$

24. Given, $y\sqrt{1-x^2} + x\sqrt{1-y^2} = 1$ ...(i)

Putting $x = \sin A$ and $y = \sin B$ in Eq. (i), we get

$\sin B \cos A + \sin A \cos B = 1$

$\Rightarrow \qquad \sin(A+B) = 1$

$\Rightarrow \qquad A + B = \sin^{-1}(1) = \dfrac{\pi}{2}$

$\Rightarrow \qquad \sin^{-1}x + \sin^{-1}y = \dfrac{\pi}{2}$ ...(ii) (1)

Now, differentiating both sides of Eq. (ii), we get

$$\frac{1}{\sqrt{1-x^2}} + \frac{1}{\sqrt{1-y^2}}\left(\frac{dy}{dx} \right) = 0$$

$\Rightarrow \qquad \dfrac{dy}{dx} = -\sqrt{\dfrac{1-y^2}{1-x^2}}$ **Hence proved.** (1)

25. $\because \vec{a}$ is a unit vector.

$\therefore \ |\vec{a}| = 1$

Now, we have

$$(\vec{x} - \vec{a}) \cdot (\vec{x} + \vec{a}) = 12$$

$\Rightarrow \vec{x} \cdot \vec{x} + \vec{x} \cdot \vec{a} - \vec{a} \cdot \vec{x} - \vec{a} \cdot \vec{a} = 12$ (1)

$\Rightarrow \qquad |\vec{x}|^2 - |\vec{a}|^2 = 12 \quad [\because \vec{x} \cdot \vec{a} = \vec{a} \cdot \vec{x}]$

$\Rightarrow \qquad |\vec{x}|^2 - 1 = 12 \qquad [\because |\vec{a}| = 1]$

$\Rightarrow \qquad |\vec{x}|^2 = 13$

$\Rightarrow \qquad |\vec{x}| = \sqrt{13}$ (1)

26. Let $I = \displaystyle\int \frac{dx}{\sqrt{3 - 2x - x^2}}$

$\therefore \qquad I = \displaystyle\int \frac{dx}{\sqrt{3 - (2x + x^2)}}$

$\Rightarrow \qquad I = \displaystyle\int \frac{dx}{\sqrt{3 - (1 + 2x + x^2 - 1)}}$

$\Rightarrow \qquad I = \displaystyle\int \frac{dx}{\sqrt{3 - [(x+1)^2 - 1]}}$

$\Rightarrow \qquad I = \displaystyle\int \frac{dx}{\sqrt{3 - (x+1)^2 + 1}}$

$\Rightarrow \qquad I = \displaystyle\int \frac{dx}{\sqrt{4 - (x+1)^2}}$ (1)

Let $(x + 1) = t$

$\Rightarrow \qquad dx = dt$

$\therefore \ I = \displaystyle\int \frac{dt}{\sqrt{4 - t^2}} = \int \frac{dt}{\sqrt{(2)^2 - t^2}}$

$\Rightarrow I = \sin^{-1}\left(\dfrac{t}{2} \right) + C \quad \left[\because \displaystyle\int \frac{dx}{\sqrt{a^2 - x^2}} = \sin^{-1}\left(\dfrac{x}{a} \right) + C \right]$

$\therefore \ I = \sin^{-1}\left(\dfrac{x+1}{2} \right) + C \qquad [\because t = x + 1]$ (2)

27. P(not obtaining an odd person in a single round)

= P(all three of them throw tails or all three of them throw heads)

= P(all three of them throw tails) + P(all three of them throw heads)

$$= \left(\frac{1}{2} \times \frac{1}{2} \times \frac{1}{2} \right) + \left(\frac{1}{2} \times \frac{1}{2} \times \frac{1}{2} \right)$$

$$\left[\because P(\text{Head}) = P(\text{Tails}) = \frac{1}{2} \right]$$

$$= 2 \times \frac{1}{2} \times \frac{1}{2} \times \frac{1}{2} = \frac{1}{4} \qquad (1)$$

Now,

P(obtaining an odd person in a single round)

= $1 - P$(not obtaining an odd person in a single round)

$= 1 - \dfrac{1}{4} = \dfrac{3}{4}$ (1)

Now, the required probability is given by P('in first round there is no odd person' and 'in second round there is no odd person' and 'in third round there is an odd person')

= P(in first round there is no odd person)

$\times P$(in second round there is no odd person)

$\times P$(in third round there is an odd person)

$= \dfrac{1}{4} \times \dfrac{1}{4} \times \dfrac{3}{4} = \dfrac{3}{64}$ (1)

Or

Let X denote the random variable defined by the number of defective items.

$\because$ Sample of two items are drawn one-by-one without replacement from an urn

$\therefore X$ can take the values 0, 1, 2

Now, $P(X = 0) = P$(no defective item)

$$= \frac{4}{6} \times \frac{3}{5} = \frac{2}{5}$$

$P(X = 1) = P$(1 defective and 1 non-defective)

= P(defective and non-defective)

+ P(non-defective and defective)

$$= \left(\frac{2}{6} \times \frac{4}{5} \right) + \left(\frac{4}{6} \times \frac{2}{5} \right)$$

$$= 2 \times \left(\frac{2}{6} \times \frac{4}{5} \right) = \frac{8}{15} \qquad (1)$$

$$P(X = 2) = P(\text{both defective}) = \frac{2}{6} \times \frac{1}{5} = \frac{1}{15}$$

X	0	1	2
P(X)	2/5	8/15	1/15

(1)

Now, required mean $= \sum X \, P(X)$

$$= 0\left(\frac{2}{5}\right) + 1\left(\frac{8}{15}\right) + 2\left(\frac{1}{15}\right)$$

$$= \frac{8}{15} + \frac{2}{15} = \frac{10}{15} = \frac{2}{3}$$

(1)

28. Let $I = \displaystyle\int_{\frac{\pi}{6}}^{\frac{\pi}{3}} \frac{dx}{1 + \sqrt{\tan x}}$

$\Rightarrow I = \displaystyle\int_{\frac{\pi}{6}}^{\frac{\pi}{3}} \frac{dx}{1 + \dfrac{\sqrt{\sin x}}{\sqrt{\cos x}}}$

$\Rightarrow I = \displaystyle\int_{\frac{\pi}{6}}^{\frac{\pi}{3}} \frac{\sqrt{\cos x}\, dx}{\sqrt{\sin x} + \sqrt{\cos x}}$ ...(i) (1)

$\Rightarrow I = \displaystyle\int_{\frac{\pi}{6}}^{\frac{\pi}{3}} \frac{\sqrt{\cos\left(\frac{\pi}{6} + \frac{\pi}{3} - x\right)}\, dx}{\sqrt{\sin\left(\frac{\pi}{6} + \frac{\pi}{3} - x\right)} + \sqrt{\cos\left(\frac{\pi}{6} + \frac{\pi}{3} - x\right)}}$

$$\left[\because \int_a^b f(x)\, dx = \int_a^b f(a + b - x)\, dx\right]$$

$\Rightarrow I = \displaystyle\int_{\frac{\pi}{6}}^{\frac{\pi}{3}} \frac{\sqrt{\cos\left(\frac{\pi}{2} - x\right)}\, dx}{\sqrt{\sin\left(\frac{\pi}{2} - x\right)} + \sqrt{\cos\left(\frac{\pi}{2} - x\right)}}$

$\Rightarrow I = \displaystyle\int_{\frac{\pi}{6}}^{\frac{\pi}{3}} \frac{\sqrt{\sin x}\, dx}{\sqrt{\cos x} + \sqrt{\sin x}}$ ...(ii) (1)

On adding Eqs. (i) and (ii), we get

$$2I = \displaystyle\int_{\frac{\pi}{6}}^{\frac{\pi}{3}} \frac{\sqrt{\cos x} + \sqrt{\sin x}}{\sqrt{\cos x} + \sqrt{\sin x}}\, dx$$

$\Rightarrow 2I = \displaystyle\int_{\frac{\pi}{6}}^{\frac{\pi}{3}} dx = [x]_{\frac{\pi}{6}}^{\frac{\pi}{3}} = \frac{\pi}{3} - \frac{\pi}{6} = \frac{\pi}{6}$

$\Rightarrow I = \dfrac{\pi}{12}$

Hence, $\displaystyle\int_{\frac{\pi}{6}}^{\frac{\pi}{3}} \frac{dx}{1 + \sqrt{\tan x}} = \frac{\pi}{12}$

(1)

Or

Let $I = \displaystyle\int_0^4 |x - 1|\, dx$

Here, $|x - 1| = \begin{cases} x - 1 & , & x \geq 1 \\ -(x - 1) & , & x < 1 \end{cases}$

$\therefore I = \displaystyle\int_0^1 -(x - 1)\, dx + \int_1^4 (x - 1)\, dx$

(1)

$\Rightarrow I = \displaystyle\int_0^1 (1 - x)\, dx + \int_1^4 (x - 1)\, dx$

$\Rightarrow I = \left[x - \dfrac{x^2}{2}\right]_0^1 + \left[\dfrac{x^2}{2} - x\right]_1^4$

$\Rightarrow I = \left(1 - \dfrac{1}{2}\right) + (8 - 4) - \left(\dfrac{1}{2} - 1\right)$

$\Rightarrow I = \dfrac{1}{2} + 4 + \dfrac{1}{2} = 1 + 4 = 5$

(2)

29. Given, $y\, dx + (x - y^2)\, dy = 0$

$\Rightarrow \quad y\, dx + x\, dy - y^2\, dy = 0$

$\Rightarrow \quad y\, dx + x\, dy = y^2\, dy$

$\Rightarrow \quad y\dfrac{dx}{dy} + x = y^2$

$\Rightarrow \quad \dfrac{dx}{dy} + \dfrac{x}{y} = y$

(1)

Which is of the form,

$$\frac{dx}{dy} + Rx = S$$

Here, $IF = e^{\int \frac{1}{y}\, dy} = e^{\log y} = y$

(1)

Now, required solution is given by

$$x\,(IF) = \int S\,(IF)\, dy + C$$

$$xy = \int y^2\, dy + C$$

$\Rightarrow \quad xy = \dfrac{y^3}{3} + C$

(1)

Or

Given, $x\, dy - y\, dx = \sqrt{x^2 + y^2}\, dx$

$\Rightarrow \quad x\, dy = \sqrt{x^2 + y^2}\, dx + y\, dx$

$\Rightarrow \quad x\, dy = (\sqrt{x^2 + y^2} + y)\, dx$

$\Rightarrow \quad \dfrac{dy}{dx} = \dfrac{\sqrt{x^2 + y^2} + y}{x}$ ...(i) (1)

Now, put $y = vx \Rightarrow \dfrac{dy}{dx} = v + x\dfrac{dv}{dx}$

From Eq. (i), we get

$$v + x\frac{dv}{dx} = \frac{\sqrt{x^2 + v^2x^2} + vx}{x}$$

$\Rightarrow \quad v + x\dfrac{dv}{dx} = \dfrac{x\sqrt{1 + v^2} + vx}{x}$

$\Rightarrow \quad v + x\dfrac{dv}{dx} = \sqrt{1 + v^2} + v$

$\Rightarrow \quad x\dfrac{dv}{dx} = \sqrt{1 + v^2}$

$\Rightarrow \quad \dfrac{dv}{\sqrt{1 + v^2}} = \dfrac{dx}{x}$ ...(ii) (1)

On integrating both sides of Eq. (ii), we get

$$\int \frac{dv}{\sqrt{1+v^2}} = \int \frac{dx}{x}$$

$$\Rightarrow \quad \log|v + \sqrt{1+v^2}| = \log|x| + \log C, C > 0$$

$$\Rightarrow \quad \log\left|\frac{y}{x} + \sqrt{1 + \frac{y^2}{x^2}}\right| = \log|x| + \log C \quad \left[\because v = \frac{y}{x}\right]$$

$$\Rightarrow \log|y + \sqrt{x^2 + y^2}| - \log|x| = \log|x| + \log C$$

$$\Rightarrow \log|y + \sqrt{x^2 + y^2}| = 2\log|x| + \log C = \log(x^2 C)$$

$$\Rightarrow \quad y + \sqrt{x^2 + y^2} = \pm Cx^2$$

$$\Rightarrow \quad y + \sqrt{x^2 + y^2} = Kx^2, \quad [\text{where}, K = \pm C, -C]$$

which is the required general solution. (1)

30. Given, objective function is maximise
$Z = 400x + 300y$

Subject to constraints,

$$x + y \le 200 \qquad \dots(i)$$
$$x \le 40 \qquad \dots(ii)$$
$$x \ge 20 \qquad \dots(iii)$$
$$y \ge 0 \qquad \dots(iv)$$

Table for line $x + y = 200$

x	200	0
y	0	200

So, the line passes through the points (200, 0) and (0, 200). (1)

On putting (0, 0) in the inequality $x + y \le 200$, we get $0 + 0 \le 200$, which is true.

So, the half plane is towards the origin.

Now, draw the graph of lines $x = 40$ and $x = 20$, which is perpendicular to X-axis.

Clearly, the half planes $x \le 40$ and $x \ge 20$ is towards the origin and away from the origin, respectively.

On solving equations $x + y = 200$ and $x = 40$, we get $B(40, 160)$

Again, solving the equations $x + y = 200$ and $x = 20$, we get $A(20, 180)$

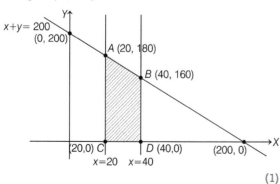

(1)

Clearly, the feasible region is *ABDCA*. The corner points of the feasible region are $A(20, 180)$, $B(40, 160)$, $C(20, 0)$ and $D(40, 0)$.

The values of Z at corner points are given below

Corner Points	Value of $Z = 400x + 300y$
$A(20, 180)$	62000
$B(40, 160)$	64000 (Maximum)
$C(20, 0)$	8000
$D(40, 0)$	16000

The maximum value of Z is 64000 at $B(40, 160)$. (1)

31. Let $I = \int \frac{(x^3 + x + 1)}{(x^2 - 1)} dx$

$$= \int \frac{x^3 - x + x + x + 1}{(x^2 - 1)} dx$$

$$= \int \frac{x(x^2 - 1) + (2x + 1)}{(x^2 - 1)} dx$$

$$\Rightarrow \quad I = \int \left(x + \frac{2x + 1}{(x^2 - 1)}\right) dx$$

$$\therefore \quad I = \int x\, dx + \int \frac{2x + 1}{x^2 - 1} dx \qquad \dots(i) \;(1)$$

Now, resolving $\frac{2x + 1}{x^2 - 1}$ into partial fraction as

$$\frac{2x + 1}{(x - 1)(x + 1)} = \frac{A}{x - 1} + \frac{B}{x + 1} \qquad \dots(ii)$$

$$\Rightarrow \quad 2x + 1 = A(x + 1) + B(x - 1)$$

$$\Rightarrow \quad 2x + 1 = x(A + B) + A - B$$

$$\Rightarrow \quad A + B = 2 \text{ and } A - B = 1$$

On solving, we get

$$A = \frac{3}{2} \text{ and } B = \frac{1}{2} \qquad (1)$$

On substituting the values of A and B in Eq. (ii), we get

$$\frac{2x + 1}{(x - 1)(x + 1)} = \frac{3}{2(x - 1)} + \frac{1}{2(x + 1)}$$

From Eq. (i), we get

$$I = \int x\, dx + \frac{3}{2} \int \frac{1}{x - 1} dx + \frac{1}{2} \int \frac{1}{x + 1} dx$$

$$I = \frac{x^2}{2} + \frac{3}{2} \log|x - 1| + \frac{1}{2} \log|x + 1| + C$$

$$I = \frac{x^2}{2} + \frac{1}{2} \log|x - 1|^3 + \frac{1}{2} \log|x + 1| + C$$

$$I = \frac{x^2}{2} + \frac{1}{2} [\log|(x - 1)^3 (x + 1)|] + C$$

(1)

32. Given, curves are

$$0 \le y \le x^2 \qquad \ldots\text{(i)}$$

$$0 \le y \le x \qquad \ldots\text{(ii)}$$

$$0 \le x \le 2 \qquad \ldots\text{(iii)}$$

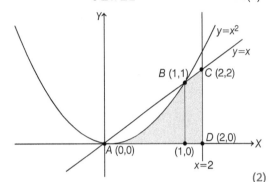

(2)

Now, plotting the curves (i), (ii) and (iii), we get

Now, on solving $y = x^2$ and $y = x$, we get $A(0, 0)$ and $B(1, 1)$.

Again, on solving $y = x$ and $x = 2$, we get $C(2, 2)$. (1)

Now, required area = Area of shaded region

$$= \int_0^1 (y_{\text{parabola}})\, dx + \int_1^2 (y_{\text{line}})\, dx$$

$$= \int_0^1 x^2 dx + \int_1^2 x\, dx$$

$$= \left[\frac{x^3}{3} \right]_0^1 + \left[\frac{x^2}{2} \right]_1^2$$

$$= \frac{1}{3} + \left(\frac{4}{2} - \frac{1}{2} \right)$$

$$= \frac{1}{3} + \frac{3}{2} = \frac{11}{6} \text{ sq units} \qquad (2)$$

33. Given, a relation R in the set $N \times N$ as $(a, b)\, R(c, d)$ iff $ad = bc$.

Now, let $(a, b) \in N \times N$

Then, we have

$ab = ba$ (by commutative property of multiplication of natural numbers)

$$\Rightarrow \qquad (a, b)\, R(a, b)$$

Hence, R is reflexive. (1)

Again, let $(a, b), (c, d) \in N \times N$

Such that $(a, b)\, R(c, d)$

$$\Rightarrow \qquad ad = bc$$

$\Rightarrow cb = da$ (by commutative property of multiplication of natural numbers)

$$\Rightarrow \qquad (c, d)\, R(a, b)$$

Hence, R is symmetric. (1)

Again, let $(a, b), (c, d), (e, f) \in N \times N$

Such that $(a, b)\, R\, (c, d)$ and $(c, d)\, R\, (e, f)$

$$\Rightarrow \qquad ad = bc \text{ and } cf = de$$

$$\Rightarrow \qquad adcf = bcde$$

$$\Rightarrow \qquad af = be$$

$$\Rightarrow \qquad (a, b)\, R(e, f)$$

Hence, R is transitive. (1)

Since, R is reflexive, symmetric and transitive.

So, R is as equivalence relation on $N \times N$. (2)

Or

Given, a relation R in the set $P(X)$, where X is a non-empty set as $(A, B) \in R$ iff $A \subset B$.

Let $\qquad A \in P(X)$

Then, $\qquad A \subset A$

$$\Rightarrow \qquad (A, A) \in R$$

Hence, R is reflexive. (2)

Now, let $\phi, A \in P(X)$

Such that $\phi \subset A$

$\therefore \qquad (\phi, A) \in R$

But $A \not\subset \phi$

$\therefore \qquad (A, \phi) \notin R$

Hence, R is not symmetric. (1)

Let $A, B, C \in P(X)$

Such that $(A, B), (B, C) \in R$

$$\Rightarrow \qquad A \subset B \text{ and } B \subset C$$

$$\Rightarrow \qquad A \subset C$$

$$\Rightarrow \qquad (A, C) \in R$$

Hence, R is transitive. (2)

34. Given, lines are

$$\vec{r} = 6\hat{i} + 2\hat{j} + 2\hat{k} + \lambda(\hat{i} - 2\hat{j} + 2\hat{k})$$

or $\dfrac{x - 6}{1} = \dfrac{y - 2}{-2} = \dfrac{z - 2}{2} = \lambda$ (say) $\ldots\text{(i)}$

and $\vec{r} = -4\hat{i} - \hat{k} + \mu(3\hat{i} - 2\hat{j} - 2\hat{k})$

or $\dfrac{x + 4}{3} = \dfrac{y}{-2} = \dfrac{z + 1}{-2} = \mu$ (say) $\ldots\text{(ii)}$ (1)

Let the insect crawling on line (i) should reach at point P and insect crawling on line (ii) should reach at point Q. Now, for distance between them to be shortest, line segment PQ must be at right angles to both the lines, then PQ is the shortest distance between them.

Now, the position vector of point P lying on line (i) is

$\overrightarrow{OP} = (6 + \lambda)\hat{i} + (2 - 2\lambda)\hat{j} + (2 + 2\lambda)\hat{k}$ for some λ and the position vector of point Q lying on line (ii) is

$\overrightarrow{OQ} = (-4 + 3\mu)\hat{i} - 2\mu\hat{j} + (-1 - 2\mu)\hat{k}$ for some μ

Now, $\overrightarrow{PQ} = \overrightarrow{OQ} - \overrightarrow{OP}$

$\therefore \overrightarrow{PQ} = (-10 + 3\mu - \lambda)\hat{i} + (-2\mu - 2 + 2\lambda)\hat{j}$
$$+ (-3 - 2\mu - 2\lambda)\hat{k} \quad (1)$$

$\because \overrightarrow{PQ}$ is perpendicular to both the lines.

$\therefore (-10 + 3\mu - \lambda)(1) + (-2\mu - 2 + 2\lambda)(-2)$
$$+ (-3 - 2\mu - 2\lambda)(2) = 0$$
$\Rightarrow \quad -10 + 3\mu - \lambda + 4\mu + 4 - 4\lambda - 6 - 4\mu - 4\lambda = 0$
$\Rightarrow \quad -12 + 3\mu - 9\lambda = 0$
$\Rightarrow \quad -4 + \mu - 3\lambda = 0$
$\Rightarrow \quad \mu - 3\lambda = 4 \qquad \ldots\text{(iii)} \quad (1)$

and $(-10 + 3\mu - \lambda)(3) + (-2\mu - 2 + 2\lambda)(-2)$
$$+ (-3 - 2\mu - 2\lambda)(-2) = 0$$
$\Rightarrow -30 + 9\mu - 3\lambda + 4\mu + 4 - 4\lambda + 6 + 4\mu + 4\lambda = 0$
$\Rightarrow \quad -20 + 17\mu - 3\lambda = 0 \Rightarrow 17\mu - 3\lambda = 20 \ \ldots\text{(iv)} \ (1)$

Now, on solving Eqs. (iii) and (iv), we get
$$\mu = 1 \text{ and } \lambda = -1$$
$\therefore \ P \equiv (5, 4, 0) \text{ and } Q \equiv (-1, -2, -3)$

$\therefore$ The insect on line (i) should reach at point $P(5, 4, 0)$ and the insect on line (ii) should reach at point $Q(-1, -2, -3)$, so that the distance between, them is shortest.

Now, $\overrightarrow{PQ} = (-1-5)\hat{i} + (-2-4)\hat{j} + (-3-0)\hat{k}$

$\overrightarrow{PQ} = -6\hat{i} - 6\hat{j} - 3\hat{k}$

$\therefore$ Shortest possible distance between them is

$|\overrightarrow{PQ}| = \sqrt{(-6)^2 + (-6)^2 + (-3)^2}$
$$= \sqrt{36 + 36 + 9} = \sqrt{81} = 9 \text{ units} \qquad (1)$$

Or

Given, equations of motion of a rocket are
$$x = 2t$$
$$y = -4t \text{ and } z = 4t$$
or $\qquad \dfrac{x}{2} = t, \dfrac{y}{-4} = t \text{ and } \dfrac{z}{4} = t$

$\Rightarrow \qquad \dfrac{x}{2} = \dfrac{y}{-4} = \dfrac{z}{4} \qquad \ldots\text{(i)} \ (1)$

which is the equation of line passing through the origin and having direction ratios $< 2, -4, 4 >$.

$\therefore$ The line (i) is the path of the rocket.

At t s rocket will be at the point $(2t, -4t, 4t)$

$\therefore$ At $t = 10$ s rocket will be at the point $P(20, -40, 40)$

Now, the distance of point $P(20, -40, 40)$ from starting point $O(0, 0, 0)$ is given by

$$OP = \sqrt{(20)^2 + (-40)^2 + (40)^2}$$
$$= \sqrt{400 + 1600 + 1600}$$
$\therefore \qquad OP = \sqrt{3600} = 60 \text{ km} \qquad (2)$

Now, the distance of point $P(20, -40, 40)$ from the given line $\vec{r} = 20\hat{i} - 10\hat{j} + 40\hat{k} + \mu(10\hat{i} - 20\hat{j} + 10\hat{k})$ is

$= \dfrac{|(\vec{a_2} - \vec{a_1}) \times \vec{b}|}{|\vec{b}|} = \dfrac{|-30\hat{j} \times (10\hat{i} - 20\hat{j} + 10\hat{k})|}{|10\hat{i} - 20\hat{j} + 10\hat{k}|}$ km

$= \dfrac{|-300\hat{i} + 300\hat{k}|}{|10\hat{i} - 20\hat{j} + 10\hat{k}|}$ km

$= \dfrac{\sqrt{(-300)^2 + (300)^2}}{\sqrt{(10)^2 + (-20)^2 + (10)^2}}$ km

$= \dfrac{300\sqrt{2}}{\sqrt{600}}$ km $= \dfrac{300\sqrt{2}}{10\sqrt{6}}$ km $= 10\sqrt{3}$ km
$\qquad (2)$

35. We have, $A = \begin{bmatrix} 2 & -3 & 5 \\ 3 & 2 & -4 \\ 1 & 1 & -2 \end{bmatrix}$

Now, $|A| = 2(-4 + 4) + 3(-6 + 4) + 5(3 - 2)$

$\therefore \qquad |A| = -6 + 5 = -1 \neq 0$

$\therefore A$ is invertible.

$C_{11} = \begin{vmatrix} 2 & -4 \\ 1 & -2 \end{vmatrix} = -4 + 4 = 0$

$C_{12} = -\begin{vmatrix} 3 & -4 \\ 1 & -2 \end{vmatrix} = -(-6 + 4) = 2$

$C_{13} = \begin{vmatrix} 3 & 2 \\ 1 & 1 \end{vmatrix} = 3 - 2 = 1$

$C_{21} = -\begin{vmatrix} -3 & 5 \\ 1 & -2 \end{vmatrix} = -(6 - 5) = -1$

$C_{22} = \begin{vmatrix} 2 & 5 \\ 1 & -2 \end{vmatrix} = -4 - 5 = -9$

$C_{23} = -\begin{vmatrix} 2 & -3 \\ 1 & 1 \end{vmatrix} = -(2 + 3) = -5$
$\qquad (1)$

$C_{31} = \begin{vmatrix} -3 & 5 \\ 2 & -4 \end{vmatrix} = 12 - 10 = 2$

$C_{32} = -\begin{vmatrix} 2 & 5 \\ 3 & -4 \end{vmatrix} = -(-8 - 15) = 23$

$C_{33} = \begin{vmatrix} 2 & -3 \\ 3 & 2 \end{vmatrix} = 4 + 9 = 13$

$\therefore$ adj $A = \begin{bmatrix} C_{11} & C_{12} & C_{13} \\ C_{21} & C_{22} & C_{23} \\ C_{31} & C_{32} & C_{33} \end{bmatrix}^T = \begin{bmatrix} 0 & 2 & 1 \\ -1 & -9 & -5 \\ 2 & 23 & 13 \end{bmatrix}^T$

$\therefore$ adj $A = \begin{bmatrix} 0 & -1 & 2 \\ 2 & -9 & 23 \\ 1 & -5 & 13 \end{bmatrix}$
$\qquad (1)$

$\therefore \quad A^{-1} = \dfrac{1}{|A|}$ adj $A = \dfrac{1}{-1}\begin{bmatrix} 0 & -1 & 2 \\ 2 & -9 & 23 \\ 1 & -5 & 13 \end{bmatrix}$

$= \begin{bmatrix} 0 & 1 & -2 \\ -2 & 9 & -23 \\ -1 & 5 & -13 \end{bmatrix}$
$\qquad (1)$

Given, system of equation is

$$2x - 3y + 5z = 11 \qquad \text{...(i)}$$
$$3x + 2y - 4z = -5 \qquad \text{...(ii)}$$
$$x + y - 2z = -3 \qquad \text{...(iii)}$$

Let $A = \begin{bmatrix} 2 & -3 & 5 \\ 3 & 2 & -4 \\ 1 & 1 & -2 \end{bmatrix}$, $B = \begin{bmatrix} 11 \\ -5 \\ -3 \end{bmatrix}$ and $X = \begin{bmatrix} x \\ y \\ z \end{bmatrix}$ (1)

$\therefore \quad AX = B$

$\Rightarrow \quad X = A^{-1}B$

$\Rightarrow \quad X = \begin{bmatrix} 0 & 1 & -2 \\ -2 & 9 & -23 \\ -1 & 5 & -13 \end{bmatrix} \begin{bmatrix} 11 \\ -5 \\ -3 \end{bmatrix} = \begin{bmatrix} 0-5+6 \\ -22-45+69 \\ -11-25+39 \end{bmatrix}$

$\Rightarrow \quad X = \begin{bmatrix} 1 \\ 2 \\ 3 \end{bmatrix} \Rightarrow \begin{bmatrix} x \\ y \\ z \end{bmatrix} = \begin{bmatrix} 1 \\ 2 \\ 3 \end{bmatrix}$

$\Rightarrow x = 1, y = 2$ and $z = 3$ (1)

36. (i) Given, function is $f(x) = -0.1x^2 + mx + 98.6$

$\because f(x)$ is a polynomial function.

$\therefore$ It is differentiable everywhere and hence, differentiable in $(0, 12)$.

(ii) We have, $f(x) = -0.1x^2 + mx + 98.6$

$\therefore \qquad f'(x) = -0.2x + m$

$\because$ 6 is the critical point of the function.

$\therefore \qquad f'(6) = 0$

$\Rightarrow \quad -0.2(6) + m = 0$

$\Rightarrow \qquad m = 1.2$

(iii) We have, $f(x) = -0.1x^2 + 1.2x + 98.6$

$\therefore \qquad f'(x) = -0.2x + 1.2 = -0.2(x - 6)$

Interval	Sign of $f'(x)$
$(0, 6)$	+ ve
$(6, 12)$	– ve

Hence, $f(x)$ is strictly increasing in the interval $(0, 6)$ and strictly decreasing in the interval $(6, 12)$.

Or

We have, $f(x) = -0.1x^2 + 1.2x + 98.6$

$\therefore \qquad f'(x) = -0.2x + 1.2 = -0.2(x - 6)$

$\therefore \qquad f'(x) = 0$

$\Rightarrow \qquad x = 6$

Now, $\quad f''(x) = -0.2$

and $\quad f''(6) = -0.2 < 0$

Hence, $x = 6$ is the point of local maximum and the local maximum value

$= f(6) = -0.1 \times (6)^2 + (1.2 \times 6) + 98.6 = 102.2$

Now, $f(0) = 98.6$, $f(6) = 102.2$ and $f(12) = 98.6$

Hence, $x = 6$ is the point of absolute maximum and the absolute maximum value of the function at $x = 6$ is 102.2 and $x = 0$, $x = 12$ both are the points of absolute minimum and the absolute minimum value of the function is 98.6.

37. (i) Elliptical sport field is given by $\dfrac{x^2}{a^2} + \dfrac{y^2}{b^2} = 1$ ...(i)

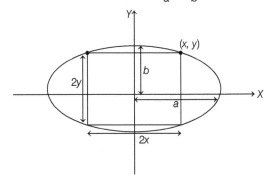

Let (x, y) be the upper right vertex of the rectangle

$\therefore$ From Eq. (i), we have $\dfrac{y^2}{b^2} = 1 - \dfrac{x^2}{a^2} = \dfrac{a^2 - x^2}{a^2}$

$\Rightarrow \qquad y = \dfrac{b}{a}\sqrt{a^2 - x^2}$

$\because$ Length and breadth of rectangular field are $2x$ and $2y$, respectively.

$\therefore$ The area function $A = (2x)(2y)$

$\therefore \quad A = (2x)2\dfrac{b}{a}\sqrt{a^2 - x^2} \qquad \left[\because y = \dfrac{b}{a}\sqrt{a^2 - x^2}\right]$

$\therefore \quad A = \dfrac{4bx}{a}\sqrt{a^2 - x^2}$, $x \in (0, a)$

(ii) We have area function A, as

$$A = \dfrac{4bx}{a}\sqrt{a^2 - x^2}$$

Now, $\dfrac{dA}{dx} = \dfrac{4b}{a}\left[x \times \dfrac{-x}{\sqrt{a^2 - x^2}} + \sqrt{a^2 - x^2}\right]$

$\therefore \quad \dfrac{dA}{dx} = \dfrac{4b}{a}\left[\dfrac{-x^2 + a^2 - x^2}{\sqrt{a^2 - x^2}}\right]$

$= \dfrac{4b}{a} \times \dfrac{(a^2 - 2x^2)}{\sqrt{a^2 - x^2}}$

or $\quad \dfrac{dA}{dx} = -\dfrac{4b}{a} \times \dfrac{2\left(x + \dfrac{a}{\sqrt{2}}\right)\left(x - \dfrac{a}{\sqrt{2}}\right)}{\sqrt{a^2 - x^2}}$

For critical point, put $\dfrac{dA}{dx} = 0$

$\therefore \qquad \dfrac{dA}{dx} = 0$

$\Rightarrow \qquad x = \dfrac{a}{\sqrt{2}}$ is the critical point.

(iii) We have,

$$\frac{dA}{dx} = \frac{-4b}{a} \times \frac{2\left(x + \frac{a}{\sqrt{2}}\right)\left(x - \frac{a}{\sqrt{2}}\right)}{\sqrt{a^2 - x^2}}$$

For the values of x less than $\frac{a}{\sqrt{2}}$ and close to $\frac{a}{\sqrt{2}}$, we have $\frac{dA}{dx} > 0$

and for the values of x greater than $\frac{a}{\sqrt{2}}$ and close to $\frac{a}{\sqrt{2}}$, we have $\frac{dA}{dx} < 0$

Hence, by the first derivative test, there is a local maximum at the critical point $x = \frac{a}{\sqrt{2}}$.

Since, there is only one critical point, therefore the area of the soccer field is maximum at this critical point $x = \frac{a}{\sqrt{2}}$

$$\therefore \quad x = \frac{a}{\sqrt{2}} \Rightarrow 2x = \frac{2a}{\sqrt{2}} = a\sqrt{2} \text{ and } x = \frac{a}{\sqrt{2}}$$

$$\Rightarrow \quad y = \frac{b}{a}\sqrt{a^2 - \frac{a^2}{2}}$$

$$= \frac{b}{a}\sqrt{\frac{a^2}{2}} = \frac{b}{a} \times \frac{a}{\sqrt{2}} = \frac{b}{\sqrt{2}}$$

$$\therefore \quad 2y = \frac{2b}{\sqrt{2}} = b\sqrt{2}$$

Thus, for maximum area of soccer field, its length should be $a\sqrt{2}$ and its width should be $b\sqrt{2}$.

Or

We have, $A = \frac{4bx}{a}\sqrt{a^2 - x^2}$ ...(i)

Squaring both sides of Eq. (i), we get

$$A^2 = \frac{16b^2x^2}{a^2}(a^2 - x^2) = \frac{16b^2}{a^2}(x^2a^2 - x^4)$$

Let $A^2 = Z$

Now, A is maximum when Z is maximum.

$$\therefore \quad \frac{dZ}{dx} = \frac{16b^2}{a^2}(2xa^2 - 4x^3)$$

$$= \frac{32b^2}{a^2}x(a + \sqrt{2}x)(a - \sqrt{2}x)$$

Now, $\frac{dZ}{dx} = 0 \Rightarrow x = \frac{a}{\sqrt{2}}$

Now, $\frac{d^2Z}{dx^2} = \frac{d}{dx}\left(\frac{32b^2}{a^2}(a^2x - 2x^3)\right)$

$$= \frac{32b^2}{a^2}(a^2 - 6x^2)$$

$$\therefore \left(\frac{d^2Z}{dx^2}\right)_{x = \frac{a}{\sqrt{2}}} = \frac{32b^2}{a^2}\left(a^2 - 6.\frac{a^2}{2}\right)$$

$$= \frac{32b^2}{a^2}(a^2 - 3a^2)$$

$$= \frac{32b^2}{a^2}(-2a^2)$$

$$= -64b^2 < 0$$

Hence, at $x = \frac{a}{\sqrt{2}}$, Z is maximum and here, A is maximum.

$$\therefore \quad x = \frac{a}{\sqrt{2}} \Rightarrow 2x = a\sqrt{2} \text{ and } x = \frac{a}{\sqrt{2}}$$

$$\Rightarrow \quad y = \frac{b}{a}\sqrt{a^2 - \frac{a^2}{2}} = \frac{b}{a} \times \frac{a}{\sqrt{2}} = \frac{b}{\sqrt{2}}$$

$$\Rightarrow 2y = \frac{2b}{\sqrt{2}} = b\sqrt{2}$$

Thus, for maximum area of the soccer field, its length should be $a\sqrt{2}$ and its width should be $b\sqrt{2}$.

38. We have,

P(Shell from A hits the plane) = 0.3

$\therefore P$(Shell from A does not hit the plane) = $1 - 0.3 = 0.7$

and P(Shell from B hits the plane) = 0.2

$\therefore P$(Shell from B does not hit the plane) = $1 - 0.2 = 0.8$

(i) P(Shell fired from exactly one of them hits the plane)

= P(Shell from A hits the plane and Shell from B does not hit the plane) or (Shell from A does not hit the plane and shell from B hits the plane)

= $0.3 \times 0.8 + 0.7 \times 0.2 = 0.38$

(ii) P(Shell fired from B hit the plane/Exactly one of them hit the plane)

$$= \frac{P(\text{Shell fired from } B \text{ hit the plane} \cap \text{Exactly one of them hit the plane})}{P(\text{Exactly one of them hit the plane})}$$

$$= \frac{P(\text{Shell fired from only } B \text{ hit the plane})}{P(\text{Exactly one of them hit the plane})}$$

$$= \frac{0.14}{0.38} = \frac{7}{19}$$

One Day

BEFORE EXAM[*]

MATHEMATICS

Time : 3 hrs   Max. Marks : 80

General Instructions

1. This question paper contains - five sections A, B, C, D and E. Each section is compulsory. However, there are internal choices in some questions.
2. Section A has 18 MCQ's and 02 Assertion-Reason based questions of 1 mark each.
3. Section B has 5 Very Short Answer (VSA) type questions of 2 marks each.
4. Section C has 6 Short Answer (SA) type questions of 3 marks each.
5. Section D has 4 Long Answer (LA) type questions of 5 marks each.
6. Section E has 3 source based/case based/passage based/integrated units of assessment (4 marks each) with sub parts.

Section A

(Multiple Choice Questions) Each question carries 1 mark

1. The magnitude of $\vec{a}$ given by
   $\vec{a} = (\hat{i} + 3\hat{j} - 2\hat{k}) \times (-\hat{i} + 3\hat{k})$ is equal to
   (a) 91   (b) $\sqrt{91}$ (c) 90   (d) $\sqrt{90}$

2. $\int \dfrac{1}{x + x \log x} dx$ is equal to
   (a) $\log(1 + \log x) + C$ (b) $\log(1 + x) + C$
   (c) $\dfrac{1}{x} + C$ (d) $\dfrac{1}{\log(1 + \log x)} + C$

3. If $y = \sqrt{x+1} + \sqrt{x-1}$, then $\sqrt{x^2 - 1}\dfrac{dy}{dx}$ is equal to
   (a) y (b) $\dfrac{y}{2}$ (c) $\dfrac{y}{3}$ (d) $-y$

4. The domain of $f(x) = \sin^{-1}(-x^2)$ is
   (a) $(-1, 1)$ (b) $[-1, 1]$ (c) $(-1, 1]$ (d) $[-1, 1)$

5. The function $f(x) = x^2 + 2$ is
   (a) one-one   (b) not one-one
   (c) one-one and onto   (d) None of these

6. The value of $\cos^{-1}\left(\sin\dfrac{\pi}{6}\right)$ is
   (a) $\dfrac{\pi}{2}$ (b) $\dfrac{\pi}{3}$ (c) $\dfrac{\pi}{6}$ (d) $\dfrac{\pi}{4}$

7. If $2A + B + X = 0$, where $A = \begin{bmatrix} -1 & 2 \\ 3 & 4 \end{bmatrix}$ and $B = \begin{bmatrix} 3 & -2 \\ 1 & 5 \end{bmatrix}$, then find the value of matrix X.
   (a) $\begin{bmatrix} -1 & -7 \\ -2 & -13 \end{bmatrix}$ (b) $\begin{bmatrix} -1 & -2 \\ -7 & -13 \end{bmatrix}$ (c) $\begin{bmatrix} 1 & 2 \\ 7 & 13 \end{bmatrix}$ (d) $\begin{bmatrix} 1 & 7 \\ 2 & 13 \end{bmatrix}$

8. The principal value of
$\sec^{-1}(-\sqrt{2}) + \csc^{-1}(-\sqrt{2})$ is
(a) $\frac{\pi}{2}$ (b) $\frac{\pi}{3}$ (c) $\frac{2\pi}{3}$ (d) $\frac{-\pi}{2}$

9. If A is a matrix of order 3×3 such that $|A| = 4$, then $|A^{-1}|$ is equal to
(a) 4   (b) $\frac{1}{4}$ (c) $\frac{1}{2}$ (d) 2

10. If $f(x) = \begin{cases} \dfrac{1 - \sqrt{2}\sin x}{\pi - 4x}, & \text{if } x \neq \dfrac{\pi}{4} \\ k, & \text{if } x = \dfrac{\pi}{4} \end{cases}$
is continuous at $\dfrac{\pi}{4}$, then k is equal to
(a) 4   (b) 3   (c) $-\dfrac{1}{2}$ (d) $\dfrac{1}{4}$

11. If $y = 2x + |x|$, then $\dfrac{dy}{dx}$ at $x = -1$ is equal to
(a) 1   (b) -1 (c) 0   (d) 2

12. $\displaystyle\int_2^3 \dfrac{dx}{1 - x^2}$ is equal to
(a) $\dfrac{1}{2}\log\dfrac{3}{2}$ (b) $\dfrac{1}{2}\log\dfrac{2}{3}$
(c) $\dfrac{1}{2}\log 6$ (d) $\dfrac{1}{2}\log\dfrac{4}{3}$

13. The degree of the differential equation
$$\left(\dfrac{d^2 y}{dx^2}\right)^3 + \left(\dfrac{dy}{dx}\right)^3 + \sin\left(\dfrac{dy}{dx}\right) + 1 = 0 \text{ is}$$
(a) 3   (b) 2
(c) not defined   (d) 1

14. If $\vec{a}$ and $\vec{b}$ are two vectors, then
$(\vec{a} \times \vec{b})^2 + (\vec{a} \cdot \vec{b})^2$ is equal to
(a) ab (b) $a^2 b$
(c) ab^2 (d) $a^2 b^2$

15. If E_1 and E_2 are two independent events such that $P(E_1) = 0.35$ and $P(E_1 \cup E_2) = 0.60$, then $P(E_2)$ is equal to
(a) $\dfrac{5}{13}$ (b) $\dfrac{13}{25}$
(c) $\dfrac{1}{2}$ (d) $\dfrac{5}{11}$

16. If the lines $\dfrac{-x+3}{\alpha - 2} = \dfrac{y+3}{-1} = \dfrac{4+2z}{6}$ and $\dfrac{x-1}{2} = \dfrac{y-3}{-5} = \dfrac{z+5}{1}$ are perpendicular, then α equals
(a) 1   (b) 2   (c) 6   (d) 8

17. $\displaystyle\int \dfrac{x\,dx}{x^4 + 4}$ is equal to
(a) $\dfrac{1}{2}\tan^{-1}\left(\dfrac{x^2}{2}\right) + C$ (b) $\dfrac{1}{4}\tan^{-1}\left(\dfrac{x^2}{2}\right) + C$
(c) $\dfrac{1}{4}\tan^{-1}\left(\dfrac{x}{2}\right) + C$ (d) $\tan^{-1}\left(\dfrac{x^2}{2}\right) + C$

18. An urn contains 10 black and 5 white balls. Two balls are drawn from the urn one after the other without replacement, then the probability that both drawn balls are black is
(a) $\dfrac{1}{7}$ (b) $\dfrac{2}{7}$ (c) $\dfrac{3}{7}$ (d) $\dfrac{4}{7}$

Assertion-Reason Based Questions

In the following questions, a statement of Assertion (A) is followed by a statement of Reason (R). Choose the correct answer out of the following choices.

(a) Both A and R are true and R is the correct explanation of A.
(b) Both A and R are true but R is not the correct explanation of A.
(c) A is true but R is false.
(d) A is false but R is true.

19. **Assertion (A)** If R is the relation defined in set $\{1, 2, 3, 4, 5, 6\}$ as $R = \{(a, b) : b = a + 1\}$, then R is reflexive

Reason (R) The relation R in the set $\{1, 2, 3\}$ given by $R = \{(1, 2), (2, 1)\}$ is symmetric.

20. **Assertion (A)** The equation of the line joining $A(1, 3)$ and $B(0, 0)$ is given by $y = 3x$.

Reason (R) The area of triangle with vertices (x_1, y_1), (x_2, y_2) and (x_3, y_3) in the form of determinant is $\Delta = \begin{vmatrix} x_1 & y_1 & 1 \\ x_2 & y_2 & 1 \\ x_3 & y_3 & 1 \end{vmatrix}$.

Section B

(This section comprises of very short answer type questions (VSA) of 2 marks each)

21. Find the equation of the line joining $A(1, 3)$ and $B(0, 0)$ using determinant and find k, if $D(k, 0)$ is a point such that area of $\triangle ABD$ is 3 sq units.

    Or Find X and Y, if $X + Y = \begin{bmatrix} 7 & 0 \\ 2 & 5 \end{bmatrix}$ and

    $X - Y = \begin{bmatrix} 3 & 0 \\ 0 & 3 \end{bmatrix}$.

22. If $\hat{a}$ and $\hat{b}$ are unit vectors, then prove that $|\hat{a} + \hat{b}| = 2\cos\dfrac{\theta}{2}$, where θ is the angle between them.

23. The probability of two students A and B coming to the school in time are $\dfrac{3}{7}$ and $\dfrac{5}{7}$, respectively. Assuming that the events

'A coming in time' and 'B coming in time' are independent. Find the probability of only one of them coming to the school in time.

    Or

    A couple has 2 children. Find the probability that both are boys, if it is known that

    (i) one of them is a boy.

    (ii) the older child is a boy.

24. Find the direction cosines of the following line $\dfrac{3 - x}{-1} = \dfrac{2y - 1}{2} = \dfrac{z}{4}$

25. Given two independent events A and B such that $P(A) = 0.3$ and $P(B) = 0.6$, find $P(A' \cap B')$.

Section C

(This section comprises of short answer type questions (SA) of 3 marks each)

26. Consider the function $f : R^+ \to [4, \infty)$ defined by $f(x) = x^2 + 4$, where R^+ is the set of all non-negative real numbers. Show that f is bijective.

27. Solve the differential equation $(\tan^{-1} x - y) dx = (1 + x^2) dy$.

    Or

    Find the particular solution of the differential equation $\dfrac{dy}{dx} + 2y \tan x = \sin x$, given that $y = 0$, when $x = \dfrac{\pi}{3}$.

28. If $x^y - y^x = a^b$, find $\dfrac{dy}{dx}$.

    Or

    Evaluate $\displaystyle\int \dfrac{\cos x}{(1 - \sin x)(2 - \sin x)} dx$.

29. Solve $\left[x\sin^2\left(\dfrac{y}{x}\right) - y \right] dx + x\, dy = 0$ such that $y = \dfrac{\pi}{4}$, at $x = 1$.

    Or

    Solve $x^2 dy + y(x + y) dx = 0$.

30. Evaluate $\displaystyle\int \dfrac{dx}{1 - 3\sin x}$.

31. Evaluate $\displaystyle\int_3^4 \dfrac{\sqrt{x}}{\sqrt{x} + \sqrt{7 - x}} dx$.

Section D

(This section comprises of long answer type questions (LA) of 5 marks each)

32. Evaluate $\int \dfrac{(x^2+1)(x^2+2)}{(x^2+3)(x^2+4)}\,dx$.

33. Using matrices, solve the following system of equations
$$x - y + 2z = 7$$
$$3x + 4y - 5z = -5$$
$$\text{and} \quad 2x - y + 3z = 12$$

Or If $A = \begin{bmatrix} 1 & 1 & 1 \\ 1 & 1 & 1 \\ 1 & 1 & 1 \end{bmatrix}$, prove that

$$A^n = \begin{bmatrix} 3^{n-1} & 3^{n-1} & 3^{n-1} \\ 3^{n-1} & 3^{n-1} & 3^{n-1} \\ 3^{n-1} & 3^{n-1} & 3^{n-1} \end{bmatrix} \text{ for all values of}$$

$n \in N$.

34. Solve the following LPP graphically maximise $Z = 2x + 3y$

Subject to constraints

$x + 2y \leq 10$, $2x + y \leq 14$ and $x, y \geq 0$.

Or

Solve the LPP graphically
Maximise $Z = 60x + 40y$
Subject to constraints
$$5x + 6y \leq 45$$
$$3x + 2y \leq 18$$
$$\text{and} \quad x, y \geq 0$$

35. The scalar product of the vector $\vec{a} = \hat{i} + \hat{j} + \hat{k}$ with a unit vector along the sum of vectors $\vec{b} = 2\hat{i} + 4\hat{j} - 5\hat{k}$ and $\vec{c} = \lambda\hat{i} + 2\hat{j} + 3\hat{k}$ is equal to one. Find the value of λ and hence, find the unit vector along $\vec{b} + \vec{c}$.

Section E

(This section comprises of 3 case-study/ passage-based questions of 4 marks each with two sub-parts. First two case study questions have three sub-parts (i), (ii), (iii) of marks 1, 1, 2 respectively. The third case study question has two sub-parts of 2 marks each)

36. If $f(x)$ is a continuous function defined on $[-a, a]$, then

$$\int_{-a}^{a} f(x)\,dx = \begin{cases} 2\displaystyle\int_0^a f(x)\,dx, & \text{if } f(x) \text{ is an even function} \\ 0, & \text{if } f(x) \text{ is a odd function} \end{cases}$$

A function $f(x)$ is even, when $f(-x) = f(x)$ and odd when $f(-x) = -f(x)$.

On the basis of above information, answer the following questions.

(i) If $f(x)$ is an even function, then evaluate $\displaystyle\int_{-1}^{1}(f(x) - f(-x))\,dx$.

(ii) If $g(x)$ is an odd function, then evaluate $\displaystyle\int_{-a}^{a}(g(x) + g(-x))\,dx$.

(iii) Evaluate $\displaystyle\int_{-\pi}^{\pi} \dfrac{x}{1 + \cos^2 x}\,dx$ and $\displaystyle\int_{-1}^{1} \log\left(\dfrac{2-x}{2+x}\right)\,dx$

Or

Evaluate $\displaystyle\int_{-\pi}^{\pi} |\sin x|\,dx$

37. By examine the test, the probability that a person is diagnosed with CORONA when he is actually suffering from it, is 0.99. The probability that the doctor incorrectly diagnosed a person to be having CORONA, on the basis of test reports, is 0.001. In a certain city, 1 in 1000 persons suffers from CORONA. A person is selected at random and is diagnosed to have CORONA.

On the basis of above information, answer the following questions.

(i) Find the probability P(person suffering from CORONA).

(ii) Find the probability P(CORONA is diagnosed, when the person actually has CORONA).

(iii) Find the probability P(CORONA is diagnosed).

Or

Find the probability P(person has CORONA given CORONA is diagnosed).

38. For any function $f(x)$, we have

$$\int_a^b f(x)\,dx = \int_a^{c_1} f(x)\,dx + \int_{c_1}^{c_2} f(x)\,dx + \ldots + \int_{c_n}^b f(x)\,dx, \text{ where,}$$

$$a < c_1 < c_2 < c_3 \ldots < c_{n-1} < c_n < b$$

On the basis of above information, answer the following questions.

(i) Evaluate $\int_0^1 |5x - 3|\,dx$

(ii) Evaluate $\int_0^2 [x]\,dx$ and $\int_{-1}^1 f(x)\,dx$, where

$$f(x) = \begin{cases} 1 - 2x & , x < 0 \\ 1 + 2x & , x \geq 0 \end{cases}$$

SOLUTIONS

1. (b) We have,

$$\vec{a} = (\hat{i} + 3\hat{j} - 2\hat{k}) \times (-\hat{i} + 0\hat{j} + 3\hat{k})$$

$$\Rightarrow \vec{a} = \begin{vmatrix} \hat{i} & \hat{j} & \hat{k} \\ 1 & 3 & -2 \\ -1 & 0 & 3 \end{vmatrix} = (9 - 0)\hat{i} - (3 - 2)\hat{j} + (0 + 3)\hat{k}$$

$$= 9\hat{i} - \hat{j} + 3\hat{k}$$

$$\therefore |\vec{a}| = \sqrt{9^2 + (-1)^2 + 3^2} = \sqrt{91}$$

2. (a) Let $I = \int \dfrac{1}{x + x\log x}\,dx = \int \dfrac{1}{x(1 + \log x)}\,dx$

Let $1 + \log x = t \Rightarrow \dfrac{1}{x}dx = dt$

$$\therefore \quad I = \int \dfrac{dt}{t} = \log t + C = \log(1 + \log x) + C$$

3. (d) Given, $y = \sqrt{x+1} + \sqrt{x-1}$

On differentiating w.r.t. x, we get

$$\dfrac{dy}{dx} = \dfrac{1}{2\sqrt{x+1}} + \dfrac{1}{2\sqrt{x-1}}$$

$$= \dfrac{1}{2}\left(\dfrac{\sqrt{x-1} + \sqrt{x+1}}{\sqrt{x^2 - 1}}\right) = \dfrac{y}{2\sqrt{x^2 - 1}}$$

$$\Rightarrow \sqrt{x^2 - 1}\dfrac{dy}{dx} = \dfrac{y}{2}$$

4. (b) The domain of $\sin^{-1} x$ is $[-1, 1]$.

Therefore, $f(x) = \sin^{-1}(-x^2)$ is defined for all x satisfying.

$$-1 \leq -x^2 \leq 1$$

$$\Rightarrow \quad 1 \geq x^2 \geq -1$$

$$\Rightarrow \quad 0 \leq x^2 \leq 1$$

$$\Rightarrow \quad x^2 \leq 1 \Rightarrow x^2 - 1 \leq 0$$

$$\Rightarrow \quad (x - 1)(x + 1) \leq 0 \Rightarrow -1 \leq x \leq 1$$

Hence, the domain of $f(x)$ is $[-1, 1]$.

5. (b) We have, $f(x) = x^2 + 2$

Let $x_1, x_2 \in R$ such that

$$f(x_1) = f(x_2)$$

$$\Rightarrow \quad x_1^2 + 2 = x_2^2 + 2$$

$$\Rightarrow \quad x_1^2 = x_2^2$$

$$\Rightarrow \quad x_1 = \pm x_2$$

$$\therefore f(x) \text{ is not one-one.}$$

6. (b) We have,

$$\cos^{-1}\left(\sin\dfrac{\pi}{6}\right) = \cos^{-1}\left(\dfrac{1}{2}\right) = \dfrac{\pi}{3}$$

7. (b) We have, $2A + B + X = 0$

$$\Rightarrow \quad X = -(2A + B)$$

Now, $2A + B = 2\begin{bmatrix} -1 & 2 \\ 3 & 4 \end{bmatrix} + \begin{bmatrix} 3 & -2 \\ 1 & 5 \end{bmatrix}$

$$= \begin{bmatrix} -2 & 4 \\ 6 & 8 \end{bmatrix} + \begin{bmatrix} 3 & -2 \\ 1 & 5 \end{bmatrix}$$

$$= \begin{bmatrix} -2+3 & 4-2 \\ 6+1 & 8+5 \end{bmatrix} = \begin{bmatrix} 1 & 2 \\ 7 & 13 \end{bmatrix}$$

$$\therefore \quad X = -(2A + B) = \begin{bmatrix} -1 & -2 \\ -7 & -13 \end{bmatrix}$$

8. (a) We have,

$$\sec^{-1}(-\sqrt{2}) + \text{cosec}^{-1}(-\sqrt{2})$$

$$= \left(\pi - \dfrac{\pi}{4}\right) + \left(-\dfrac{\pi}{4}\right)$$

$$= \pi - \dfrac{\pi}{2} = \dfrac{\pi}{2}$$

9. (b) We have,

$$|A| = 4$$

Now, $\quad |A^{-1}| = \dfrac{1}{|A|} = \dfrac{1}{4}$

10. (d) We have, $f(x) = \begin{cases} \dfrac{1-\sqrt{2}\sin x}{\pi - 4x}, & \text{if } x \neq \dfrac{\pi}{4} \\ k, & \text{if } x = \dfrac{\pi}{4} \end{cases}$

$f(x)$ is continuous at $x = \dfrac{\pi}{4}$

$$\lim_{x \to \frac{\pi}{4}} f(x) = k$$

$\Rightarrow \quad \lim_{x \to \frac{\pi}{4}} \dfrac{1 - \sqrt{2}\sin x}{\pi - 4x} = k$

$\Rightarrow \quad \lim_{h \to 0} \dfrac{1 - \sqrt{2}\sin\left(\dfrac{\pi}{4} - h\right)}{\pi - 4\left(\dfrac{\pi}{4} - h\right)} = k$

$\Rightarrow \quad \lim_{h \to 0} \dfrac{1 - \sqrt{2}\left(\sin\dfrac{\pi}{4}\cos h - \cos\dfrac{\pi}{4}\sin h\right)}{\pi - \pi + 4h} = k$

$\Rightarrow \quad \lim_{h \to 0} \dfrac{1 - \sqrt{2}\left(\dfrac{\cos h}{\sqrt{2}} - \dfrac{\sin h}{\sqrt{2}}\right)}{4h} = k$

$\Rightarrow \quad \lim_{h \to 0} \dfrac{1 - \cos h + \sin h}{4h} = k$

$\Rightarrow \quad \dfrac{1}{4}\left[\lim_{h \to 0} \dfrac{1 - \cos h}{h} + \lim_{h \to 0} \dfrac{\sin h}{h}\right] = k$

$\Rightarrow \quad \dfrac{1}{4}[0 + 1] = k$

$\Rightarrow \quad k = \dfrac{1}{4}$

11. (a) We have,

$$y = 2x + |x|$$

$\Rightarrow \quad y = 2x - x \quad\quad [\because |x| = -x, x < 0]$

$\Rightarrow \quad y = x$

$\therefore \quad \dfrac{dy}{dx} = 1$

12. (b) Let $\quad I = \displaystyle\int_2^3 \dfrac{dx}{1 - x^2}$

$\Rightarrow \quad I = \dfrac{1}{2}\left[\log\left|\dfrac{1+x}{1-x}\right|\right]_2^3$

$\Rightarrow \quad I = \dfrac{1}{2}\left[\log\dfrac{4}{2} - \log\dfrac{3}{1}\right]$

$\therefore \quad I = \dfrac{1}{2}\log\dfrac{2}{3}$

13. (c) The given differential equation is not a polynomial equation in $\dfrac{dy}{dx}$. Therefore, its degree is not defined.

14. (d) $(\vec{a} \times \vec{b})^2 = |\vec{a} \times \vec{b}|^2 \quad\quad [\because (\vec{a})^2 = \vec{a} \cdot \vec{a} = |\vec{a}|^2]$

$= |\vec{a}|^2 |\vec{b}|^2 \sin^2\theta = a^2 b^2 (1 - \cos^2\theta) \quad\quad (1)$

$= a^2 b^2 - a^2 b^2 \cos^2\theta$

$= a^2 b^2 - |\vec{a}|^2 |\vec{b}|^2 \cos^2\theta$

$= a^2 b^2 - (\vec{a} \cdot \vec{b})^2 \quad\quad [\because \vec{a} \cdot \vec{b} = |\vec{a}||\vec{b}|\cos\theta]$

$\therefore (\vec{a} \times \vec{b})^2 + (\vec{a} \cdot \vec{b})^2 = a^2 b^2 \quad\quad (1)$

15. (a) Let $P(E_2) = x$

Then, E_1 and E_2 being independent events, we have

$P(E_1 \cap E_2) = P(E_1) \times P(E_2) = 0.35x$

Now, $\quad P(E_1 \cup E_2) = P(E_1) + P(E_2) - P(E_1 \cap E_2)$

$\Rightarrow \quad 0.60 = 0.35 + x - 0.35x \Rightarrow 0.65x = 0.25$

$\therefore \quad x = \dfrac{0.25}{0.65} = \dfrac{5}{13}$

16. (c) Given, lines can be rewritten as

$$\dfrac{x-3}{2-\alpha} = \dfrac{y+3}{-1} = \dfrac{z+2}{3} \quad\quad \dots(i)$$

$$\dfrac{x-1}{2} = \dfrac{y-3}{-5} = \dfrac{z+5}{1} \quad\quad \dots(ii)$$

$\because$ Lines (i) and (ii) are perpendicular.

$\therefore 2(2-\alpha) + (-1)(-5) + 3(1) = 0$

$4 - 2\alpha + 5 + 3 = 0$

$\Rightarrow \quad 2\alpha = 12 \Rightarrow \alpha = 6$

17. (b) Let $I = \displaystyle\int \dfrac{x}{4 + x^4}\,dx = \dfrac{1}{2}\int \dfrac{2x}{(2)^2 + (x^2)^2}\,dx \quad\quad \dots(i)$

Put $x^2 = t \Rightarrow 2x\,dx = dt$

Putting these values in Eq. (i), we get

$I = \dfrac{1}{2}\displaystyle\int \dfrac{dt}{(2)^2 + t^2} = \dfrac{1}{2} \times \dfrac{1}{2}\tan^{-1}\left(\dfrac{t}{2}\right) + C$

$\left[\because \displaystyle\int \dfrac{1}{a^2 + x^2}dx = \dfrac{1}{a}\tan^{-1}\dfrac{x}{a} + C\right]$

$= \dfrac{1}{4}\tan^{-1}\left(\dfrac{x^2}{2}\right) + C \quad\quad [\text{putting } t = x^2]$

18. (c) Let E and F denote respectively the events first and second ball drawn are black.

$\therefore \quad P(E) = \dfrac{10}{15}$ and $P\left(\dfrac{F}{E}\right) = \dfrac{9}{14}$

$\therefore$ Required probability,

$P(E \cap F) = P(E) \times P\left(\dfrac{F}{E}\right) = \dfrac{10}{15} \times \dfrac{9}{14} = \dfrac{3}{7}$

19. (d) **Assertion** Let $A = \{1, 2, 3, 4, 5, 6\}$

A relation R is defined on set A is

$R = \{(a, b) : b = a + 1\}$

$\therefore \quad R = \{(1, 2), (2, 3), (3, 4), (4, 5), (5, 6)\}$

Now, $6 \in A$ but $(6, 6) \notin R$

$\therefore R$ is not reflexive.

Hence, Assertion is false.

Reason Given, set $A = \{1, 2, 3\}$

A relation R on A is defined as

$$R = \{(1, 2), (2, 1)\}$$

$\because (1, 2) \in R$ and $(2, 1) \in R$.

So, R is symmetric.

Hence, Reason is true.

20. (a) **Assertion** Let $P(x, y)$ be any point on AB.

Then, area of $\triangle ABP$ is zero.

$$\qquad\qquad \text{[since, the three points are collinear]}$$

$$\therefore \quad \frac{1}{2}\begin{vmatrix} 1 & 3 & 1 \\ 0 & 0 & 1 \\ x & y & 1 \end{vmatrix} = 0$$

This gives $\dfrac{1}{2}(3x - y) = 0 \;$ or $\; y = 3x$

which is the equation of required line AB.

Hence, Assertion is true.

Reason The area of triangle with vertices $(x_1, y_1), (x_2, y_2)$ and (x_3, y_3) is given by

$$\Delta = \frac{1}{2}\begin{vmatrix} x_1 & y_1 & 1 \\ x_2 & y_2 & 1 \\ x_3 & y_3 & 1 \end{vmatrix}$$

Hence, Reason is also true and it is the correct explanation of Assertion.

21. Let $P(x, y)$ be the any point on line AB.

Then, $\qquad$ area of $\triangle ABP = 0$

$$\Rightarrow \qquad \frac{1}{2}\begin{vmatrix} 1 & 3 & 1 \\ 0 & 0 & 1 \\ x & y & 1 \end{vmatrix} = 0$$

$$\Rightarrow \qquad \frac{1}{2}\{1(0 - y) - 3(0 - x) + 1(0 - 0)\} = 0$$

$\Rightarrow 3x - y = 0$, which is the required equation of AB. (1)

Now, area of $\triangle ABD = 3$ sq units.

$$\Rightarrow \quad \frac{1}{2}\begin{vmatrix} 1 & 3 & 1 \\ 0 & 0 & 1 \\ k & 0 & 1 \end{vmatrix} = \pm 3 \Rightarrow \begin{vmatrix} 1 & 3 & 1 \\ 0 & 0 & 1 \\ k & 0 & 1 \end{vmatrix} = \pm 6$$

$$\Rightarrow \qquad 1(0 - 0) - 3(0 - k) + 1(0 - 0) = \pm 6$$

$$\Rightarrow \qquad 3k = \pm 6$$

$$\therefore \qquad k = \pm 2 \qquad\qquad\qquad (1)$$

Or

We have,

$$X + Y = \begin{bmatrix} 7 & 0 \\ 2 & 5 \end{bmatrix} \text{and } X - Y = \begin{bmatrix} 3 & 0 \\ 0 & 3 \end{bmatrix}$$

$$\therefore \qquad (X + Y) + (X - Y) = \begin{bmatrix} 7 & 0 \\ 2 & 5 \end{bmatrix} + \begin{bmatrix} 3 & 0 \\ 0 & 3 \end{bmatrix}$$

$$\Rightarrow \qquad 2X = \begin{bmatrix} 7 + 3 & 0 + 0 \\ 2 + 0 & 5 + 3 \end{bmatrix} = \begin{bmatrix} 10 & 0 \\ 2 & 8 \end{bmatrix}$$

$$\Rightarrow \qquad X = \frac{1}{2}\begin{bmatrix} 10 & 0 \\ 2 & 8 \end{bmatrix} = \begin{bmatrix} 5 & 0 \\ 1 & 4 \end{bmatrix} \qquad (1)$$

and $\quad (X + Y) - (X - Y) = \begin{bmatrix} 7 & 0 \\ 2 & 5 \end{bmatrix} - \begin{bmatrix} 3 & 0 \\ 0 & 3 \end{bmatrix}$

$$= \begin{bmatrix} 7 & 0 \\ 2 & 5 \end{bmatrix} + \begin{bmatrix} -3 & 0 \\ 0 & -3 \end{bmatrix}$$

$$2Y = \begin{bmatrix} 7 - 3 & 0 + 0 \\ 2 + 0 & 5 - 3 \end{bmatrix} = \begin{bmatrix} 4 & 0 \\ 2 & 2 \end{bmatrix}$$

$$Y = \frac{1}{2}\begin{bmatrix} 4 & 0 \\ 2 & 2 \end{bmatrix} = \begin{bmatrix} 2 & 0 \\ 1 & 1 \end{bmatrix}$$

Hence, $X = \begin{bmatrix} 5 & 0 \\ 1 & 4 \end{bmatrix}$ and $Y = \begin{bmatrix} 2 & 0 \\ 1 & 1 \end{bmatrix}$

$$\qquad\qquad\qquad\qquad\qquad\qquad (1)$$

22. Given, $|\hat{a}| = |\hat{b}| = 1$

Now, consider $|\hat{a} + \hat{b}|^2 = (\hat{a} + \hat{b}) \cdot (\hat{a} + \hat{b})$

$$\Rightarrow \qquad |\hat{a} + \hat{b}|^2 = |\hat{a}|^2 + |\hat{b}|^2 + 2(\hat{a} \cdot \hat{b}) \quad (1)$$

$$\Rightarrow \qquad |\hat{a} + \hat{b}|^2 = 1 + 1 + 2|\hat{a}||\hat{b}|\cos\theta$$

$$= 2 + 2\cos\theta$$

$$= 2(1 + \cos\theta)$$

$$\Rightarrow \qquad |\hat{a} + \hat{b}|^2 = 2\left(2\cos^2\frac{\theta}{2}\right) = 4\cos^2\frac{\theta}{2}$$

$$\therefore \qquad |\hat{a} + \hat{b}| = 2\cos\frac{\theta}{2} \quad \textbf{Hence proved.} \;(1)$$

23. Given, probability of student A coming in time,

$$P(A) = \frac{3}{7}$$

$$\therefore \; P(\overline{A}) = 1 - P(A) = 1 - \frac{3}{7} = \frac{4}{7}$$

$$\qquad\qquad\qquad\qquad\qquad\qquad (1/2)$$

Probability of student B coming in time, $P(B) = \dfrac{5}{7}$

$$\therefore \; P(\overline{B}) = 1 - P(B) = 1 - \frac{5}{7} = \frac{2}{7}$$

$$\qquad\qquad\qquad\qquad\qquad\qquad (1/2)$$

Required probability $= P(A \cap B') + P(A' \cap B)$

$$= P(A) \times P(B') + P(A') \times P(B)$$

$$= \frac{3}{7} \times \frac{2}{7} + \frac{4}{7} \times \frac{5}{7}$$

$$= \frac{6 + 20}{49} = \frac{26}{49} \qquad (1)$$

Or

Let B represents the boy and G represents the girl. Then, the sample space of given problem is

$$S = \{BB, GB, BG, GG\}$$

$$\therefore \qquad n(S) = 4$$

Now, let E be the event that both children are boys, i.e. $\qquad E = \{BB\}$

(i) Let F_1 be the event that one of the children is boy.

Then, $F_1 = \{BB, GB, BG\}$

$\therefore$ Required probability

$$= P(E / F_1) = \frac{P(E \cap F_1)}{P(F_1)} = \frac{P(BB)}{P(F_1)} = \frac{\dfrac{1}{4}}{\dfrac{3}{4}} = \frac{1}{3}$$

$$\qquad\qquad\qquad\qquad\qquad\qquad (1)$$

(ii) Let F_2 be the event that the older child is a boy.
Then, $F_2 = \{BB, BG\}$

∴ Required probability $= P(E / F_2) = \dfrac{P(E \cap F_2)}{P(F_2)}$

$$= \dfrac{P(BB)}{P(F_2)} = \dfrac{1/4}{2/4} = \dfrac{1}{2}$$ (1)

24. Given, line is $\dfrac{3-x}{-1} = \dfrac{2y-1}{2} = \dfrac{z}{4}$

or $\dfrac{x-3}{1} = \dfrac{y-\dfrac{1}{2}}{1} = \dfrac{z}{4}$ ...(i) (1)

Now, comparing Eq. (i) with $\dfrac{x - x_1}{a} = \dfrac{y - y_1}{b} = \dfrac{z - z_1}{c}$,

we get direction ratios as $< 1, 1, 4 >$

∴ Its direction cosines are given by

$$\left(\dfrac{1}{\sqrt{1^2 + 1^2 + 4^2}}, \dfrac{1}{\sqrt{1^2 + 1^2 + 4^2}}, \dfrac{4}{\sqrt{1^2 + 1^2 + 4^2}} \right)$$

$$= \left(\dfrac{1}{3\sqrt{2}}, \dfrac{1}{3\sqrt{2}}, \dfrac{4}{3\sqrt{2}} \right)$$ (1)

25. Given, $P(A) = 0.3$ and $P(B) = 0.6$

Now, $P(A' \cap B') = P(A \cup B)' = 1 - P[A \cup B]$

$$= 1 - [P(A) + P(B) - P(A \cap B)]$$ (1)

$$= 1 - \{0.3 + 0.6 - 0.3 \times 0.6\}$$

$[\because A$ and B are independent events

$\therefore P(A \cap B) = P(A)P(B)]$

$$= 1 - \{0.9 - 0.18\} = 1 - \{0.72\} = 0.28 \text{ (1)}$$

26. We have a mapping $f : R^+ \rightarrow [4, \infty)$ given by $f(x) = x^2 + 4$.

To prove f is invertible.

For f to be one-one

Let $x_1, x_2 \in R^+$ be any arbitrary elements, such that

$$f(x_1) = f(x_2)$$

$$\Rightarrow \quad x_1^2 + 4 = x_2^2 + 4 \Rightarrow x_1^2 - x_2^2 = 0$$

$$\Rightarrow \quad (x_1 - x_2)(x_1 + x_2) = 0$$

$$\Rightarrow \quad x_1 - x_2 = 0$$

$$[\because x_1 + x_2 \neq 0 \text{ as } x_1, x_2 \in R^+]$$

$$\Rightarrow \quad x_1 = x_2$$

So, f is one-one.   (1)

For f to be onto

Let $y \in [4, \infty)$ be any arbitrary element and let $y = f(x)$
Then, $y = x^2 + 4$

$$x^2 = y - 4$$

$$x = \pm \sqrt{y - 4}$$

$\because x \in R^+$, therefore $x \neq -\sqrt{y - 4}$.

Now, $x = \sqrt{y - 4} \in R^+$ (1)

$$[\because 4 \leq y < \infty \Rightarrow 0 \leq y - 4 < \infty \Rightarrow 0 \leq \sqrt{y - 4} < \infty]$$

Thus, for each $y \in [4, \infty)$, there exist $x = \sqrt{y - 4} \in R^+$
such that $f(x) = y$

So, f is onto.   (1)

Hence, f is bijective.   **Hence proved.**

27. Given, $(\tan^{-1} x - y)\, dx = (1 + x^2)\, dy$

$$\Rightarrow \quad \dfrac{dy}{dx} = \dfrac{\tan^{-1} x - y}{(1 + x^2)}$$

$$\Rightarrow \quad \dfrac{dy}{dx} = \dfrac{\tan^{-1} x}{1 + x^2} - \dfrac{1}{1 + x^2} y$$

$$\Rightarrow \quad \dfrac{dy}{dx} + \dfrac{1}{1 + x^2} y = \dfrac{\tan^{-1} x}{1 + x^2}$$ ...(i) (1)

which is a linear differential equation of the form
$\dfrac{dy}{dx} + Py = Q$.

Here, $P = \dfrac{1}{1 + x^2}$ and $Q = \dfrac{\tan^{-1} x}{1 + x^2}$

Now, $IF = e^{\int P dx} = e^{\int \frac{1}{1 + x^2} dx} = e^{\tan^{-1} x}$

∴ The general solution is given by

$$y \cdot IF = \int Q \cdot IF \, dx + C$$

$$\Rightarrow \quad y \cdot e^{\tan^{-1} x} = \int \dfrac{\tan^{-1} x}{1 + x^2} \cdot e^{\tan^{-1} x} dx + C$$ (1)

On putting $\tan^{-1} x = t \Rightarrow \dfrac{1}{1 + x^2} dx = dt$

$$\therefore \quad y e^{\tan^{-1} x} = \int t \cdot e^t dt = t \cdot e^t - \int 1 \cdot e^t \, dt + C$$

[using integration by parts]

$$\Rightarrow \quad y e^{\tan^{-1} x} = t \cdot e^t - e^t + C$$

$$\Rightarrow \quad y e^{\tan^{-1} x} = \tan^{-1} x \cdot e^{\tan^{-1} x} - e^{\tan^{-1} x} + C$$

$$[\because \text{put } t = e^{\tan^{-1} x}]$$

$$\Rightarrow \quad y e^{\tan^{-1} x} = (\tan^{-1} x - 1)e^{\tan^{-1} x} + C$$ (1)

Or

Given, differential equation is

$$\dfrac{dy}{dx} + 2y \tan x = \sin x$$

which is a linear differential equation of the form
$\dfrac{dy}{dx} + Py = Q$.

Here, $P = 2 \tan x$ and $Q = \sin x$

$$\therefore \quad IF = e^{\int P dx} = e^{2 \int \tan x \, dx}$$

$$= e^{2 \log |\sec x|}$$

$$= e^{\log \sec^2 x} \qquad [\because m \log n = \log n^m]$$

$$= \sec^2 x \qquad [\because e^{\log x} = x] \text{ (1)}$$

The general solution is given by

$$y \cdot \text{IF} = \int (Q \cdot \text{IF}) dx + C \qquad \ldots(i)$$

$$\Rightarrow \qquad y \sec^2 x = \int (\sin x \cdot \sec^2 x) dx + C$$

$$\Rightarrow \qquad y \sec^2 x = \int \sin x \cdot \frac{1}{\cos^2 x} dx + C$$

$$\Rightarrow \qquad y \sec^2 x = \int \tan x \sec x \, dx + C$$

$$\Rightarrow \qquad y \sec^2 x = \sec x + C \qquad \ldots(ii)$$

Also, given that $y = 0$, when $x = \dfrac{\pi}{3}$.   (1)

On putting $y = 0$ and $x = \dfrac{\pi}{3}$ in Eq. (ii), we get

$$0 \times \sec^2 \frac{\pi}{3} = \sec \frac{\pi}{3} + C$$

$$\Rightarrow \qquad 0 = 2 + C \Rightarrow C = -2$$

On putting the value of C in Eq. (ii), we get

$$y \sec^2 x = \sec x - 2$$

$$\therefore \qquad y = \cos x - 2 \cos^2 x$$

which is the required particular solution of the given differential equation.   (1)

28. Given, $\quad x^y - y^x = a^b$

Let $x^y = u$ and $y^x = v$

Then, $\quad u - v = a^b \Rightarrow \dfrac{du}{dx} - \dfrac{dv}{dx} = 0 \qquad \ldots(i)$

Now, $\quad u = x^y \Rightarrow \log u = y \log x$

$$\Rightarrow \frac{1}{u} \frac{du}{dx} = \frac{y}{x} + \log x \frac{dy}{dx}$$

$$\Rightarrow \frac{du}{dx} = y \cdot x^{y-1} + x^y \cdot \log x \frac{dy}{dx} \qquad (1)$$

and $\quad v = y^x \Rightarrow \log v = x \log y$

$$\Rightarrow \frac{1}{v} \frac{dv}{dx} = \frac{x}{y} \frac{dy}{dx} + \log y$$

$$\Rightarrow \frac{dv}{dx} = x y^{x-1} \frac{dy}{dx} + y^x \log y \qquad (1)$$

Now, Eq. (i) becomes,

$$y \cdot x^{y-1} + x^y \cdot \log x \frac{dy}{dx} - x y^{x-1} \frac{dy}{dx} - y^x \log y = 0$$

$$\Rightarrow \frac{dy}{dx} (x^y \log x - x y^{x-1}) = y^x \log y - y \cdot x^{y-1}$$

$$\Rightarrow \qquad \frac{dy}{dx} = \frac{y^x \cdot \log y - y \cdot x^{y-1}}{x^y \cdot \log x - x \cdot y^{x-1}} \qquad (1)$$

Or

Let $I = \displaystyle\int \frac{\cos x}{(1 - \sin x)(2 - \sin x)} dx$

Put $\sin x = t \Rightarrow \cos x = \dfrac{dt}{dx} \Rightarrow dx = \dfrac{dt}{\cos x}$

$$\therefore \quad I = \int \frac{\cos x}{(1-t)(2-t)} \frac{dt}{\cos x} = \int \frac{1}{(1-t)(2-t)} dt$$

$$= \int \left[\frac{A}{1-t} + \frac{B}{2-t} \right] dt \qquad \ldots(i)$$

$$\therefore \quad \frac{1}{(1-t)(2-t)} = \frac{A(2-t) + B(1-t)}{(1-t)(2-t)}$$

$$\Rightarrow \qquad 1 = 2A - tA + B - Bt$$

$$\Rightarrow \qquad 1 = (2A + B) + t(-A - B) \qquad (1\tfrac{1}{2})$$

On comparing the coefficients of t and constant term both sides, we get

$$2A + B = 1 \text{ and } -A - B = 0$$

On adding above equations, we get

$$A = 1 \quad \text{and} \quad \text{then } B = -1$$

$$\therefore \qquad I = \int \left(\frac{1}{1-t} - \frac{1}{2-t} \right) dt \qquad \text{[from Eq. (i)]}$$

$$= \int \frac{1}{(1-t)} dt - \int \frac{1}{(2-t)} dt$$

$$= \frac{\log|1-t|}{(-1)} - \frac{\log|2-t|}{(-1)} + C$$

$$= \log \left| \frac{2-t}{1-t} \right| + c = \log \left| \frac{2 - \sin x}{1 - \sin x} \right| + C$$

$$[\because \text{put } t = \sin x] \quad (1\tfrac{1}{2})$$

29. Given, differential equation is

$$\left[x \sin^2 \left(\frac{y}{x} \right) - y \right] dx + x \, dy = 0$$

$$\Rightarrow \qquad \frac{dy}{dx} = \frac{y - x \sin^2 \left(\dfrac{y}{x} \right)}{x} \qquad \ldots(i)$$

On putting $y = vx$ and $\dfrac{dy}{dx} = v + x \dfrac{dv}{dx}$ in Eq. (i), we get

$$v + x \frac{dv}{dx} = \frac{vx - x \sin^2 \left(\dfrac{vx}{x} \right)}{x}$$

$$\Rightarrow \quad v + x \frac{dv}{dx} = v - \sin^2 (v) \Rightarrow x \frac{dv}{dx} = -\sin^2 (v)$$

$$\Rightarrow \qquad \text{cosec}^2 v \, dv = -\frac{dx}{x}$$

$$\Rightarrow \qquad \text{cosec}^2 v \, dv + \frac{dx}{x} = 0 \qquad (1\tfrac{1}{2})$$

On integrating both sides, we get

$$\int \text{cosec}^2 v + \int \frac{dx}{x} = 0$$

$$\Rightarrow \qquad -\cot v + \log |x| = C$$

$$\Rightarrow \qquad -\cot \left(\frac{y}{x} \right) + \log |x| = C \qquad \left[\because \text{put } v = \frac{y}{x} \right] \ldots(ii)$$

Also, given that $y = \dfrac{\pi}{4}$, when $x = 1$

$$\therefore \quad -\cot \frac{\pi}{4} + \log |1| = C \Rightarrow C = -1 + 0 \Rightarrow C = -1$$

So, the required particular solution is

$$-\cot\left(\frac{y}{x}\right) + \log|x| = -1$$

$$\Rightarrow \quad 1 + \log|x| - \cot\left(\frac{y}{x}\right) = 0 \qquad (1\frac{1}{2})$$

Or

Given differential equation $x^2 dy + y(x + y) dx = 0$ can be written as $x^2 dy + (xy + y^2) dx = 0$

$$\Rightarrow \qquad x^2 dy = -(xy + y^2) dx$$

$$\Rightarrow \qquad \frac{dy}{dx} = -\left(\frac{yx + y^2}{x^2}\right)$$

$$\Rightarrow \qquad \frac{dy}{dx} = -\left(\frac{y}{x}\right) - \left(\frac{y}{x}\right)^2 \qquad \ldots\text{(i)}$$

which is a homogeneous, as $\frac{dy}{dx} = f\left(\frac{y}{x}\right)$.

$$(1)$$

On putting $y = vx$ and $\frac{dy}{dx} = v + x\frac{dv}{dx}$ in Eq. (i), we get

$$v + x\frac{dv}{dx} = -v - v^2 \Rightarrow \quad x\frac{dv}{dx} = -2v - v^2$$

$$\Rightarrow \qquad \frac{1}{2v + v^2} dv = -\frac{1}{x} dx$$

$$\Rightarrow \qquad \frac{1}{v(2 + v)} dv = -\frac{1}{x} dx$$

$$\Rightarrow \qquad \frac{2}{2v(2 + v)} dv = -\frac{1}{x} dx$$

$$\Rightarrow \qquad \frac{1}{2}\left(\frac{1}{v} - \frac{1}{v + 2}\right) dv = -\frac{1}{x} dx$$

$$\Rightarrow \qquad \frac{1}{2}\int\frac{1}{v} dv - \frac{1}{2}\int\frac{1}{v + 2} dv = -\int\frac{1}{x} dx$$

$$\Rightarrow \frac{1}{2}\log|v| - \frac{1}{2}\log|v + 2| = -|\log x| + \log C$$

$$\Rightarrow \qquad \frac{1}{2}\log\left|\frac{v}{v + 2}\right| = \log\left|\frac{C}{x}\right|$$

$$\Rightarrow \qquad \log\left|\frac{v}{v + 2}\right| = 2\log\left|\frac{C}{x}\right| \Rightarrow \frac{v}{v + 2} = \left(\frac{C}{x}\right)^2$$

$$\Rightarrow \qquad \frac{\frac{y}{x}}{\frac{y}{x} + 2} = \left(\frac{C}{x}\right)^2 \qquad \left[\because \text{put } v = \frac{y}{x}\right]$$

$$\Rightarrow \qquad \frac{y}{y + 2x} = \left(\frac{C}{x}\right)^2 \qquad (2)$$

30. Let $I = \int\frac{dx}{1 - 3\sin x}$

$$= \int\frac{dx}{1 - 3\left(\frac{2\tan\frac{x}{2}}{1 + \tan^2\frac{x}{2}}\right)} \qquad \left[\because \sin x = \frac{2\tan\frac{x}{2}}{1 + \tan^2\frac{x}{2}}\right]$$

$$= \int\frac{dx}{\frac{1 + \tan^2\frac{x}{2} - 6\tan\frac{x}{2}}{1 + \tan^2\frac{x}{2}}} = \int\frac{\sec^2\frac{x}{2}}{\tan^2\frac{x}{2} - 6\tan\frac{x}{2} + 1} dx$$

$$[\because 1 + \tan^2\theta = \sec^2\theta] \; (1)$$

On putting $\tan\frac{x}{2} = t$

$$\Rightarrow \quad \sec^2\frac{x}{2} \cdot \frac{1}{2} = \frac{dt}{dx} \Rightarrow \sec^2\frac{x}{2} dx = 2\, dt$$

$$\therefore \quad I = 2\int\frac{dt}{t^2 - 6t + 1} = 2\int\frac{dt}{t^2 - 6t + 1 + (3)^2 - (3)^2}$$

$$= 2\int\frac{dt}{(t - 3)^2 - 8} = 2\int\frac{dt}{(t - 3)^2 - (2\sqrt{2})^2}$$

$$= 2 \times \frac{1}{2 \times 2\sqrt{2}}\log\left|\frac{t - 3 - 2\sqrt{2}}{t - 3 + 2\sqrt{2}}\right| + C$$

$$\left[\because \int\frac{1}{x^2 - a^2} dx = \frac{1}{2a}\log\left|\frac{x - a}{x + a}\right| + C\right]$$

$$= \frac{1}{2\sqrt{2}}\log\left|\frac{\tan\frac{x}{2} - 3 - 2\sqrt{2}}{\tan\frac{x}{2} - 3 + 2\sqrt{2}}\right| + C$$

$$\left[\because \text{putting } t = \tan\frac{x}{2}\right] \; (2)$$

31. Let $I = \int_3^4\frac{\sqrt{x}}{\sqrt{x} + \sqrt{7 - x}} dx \qquad \ldots\text{(i)}$

Using $\int_a^b f(x) dx = \int_a^b f(a + b - x) dx$ in Eq. (i), we get

$$I = \int_3^4\frac{\sqrt{3 + 4 - x}}{\sqrt{3 + 4 - x} + \sqrt{7 - (3 + 4 - x)}} dx$$

$$= \int_3^4\frac{\sqrt{7 - x}}{\sqrt{7 - x} + \sqrt{x}} dx \qquad \ldots\text{(ii)} \; (1)$$

On adding Eqs. (i) and (ii), we get

$$2I = \int_3^4\frac{\sqrt{x}}{\sqrt{x} + \sqrt{7 - x}} dx + \int_3^4\frac{\sqrt{7 - x}}{\sqrt{7 - x} + \sqrt{x}} dx$$

$$= \int_3^4\frac{\sqrt{x} + \sqrt{7 - x}}{\sqrt{x} + \sqrt{7 - x}} dx = \int_3^4 dx = [x]_3^4$$

$$\Rightarrow \qquad 2I = [4 - 3] = 1$$

$$\therefore \qquad I = \frac{1}{2} \qquad (2)$$

32. Let $I = \int\frac{(x^2 + 1)(x^2 + 2)}{(x^2 + 3)(x^2 + 4)} dx$

Here, the degree of numerator and denominator is 4.

So, we convert the integral into simple form by putting $x^2 = t$.

$$\therefore \quad \frac{(x^2 + 1)(x^2 + 2)}{(x^2 + 3)(x^2 + 4)} = \frac{(t + 1)(t + 2)}{(t + 3)(t + 4)} = \frac{t^2 + 3t + 2}{t^2 + 7t + 12} \; (1)$$

Since, degree of numerator and denominator is same,

so it can be written as $\dfrac{t^2 + 3t + 2}{t^2 + 7t + 12} = 1 - \dfrac{4t + 10}{t^2 + 7t + 12}$

[on dividing numerator by denominator]

Let $\dfrac{4t + 10}{(t + 4)(t + 3)} = \dfrac{A}{(t + 4)} + \dfrac{B}{(t + 3)}$

$\Rightarrow \dfrac{4t + 10}{(t + 4)(t + 3)} = \dfrac{A(t + 3) + B(t + 4)}{(t + 4)(t + 3)}$

$\Rightarrow \quad 4t + 10 = At + 3A + Bt + 4B$

$\Rightarrow \quad 4t + 10 = t(A + B) + (3A + 4B) \qquad (1)$

On comparing the coefficients of t and constant terms from both sides, we get

$A + B = 4 \qquad \qquad \text{...(i)}$

and $\quad 3A + 4B = 10 \qquad \qquad \text{...(ii)}$

On multiplying Eq. (i) by 3 and then subtracting Eq. (ii) from Eq. (i), we get

$-B = 2 \Rightarrow B = -2$

Then, from Eq. (i), we get $A = 6$

$\Rightarrow \dfrac{4t + 10}{(t + 4)(t + 3)} = \dfrac{6}{(t + 4)} - \dfrac{2}{(t + 3)} \qquad (1)$

$\therefore I = \int 1 dx - \left[\int \left(\dfrac{6}{x^2 + 4} - \dfrac{2}{x^2 + 3} \right) dx \right] \qquad [\text{put } t = x^2]$

$= x - 6 \int \dfrac{1}{x^2 + (2)^2} dx + 2 \int \dfrac{1}{x^2 + (\sqrt{3})^2} dx \qquad (1)$

$= x - 6 \times \dfrac{1}{2} \tan^{-1} \dfrac{x}{2} + 2 \times \dfrac{1}{\sqrt{3}} \tan^{-1} \dfrac{x}{\sqrt{3}} + C$

$\left[\because \int \dfrac{1}{a^2 + x^2} dx = \dfrac{1}{a} \tan^{-1} \dfrac{x}{a} + C \right]$

$= x - 3\tan^{-1} \dfrac{x}{2} + \dfrac{2}{\sqrt{3}} \tan^{-1} \dfrac{x}{\sqrt{3}} + C \qquad (1)$

33. Given, system of equations is

$x - y + 2z = 7$

$3x + 4y - 5z = -5$

and $\quad 2x - y + 3z = 12$

In matrix form, it can be written as

$AX = B \qquad \qquad \text{...(i)}$

where, $A = \begin{bmatrix} 1 & -1 & 2 \\ 3 & 4 & -5 \\ 2 & -1 & 3 \end{bmatrix}, X = \begin{bmatrix} x \\ y \\ z \end{bmatrix}$ and $B = \begin{bmatrix} 7 \\ -5 \\ 12 \end{bmatrix}$

Here, $\quad |A| = 1(12 - 5) + 1(9 + 10) + 2(-3 - 8)$

$= 1(7) + 1(19) + 2(-11) = 7 + 19 - 22 = 4$

$\Rightarrow \quad |A| \neq 0 \qquad \qquad (1)$

So, A is non-singular and its inverse exists.

Now, cofactors of elements of $|A|$ are

$A_{11} = (-1)^2 \begin{vmatrix} 4 & -5 \\ -1 & 3 \end{vmatrix} = 1(12 - 5) = 7$

$A_{12} = (-1)^3 \begin{vmatrix} 3 & -5 \\ 2 & 3 \end{vmatrix} = -1(9 + 10) = -19$

$A_{13} = (-1)^4 \begin{vmatrix} 3 & 4 \\ 2 & -1 \end{vmatrix} = 1(-3 - 8) = -11$

$A_{21} = (-1)^3 \begin{vmatrix} -1 & 2 \\ -1 & 3 \end{vmatrix} = -1(-3 + 2) = 1$

$A_{22} = (-1)^4 \begin{vmatrix} 1 & 2 \\ 2 & 3 \end{vmatrix} = 1(3 - 4) = -1$

$A_{23} = (-1)^5 \begin{vmatrix} 1 & -1 \\ 2 & -1 \end{vmatrix} = -1(-1 + 2) = -1$

$A_{31} = (-1)^4 \begin{vmatrix} -1 & 2 \\ 4 & -5 \end{vmatrix} = 1(5 - 8) = -3$

$A_{32} = (-1)^5 \begin{vmatrix} 1 & 2 \\ 3 & -5 \end{vmatrix} = -1(-5 - 6) = 11$

$A_{33} = (-1)^6 \begin{vmatrix} 1 & -1 \\ 3 & 4 \end{vmatrix} = 1(4 + 3) = 7 \qquad (2)$

$\therefore \text{adj}(A) = \begin{bmatrix} A_{11} & A_{12} & A_{13} \\ A_{21} & A_{22} & A_{23} \\ A_{31} & A_{32} & A_{33} \end{bmatrix}^T$

$= \begin{bmatrix} 7 & -19 & -11 \\ 1 & -1 & -1 \\ -3 & 11 & 7 \end{bmatrix}^T = \begin{bmatrix} 7 & 1 & -3 \\ -19 & -1 & 11 \\ -11 & -1 & 7 \end{bmatrix}$

and $A^{-1} = \dfrac{\text{adj}(A)}{|A|} \Rightarrow A^{-1} = \dfrac{1}{4} \begin{bmatrix} 7 & 1 & -3 \\ -19 & -1 & 11 \\ -11 & -1 & 7 \end{bmatrix} \qquad (1)$

Now, from Eq. (i), we get

$X = A^{-1}B$

$\Rightarrow \begin{bmatrix} x \\ y \\ z \end{bmatrix} = \dfrac{1}{4} \begin{bmatrix} 7 & 1 & -3 \\ -19 & -1 & 11 \\ -11 & -1 & 7 \end{bmatrix} \begin{bmatrix} 7 \\ -5 \\ 12 \end{bmatrix}$

$\Rightarrow \begin{bmatrix} x \\ y \\ z \end{bmatrix} = \dfrac{1}{4} \begin{bmatrix} 49 - 5 - 36 \\ -133 + 5 + 132 \\ -77 + 5 + 84 \end{bmatrix} = \dfrac{1}{4} \begin{bmatrix} 8 \\ 4 \\ 12 \end{bmatrix} = \begin{bmatrix} 2 \\ 1 \\ 3 \end{bmatrix}$

On comparing corresponding elements, we get

$x = 2, \ y = 1 \text{ and } z = 3 \qquad (1)$

Or

We shall prove that result by using the principle of mathematical induction.

When $n = 1$, we have

$A^1 = \begin{bmatrix} 3^{1-1} & 3^{1-1} & 3^{1-1} \\ 3^{1-1} & 3^{1-1} & 3^{1-1} \\ 3^{1-1} & 3^{1-1} & 3^{1-1} \end{bmatrix} = \begin{bmatrix} 3^0 & 3^0 & 3^0 \\ 3^0 & 3^0 & 3^0 \\ 3^0 & 3^0 & 3^0 \end{bmatrix} = \begin{bmatrix} 1 & 1 & 1 \\ 1 & 1 & 1 \\ 1 & 1 & 1 \end{bmatrix} \quad (1)$

Thus, the result is true for $n = 1$.

Let it be true for $n = k$. Then,

$A^k = \begin{bmatrix} 3^{k-1} & 3^{k-1} & 3^{k-1} \\ 3^{k-1} & 3^{k-1} & 3^{k-1} \\ 3^{k-1} & 3^{k-1} & 3^{k-1} \end{bmatrix}$

$\therefore A^{k+1} = A \cdot A^k$

$$= \begin{bmatrix} 1 & 1 & 1 \\ 1 & 1 & 1 \\ 1 & 1 & 1 \end{bmatrix} \times \begin{bmatrix} 3^{k-1} & 3^{k-1} & 3^{k-1} \\ 3^{k-1} & 3^{k-1} & 3^{k-1} \\ 3^{k-1} & 3^{k-1} & 3^{k-1} \end{bmatrix}$$ (1)

$$= \begin{bmatrix} 3(3^{k-1}) & 3(3^{k-1}) & 3(3^{k-1}) \\ 3(3^{k-1}) & 3(3^{k-1}) & 3(3^{k-1}) \\ 3(3^{k-1}) & 3(3^{k-1}) & 3(3^{k-1}) \end{bmatrix}$$

$$= \begin{bmatrix} 3^k & 3^k & 3^k \\ 3^k & 3^k & 3^k \\ 3^k & 3^k & 3^k \end{bmatrix}$$ (1)

Thus, the result is true for $n = (k+1)$, whenever it is true for $n = k$. (1)

So, the result is true for all $n \in N$.

Hence, $A^n = \begin{bmatrix} 3^{n-1} & 3^{n-1} & 3^{n-1} \\ 3^{n-1} & 3^{n-1} & 3^{n-1} \\ 3^{n-1} & 3^{n-1} & 3^{n-1} \end{bmatrix}$

for all values of $n \in N$. (1)

34. Given, maximise $Z = 2x + 3y$

Subject to constraints

$$x + 2y \le 10 \qquad \ldots(i)$$
$$2x + y \le 14 \qquad \ldots(ii)$$
and $\qquad x \ge 0, y \ge 0 \qquad \ldots(iii)$

Shade the region to the right of Y-axis to show $x \ge 0$ and above X-axis to show $y \ge 0$.

Table for line $x + 2y = 10$ is

x	0	4	10
y	5	3	0

So, the line is passing through the points $(0, 5)$, $(4, 3)$ and $(10, 0)$. (1)

On putting $(0, 0)$ in the inequality $x + 2y \le 10$, we get $0 + 0 \le 10$, which is true.

So, the half plane is towards the origin.

Table for line $2x + y = 14$ is

x	4	6	7
y	6	2	0

So, the line is passing through the points $(4, 6)$, $(6, 2)$ and $(7, 0)$. (1)

On putting $(0, 0)$ in the inequality $2x + y \le 14$, we get $0 + 0 \le 14$, which is true.

So, the half plane is towards the origin.

The intersection point of lines corresponding to Eqs. (i) and (ii) is $B(6, 2)$.

On shading the common region, we get the feasible region $OABD$. (1)

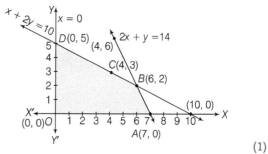

(1)

The values of Z at corner points are given below

Corner points	Value of $Z = 2x + 3y$
$O(0, 0)$	$Z = 2 \times 0 + 3 \times 0 = 0$
$A(7, 0)$	$Z = 2 \times 7 + 3 \times 0 = 14$
$B(6, 2)$	$Z = 2 \times 6 + 3 \times 2 = 18$
$D(0, 5)$	$Z = 2 \times 0 + 3 \times 5 = 15$

Hence, the maximum value of Z is 18 at the point $B(6, 2)$. (1)

Or

We have to maximize $Z = 60x + 40y$,

Subject to the constraints

$$5x + 6y \le 45,$$
$$3x + 2y \le 18,$$
and $\qquad x, y \ge 0$

Now, $5x + 6y = 45$

$\Rightarrow \qquad \dfrac{x}{9} + \dfrac{y}{(15/2)} = 1$

This line meets the axes at $A(9, 0)$ and $B\left(0, \dfrac{15}{2}\right)$. (1)

Plot these points and join them to obtain the line $5x + 6y = 45$.

Clearly, $(0, 0)$ satisfies $5x + 6y \le 45$.

So, the region below AB represents $5x + 6y \le 45$.

Again, $3x + 2y = 18$

$\Rightarrow \qquad \dfrac{x}{6} + \dfrac{y}{9} = 1$.

This line meets the axes at $C(6, 0)$ and $D(0, 9)$.

Plot these points and join them to obtain the line $3x + 2y = 18$.

Clearly, $(0, 0)$ satisfies $3x + 2y \le 18$.

So, the region below CD represents $3x + 2y \le 18$.

$x \ge 0$ is the region to the right of the Y-axis.

and $y \ge 0$ is the region above the X-axis.

On solving $5x + 6y = 45$ and $3x + 2y = 18$, we get

$$x = \frac{9}{4} \text{ and } y = \frac{45}{8}$$ (1)

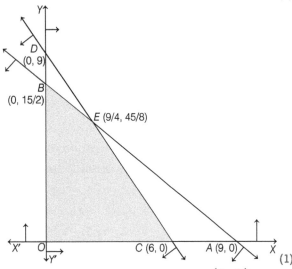

(1)

So, the lines AB and CD intersect at $E\left(\dfrac{9}{4}, \dfrac{45}{8}\right)$.

Thus, the corner points of the feasible region are

$O(0, 0)$, $C(6, 0)$, $E\left(\dfrac{9}{4}, \dfrac{45}{8}\right)$ and $B\left(0, \dfrac{15}{2}\right)$. (1)

Corner points	Value of $Z = 60x + 40y$
$O(0, 0)$	$Z = 60 \times 0 + 40 \times 0 = 0$
$C(6, 0)$	$Z = 60 \times 6 + 40 \times 0 = 360$
	(Maximum)
$E\left(\dfrac{9}{4}, \dfrac{45}{8}\right)$	$Z = 60 \times \dfrac{9}{4} + 40 \times \dfrac{45}{8} = 360$
	(Maximum)
$B\left(0, \dfrac{15}{2}\right)$	$Z = 60 \times 0 + 40 \times \dfrac{15}{2} = 300$

So, Z is maximum at either at $(6, 0)$ or $\left(\dfrac{9}{4}, \dfrac{45}{8}\right)$ and maximum value of Z is 360. (1)

35. Given, $\vec{a} = \hat{i} + \hat{j} + \hat{k}, \vec{b} = 2\hat{i} + 4\hat{j} - 5\hat{k}$

and $\vec{c} = \lambda\hat{i} + 2\hat{j} + 3\hat{k}$.

Now, $\vec{b} + \vec{c} = 2\hat{i} + 4\hat{j} - 5\hat{k} + \lambda\hat{i} + 2\hat{j} + 3\hat{k}$

$= (2 + \lambda)\hat{i} + 6\hat{j} - 2\hat{k}$

$\therefore |\vec{b} + \vec{c}| = \sqrt{(2 + \lambda)^2 + (6)^2 + (-2)^2}$

$= \sqrt{4 + \lambda^2 + 4\lambda + 36 + 4}$

$= \sqrt{\lambda^2 + 4\lambda + 44}$ (1)

Now, the unit vector along $\vec{b} + \vec{c}$

$= \dfrac{\vec{b} + \vec{c}}{|\vec{b} + \vec{c}|} = \dfrac{(2 + \lambda)\hat{i} + 6\hat{j} - 2\hat{k}}{\sqrt{\lambda^2 + 4\lambda + 44}}$ ...(i) (1)

Given, scalar product of $(\hat{i} + \hat{j} + \hat{k})$ with unit vector $\vec{b} + \vec{c}$ is 1.

$\therefore \qquad (\hat{i} + \hat{j} + \hat{k}) \cdot \dfrac{\vec{b} + \vec{c}}{|\vec{b} + \vec{c}|} = 1$

$\Rightarrow \quad (\hat{i} + \hat{j} + \hat{k}) \cdot \dfrac{(2 + \lambda)\hat{i} + 6\hat{j} - 2\hat{k}}{\sqrt{\lambda^2 + 4\lambda + 44}} = 1$ (1)

$\Rightarrow \quad \dfrac{1(2 + \lambda) + 1(6) + 1(-2)}{\sqrt{\lambda^2 + 4\lambda + 44}} = 1$

$\Rightarrow \quad \dfrac{(2 + \lambda) + 6 - 2}{\sqrt{\lambda^2 + 4\lambda + 44}} = 1$

$\Rightarrow \qquad \lambda + 6 = \sqrt{\lambda^2 + 4\lambda + 44}$

$\Rightarrow \qquad (\lambda + 6)^2 = \lambda^2 + 4\lambda + 44$

[squaring both sides]

$\Rightarrow \qquad \lambda^2 + 36 + 12\lambda = \lambda^2 + 4\lambda + 44$

$\Rightarrow \qquad 8\lambda = 8 \Rightarrow \lambda = 1$

Hence, the value of λ is 1. (1)

On substituting the value of λ in Eq. (i), we get

Unit vector along $\vec{b} + \vec{c}$

$= \dfrac{(2 + 1)\hat{i} + 6\hat{j} - 2\hat{k}}{\sqrt{(1)^2 + 4(1) + 44}} = \dfrac{3\hat{i} + 6\hat{j} - 2\hat{k}}{\sqrt{1 + 4 + 44}}$

$= \dfrac{3\hat{i} + 6\hat{j} - 2\hat{k}}{\sqrt{49}} = \dfrac{3}{7}\hat{i} + \dfrac{6}{7}\hat{j} - \dfrac{2}{7}\hat{k}$ (1)

36. (i) Let $I = \displaystyle\int_{-1}^{1} (f(x) - f(-x))\,dx$

Again, let $h(x) = f(x) - f(-x)$

$\therefore \qquad h(-x) = f(-x) - f(x)$

$= -[f(x) - f(-x)] = -h(x)$

$\therefore h(x)$ is a odd function.

So, $\displaystyle\int_{-1}^{1} (f(x) - f(-x))\,dx = 0$

(ii) Let $I = \displaystyle\int_{-a}^{a} (g(x) + g(-x))\,dx$

Since, $g(x)$ is a odd function

$\therefore \qquad g(-x) = -g(x) \Rightarrow g(x) + g(-x) = 0$

$\therefore \displaystyle\int_{-a}^{a} (g(x) + g(-x))\,dx = 0$

(iii) Let $I = \displaystyle\int_{-\pi}^{\pi} \dfrac{\pi}{1 + \cos^2 x}\,dx$

Let $k(x) = \dfrac{x}{1 + \cos^2 x}$

$\therefore \quad k(-x) = \dfrac{-x}{1 + \cos^2 (-x)} = \dfrac{-x}{1 + \cos^2 x} = -k(x)$

$\therefore k(x)$ is a odd function

$$\therefore I = \int_{-\pi}^{\pi} \frac{x}{1+\cos^2 x}\,dx = 0$$

Now, let $w(x) = \log\left(\dfrac{2-x}{2+x}\right)$

$$\therefore \quad w(-x) = \log\left(\frac{2+x}{2-x}\right) = \log\left(\frac{2-x}{2+x}\right)^{-1}$$

$$= -\log\left(\frac{2-x}{2+x}\right) = -w(x)$$

$\therefore w(x)$ is a odd function.

$$\therefore \int_{-1}^{1} \log\left(\frac{2-x}{2+x}\right) dx = 0$$

Or

Let $\phi(x) = |\sin x|$

$\Rightarrow \quad \phi(-x) = |\sin(-x)| = |-\sin x| = |\sin x| = \phi(x)$

$\therefore \phi(x)$ is an even function

$$\therefore \int_{-\pi}^{\pi} |\sin x|\,dx = 2\int_{0}^{\pi} |\sin x|\,dx$$

$$= 2\int_{0}^{\pi} \sin x\,dx \qquad [\because |\sin x| = \sin x,\ 0 < x < \pi]$$

$$= 2\,[-\cos x]_0^{\pi} = 2\,[1+1] = 4$$

37. (i) Let E = event that the doctor diagnoses CORONA.
E_1 = event that the person selected is suffering from CORONA.
E_2 = event that the person selected is not suffering from CORONA.

We have,

Required probability $= P(E_1) = \dfrac{1}{1000} = 0.001$

Also, $P(E_2) = 1 - P(E_1) = 1 - \dfrac{1}{1000} = \dfrac{999}{1000} = 0.999$

(ii) Required probability $= P\left(\dfrac{E}{E_1}\right) = \dfrac{99}{100} = 0.99$

(iii) Required probability $= P(E)$

$$= \sum_{i=1}^{2} P(E_i)\, P\left(\frac{E}{E_i}\right)$$

$$= P(E_1)\, P\left(\frac{E}{E_1}\right) + P(E_2)\, P\left(\frac{E}{E_2}\right)$$

$$= 0.001 \times 0.99 + 0.999 \times 0.001$$

$$\left[\because P\left(\frac{E}{E_2}\right) = \frac{1}{1000} = 0.001\right]$$

$$= 0.00099 + 0.000999 = 0.001989$$

Or

Required Probability

$$= P(E_1/E) = \dfrac{P(E_1)P(E/E_1)}{P(E_1)P(E/E_1) + P(E_2)P(E/E_2)}$$

$$= \frac{0.001 \times 0.99}{0.001 \times 0.99 + 0.999 \times 0.001}$$

$$= \frac{0.00099}{0.00099 + 0.000999}$$

$$= \frac{0.00099}{0.001989} = \frac{110}{221}$$

38. (i) $|5x-3| = \begin{cases} -(5x-3), & \text{when } 5x-3 < 0 \ \text{ i.e., } x < \dfrac{3}{5} \\ 5x-3, & \text{when } 5x-3 \geq 0 \ \text{ i.e., } x > \dfrac{3}{5} \end{cases}$

The graph of $y = |5x-3|$ is shown in figure

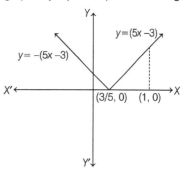

Let $I = \int_0^1 |5x-3|\,dx$. Then,

$$I = \int_0^{3/5} |5x-3|\,dx + \int_{3/5}^1 |5x-3|\,dx$$

$$\Rightarrow I = \int_0^{3/5} -(5x-3)\,dx + \int_{3/5}^1 (5x-3)\,dx$$

$$\Rightarrow I = \left[3x - \frac{5x^2}{2}\right]_0^{3/5} + \left[\frac{5x^2}{2} - 3x\right]_{3/5}^1$$

$$= \left(\frac{9}{5} - \frac{9}{10}\right) + \left(-\frac{1}{2} + \frac{9}{10}\right) = \frac{13}{10}$$

(ii) Clearly, $[x] = \begin{cases} 0 & 0 \leq x < 1 \\ 1 & 1 \leq x < 2 \end{cases}$

$$\therefore \int_0^2 [x]\,dx = \int_0^1 [x]\,dx + \int_1^2 [x]\,dx$$

$$= \int_0^1 0\,dx + \int_1^2 1\,dx$$

$$= 0 + [x]_1^2$$

$$= 2 - 1 = 1$$

Now, $f(x) = \begin{cases} 1-2x, & x \leq 0 \\ 1+2x, & x \geq 0 \end{cases}$

$$\therefore \int_{-1}^1 f(x)\,dx = \int_{-1}^0 f(x)\,dx + \int_0^1 f(x)\,dx$$

$$\Rightarrow \int_{-1}^1 f(x)\,dx = \int_{-1}^0 (1-2x)\,dx + \int_0^1 (1+2x)\,dx$$

[by using the definition of $f(x)$]

$$\Rightarrow \int_{-1}^1 f(x)\,dx = [x - x^2]_{-1}^0 + [x + x^2]_0^1$$

$$= [0 - (-1-1)] + [(1+1) - (0)] = 4$$

9 789327 195682